Dominie
July 80

ENGINEERING LAW
AND THE
I.C.E. CONTRACTS

To the memory of

LEONARD ABRAHAMSON

incomparable parent and teacher

and to

EDNA

and

GAIL, LYNNE, LEONARD and EMILY

for joy received

Engineering Law
and the
I.C.E. Contracts

MAX W. ABRAHAMSON
(Mod.) B.A., LL.B., Solicitor

Sometime Scholar in Law of Trinity College, Dublin
Honorary Fellow of the Institution of Engineers of Ireland
Companion of the Institution of Civil Engineers

FOURTH EDITION

With a Foreword by
Sir William Harris

APPLIED SCIENCE PUBLISHERS LTD
LONDON

APPLIED SCIENCE PUBLISHERS LTD
RIPPLE ROAD,.BARKING, ESSEX, ENGLAND

First Edition published 1965
Second Edition published 1969
Reprinted 1970
Reprinted 1972
Third Edition published 1975
Reprinted 1978
Fourth Edition published 1979

British Library Cataloguing in Publication Data

Abrahamson, Max William
    Engineering law and the ICE contracts. — 4th ed.
    1. Civil engineering — Contracts and specifications
    — England
    I. Title
    343'.42'078   KD1641

ISBN 0-85334-826-X

Printed in Great Britain by Galliard (Printers) Ltd, Great Yarmouth

Preface to the Fourth Edition

As the bible of the civil engineering industry the I.C.E. Conditions have the distinction, in common with other scripture reflecting diverse and unfortunately combative activity, that the more they are analysed and used, the more issues appear. That is one of the excuses for the extra pages in this edition. Some of the problems dealt with have already arisen in practice, and it would be optimistic to believe that even those that seem most abstruse and academic will not sooner or later complicate construction or some final accounts.

Many other additions are due to the recent enthusiasm of judges and parliament for reform, and will surprise those who attribute rigor mortis to law and lawyers. The industry itself can of course bring pressure and carry out research and investigation to make sure that all future reforms are beneficial.

A new edition of the F.I.D.I.C. International Conditions was published in 1977, moving in a different direction to the I.C.E. Conditions. As a result it is no longer adequate to deal with international contracts in one chapter of a book on the domestic forms. The chapter on the F.I.D.I.C. Conditions in previous editions of this book therefore has been omitted, but may be expanded later into a separate volume.

Topics dealt with in new or expanded notes in this edition include—adjustment and balancing items (pp. 15–16), ingredients of a letter of intent (pp. 18–19), assignment of contract payments (p. 39), responsibility for temporary works and the contractor's responsibility for design of permanent works (pp. 52–5), new decisions relevant to site and other information supplied by the employer (pp. 61–3) and to cl. 20 of the Conditions (p. 97), general note on cl. 44 (pp. 138–9), variations to temporary works (p. 170), variations permitted by cl. 51 (pp. 172–4), design changes contributed by or as concessions to the contractor (pp. 179–84), an important decision on concessions obtained by the contractor by pressures on the employer (p. 182), errors in and omissions from the bill (pp. 206–9), contractual aspects of the new Civil Engineering Standard Method of Measurement (pp. 213–18) and method-related charges (pp. 218–20), retention of title clauses (p. 262), counterclaims (pp. 269–72), the contract price fluctuations clause (pp. 316–19), disruption claims and their assessment, and acceleration claims (pp. 364–72), the expanding extent and period of liabilities and side effects on the Conditions (pp. 393–9 and 430–1), the Unfair Contract Terms Act 1977 (pp. 431–4), tendermanship and claimsmanship (ch. 17). More than a score of newly unearthed detailed issues on the Conditions and 102 additional court decisions are included.

M.W.A.

Preface to the First Edition

The Institution of Civil Engineers, etc., forms of construction contract are now used for most English and Irish engineering works, and also abroad. My major aim in this book is to supply the engineer or contractor turning to any particular clause in the forms with an analysis of the clause and cross-references, and the background law necessary to apply it. At the same time the notes and general chapters are planned to give an outline of general engineering law independent of these forms.

The Association of Consulting Engineers' service agreements are dealt with in the same way.

This book is therefore not primarily written for lawyers, and I have shunned legal jargon not only because outsiders find it pompous and out of date, but because I feel that it is in practice a real obstacle to understanding and useful co-operation between the engineer and lawyer. At the same time I hope that this book will be helpful to my colleagues—the arguments and authorities on doubtful points are set out fully, and I have tried to make clear the unique problems of engineering, since lawyers almost always equate civil engineering works, however vast, with having a house built.

The engineers I have had the pleasure of lecturing and advising have, in the nicest way, made it plain that they generally prefer to steer clear of law and lawyers. As a result the parties do not always consider the contract forms properly before signature, or even when there is trouble on the works—but it is certain that they would avoid much eventual suffering at the hands of lawyers if they did. A knowledge of the contract is obviously essential to a contractor if he is to value the risks he is taking, and the contractor, employer and engineer should find the forms, if completely understood, a useful guide on avoiding or solving many problems.

It is even possible that the engineer may learn some general lessons from the lawyer—particularly about precision of language and the proper approach to disputes. I hope that this book will make a small contribution to that also.

Foreword

by

SIR WILLIAM HARRIS, K.B.E., C.B., D.Sc.(Hon.), M.A., F.Eng., F.I.C.E.
Past President of the Institution of Civil Engineers

When, after three years' hard labour by the Joint Contracts Committee of the I.C.E., A.C.E. and F.C.E.C., under my chairmanship, the 5th Edition of the I.C.E. Conditions of Contract was published by the sponsors in June 1973, there was a great deal of public debate among engineers, contractors and lawyers. Articles were written, lectures given and conferences organised and, not surprisingly, opinions differed—even among the lawyers—on the interpretation and probable effects of a number of the changes that had been made.

It was at that time that I first got to know Max Abrahamson personally and began to appreciate his deep interest in and knowledge of the law and practice of civil engineering contracts. He was one of the first to analyse and, in some respects, criticise the new 5th Edition and he and I had several meetings to discuss the opinions he expressed. I was greatly impressed by the depth of thought Mr. Abrahamson had given to the whole subject and also by his reasonable and constructive attitude throughout our discussions—even though we continued to differ on a number of issues.

The first two editions of Mr. Abrahamson's book (1965 and 1969) were based on the 4th Edition of the I.C.E. Conditions of Contract and, in 1975, after a major re-writing, his third edition, incorporating the 5th Edition of the I.C.E. Conditions, was published. By this time these were in fairly general use for new contracts, but there was little experience of operating them and, of course, no case law at all. Nevertheless, Mr. Abrahamson's careful and detailed analysis of the Conditions themselves and of the duties and responsibilities of the several parties involved in the practical operation of contracts based on them has been a most valuable aid to all concerned. There must be few engineers' or contractors' offices in which his third edition is not regarded as an essential reference book.

Since then there has been a number of important developments, such as the publication of the C.E.S.M.M. in 1976, the Unfair Contract Terms Act 1977 and the changing attitude to liability for negligence. Moreover, experience in the use of the new I.C.E. Conditions, the Baxter Indices and the C.E.S.M.M. is accumulating: and although there is, as yet, little (if any) case law arising from the 5th Edition, there have been further important court decisions on construction contracts generally. So, once again, Max Abrahamson has up-dated and expanded his book to take account of all these and to make available to engineers, contractors, arbitrators and

ix

clients contemporary and comprehensive practical guidance in what is still a complex, though fascinating, subject.

Far be it from me to attempt a critical analysis of Max Abrahamson's latest work, as he has done of mine (the 5th Edition itself!). But I have read through all the amendments and additions and am, once again, impressed by the extent of his knowledge and by his insight into the many problems which, however good the Conditions of Contract and other documents may be, will continue to beset those who are concerned with civil engineering contracts. There are still a few issues on which our opinions differ, to a greater or lesser extent, but in this field there are no absolute answers: even court decisions can be reversed. The importance of this book lies in the thoroughness with which every conceivable facet of the contractual process has been examined and exposed, the clarity with which the argument is developed and the relevance of the cases quoted. The fact that I and probably others may differ, here and there, on matters of opinion, in no way detracts from the value of the wise guidance which the book contains.

This new, up-to-date edition of Mr. Abrahamson's book should be kept within easy reach of all those engaged in drawing up contract documents and in supervising, operating and settling civil engineering contracts — and especially those who (should they have failed to read and learn from it) get involved in arbitration.

Acknowledgements

Sir William Harris' reputation inside and beyond the construction industry is such that he needs no commendation from me; but if I may say so, it is typical of him to accept that controversy does not preclude friendly discussion. I have learned much about the practical realities of the industry from discussions with him, started in print and happily continued in person. I am heartened and grateful that he has been kind enough to grace this edition with a foreword.

Martin Barnes and Peter Madge have read and commented helpfully on my views on measurement and insurance, respectively, on which they are so expert. As always, I have shamelessly exploited friends and clients, and indeed so many have helped me with this edition, directly and indirectly, that I must thank them collectively rather than choose some names to mention.

My associate Tim Bouchier-Hayes has borne with skill much of the burden of checking and proof-reading this edition. I realise it was his sense of duty rather than the quality of my prose that caused him to read the proofs up to and including the day of his wedding, and I hope Sinead will forgive me.

While I have been coping with this edition all the members of my office have been even more patient with me than they usually have to be. I am particularly grateful to Michael O'Reilly for stalwart help with the proofs, and also to Philip Lee. I am sure that Rosanna Flanagan will enjoy her retirement all the more with the thought that she does not again have to translate my drafts into a manuscript, but her help with several editions has been invaluable. For this edition she has been aided by Helen Casey and Rachel O'Callaghan.

My publishers, personified by the indefatigable Sheila Graham, have co-operated beyond the bounds of duty to get this edition into print, despite pressures on me which, amongst other reasons, have required them to contend with what I have to describe with some understatement as a less than ideal author.

Finally, Edna and our children have allowed me to write this edition in what should have been their time. But then there is so much for which I can never thank them adequately.

M.W.A.

Contents

CHAPTER 1

Background to the Contract Forms:
General Law of Contract

The forms of tender, agreement, conditions and bond published by the
Institution of Civil Engineers, etc., and the Association of Consulting
Engineers' Service Agreements are designed to standardise the duties of
contractors, employers and engineers and to distribute fairly the risks
inherent in civil engineering.

The contract system on which these forms are based has been in use for
over a century, and the present practice is outlined in a report published by
the Institution, so that it is not necessary to say anything about it here.   *a*

The forms themselves—in general use since about 1950—have defects,
but are not as defective as many of the forms concocted by individual
engineers and contractors used before then. They have the great advantage
that their contents become known and understood with constant use, so
that they have reduced the number of disputes and misunderstandings.   *b*

From a practical point of view the use of the forms is now so widespread
that they are really a private code of legislation which is automatically
accepted by individual employers and contractors, subject to adjustments
for special cases, rather than an agreement on terms which are bargained
for in detail between them. Nevertheless, it is normally the ordinary law of
contract which applies—the branch of the law which regulates rights and
duties not imposed by the law but created by the parties' own agreement
with each other. To be dealt with first, therefore, are four general topics   *c*
relating to the law of contract.

Essentials of a valid contract. The basic requirements of the courts before
they will enforce a private agreement as a legal contract are, very briefly
because they will not often be in question in relation to construction or
service contracts—

(*a*) CERTAINTY. Since it is the agreement of the parties which gives
binding force to a contract, the terms of their agreement must be sufficiently
certain to have a practical meaning. To create a contract the parties must
not have failed to agree on any term which "*even though the parties did not
realise it, was in fact essential to be agreed, as a term of the contract, if the*

(*a*) "Civil Engineering Procedure" published by the Institution of Civil Engineers.
(*b*) This comment has been allowed to stand from previous editions, because there can be little
doubt that there would be more disputes if a variety of home-made forms were used instead
of the I.C.E. Conditions. That is not to say that there is any shortage of disputes in the
industry; hence the finale of this book is on "Tendermanship and Claimsmanship".
(*c*) There are many books available for those who wish to obtain a grasp of the general law of
contract—e.g. "Sutton & Shannon on Contracts", 7th ed.; Cheshire & Fifoot "The Law of
Contract", 9th ed.; Treitel "The Law of Contract", 4th ed.; John Uff "Construction Law",
2nd ed., which covers a number of other relevant topics.

contract was to be commercially workable". The courts will help—if, for example, no price is fixed they may imply that a reasonable price is to be paid—but they cannot make the contract for the parties:

> Defendant sued on an agreement to buy a van. A deposit had been made but all that was said about the balance of the price was that it was to be paid "on hire-purchase terms".
> Held: "hire-purchase terms" vary so much that it was impossible to say what the parties intended to agree to, and there was no binding contract.

> Contractors submitted two tenders for construction of a freight terminal. One tender was at a fixed price, and the other had a price variation clause. There was a steep rise in costs after tender, and the contractors wrote to the employers asking for sympathetic consideration of revision of the prices quoted for the fixed price tender. The employers wrote to the contractors that they accepted "your tender". No contract was signed, and it was held that as the employers had not made it clear which tender they were accepting, there was no concluded contract and the contractors were entitled to payment on a *quantum meruit* (see below) for the works, which they had completed.

> Agreement that a developer's quantity surveyor would negotiate with a builder—"fair and reasonable contract sums in respect of each of the three projects as they arise. (These would incidentally be based upon agreed estimates of the net cost of work and the general overheads with a margin for profit of five per cent) . . .". Negotiations on prices eventually broke down. Held that there was no concluded contract. There was no agreement on the price or any method by which the price was to be calculated, not dependent on agreement being reached by the parties in further negotiations. An agreement to negotiate a fundamental term of a contract such as price is too uncertain to be enforced by the courts.

It is not often nowadays that the main contract is not tied up, because the procedure has become stereotyped. Lack of similar procedure in engineers' offices (in the case of nominated sub-contractors) and on the part of contractors and sub-contractors for making sure that all sub-contracts are in order, is one of the reasons why a high proportion of the legal troubles in construction work now are about sub-contracting.

A common sequence is a quotation from a sub-contractor containing on the back, in small print, conditions of contract trying hard (but not always successfully in law) to shed legal responsibility. The main contractor replies with an "acceptance" of tender, which says that all conditions put forward by the sub-contractor are to be null and void and contains its own conditions, placing the sub-contractor at the mercy of the main contractor. There may also be discrepancies between the quotation and acceptance about attendances and co-ordination of programmes. These differences are

(d) *Trollope & Colls Ltd.* v. *Atomic Power Construction Ltd.* [1963] 1 W.L.R. 333, 336 per Megaw J.

(e) *Scammell and Nephew Ltd.* v. *Ouston* [1941] A.C. 251. In *Love & Stewart Ltd.* v. *S. Instone & Co. Ltd.* [1917] 33 T.L.R. 475 it was held that an agreement to deliver goods by a specified date subject to "strike and lock-out clause" was not enforceable because the parties had not agreed on the terms of that clause and there was no evidence of a particular usual or customary form of such a clause intended by the parties to apply. *See also* p. 45 (vi).

(f) *Peter Lind & Co.* v. *Mersey Docks & Harbour Board* [1972] 2 Lloyd's Rep. 234.

(g) *Courtney & Fairbairn Ltd.* v. *Tolaini Bros. (Hotels) Ltd.* [1975] 1 All E.R. 716, C.A. The line between a case such as this where the parties are still negotiating about price and therefore there is no contract, and cases where the courts have recognised that there is a binding contract because the parties' silence about price can be interpreted as an intention that a reasonable price is to be paid (p. 175 on variations) is by no means crystal clear from the judgments in this decision.

either ignored or, while efforts are being made to sort them out, the work starts. As a result it may be extremely difficult to decide what are the terms of the contract between the parties, or because of the lack of agreement on all the points raised there may be no contract at all and either party may lose unfairly. The sub-contractor may have no remedy for breach of contract if he is put off the site. Because even an agreed price does not bind unless the contract as a whole is agreed, the sub-contractor may be entitled to payment on a *quantum meruit* for the work done (i.e. literally "as much as he has earned", that is reasonable payment, which may be based on cost plus profit).

For letters of intent refer to p. 18, and for incorporation of standard terms p. 26.

A word of warning is necessary: legislation intended to prevent abuse of the freedom to contract may now alter the effect of the agreed terms of a contract. Chapter 16 deals with the most important cases.

(*b*) CONSIDERATION. The law of contract was originally developed to meet the needs of the commercial world, and this is still reflected in the rule that only an agreement which has an element of bargain will be enforced by the courts—that is, an agreement by which each party "gives something" to the other in return for the benefit he is receiving. For example, the employer agrees to pay the price in consideration of the contractor building the works. The benefit given—the consideration—need not be equal in any way to the benefit being received, and may be actually doing something for the other party, or not doing something which would be to his disadvantage, or promising to do either in the future. Where one party receives no consideration of any of these kinds, an agreement will not be enforced:

> A contractor refused to do work unless the employer agreed to pay for it as an extra. In fact the work was included in the contract work which the contractor was bound to do for the original contract price.
> Held: The contractor gave no consideration for the employer's promise to pay him extra, which therefore was not binding.

> A contractor submits a tender for works and agrees that it will be open for acceptance for one week.
> The contractor may still withdraw his tender at any time because the employer

(*h*) In *Butler Machine Tools Co. Ltd.* v. *Ex-Cell-O Corp. (England) Ltd.* (1977) 121 S.J. 406, C.A. conditions of sale were included on the back of a quotation from the seller for delivery of a machine. The conditions opened by saying they were to prevail over any terms and conditions in the buyer's order. Nevertheless the buyer replied with an order on his terms "and conditions as appearing overleaf" and including a tear-off acknowledgement slip stating that those terms and conditions were accepted and with a blank for the delivery date. The slip was completed and returned by the seller.

Held: the documents were to be considered as a whole. The acknowledgement made it clear that the contract was on the buyer's, not the seller's, terms of contract and therefore the price fluctuations clause that was included only in the latter did not apply. The judgments in the Court of Appeal contain a divergence of opinion which illustrates the extreme difficulty for themselves and the courts that parties may create if they do not take proper precautions in making a contract to avoid the "battle of the forms".

Refer also to *Davies and Co. Shopfitters Ltd.* v. *William Old* (1969) 67 L.G.R. 395, summarised in footnote (*g*), p. 26.

(*i*) For possible limitations on this result see *Way* v. *Latilia* [1937] 3 All E.R. 759, H.L.

(*j*) Unreported, but see *Sharpe* v. *San Paulo Ry.* (1873) L.R. 8 Ch.App. 597, at p. 608. *See also* p. 179, N. 2 and particularly p. 182, footnote (*c''*).

has given no consideration for his promise to keep it open. But the contractor is
k　　bound by the promise if the employer makes any payment for it, however small.

The only exception to this rule, again for historical reasons, is that a
promise by a party in a document on which he has put a seal—e.g. the
Agreement (p. 22)—is binding without consideration.

It follows from these principles that an employer or main contractor who
requires a tender which may not be withdrawn should specify in the tender
form that it is to remain open for a stated time and insist on having the
tender made under seal. Another expedient is to state in the tender form
that the tender will be kept open for the specified time in consideration of
the employer having supplied the contract documents to the tenderer at his
l　　request. The obligation to abide by an offer may then be secured by a bid
bond or cash deposit.

Although a time limit for validity of a tender may not bind the tenderer, it
does have the effect that the tender ends automatically when the time
expires (p. 134, N. 2). An employer or main contractor should be careful not
to let the time go by before accepting, or the tenderer may demand
improved terms for revival of his tender.

As to waiver, *see* p. 157.

(*c*) WRITING. Generally, provided the courts believe verbal evidence that
a contract was made, it is perfectly effective even though not recorded in
writing. But in some cases—e.g. contracts of guarantee (pp. 320-2) and
m　　(unless the contract has been partly performed) contracts relating to land or
n　　easements (p. 423)—a contract is not enforceable without written evidence
however much verbal proof of it there may be.

And the whole business of tying everything up in a proper written
contract is strongly recommended by lawyers in all cases, and not for self-
interest—without being cynical the following may be given as a general
warning:

> A trading agreement was made to which the parties added what they called an
> "honourable pledge" clause—that the agreement was to be binding in honour
> only and not to be enforceable by the courts.
>
> Presumably the parties had particular confidence in the integrity of each
> other, but in fact they eventually fell out and one party took proceedings to the
> House of Lords in an unsuccessful effort to have the agreement enforced. The
o　　> result was a five-figure profit to the legal profession in costs.

Of course, legal and moral right should not be confused and it is not
generally profitable in the long run to pay too much attention to the legal
limits of one's duties, but a detailed written contract does supply a
framework for preventing and settling disputes.

(*k*) This rule may particularly cause trouble in the case of a quotation for a sub-contract. A
quotation may be withdrawn although a main contract has been made including prices based
on the quotation, unless it has actually been accepted by the main contractor or there is a
binding contract with consideration to keep it open—*Pigott Structures Ltd.* v. *Keiller
Construction Co. Ltd.* (1965) 50 D.L.R. (2d) 97 Can.

(*l*) The effectiveness of this expedient is deduced from *Casey's Patents, re Stewart* v. *Casey*
[1892] 1 Ch. 104 and *Chappell & Co. Ltd.* v. *Nestlé & Co. Ltd.* [1960] A.C. 87.

(*m*) By the Statute of Frauds, 1677, as amended by the Law Reform (Enforcement of
Contracts) Act, 1954.

(*n*) By Sec. 40 (i) of the Law of Property Act, 1925, which applies to "any contract for the sale or
disposition of land or of any interest in land".

(*o*) *Rose and Frank Co.* v. *Crompton Bros. Ltd.* [1925] A.C. 445.

(*d*) CAPACITY. A person under 18 is in some circumstances not bound by a *p* contract. More important, a corporation may have only limited capacity to make a contract. A local authority or other statutory corporation has only the power to make contracts given to it by statute, and contracts outside these powers (technically *ultra vires*) are not binding. In the case of the ordinary commercial company legislation and the wide powers traditionally conferred by the memorandum of association, which is the constitution of the company, have made the *ultra vires* rule unimportant in practice.

The rule which formerly required a contract by a corporation to be under seal has been repealed.

The Crown is now fully liable on contracts made on its behalf, provided the agent making the contract has authority, and no special formalities are necessary. *q*

(*e*) DEFECTS. An apparently good contract may be affected by certain defects—for example, illegality (p. 110), mistake or misrepresentation (pp. 12, 60) or economic duress (p. 182), and a contract which was valid originally may become frustrated (p. 281) or be brought to an end when it is broken (p. 425).

Interpretation of the Contract forms by the courts—drafting. The courts interpret and apply a written contract literally—when there is a dispute they assume that the written words were chosen by the parties with the possibility of that dispute in mind, and that they accurately set out their intention when they made the contract as to the solution of the dispute. That is the rule even where the circumstances of the dispute in fact could not have been anticipated when the contract was made. The reasonable solution in view of what has actually happened or the real intention of the parties when they made the contract will not usually be given effect to if not expressed by the written words:

> Partners in a firm, by a deed which set out that the firm could not pay its creditors, assigned the firm's business and property absolutely to trustees. The deed directed the trustees to sell the business and property and to divide the proceeds amongst the firm's creditors rateably in proportions according to the amount of their debts. On sale there was found to be enough to satisfy the debts due to the creditors and to leave a surplus.
>
> Held: The partners had assigned outright their whole interest in the business and the property, and not merely enough to pay their debts, and the creditors were entitled to the surplus. *r*

The rules are not always applied as strictly as that (*see* p. 43 (*e*)) and there are also cases where the written contract may be superseded (p. 58, N. 3). But by and large the courts do not give the draftsmen enough help, and make little allowance for the real difficulties when a contract is being made of anticipating all possibilities, and wording the contract so as to cover them precisely.

The very detailed terms of the I.C.E. Contract forms, which might be thought over-elaborate, are necessary to see that they stand up to this type

(*p*) Family Law Reform Act, 1969.
(*q*) Subject to possible constitutional limits not relevant in this context.
(*r*) *Smith* v. *Cooke* [1891] A.C. 297, and see *Trollope & Colls Ltd.* v. *North West Metropolitan Regional Hospital Board* [1973] 2 All E.R. 260, H.L., summarised below on p. 42 and *Federazione Italiana* v. *Federal Commerce and Navigation Co.* [1949] 82 Ll.L. Rep. 717.

of interpretation and to the dissection which they may have to face in court. And the attitude of the courts does fulfil some useful purpose in so far as it causes contracting parties and their advisers to consider and record what, and the exact implications of what, they are agreeing to. It is failing to do this which causes most trouble, not the rules of interpretation.

For the detailed rules of interpretation *see* p. 41, N. 1, and p. 446 on the adverse effects of the attitude of the courts.

Guides to drafting. Apart from writing changes and extra clauses for the Conditions of contract, the engineer has to face the difficulties of effective drafting in preparing the technical documents, bill of quantities, specification, etc., and the contractor in preparing tender qualifications (p. 20) (all of which as part of the contract are legal documents ultimately to be interpreted by the courts (p. 302)). Bad drafting even in writing minutes of meetings and letters may cause unnecessary disputes (p. 18). Some hints for the draftsman:

(*a*) Insist on having full and clear instructions and information as to what the document to be drafted is to achieve. Do not draft a clause without visualising clearly all possibilities intended to be covered. Refer to the instructions and information often to make sure that the draft has not drifted away from what is intended. Preserve the instructions and information.

(*b*) Generally find out as much as possible about the subject matter, and ask as many questions as necessary—when in doubt ask, do not assume.

(*c*) Do not rely on memory more than is essential. In particular, make (and keep up to date) a check list of the points to be covered.

(*d*) Make a skeleton plan of the document and do not add details, which may obscure basic faults, until this ground plan is correct and logically organised. As far as possible in the whole document and each part follow some logical sequence—why (it often helps to make a clause clearer if the reason for the clause is put first), who, what, when.

(*e*) Use published forms and forms from previous documents wherever possible, but as an aid only. Avoid the scissors and paste drafting of using undigested clauses from previous contracts; there is no substitute for thought about the particular works.

(*f*) Make "across the board" checks of the draft. Check definitions one by one, then cross-references, and so on, i.e. take one point at a time and check that it is fully and consistently dealt with in the various sections of the document.

(*g*) Any special alteration or addition to the standard forms must be explicit and precise, and each of the other terms of the forms must be run through to see if any consequential changes are necessary.

(*h*) Simple words and sentences are best. Pompous and tortuous phrases and legal jargon often hide (even from the draftsman himself) the fact that the draftsman is confused about what he wants to say. But the use of words and phrases with a meaning settled by the courts in past cases (*see* the doctrine of precedent below) is often wise, however out of date they may have become in ordinary language. Do not use more words than necessary or use any word the purpose of which is not fully understood.

(*i*) Take special care about the position of words in a sentence. An American statute reads: "No one shall carry any dangerous weapon upon the public highway except for the purpose of killing a noxious animal or a policeman in the execution of his duty." Take care in choosing between "and", "or" and "and/or".

(*j*) Above all, time and pride are the enemies of good drafting. Do not be too proud to prepare as many revised drafts as necessary, or to have the document read and checked by others if at all possible. However urgent it is, never finalise an important document without putting it aside for a time, forgetting about it, and considering it again with an open mind. Compare the usual hurry in which construction documents are drafted with the following appreciation of the difficulties of drafting, written by a parliamentary draftsman:

> A friend of a draftsman walked into his office late one evening and enquired: "Done any useful work today?" The draftsman replied: "Well, to be frank, I inserted a comma before a particular word this morning. I took it off in the afternoon and just as you were entering my room I was thinking of putting it back. That is all the work I have done today."

(*k*) It is better to consult a lawyer too soon rather than too late. In consulting a lawyer on the preparation of a draft it must be remembered that his work can be no better than the instructions he receives.

(*l*) It may be expensive for the employer or contractor if a decision of the engineer on the basis of which the works were completed is eventually overruled. The engineer—unlike the courts—may tend to read the contract on the basis of what it should say or was meant to say, rather than what it literally does say, so that legal advice may be particularly necessary if the draftsman's efforts have failed and a dispute does arise on a question of interpretation.

The doctrine of precedent. Many of the statements about the law in this book are supported by references to published law reports of court decisions. It should be explained that these cases are not simply examples of the application of the law by the courts, but are themselves the law. A judge is bound by all decisions on matters of principle made in similar cases by courts of higher (or in some cases equal) standing, whether he agrees with them or not—e.g. a House of Lords decision binds all courts except the House itself unless altered by legislation, a High Court decision binds a County Court judge but not of course the Court of Appeal or House of Lords.

It is very natural for a judge to refer to previous decisions for guidance and to follow a decision which he considers right. The pecularity of the doctrine of precedent of the English common law, and legal systems based on it, is that it binds a judge to follow a previous decision whether he likes it or not and even if he thinks it is based on defective reasoning. However, only those conclusions of the judge in the previous case which were necessary for the purpose of deciding that case (the *ratio decidendi*— literally the reason for or ground of a decision) are binding in this way, and not his conclusions on other questions discussed in his judgment (*obiter dicta*— remarks by the way).

Commonwealth and U.S.A. decisions are, of course, only persuasive, not

(*s*) S. K. Hiranandami "Legislative Drafting; an Indian View" (1964) 27 Modern Law Review 1.

(*t*) Useful books on drafting are Piesse and Smith "Elements of Drafting", 3rd ed.; and Dickerson "Fundamentals of Legal Drafting".

binding, authority in the English courts. As with the *obiter dicta* of judges in English cases, whether they are followed or not will depend on the standing and reputation of the particular judge and the cogency of his reasoning.

The purpose of the doctrine of precedent is to make the law certain—so that contracts may be made and disputes settled knowing what the law is on the basis of past decisions which the courts will follow. In practice the law is about as certain as are the principles of civil engineering.

Engineering law particularly is made up largely of case law of this kind rather than legislation, but the decisions of arbitrators are not of course binding in other cases or even made public, so that the law has not developed greatly since arbitration became fashionable, and this accounts for the age of many of the cases referred to in the following chapters. However, there are signs of the courts obtaining a more active role, with an increasing number of court decisions—for good or ill.

(*u*) Effective operation of the doctrine of precedent depends on publication of court judgments, so that lawyers and others may consult past decisions in order to advise and to arrange contracts and other affairs on the basis of the existing judge-made law, and foretell how any dispute that does arise would be likely to be decided if it were brought to court. Decisions have been recorded and published for several centuries, and there are now many series of official and unofficial law reports.

Many important decisions are recorded in several reports, but the scheme adopted in this book is to refer to one report only, because that should be sufficient to enable the decision readily to be found in any law library. Where available the All England Reports are cited. Reports in the recently commenced Building Law Reports are cited for some cases.

The citation that appears after the name of each decision consists usually of the year of the report in brackets, then the abbreviation for the series of reports ("All E.R.", "B.L.R.") followed by the volume number for the year, and then the page number at which the report starts and the page number at which any quotation or observation specially referred to is to be found. Decisions of the august Court of Appeal and House of Lords are noted by their initials in the citation. Where necessary the country of origin of the decision also is identified.

CHAPTER 2

Tender and Agreement

SHORT DESCRIPTION OF WORKS:—

All Permanent and Temporary Works in connection with*...............................

....

Form of Tender[1,2]

NOTE: The Appendix forms part of the Tender.

To ....

....

....

GENTLEMEN,

Having examined the Drawings, Conditions of Contract,[3] Specification and Bill of Quantities for the construction of the above-mentioned Works (and the matters set out in the Appendix hereto), we offer to construct and complete the whole of the said Works and maintain the Permanent Works in conformity with the said Drawings, Conditions of Contract, Specification and Bill of Quantities for such sum as may be ascertained in accordance with the said Conditions of Contract.[4,5,6,7,14]

We undertake to complete and deliver the whole of the Permanent Works comprised in the Contract within the time stated in the Appendix hereto.[8]

If our tender is accepted we will, when required, provide two good and sufficient sureties or obtain the guarantee of a Bank or Insurance Company (to be approved in either case by you) to be jointly and severally bound with us in a sum equal to the percentage of the Tender Total as defined in the said Conditions of Contract for the due performance of the Contract under the terms of a Bond in the form annexed to the Conditions of Contract.

Unless and until a formal Agreement is prepared and executed this Tender, together with your written acceptance thereof, shall constitute a binding Contract between us.[9]

We understand that you are not bound to accept the lowest or any tender you may receive.[10,11]

†To the best of our knowledge and belief we have complied with the general conditions required by the Fair Wages Resolution for the three months immediately preceding the date of this tender.[12]

We are, Gentlemen,
Yours faithfully,

Signature ....

Address ....

....

Date ....
* Complete as appropriate.
† Delete if not required.

APPENDIX P.T.O.

APPENDIX

NOTE: Relevant Clause numbers are shown in brackets following the description.

Amount of Bond (if any)   (10)   .... % of Tender Total

Minimum Amount of   £ ....
Insurance   (23 (2))

Time for Completion   (43)   Liquidated Damages for Delay   (47)

Column 1
(see Clause 47 (1))

For the Whole of   £....................[b] per Day/Week[c]
the Works   [a]8 Weeks

For the following Sections   Column 2   Column 3
     (see Clause 47 (2))

Section[d]13 ....   £.....................   £...................
     Weeks   per Day/Week[c]   per Day/Week[c]

Section[d]......................   £....................   £....................
     Weeks   per Day/Week[c]   per Day/Week[c]

Section[d]......................   £....................   £....................
     Weeks   per Day/Week[c]   per Day/Week[c]

Section[d]......................   £....................   £....................
     Weeks   per Day/Week[c]   per Day/Week[c]

Period of Maintenance   (49 (1))   ....Weeks

Vesting of Materials not on Site   (54 (1) and 60 (1))[e]

1 ....   4 ....

2 ....   5 ....

3 ....   6 ....

Standard Method of Measurement adopted in preparation of Bills of Quantities (57)[f] ....

Percentage for adjustment of P.C. Sums (59A (2) (b) and (5) (c))[14]   ....%

Percentage of the Value of Goods and Materials to be included in Interim Certificates (60 (2) (b))   ....%

Minimum Amount of Interim Certificates (60 (2))   £............

[a] To be completed in every case (by Contractor if not already stipulated).
[b] To be completed by Engineer in every case.
[c] Delete which not required.
[d] To be completed if required, with brief description.[13]
[e] (If used) materials to which clauses apply are to be filled in by Engineer prior to inviting tenders.
[f] Insert here any amendment or modification adopted if different from that stated in Clause 57.

1. RESTRICTIVE PRACTICE AND TENDER PROCEDURES. Until the passing of the Restrictive Trade Practices Act of 1956 the law developed by the courts on restrictive practices was unsatisfactory and there was no administrative machinery to prevent enforcement of tendering agreements contrary to the public interest. The Restrictive Trade Practices Acts 1956 & 1968 have now largely been replaced and consolidated by the Restrictive Trade Practices Act 1976. The Act defines restrictive agreements widely, requires them to be registered and provides for their judicial examination. There is a statutory presumption that any agreement falling within the definition is against the public interest and void, and the Restrictive Trade Practices Court can prevent enforcement of the agreement.

Recommendations by a building trade association that members should refuse to tender for contracts over a specified amount unless the employer supplies a bill of quantities, that they should always charge rates for day work in the building federation schedule and that they should press for use of the R.I.B.A. contract forms wherever appropriate, have been held to infringe the legislation. An agreement not to offer to supply goods in *a* response to an invitation to tender save after discussions with any other person or persons invited to tender for the supply of such goods has also been held to be a restrictive agreement, on the principle that a broad construction of the Acts is to be favoured. *b*

Agreements between contractors fixing tender prices or agreeing not to compete do not affect the validity of the actual contract if a tender is accepted unless before the contract is made the tenderer is asked for and gives the employer an assurance that there has been no such agreement, in which case the employer has remedies for misinformation. Most important, if an agreement which is registrable under the Restrictive Trade Practices Acts is not registered, any person whose interests are affected by the carrying out of its terms may sue the parties to the agreement for damages *c* for breach of statutory duty.

Article 85(1) of the Rome Treaty establishing the Common Market prohibits and imposes severe sanctions against a wide category of restrictive agreements. The Article will, however, only apply where trade between member states of the Common Market is or is likely to be affected and therefore only to construction contracts of international significance.

The procedures to be followed by the employer in inviting tenders for public works are subject to regulation, under local authority standing orders, directives of the Council of the European Communities, etc. Such *d* regulation is outside the scope of this book.

2. TENDERS AND ESTIMATES. In an old case it was held that a contractor who submitted a quotation headed "estimate" in reply to an invitation to tender had not made it sufficiently clear that he was not giving a firm tender, so that he was bound by the figure. And, in fact, what are called "estimates" *e* for small jobs are generally worded as binding lump sum offers (p. 27).

(a) *Re Birmingham Association of Building Trades Employers Agreement* [1963] 2 All E.R. 361.
(b) *Re Electrical Installation at Exeter Hospital Agreement* [1971] 1 All E.R. 347.
(c) Restrictive Trade Practices Act 1976 section 35(2).
(d) Refer to Halsbury's "Laws of England", 4th ed., vol. iv, paras. 138, and 1149–50.
(e) *Crowshaw* v. *Pritchard*, Hudson "Building Contracts", 4th ed., vol. ii, p. 274. The contractor may also have other liabilities in respect of an estimate—p. 396. In *Jardine Renovations Ltd.* v. *Holland* (1976) 13 N.B.R. (2d) 343 Can. "an approximate sum" named by contractors for carrying out work, in a letter to the employer's bank, was held not to amount to a firm quotation.

3. "HAVING EXAMINED THE . . . CONDITIONS OF CONTRACT", ETC. Although the contractor is fixed with notice of the terms of the contract documents whether he reads them or not, it may avoid disputes if attention is drawn to any changes from the standard forms. For the I.C.E. recommended method of incorporating and altering the Conditions refer to p. 25.

4. "SUCH SUM AS MAY BE ASCERTAINED IN ACCORDANCE WITH THE SAID CONDITIONS OF CONTRACT". The reality is now fully recognised that under this form of contract the contract price can be determined only when the works are finished, on final re-measurement under cl. 56. There is no initial lump sum contract price.

It is therefore particularly essential for the engineer to check the individual rates in the bills of quantities when comparing tenders (p. 17), and to bring home to the employer that what matters is not the starting total of the bill, but the finishing price, which will depend on a number of factors. A key to the payments to which the contractor may become entitled is contained in ch. 11, and "Tendermanship and Claimsmanship" are discussed in ch. 17.

5. MISTAKE IN THE TENDER PRICE. Where a mistake is made by the contractor in writing the bulk price into the tender form from the total of the bill of quantities the position is quite clear—the mistake is binding unless before the tender is accepted the employer or the engineer discovers the difference and realises that it is not intentional (N. 6). If the error is discovered the general rule which applies is that a party cannot effectively accept an offer to contract if he knows that the terms of the offer were not intended by the other party:

> A offered to sell property to B, naming a price of £1,250. B knew perfectly well that this was a slip for £2,250 but attempted to accept the offer as it stood. The court refused to order A to sell at £1,250.

This problem does not arise under the I.C.E. 5th edition, since there is no figure in the tender. More difficult are the problems that may arise where there is a mathematical or clerical error by the contractor in pricing the bill of quantities. The error may be in inserting the amount of a rate or failing to price an item; in extending a rate or in totalling or carrying forward totals:

(a) In a lump sum contract (p. 27) errors not discovered by the employer or engineer before the tender is accepted, whether in rates, extension or totalling, bind the contractor in relation to the original contract work, which is paid for at the actual lump sum price in the tender. In valuing extras—and in a quantities contract additional quantities—it seems on balance that errors in rates only are included, since the price for extras is

(f) Although this form of tender later refers to the "lowest" tender.
(g) *Webster* v. *Cecil* (1861) 132 R.R. 185, followed in *McMaster University* v. *Wilchar Construction Ltd.* [1971] 22 D.L.R. (3d) 9 Can., where an employer purported to accept a tender knowing that the contractor had omitted the entire first page of his bid, a page which included an intended escalation clause.
(h) See *Riverlate Properties Ltd.* v. *Paul* [1974] 2 All E.R. 656, C.A.
(i) In *Dudley Corp.* v. *Parsons & Morrin Ltd.*, Building Industry News, Feb. 17, 1967, an item for excavating 750 cube yds. in rock was priced out at £75, i.e. 2s. per cube yard. A fair and reasonable price would have been £2 per cube yard. It was not known beforehand whether or not rock would be met, but in fact 2,230 cube yds. of rock was excavated. The architect (under a contract in the R.I.B.A. quantities form) valued the excavation at 750 yds. at 2s. (i.e. the original extension of £75) and the balance at £2 per cube yd. Held: the contractors were entitled to 2s. per cube yd. only for the whole quantity excavated.

calculated on the basis of the individual rates and there does not seem to be any reason to apply to extra work a mistake made by the contractor in calculating his price for the original contract work from his rates. *j* Omissions and substitutions are dealt with as in the case of intentional deductions (N. 6).

For the omission of a rate, *see* p. 187.

It has been argued that in this case the discovery of the error by the employer does not alter the legal position, and that he may still keep the contractor to the mistaken price. The argument is that the contractor's offer as to price is the lump sum stated in the tender and is the offer which the contractor intended to make; that it is immaterial that his reason for offering to do the work at this figure was his mistaken belief that it represented the correct total of correct rates and calculations in his bill of quantities, particularly since the bill is completed for pricing variations only. The mistake is said to be on a par with the case of a contractor who prices the bill as he intends but bases his rates on bad costing, in which case, of course, the employer may validly accept the tender even if he realises that the contractor's price is uneconomic.

This argument is artificial:

> Employers directed their quantity surveyors to prepare a bill of reductions of a contractor's tender. Because a reference letter was misplaced, there was an error in the total of the bill. The contractor's re-tender for the reduced work with a lump sum price was accepted. Held: that "the intention of the parties . . . was that the tender for the original amount of the priced section less the priced bill of reductions should be accepted. The sum of £167,000 was erroneously taken to be the figure and erroneously embodied in the (re-tender and) contract" and was *k* therefore rectified to the correct figure.

It is suggested, therefore, that once the employer or engineer does, in fact, read the bill of quantities as the breakdown of the bulk tender price and realises that there is a mistake which has been carried over into the tender price, the courts will rectify the mistake:

> A contractor made errors in extension in a quantities contract, some in his favour, some against. The net result was an error of £1,881 in favour of the employers in the lump sum price.
> Held: That the mistakes were so palpable that it was strange that the employers wished to take advantage of them, and the errors were rectified by inserting the correct extensions. *l*

(*j*) The practice in the case of an error in extension of dividing the extended figure by the number of units included in the extension, so as to get a new rate proportionate to the actual total extended, is not correct. Where a mistaken extension is not discovered it stands insofar as it affects the lump sum price for the original contract work in a lump sum contract; in valuing variations and extra quantities (and in a measure and value contract in valuing all the work—below) there does not seem, for the reasons stated in the text, to be any basis on which the engineer should hold that the mistaken extension overrides the correct rate inserted. In *Jamieson* v. *McInnes* (1887) 15 R. (Ct. of Sess.) 17, it was held that an error in extension is lost on remeasurement.

(*k*) *Collen* v. *Dublin County Council* [1908] 1 Ir.R. 503.

(*l*) *Neill* v. *Midland Railway Company* (1869) 20 L.T. 864. See also *A. Roberts & Co. Ltd.* v. *Leicestershire C.C.* [1961] 2 All E.R. 545, where a contract was rectified because the date for completion as tendered by the contractor was put forward for one year in the formal agreement prepared by the employer, by altering the year of the date, without telling the contractor. The contractor (to the knowledge of a responsible officer of the employer) then executed the agreement without noticing the change. The decision was followed in *Weeds* v. *Blaney* [1978] 247 E.G. 211. In *Imperial Glass Ltd.* v. *Consolidated Supplies Ltd.* [1960] 22 D.L.R. (2d) 759 Can., where a sub-contractor was held to a mistake although it had been discovered, there were special circumstances, since the contractors taking advantage of the

And whatever the legal position, if the contractor is in the position that he must go on with the contract despite the mistake rather than pay damages, or where it is found during the progress of the works, in many cases he should not be held to the mistake. A contractor who is treated badly has openings for revenge in carrying out any major works, and usually only lawyers do well from the battle which results. There is also the point that if a bond is required the contractor may have difficulty in getting it if his tender is obviously too low, or if he gets a bond on a mistaken tender it may possibly be void (p. 14).

On the other hand, of course, a contractor may make a judicious "mistake" in the hope of being given an opportunity to decide whether or not to correct it after the amounts of the other tenders have become known. If the engineer suspects that this has been done, he may advise the employer to give the contractor an opportunity of withdrawing or standing by his tender, but not of changing it. If the contractor stands by the mistake it is left in if it is in a rate; in other cases it is treated as an intentional deduction and the effect should be explained to and agreed with the contractor at the outset (*see* N. 6).

m

Since the engineer normally has no implied authority to accept any tender, decisions at the tender stage on a mistake by a tenderer must be made by or with the specific authority of the employer.

Although it may fix the employer with notice of mistakes, the engineer should even with a pure lump sum contract go through the rates in detail *see* in particular N. 7 below.

(*b*) It is generally accepted that in a measure and value contract such as the I.C.E. 5th edition, the contract price is on final measurement recalculated from the individual rates without any adjustment, so that errors in extension, totalling or carrying forward of rates have no effect. It is therefore particularly necessary for the engineer to check the individual rates.

n

Mistakes in the rates themselves not found by or on behalf of the employer before acceptance of the tender bind the contractor for all work done, including variations unless they fall outside the variation clause in the original contract (pp. 169, 172).

mistake had before discovery committed themselves to a main contract on the basis of the sub-contractor's mistaken tender. "The *Imperial Glass* case has been criticised (see 39 Can. Bar. Rev. 625 (1961)), and in my humble opinion rightly so, and as far as I am able to ascertain has not been followed in any subsequently reported case." *McMaster University* v. *Wilchar Construction Ltd.* [1971] 22 D.L.R. (3d) 9 Can. In *Belle River* v. *W. J. C. Kaufman* (1977) 15 O.R. (2d) 738 Can. also it was suggested that relief would be given where a mistake is discovered before a tender is accepted.

(*m*) The Code of Procedure for Selective Tendering, published by the National Joint Consultative Committee of Architects, Quantity Surveyors and Builders, originally advised that in all cases a building contractor should be required either to abide by an erroneous tender or withdraw it completely. The 1969 edition introduced the alternative of allowing the tenderer to correct "genuine errors" as suggested above, presumably to avoid the employer having to pay a price to the next tenderer higher than he would pay even on correction of the lowest tender. This change has been criticised, but is retained in the 1977 edition. It may be less easy for a contractor to cheat by making a deliberate "error" in a tender for engineering works, compared with a building tender. The bill of quantities normally is returned with the tender, whereas in a building contract the bill may be submitted after tenders have been opened, when a contractor will usually have learned of the prices of his rivals. The problem remains that if errors may be corrected, in theory all bills should be examined because after correction of errors the apparently highest tenderer may become the lowest.

(*n*) *See* p. 13, footnote (*j*).

In this case it is obviously the individual rates and prices in the bill of quantities which are the contractor's offer as to price and there is no total price in the tender, so that there is no doubt that if the employer accepts a tender as it stands after he or the engineer has discovered a mistake in a rate, the mistake will be rectified. But as we have seen, that is so only if the employer or engineer realises that the contractor did not put in the rate he intended, not merely that a particular rate is uneconomic or the tender unbalanced (N. 7), so that this rule will generally only apply to obvious clerical errors or where the rate makes the whole bid so low that it is obvious there has been a mistake.

6. INTENTIONAL DEDUCTIONS FROM THE TOTAL OF THE BILL. In a measure and value contract, since the works are remeasured on completion and no distinction is made between the original work and extras, it is suggested that where the contractor in his bill of quantities makes a deduction from the total, the natural interpretation is that it is a short way of reducing all his rates proportionately. So that if the total of the bill is £1,000 and the contractor makes a reduction to "say £950" and tenders at that figure, he must be taken to have reduced all his rates by 5% for all work, including extras. That is, unless he makes it clear that he is simply making a bulk reduction limited to £50 whatever the final contract price may be. For example, sections 5.26 and 6 of the C.E.S.M.M. (p. 231) require a bill of quantities prepared in accordance with the method to include an adjustment item in the grand summary, against which the tenderer may insert "a lump sum addition or deduction". The method clarifies the implications of the lump sum nature of the adjustment.

The method says that in each interim certificate a part of the item is added or deducted in the proportion that "the amount referred to in cl. 60(2)(a)" of the Conditions included in the interim certificate bears to the total of the bill of quantities without the item (provisional items and P.C. sums, etc. are not deducted). Cl. 60(2)(a) refers to "*the amount ... less a retention*" and it appears, and makes sense, that the words just quoted from the method mean the initial amount. The method says specifically that any interim addition or deduction is to be made before deduction of retention, and therefore will affect the amount of retention. Such interim additions or deductions are not to exceed the amount of the item, and conversely if the whole of the item has not been added or deducted by the date of issue of the completion certificate for the whole works the balance is to be added to or deducted from the retention money due on the certificate. (What if the retention is used up by the employer to make good defects, etc?)

(*o*) The Code of Procedure for Single Stage Selective Tendering 1977 for building points out that in making this calculation provisional sums and P.C. items should not be included (presumably including their associated items for attendances and profit), and they are not reduced by the percentage, since they are items of outlay for the contractor and subject to change. The Code also suggests that the preliminary items in the bill should not be reduced by the percentage, but it is difficult to see why — *see* Johnson "Making the Contract", The Chartered Surveyor, 98 (1965–66), p. 651.

(*p*) The use of the adjustment item is discussed in Barnes, "Measurement in Contract Control" at pp. 63–67. The purpose of the item is stated to be to supply a convenient place where the tenderer can make a last minute adjustment to his tender without altering rates and prices within the work items themselves, for example if changed quotations are received late from sub-contractors or the contractor's senior staff have second thoughts about the level of the tender.

It is a question why such a solution to a mechanical difficulty should produce the results

Thus under an adjustment item where the contractor is entitled to payment for variations at or based on his rates in the bill only the figures in the rates column of the bill apply and not the item. Where the contractor is entitled to payment of his costs or a fair valuation under cl. 52(2), or possibly even an "*appropriate increase or decrease of any rates or prices*" under cl. 56(2), the rates and prices in the bill strictly speaking do not govern (p. 211), but if either party refers to those rates and prices as having some relevance to the payment due to the contractor it seems that the contractor in the case of an addition or the employer in the case of a deduction may refer to the fact that the rates and prices were to some extent affected by an adjustment item.

The effects of a bulk addition or omission can be settled definitely by adding after it in the bill that it is a lump sum item and to be dealt with in accordance with section 6 of the C.E.S.M.M. It is, of course, open to the employer to exclude the method and to state in the tender documents that any bulk addition or deduction by the contractor will be adjusted for variations alone or both variations and changes in quantities, or for the contractor to tender specifically on the terms that all his rates or the rates in a particular section of the bill are to be taken to have been altered by a percentage as illustrated above. The Department of Transport allows for a "balancing item" in the bill, and alters cl. 56 to specify that the rates and prices in the bill other than those "in respect of any Preliminaries Prime Cost Items (together with their associated items for attendance and profit) and Dayworks" when "used for valuing work in accordance with cls. 52 or 56" are to be adjusted by an appropriate addition or deduction "in proportion that the sum against the balancing item bears to the Tender Total before the addition or deduction of the balancing item and less the above amounts".

If the contractor makes a deduction in a pure lump sum or quantities contract the original contract work is paid for at the net price shown in the tender. Unless otherwise stated it does not seem that any percentage alterations should be made in the rates for extra work (or increases in quantities) since in this case the mere fact that the contractor makes a deduction for the original contract work does not imply that he is agreeing to a similar deduction for extra work the extent of which he does not know in advance. Where work is omitted, the net price only, after percentage adjustment for the deduction by the contractor, should be subtracted from the lump sum price. Where work is substituted, no percentage adjustment need be made since adjustments of the omitted work and of the new work (which would only be adjusted up to the value of the omitted work) would cancel themselves out.

Bulk deductions and additions in the bill made initially or after tender to correct mistakes give trouble constantly and create surprises where the

---

that (in a measurement contract with no original contract price (N.4)) additional quantities and extras may be valued at a higher or lower level than the rest of the works and an omission or reduced quantities will mean that the work remaining is effectively paid for at a lower or higher rate than that in the bill. The payment received by the contractor may even differ from that payable to the sub-contractor whose late quotation made the adjustment item necessary. The employer may minimise the opportunities for illicit use of an adjustment item by specifying in the invitation to tender that it must not exceed a stated percentage of the total of the rest of the bill, and the engineer will have to consider the item when reporting on tenders (p. 17, N. 7).

quantities of the works change substantially or there are major variations. It is important for both parties to consider the implications of the system for adjustment agreed to, and except where the C.E.S.M.M. adjustment item is adopted without change the intention should be defined in detail by a special term in the contract or endorsement on the bill signed on behalf of both parties, rather than leaving the result to any of the above disputable principles.

7. UNBALANCED BIDS. The comparison by the engineer of the detailed pricing of tenders is a safeguard against an unbalanced bid, where the contractor prices some work high and other work low (e.g. rock and earth in foundations) in the belief that variations or increases in quantities will mean more of the high-priced and less of the low-priced work than estimated in the bill. Obviously such a bid should not be accepted unless it is certain that the contractor's gamble is wrong, and there may be general doubts as to the integrity of the contractor who makes it. *See also* pp. 184 9 and 211. Under the I.C.E. 5th edition comparison of rates is the only way of evaluating tenders, since there is no initial contract price, and it is quite misleading to an employer to compare tenders under a remeasurement contract by reference to the tender total (N. 4, p. 12).

For unbalanced method-related charges refer to pp. 219 20.

8. TIME FOR COMPLETION. If no completion time is filled in to the Appendix, unless there is a case for rectification (p. 41 (*a*)) the contractor has a reasonable time in which to complete the work, and any liquidated damages clause for delay is void since there is no date from which to calculate the damages.

9. "TENDER ... WITH ... WRITTEN ACCEPTANCE ... A BINDING CONTRACT" —so that it is generally too late after acceptance for the contractor, e.g., to make enquiries about the employer's financial position or to raise queries on the contract documents, and too late for the employer to incorporate new terms relating to co-ordination of the main contract and nominated sub-contract programmes, or attendances on nominated sub-contractors.

The tender generally may be withdrawn at any time before acceptance even if the contractor has agreed to keep it open (p. 3 (*b*)). An acceptance sent by post normally binds both parties immediately it is posted, not merely when it is received. For enquiries by the engineer before acceptance *see* p. 377, N. 12.

Outright acceptance by the employer should say in writing simply that the tender is accepted (as envisaged by the words from the form of tender quoted at the head of this note).

There are several alternatives to an outright tender and acceptance making a full and complete binding contract. The traditional form of words to show that although negotiations have reached an advanced stage neither party is actually to be bound at all by a legal agreement, is to say that the tender or acceptance is "subject to contract". The parties then have a breathing space for second thoughts and advice; they are not normally

q

(*q*) At 3.50 p.m. on July 8th H. posted a letter accepting an offer to contract previously made by F., which F. received on the following morning, At 5 p.m. on the 8th H. had received a letter from F. revoking his offer. Held: that the acceptance took effect on posting, the revocation only on receipt. Therefore there was a binding contract (*Henthorn* v. *Fraser* [1892] 2 Ch. 27).

committed in law unless they eventually sign a formal contract, which neither is bound to do.

A tender or acceptance may be subject to some other condition, which will take effect if accepted by the other party. The nature of the condition should be defined carefully, rather than leaving it to a court to determine. Is the agreement to be binding subject only to termination if the condition, such as receipt of financing or planning permission, is not fulfilled (within a stated time if appropriate) and possibly saying that only one party has the option to terminate? Alternatively, is the agreement intended not to bind either party at all unless and until the condition is fulfilled, so that either may withdraw in the meantime? Is either party under a duty to use his best endeavours or reasonable efforts to ensure that the condition is met or at least not to prevent the condition being fulfilled?

Too often in practice one of the parties wishes to have it both ways—to write a letter which will bind the other party but leaves himself free to decide whether or not to contract. That is not possible except by openly and with the agreement of the other party making a contract with a one-sided right of termination (above) or entering into a separate option agreement under seal or for consideration (p. 3 (b)).

Where the intention is to bind both parties to a halfway house between a full contract and no contract at all, the practice is for the employer to issue a letter of intent that is then accepted by the contractor. Unfortunately many letters dignified with that title merely say that the employer "intends to make" a contract and are ambiguous as to whether he intends to make a contract immediately, and if so exactly what contract, or merely is in mind at the moment to make a contract in the future. A recent case illustrates the apparently irresistible wish in the industry to donate money to lawyers:

Employer's representatives announced at a meeting that they intended awarding a design and construct contract to the contractors. This meant that the contractors had to embark on a period of intensive and expensive work, including preparation of detailed plans and specifications, but it was clear that the formal contract could not be agreed and signed for some time.

The Official Referee held that the contractors had made known to the employers that they required an indemnity in respect of work done between the meeting referred to and the execution of the formal contract. He held also that the contractors regarded a letter of intent issued by the employers as agreeing to give such an indemnity, although the letter merely said that the contract was to be awarded to them and "the whole to be subject to agreement on an acceptable contract". The representatives of the employers had stated in evidence that the letter of intent actually was intended to exclude any ancillary contract.

Held: viewing the events objectively as a court is bound to do, a contract had been made, ancillary to the intended contract to construct the works, by which the employers were bound to pay the contractors their interim costs.

Ingredients of a good letter of intent are:

(a) A definition of the employer's commitment, for example whether he authorises the contractor to place orders for supply of steel, or fabrication also, or to do work on site.

(b) A statement that the employer is not binding himself to a full

---

(r) The normal effectiveness of those words has been confirmed by the Court of Appeal in *Tiverton Estates Ltd.* v. *Wearwell Ltd.* [1974] 1 All E.R. 209, C.A., but difficulty may still be caused if they are used but at the same time (often in the same letter) the contractor is inconsistently ordered to start work immediately.

(s) For the meaning of "best endeavours" *see* p. 313 (d').

(t) *Turriff Construction Ltd.* v. *Regalia Knitting Mills Ltd.* (1971) 222 E.G.R. 169.

contract, and that the contractor's authority under the letter will end on a named date or may be ended at will by the employer if no full contract is made in the meantime.

(c) Method of paying the contractor for orders placed or work done during the currency of the letter of intent—a reasonable lump sum or rates in a bill, paid at some specified date or by monthly interim certificates to be deducted from the first contract certificate (if any), deduction and eventual payment to the contractor of retention, etc.

(d) Provision that any materials bought are to pass into the immediate ownership of the employer, with safeguards against retention of title clauses (p. 262). The purpose of a letter of intent often is to place early orders for materials, and the employer will be in the contractor's hands if the ownership of those materials remains with the contractor.

(e) The contractor to insure the materials bought and the work on site and against third party claims, generally in accordance with the insurance clauses of the Conditions notwithstanding that the full contract has not been made.

(f) It may be relevant to specify from what date the contract period is to start for the purpose of cl. 43 if a full contract is made eventually—whether from the date notified under cl. 41 or from the date of the letter of intent.

(g) Quality of work done under the letter of intent to be in accordance with the specification, etc.

(h) The terms of the tender documents should be read through carefully to see which, if any, should be specifically applied to the interim arrangement. For example, the arbitration or variation clause or price fluctuation formula. Other terms may be excluded specifically so as to avoid doubt.

The engineer must have his client's authority to accept a tender or issue a letter of intent (p. 399).

The gist of this long note is that the essential step at the culmination of negotiations for a contract is for the parties to make up their minds and record clearly what they intend.

For execution of a formal agreement *see* p. 21, and for matters which may affect the validity of the contract, p. 5 (e).

10. "NOT BOUND TO ACCEPT ... ANY TENDER". Even in the absence of a specific statement a person inviting tenders (or competition drawings) is not obliged to accept the lowest of any tender or to pay anything even though the parties tendering have been put to expense. The invitor may, however, be liable, in the case of a competition, for preventing the judges from considering an entry, or to pay for a tender or entry if he makes use of it for any purpose:

Plans submitted on approval were not used for the works, but they were used to show intended purchasers how the site land could be developed.
Held: that they must be paid for.

Cases are not unknown where it is suspected that although for various reasons it was thought wise to invite open tenders for a job, the contractor

(u) *Landless* v. *Wilson* (1880) 8 R. (Ct. of Sess.) 289. In *William Lacey (Hounslow)* v. *Davis* [1957] 2 All E.R. 712, builders prepared estimates of the cost of reconstructing a building in the belief, shared at that time by the owners, that they would be given the contract to do the work. The estimate was used by the owners in negotiations with the War Damage Commission for compensation. Held: that the builders were entitled to reasonable remuneration, because their work went beyond that normally done in preparing a tender and therefore a promise to pay for it could be implied.

was, in fact, chosen in advance, or tenders may be invited in order to check the prices of a favoured contractor with whom negotiations have already taken place. Where that can be proved, the other tenderers will be entitled to damages.

In addition, if the tender is accepted and the contract is then broken by the employer refusing to allow the contractor to carry it out, instead of claiming his loss of profit as damages the contractor may elect to claim for the wasted expenditure incurred in relation to the contract, including expenditure on tendering before the contract was made (but he is not entitled to both profit and expenses).

11. TENDER QUALIFICATIONS. From a contractor's point of view the perfect tender qualification is a wolf in sheep's clothing, in the sense of giving the contractor full protection while looking as innocuous as possible. Unfortunately, because of bad drafting combined with the narrow interpretation which the courts tend to place on these qualifications, it is often the opposite result which is achieved:

A contractor agreed to build a number of houses for a lump sum, to be completed in eight months. Attached to his tender was a letter which said that his tender was subject to adequate supplies of labour being available as and when required. This letter was not referred to in the agreement eventually sealed. Held: the letter was not a contract document, and even if it had been it meant only that the contractor would be entitled to an extension of time for any difficulty in getting labour, not that he was to be entitled to extra payment.

There are therefore two problems—to ensure both that the qualification will be accepted by the courts as part of the contract, and that the wording of the qualification is sufficient to give the contractor the protection on which he is relying in pricing the works.

There is a presumption that if the parties enter into a written contract, the writing is intended to set out all the terms of their agreement and to supersede any terms discussed or agreed on during negotiations. This presumption has hardened into a rule which may be applied even though it defeats the parties' intention, as in the case last cited.

There are exceptions to this rule (p. 58); however, the wise course is for any tender qualification to be put in writing and added to the list of tender documents in clause 2 of the agreement and 1 (1) (e) of the Conditions.

(v) *Anglia Television Ltd.* v. *Reed* [1971] 3 All E.R. 690. See also *Gilmore Hankey Kirke Partnership* v. *Cross* (1978) N.L.J. 87.

(w) *Davis Contractors* v. *Fareham U.D.C.* [1956] 2 All E.R. 145, H.L. In that case the contract was in the R.I.B.A. form. For a (doubtful) unreported decision where the contractor was given extra payment under the 4th ed. of the I.C.E. Contract forms on foot of a similar qualification see *Holland and Hannen & Cubitts Ltd.* v. *Yeovil R.D.C.* (1964) Hudson "Building & Engineering Contracts" 10th ed. by I. N. Duncan Wallace, p. 222. It is there pointed out that to read the qualification in the *Davis* case as relating to the right to an extension of time only was still to give it some purpose, since under that contract the right to an extension was limited to specific events which did not include shortage of labour; on the other hand, cl. 44 of these Conditions is very general.

(x) It must in any case be made clear that the employer agrees to the qualification. In *Royston U.D.C.* v. *Royston Builders Ltd.* (1961) 177 E.G. 589, notification to the employer's surveyor by the contractors that they would require the fluctuation clause to apply to materials not in the list of materials attached to the bill was ineffective, because although the surveyor did not repudiate the qualification neither did he agree to it. *Leslie & Co.* v. *Commissioners of Works* (1914) 78 J.P. 462 is a similar decision. See also *Boot & Sons Ltd.* v. *L.C.C.* [1959] 1 W.L.R. 1069, where it was the employer who was caught out.

The problem in writing a qualification is that if it is worded very generally it may be interpreted restrictively by the courts so as to alter the other contract terms as little as possible, in accordance with the principle of reconciling and giving effect to all the terms of the contract as far as possible (p. 43 (e)). If, on the other hand, the qualification is specific, some points in the contract documents which should be changed may be missed inadvertently. The solution is a general clause followed by some such phrase as "in particular but not so as to affect the generality of the foregoing" or "by way of illustration but not enumeration" or (if that legal jargon is too much) simply "in particular" or "by way of illustration only", and a list of clauses in the contract which are to be altered, for which the draftsman should go through even the standard contract forms clause by clause rather than rely on his memory. Since, regrettable as it is, lawyers have a monopoly of ultimately interpreting qualifications, of all things tender qualifications should be settled by lawyers (p. 302).

12. Fair Wages Resolution. *See* p. 122 for the Resolution. If this certificate of compliance with the Resolution is untrue the employer is entitled to end the contract and to damages.

13. Section to be completed early. For the importance of a clear and accurate description of the section, despite this footnote to the form of tender, refer to p. 98, N. 3. It may be necessary to specify that access and services to a section are to be completed with it.

14. Percentage for adjustment of P.C. Sums. For the contractor's right to this percentage, in some cases even if a P.C. item is omitted from the contract, *see* p. 240, N. 7.

AGREEMENT

The tender and acceptance provide a satisfactory binding contract (*see* p. 17, N. 9) to which the execution of this agreement under seal adds nothing, except an extra six years for limitation of actions (p. 430).

If it is used, a copy of the agreement should be executed for each party, and copies of the other contract documents initialled (including the price variation sheets, p. 312).

For matters which may affect the validity of the agreement *see* p. 5 (e).

1. "The payments to be made". There is no initial contract price—p. 12, N. 4. For a key to the payments to which the contractor may become entitled *see* ch. 11. For deductions from payments *see* p. 269.

2. The written acceptance of tender is a contract document by cl. 1(1)(e) of the Conditions, although it is not mentioned here.

3. Execution. This first form of execution under seal is for a party which is a limited company or other corporation, the second for an individual.

(*y*) In this case—as almost invariably happens with problems of interpretation—two rules conflict, *see* p. 44 (ii), and it may be very difficult to forecast how a judge will balance them.

Form of Agreement

THIS AGREEMENT made the .... day of ....
19 .... BETWEEN ....
of .... in the
County of.................... (hereinafter called "the Employer") of the one part and
.... of...
in the County of..
.... (hereinafter called "the Contractor") of the other part

WHEREAS the Employer is desirous that certain Works should be constructed, viz. the Permanent and Temporary Works in connection with............................
.... and has accepted a Tender by the Contractor for the construction and completion of such Works and maintenance of the Permanent Works NOW THIS AGREEMENT WITNESSETH as follows:

1. In this Agreement words and expressions shall have the same meanings as are respectively assigned to them in the Conditions of Contract hereinafter referred to.

2. The following documents shall be deemed to form and be read and construed as part of this Agreement, viz:

     (a)   The said Tender.
     (b)   The Drawings.
     (c)   The Conditions of Contract.
     (d)   The Specification.
     (e)   The Priced Bill of Quantities.[2]

3. In consideration of the payments to be made by the Employer to the Contractor as hereinafter mentioned[1] the Contractor hereby covenants with the Employer to construct and complete the Works and maintain the Permanent Works in conformity in all respects with the provisions of the Contract.

4. The Employer hereby covenants to pay to the Contractor in consideration of the construction and completion of the Works and maintenance of the Permanent Works the Contract Price at the times and in the manner prescribed by the Contract.

IN WITNESS whereof the parties hereto have caused their respective Common Seals to be hereunto affixed (or have hereunto set their respective hands and seals) the day and year first above written.

The Common Seal of..
.... Limited
was hereunto affixed in the presence of[2]:

    or

SIGNED SEALED AND DELIVERED by the
said..
....
in the presence of[3]:—

CHAPTER 3

Conditions of Contract
Clauses 1–19

DEFINITIONS AND INTERPRETATION

THE EMPLOYER AND CONTRACTOR

1. (1) In the Contract (as hereinafter defined) the following words and expressions shall have the meanings hereby assigned to them except where the context otherwise requires:

(a) "Employer" means ....
of ....
and includes the Employer's personal representatives,[1] or successors.[2,3]

(b) "Contractor" means the person or persons firm or company whose tender has been accepted by the Employer and includes the Contractor's personal representatives[1] successors[2] and permitted assigns.[4]

For interpretation generally *see* pp. 5 6 and cl. 5.

1. "EMPLOYER (CONTRACTOR) ... INCLUDES THE EMPLOYER'S (CONTRACTOR'S) PERSONAL REPRESENTATIVES". By these words the contract continues in force despite the death of either party. So the executors or administrators of a contractor who dies are entitled, and may be required by the employer, to complete the works. And the executors or administrators of an employer who dies may require, and must allow the contractor if he wishes, to complete the works, and must pay for them.

Even in the absence of an express term of this kind in the contract, an engineering contract is not normally affected by the death of the employer. This is because the employer's assets remain available in the hands of his personal representatives to meet the contract payments so that the contractor does not suffer by having to perform the contract despite the employer's death. In the absence of a specific term a contract will come to an end on the death of the contractor if, as will very often be the case, the circumstances show that the exercise by the contractor of his personal skill and judgment in relation to the construction of the works was to the employer a material consideration in entering into the contract with him.

Where completion by the contractor's executors or administrators would not be satisfactory to the employer, "*personal representatives*" may be struck out in (b) of this clause and "*but not the contractor's personal representatives*" added after "*assigns*".

2. "EMPLOYER (CONTRACTOR) ... INCLUDES THE EMPLOYER'S (CONTRACTOR'S) ... SUCCESSORS". The reference to "*successors*" covers, for example, a change of Minister where the employer is a Minister of the

23

Crown acting in his official capacity, or an amalgamation by a limited company party. It also covers an assignment of his whole business by a contractor and, where the contractor is a partnership, any change in the membership of the firm by death or retirement, etc., of a partner.

Where the personal ability of the original contractor or members of a contracting firm is important to the employer, "*successors*" should therefore be struck out here in relation to the contractor, particularly as the right to have successors take over the contract could be made use of in devious ways, so as to by-pass the provision in cl. 3 against assignment of the contract by itself.

As to a change of management where the contractor is a limited company, *see* cl. 3, N. 1.

3. THE EMPLOYER is given no right *to assign* the contract, for the reasons set out in cl. 3, N. 1.

4." . . . PERMITTED ASSIGNS". *See* cl. 3.

ENGINEER — DEFINITION

1 (1) (c) "Engineer" means . . . .
or other the Engineer appointed from time to time[6] by the Employer and notified in writing to the Contractor to act as Engineer for the purposes of the Contract in place of the said. . . . .

5. JOINT ENGINEERS. If joint engineers or an engineer and architect are appointed, it seems that a certificate is valid if it is signed by one of them expressly on his own behalf and on behalf of the other, but both must have
a   considered and decided the points dealt with in it (*see* p. 403, N. 38), and it is
b   safer for both to sign.

6. " . . . OR OTHER THE ENGINEER APPOINTED FROM TIME TO TIME . . . AND NOTIFIED IN WRITING TO THE CONTRACTOR", i.e. the employer may end the named engineer's powers to act for and bind him under the contract, and appoint a substitute or series of substitutes. But dismissal of the engineer, although it will be effective to end his powers, may be a breach of his service contract, for which he will be entitled to damages from the employer (p. 427).

This clause obviously cannot be read as giving *carte blanche* to the employer in changing the engineer, so that the contractor will be entitled to object to any appointee who has a disqualifying interest at the time of his
c   appointment (p. 411).

(*a*) In *Lamprell* v. *Billericay Union* (1849) 3 Exch 283, it was held that a certificate signed by one of two architects named in the contract was not valid. The wording of that contract, however, specified written instructions for variations from the two architects "signed by them", and the decision was based mainly on other factors. In *Tuta Products Pty. Ltd.* v. *Hutcherson Bros. Pty. Ltd.* [1972] 46 A.L.J.R. 479 Aus. it was questioned, but not decided, whether certificates issued from the architect's office signed not by the architect but by a person authorised to sign on his behalf were certificates "given by the architect" within the contract.

(*b*) In *Marryat* v. *Broderick* (1837) 150 E.R. 799, all disputes were to be settled by racing stewards, of whom two were named. An opinion in writing of one only was held invalid, although the other had said that he would acquiesce in whatever his colleague did.

(*c*) An arguable point is whether the employer is entitled under this clause to appoint a full-time employee in place of an independent consultant originally named as engineer (*see* p. 414). The employer would not be entitled to appoint himself, or apparently itself if a company or statutory corporation, as replacement engineer:—*see* in a different context *Finchbourne Ltd.* v. *Rodrigues* [1976] 3 All E.R. 581, C.A.

In the absence of a clause of this kind the employer generally cannot end
the independent powers of the engineer under the contract (p. 411), but in   *d*
some cases he may be bound to act under this clause (p. 416).

It is clear from the wording of this clause that in the case of a change of
engineer it is the employer's engineer at the time of the certificate who must
certify and not the engineer who supervised the work, etc. to which it relates.
Conversely, the new engineer cannot generally repudiate his predecessor's
decisions, but he has power to "*correct or modify*" interim certificates (cl.   *e*
60 (7)), and apparently he may go back on approval of work or materials—
cl. 39, N. 2.

SUPERVISORS

1 (1) (d) "Engineer's Representative" means a person being the resident
engineer or assistant of the Engineer or clerk of works appointed from
time to time by the Employer or the Engineer and notified in writing to
the Contractor by the Engineer to perform the functions set forth in
Clause 2 (1);[7]

7. SUPERVISORS. Refer to cl. 2 for elaborate new provisions about the
engineer's representative and other aides of the engineer.

PAYMENT

1 (1) (e) "Contract" means the Conditions of Contract[8] Specification Drawings
Priced Bill of Quantities the Tender the written acceptance thereof[9]
and the Contract Agreement (if completed);[10]

(f) "Specification" means the specification referred to in the Tender and
any modification thereof or addition thereto as may from time to time
be furnished or approved in writing by the Engineer;

(g) "Drawings" means the drawings referred to in the Specification and
any modification of such drawings approved in writing by the Engineer
and such other drawings as may from time to time be furnished or
approved in writing by the Engineer;

(h) "Tender Total" means the total of the Priced Bill of Quantities at the
date of acceptance of the Contractor's Tender for the Works;[11]

(i) "Contract Price" means the sum to be ascertained and paid in
accordance with the provisions hereinafter contained for the
construction completion and maintenance of the Works in accordance
with the Contract;[12]

8. GENERAL AND SPECIAL CONDITIONS OF CONTRACT. "*General*" is
omitted before "*Conditions of Contract*", so as to include any special
conditions added for the particular works. Space is provided for special
conditions in cl. 72 (p. 314).

The I.C.E. Conditions of Contract Standing Joint Committee has issued
Guidance Note 2B, which says that "When Clauses 1 to 71 of the I.C.E.
Conditions of Contract are incorporated in a Contract they are best
incorporated unaltered. The Clauses comprise closely inter-related
conditions and any changes made in some may have unforeseen effects on
others. . . . If it is necessary in a particular Contract to make any contractual

(*d*) Certificate of engineer valid despite dismissal, where there is no provision for a change of
engineer in the contract—*Burns & Kenealy* v. *Furby* (1885) 4 N.Z.L.R. 110, *Melvin* v. *St.
Cyprian's Society Building Committee* (1894) 9 E.D.C. 1 S. Af.

(*e*) *Kellett* v. *Mayor of Stockport* (1906) 70 J.P. 154.

arrangements these should be effected by the addition of special conditions in accordance with Clause 72".

The note also says that special conditions "should be kept to the minimum necessary to cover the special circumstances of the particular project. The practice of including as special conditions matters which are more appropriate to the Specification should be avoided". As that advice recognises, if guardedly, the standard Conditions are not holy writ; whilst they cover more or less adequately the generality of works the engineer has a duty for any particular project carefully to consider whether any addition or alteration is necessary (*see* pp. 6 and 161).

Finally, the note says that "Whether or not the I.C.E. Conditions are bound in (the documents prepared for tenderers) the following should appear in the documents of the Contract:

> The Conditions of Contract are Clauses 1 to 71 inclusive of the Conditions of Contract and Forms of Tender, Agreement and Bond for use in connection with Works of Civil Engineering Construction Fifth Edition (June 1973) approved by the Institution of Civil Engineers, the Association of Consulting Engineers and the Federation of Civil Engineering Contractors and commonly known as the I.C.E. Conditions of Contract together with the following special conditions:
> 72. The following special conditions form part of the Conditions of Contract.
> *f*   73. etc."

9. "THE WRITTEN ACCEPTANCE" OF TENDER is for the first time made a contract document (p. 20), although that is overlooked in the Agreement (p. 21).

If an acceptance is qualified, by refusing terms in the contractor's tender or adding new terms, there is no contract unless and until the qualification is accepted by the contractor expressly or by starting work without objection. A qualified acceptance may be dangerous, since it determines the contractor's tender, which cannot subsequently be accepted (even without
g   the qualification) unless it is renewed.

(*f*) The courts may come to the rescue of the parties and hold that a standard form has been incorporated into their contract even though the form is not accurately described in it. For example, the words "in full accordance with the appropriate form for nominated Sub-Contractors (R.I.B.A. 1965 edition)" were held to incorporate the "green form" of building sub-contract (for sub-contractors nominated under the R.I.B.A. form of main contract) into a contract between a main contractor and a sub-contractor so nominated, even though the green form is issued by the Builders' & Sub-Contractors' Federations and not by the R.I.B.A. and there is no 1965 edition, in *Modern Building Wales Ltd.* v. *Limmer & Trinidad Co. Ltd.* [1975] 2 All E.R. 549, C.A.

It has even been held in *British Crane Hire* v. *Ipswich Plant Hire* [1974] 1 All E.R.1059, C.A., that a standard form not referred to in the contract may be incorporated. In that case terms similar to those normally used by firms in the plant hire trade were held to be incorporated in a contract of plant hire between parties both of whom were in the trade and who were of equal bargaining power. But it is unsafe to rely on that exceptional decision— contrast *Hollier* v. *Rambler Motors Ltd.* [1972] 1 All E.R. 399, C.A.

(*g*) *Hyde* v. *Wrench* (1840) 49 E.R. 132—June 6th, offer to sell estate for £1,000. June 8th reply offering to pay £950. Offer refused June 27th. June 29th, plaintiff wrote that he would accept £1,000. Held: no contract. In *Davies & Co. Shopfitters Ltd.* v. *William Old* (1969) 67 L.G.R. 395, main contractor placed an order with a nominated sub-contractor whose tender had been accepted by the architect. Main contractor's order included a special term which conflicted with the earlier documents. Nominated sub-contractor replied thanking the main contractor for the order and started work. Held: the architect's acceptance of the tender did not bind the main contractor and the main contractor's order constituted a counter-offer because it was qualified by the new term. Nevertheless there was a binding contract because the nominated sub-contractor had accepted the counter-offer at the latest by starting work.

10. No Schedule of Rates and Prices. The references to a schedule of rates and prices in the previous edition have been omitted because no function was assigned to the schedule.

11. "Tender Total" as defined here is referred to in cls. 10 (amount of bond) and 60 (4) (limit of retention).

This definition assumes that all errors in arithmetic in the tender will have been corrected prior to acceptance. Where errors remain it is not absolutely clear that it is the correct total and not the stated total which applies. This ambiguity is unlikely to be of great practical importance.

12. "Contract Price". The payment due to the contractor depends on the classification of the contract, generally as either (a) pure lump sum; (b) quantities; (c) measure and value; or (d) cost plus.

(a) *Pure lump sum.* An agreement to complete a whole work—to build a house or a bridge or a dock—for a lump sum. In law this is an undertaking to get a certain result for a fixed sum of money. The contractor is entitled to that sum only, however difficult it may unexpectedly turn out to be to get the result:

> Pure lump sum contract to lay the San Paulo Railway from terminus A to terminus B. As a result of errors in the engineer's plan almost twice the quantities of excavation originally estimated were needed to complete the line.
> Held: The contractor was entitled to no extra payment beyond the lump sum price in his tender. *h*

And no work indispensably necessary to get the result is an extra:

> In a lump sum contract to build a house, flooring was omitted from the specifications.
> Held: The contractor must put it in without extra payment, as it was clearly indispensably necessary to complete the house. *i*

Therefore in a pure lump sum contract the contract price will be altered only where the plans, etc., are varied by the employer because he decides that a change is preferable, although it is not absolutely necessary; not where the change is necessary to complete the project:

> Pure lump sum contract to build a bridge. If it is found that the piling specified cannot support the superstructure, the contractor must change it without extra payment so far as necessary to complete the works. If the piles will support the superstructure but the engineer decides that a change is preferable to improve on the original scheme, he must give a variation order and the contractor will be entitled to extra payment for any additional work. *j*

And an express promise to pay extra for work in fact included in the contract price is not normally binding (pp. 3–4 and 179, N.2).

A contractor who agrees to a pure lump sum contract for work that is uncertain and unforeseeable in extent will be considered by the courts simply to have taken a voluntary gamble, and will be bound by the contract.

(h) *Sharpe* v. *San Paulo Ry.* (1873) L.R. 8 Ch. App. 597.
(i) *Williams* v. *Fitzmaurice* (1858) 177 R.R. 1004.
(j) Of course, this principle works both ways. An employer has no right to make a deduction from a pure lump sum contract price merely because the quantities are less than he expected—*Peters* v. *Quebec Harbour Commrs.* (1891) 19 S.C.R. 685 Can. and *Ibmac* v. *Marshall (Homes)* (1968) 208 E.G. 851, C.A.

The attitude of the judges in the early cases which settled the law was clearly influenced by the feeling that an employer obtains a tender and fixes a contract price for work in order to know what he is in for, and that any relaxation of these rules would destroy the whole object of getting a tender. This, of course, ignores the difference in extent and difficulties between large-scale engineering works and the ordinary relatively simple building work. Nevertheless, following from this attitude the courts hold that in inviting a tender there is no implied guarantee by the employer that the plans, bill of quantities or specifications supplied to tenderers are accurate, or that the work can be carried out in accordance with them:

> By the plans to build Blackfriars Bridge the foundations were to be put in with caissons. The contractors found this impossible and eventually had to abandon the attempt and complete the bridge in accordance with altered plans.
> Held: While they were entitled to the contract payments for the original work actually completed and, under the particular form of contract, to extra for the work in the new plans, they were not entitled to damages for the added expense
k and delay in trying to do the original work.

The courts hold that in putting forward plans, specifications and a bill of quantities with the invitation to tender, the employer is merely putting forward the estimate of an engineer as to how the required result may be achieved—he is not guaranteeing that the engineer is right. The courts know that it is the custom for the contractor to rely on these documents, but insist that if he does that to save himself trouble in tendering, it is "a usage of
l blind confidence".

But since that last decision in 1876 much development has taken place around this area of law and the employer is liable for misleading contract documents in the several cases discussed on pp. 58–63.

(*b*) *Quantities contract.* The ordinary features of a lump sum contract may be altered by making the quantities in the bill of quantities part of the description of the works to be done. Then the contractor is entitled to his lump sum for carrying out the quantities of work set out in the bill, but to extra payment for any work beyond that.

Note that in a quantities contract the rule that the employer is not taken to warrant that the works can be completed in accordance with the contract documents may still be important in relation to the documents other than the bill of quantities—the last cited case was decided on a quantities form. And the pure lump sum principle still applies to the individual rates in the bill. For example, the rate per cubic metre of excavation includes upholding the sides of excavations and keeping excavations free of water specifically by note 9 to Class E of the Civil Engineering Standard Method of Measurement (*see* p. 213), in which case, however unexpectedly much of those operations there may be, the contractor is not ordinarily entitled to an increase in the rate, and has only very limited rights under cl. 12 of these Conditions.

(*c*) *Measure and value contract:*

> "The whole of the work will be remeasured, and payment made for the work actually done".

(*k*) *Thorn* v. *London Corporation* (1876) 1 App. Cas. 120, and see *McDonald* v. *Workington Corporation* (1893) Hudson "Building Contracts", 4th ed., vol. ii, p. 228 (no extra payment for unexpected work due to water in the soil).
(*l*) Quotation *Thorn's* case above at p. 132.

Here the bill of quantities is incorporated in the contract principally as a schedule that fixes the rates of payment. With the 5th edition the I.C.E. contract is now firmly measure and value, but the quantities in the bill may be the foundation of a claim by the contractor (p. 210).

The essential legal differences between a measure and value and a quantities contract are small. They occur where the contractor makes a mistake in extension or totalling or a deduction from the total of the bill of quantities, *see* fully pp. 12–15. The general binding effect of the individual rates and the rule that the employer is not taken to warrant the contract documents (above) apply also to this form.

(*d*) *Cost*—plus a fixed fee or percentage for profit, with or without a deduction or bonus if the cost is above or below a fixed target.

A private client should always be warned by the engineer that the bill total in a quantities or measure and value contract is, in effect, only an estimate. His attention should be drawn to the importance of comparing the reputations and the individual rates of the various tenderers and to the cases listed in ch. 11 in which he may become liable for extra payment.

Permanent and Temporary Works

1 (1) (j)   "Permanent Works"[13] means the permanent works to be constructed completed and maintained in accordance with the Contract;

     (k) "Temporary Works"[13] means all temporary works of every kind required in or about the construction completion and maintenance of the Works;

     (l)   "Works"[13] means the Permanent Works together with the Temporary Works;

     (m) "Section"[14] means a part of the Works separately identified in the Appendix to the Form of Tender;

     (n) "Site"[15] means the lands and other places on under in or through which the Works are to be executed and any other lands or places provided by the Employer for the purposes of the Contract;

     (o) "Constructional Plant" means all appliances or things of whatsoever nature required in or about the construction completion and maintenance of the Works but does not include materials or other things intended to form or forming part of the Permanent Works.

13. "Permanent Works", "Temporary Works", "Works". These definitions produce a welcome clarification of the previous edition.

The further category of Temporary Works "*designed*" or "*specified or designed*" by the engineer is introduced in cls. 8 and 26 (2) (c).

Other references to "*Works*" without more in the 4th edition of the conditions are allowed to stand in this edition, combining with this new definition to give the engineer and his aides wide powers to control temporary works, whether designed by the engineer or the contractor's own temporary works. *See* cl. 14 for the contractor's right to extra payment arising out of that control, and p. 52 on liability for injury and damage by temporary works.

The words "*together with*" in this definition are a little strange. For

(*m*) For model form of cost-plus contract see Royal Institute of British Architects, etc. fixed fee form of prime cost contract. For criticisms of the form see I. N. Duncan Wallace "Building and Engineering Standard Contract Forms", ch. 8. Refer also to Perry and Thompson "Target and costs-reimbursable construction contracts—a study of their use and implications", Construction Industry Research & Information Assoc. report No. 56.

example, does cl. 12 (1) apply only if physical conditions, etc., are encountered "during the execution of the Permanent Works together with the Temporary Works", and not during the execution of preliminary temporary works before the permanent works are started? A similar question arises on cls. 18 and 19. Does cl. 51 apply to a variation of temporary works by themselves, or only as incidental to a variation of permanent works? Does "Site" as defined in cl. 1 (1) (n) include places where temporary works are being executed only if permanent works are also being executed there? *See* p. 110, N.3 and p. 262, N.9. It is reasonably clear that none of these limitations is intended to apply; that the definition means that both permanent and temporary works are separately included in "*Works*".

14. "Section". This definition is relevant to cls. 20, 43, 47, 48, 49 and 60 (5), which provide for early completion of sections of the works, with liquidated damages for delay, and, on completion of the section, passage to the employer of liability for damage, commencement of the maintenance period and release of a proportion of the first half of the retention.

15. "Site". For the importance of clearly delineating the site boundaries in the contract documents *see* p. 135. "*Works*" in this definition now include temporary works by cl. 1 (1) (l) above, but *see* N. 13.

Singular and Plural

1.   (2) Words importing the singular also include the plural and *vice-versa* where the context requires.

Headings and Marginal Notes

(3) The headings and marginal notes in the Conditions of Contract shall not be deemed to be part thereof or be taken into consideration in the interpretation or construction thereof or of the Contract.[16]

Clause References

(4) All references herein to clauses are references to clauses numbered in the Conditions of Contract and not to those in any other document forming part of the Contract.[17]

Cost

(5) The word "cost" when used in the Conditions of Contract shall be deemed to include overhead costs whether on or off the Site[18] except where the contrary is expressly stated.[19]

16. "Headings and Marginal Notes". A drafting error in the previous edition is corrected.

17. Clause references. This definition permits omission of the "*hereof*" which appears in the previous edition after each cross-reference to a clause number.

This tiny nod in the direction of modern and clear drafting appears to have exhausted the draftsman of this edition.

The definition applies only to clause references "*herein*", i.e. in the conditions (general or special), not in the specification or other documents.

18. "'COST' ... DEEMED TO INCLUDE OVERHEAD COSTS WHETHER ON OR OFF ... THE SITE". Note that this definition only applies to references to cost in the conditions of contract (general or special), not in other contract documents.

Under cl. 13 (3) the contractor is entitled to cost incurred due to instructions and similarly restricted to cost in cls. 12 (3), 14 (6) and 31 (2).   *m'*

Extra work or delay may cause real additional overhead costs to the contractor, for example where he has to engage extra supervisors on or off the site to deal with the additional work, or to employ for a longer period supervisors specially engaged for the particular works. Such cost is clearly recoverable under this definition. The contractor's fixed overheads, for example rent of head office premises, are much more difficult.

In claiming for breach of contract where the contractor is not limited to recovering costs (p. 427), contractors traditionally include loss of overhead return. The example may be taken of a delay of six months for which the employer is responsible, in a contract that would have been performed in a year but for the delay. The contractor will show the annual amount towards payment of these fixed overheads that would have been earned by his resources engaged on the contract, and will seek to recover half that amount by way of damages on the grounds that had his resources been freed from the site and not retained there unproductively for a further six months they would have earned on another contract that further contribution to overheads (*see further* p. 370 on this formula). Such a claim is not for cost incurred because of the delay, in the sense that the contractor would have had to pay these overhead costs even if the delay had not happened, but is for loss of the opportunity to earn money out of which to pay those costs.

It might well be argued, therefore, that if a contractor is detained on the works unproductively for an extra six months because of an instruction of the engineer, the proportion of his head office costs equal to the proportion of his total turnover represented by the works does not constitute cost, in the sense of expenditure, incurred by reason of the instruction. That is, except in so far as he can show that during the period of the delay supervisors (with attendant office space, secretarial staff, etc.) in fact spent extra time dealing with the works by reason of the instruction.

It is possible that a wider interpretation will be adopted by the courts, in keeping with what seems to be the intention; that in so far as the contractor incurs extra costs on a site he is deemed to incur with them the appropriate proportion of the off-site expenses which, so to speak, "go with" the resources on site. A more forthcoming definition would have avoided this ambiguity.

There will be other, unavoidable, anomalies in restricting the contractor to recovery of cost without loss of profits. For example, in an identical   *n*

(*m'*) Note the contrast between cost only and cost plus profit drawn in cl. 12(3), and see the dictum in the *Crosby* case quoted on p. 367 below.

(*n*) Although about very different circumstances the decision in *Litherland U.D.C.* v. *Liverpool Corp.* [1958] 2 All E.R. 489 has some relevance. The Corporation permitted elderly people to use its bus services without payment, and had a statutory right to recover from the Council "any cost incurred by" the Corporation in granting this travel concession in the Council's district. Held that the total cost attributable to passengers travelling free should be calculated on the basis of the cost of a passenger journey obtained by dividing the total expenditure of the undertaking in a given year by the total number of journeys made by both fare-paying passengers and those who travelled free. "It seems clear enough that, if a proportion of passengers is carried free, it must cost something. If all passengers were carried free, clearly the whole expense of the transport undertaking would be borne out of the rates. If a proportion is carried free, a proportion of the expense has to be borne out of the rates, and that may be said to be what it costs to grant the concession" (p. 491).

situation the costs recoverable by a contractor who hires plant will be greater than the costs recoverable by a contractor doing the work with his own plant (for which he will normally be entitled only to depreciation and other costs actually incurred while the plant is standing). A contractor doing the works on borrowed money will incur and presumably be entitled to recover interest charges; a contractor financing the works from his own resources may have no such head of recovery, since his equivalent loss will be the profit he would have made using elsewhere the money tied up in the works. Judicious arrangements when a job is undertaken, or even when some occurrence takes place for which the employer is bound to pay the contractor his cost, may increase the amount recoverable.

A distinction must be drawn between those clauses in these conditions which entitle the contractor only to cost incurred (e.g. cls. 13 (3) and 14 (6)), and the clauses which say that particular work shall be done "*at the expense (cost) of the Employer*" (cls. 20 (2), 36 (2)) or that "*cost . . . shall be borne by the Employer*" (cls. 17, 36 (3), 38 (2), 50). It is suggested that under both of the latter formulae the employer is bound to make reasonable payment to the contractor for the work, i.e. normally cost plus a reasonable percentage for profit. It might be argued that a subtle distinction is intended between the two formulae on the grounds that the definition of "*cost*" in this sub-clause means that under the last four clauses overheads but not profit are payable; but there is no statement in any of those cases that it is the cost "incurred by the contractor" that is being referred to, and it is suggested that in context the word cost is used in the sense that the price for the operations is to be borne by the employer. For disruption claims *see* p. 370.

19. "EXCEPT WHERE THE CONTRARY IS EXPRESSLY STATED". The contrary is not expressly stated anywhere in the general conditions. It is important to state the contrary in any special conditions in which "*cost*" is not intended to include overheads.

ENGINEER'S REPRESENTATIVE—FUNCTIONS AND POWERS

2.   (1)[1] The functions of the Engineer's Representative[2] are to watch and supervise the construction completion and maintenance of the Works. He shall have no authority to relieve the Contractor of any of his duties or obligations under the Contract[3] nor except as expressly provided hereunder to order any work involving delay or any extra payment by the Employer nor to make any variation of or in the Works.[4,5,6]

APPOINTMENT OF ASSISTANTS

(2) The Engineer or the Engineer's Representative may appoint any number of persons to assist the Engineer's Representative in the exercise of his functions under sub-clause (1) of this Clause. He shall notify to the Contractor the names and functions of such persons.[13] The said assistants shall have no power to issue any instructions to the Contractor save in so far as such instructions may be necessary to enable them to discharge their functions and to secure their acceptance of materials or workmanship as being in accordance with the Specification and Drawings and any instructions given by any of them for those purposes shall be deemed to have been given by the Engineer's Representative.[7]

(*n'*) Any further compensation would be for loss of the opportunity to earn profit with the plant—*see* Hudson "Building and Engineering Contracts", 10th ed. by I. N. Duncan Wallace at p. 600.

DELEGATION BY ENGINEER

(3) The Engineer may from time to time[8] in writing authorise the Engineer's Representative or any other person responsible to the Engineer[9,10] to act on behalf of the Engineer either generally in respect of the Contract or specifically in respect of particular Clauses of these Conditions of Contract and any act of any such person[11] within the scope of his authority shall for the purposes of the Contract[12] constitute an act of the Engineer. Prior notice in writing of any such authorisation shall be given by the Engineer to the Contractor. Such authorisation shall continue in force until such time as the Engineer shall notify the Contractor in writing that the same is determined.[13] Provided that such authorisation shall not be given in respect of any decision to be taken or certificate to be issued under Clauses 12 (3), 44, 48, 60 (3), 61, 63 and 66.[14]

REFERENCE TO ENGINEER OR ENGINEER'S REPRESENTATIVE

(4) If the Contractor shall be dissatisfied by reason of any instruction of any assistant of the Engineer's Representative duly appointed under sub-clause (2) of this Clause he shall be entitled to refer the matter to the Engineer's Representative who shall thereupon confirm reverse or vary such instruction. Similarly if the Contractor shall be dissatisfied by reason of any act of the Engineer's Representative, or other person duly authorised by the Engineer under sub-clause (3) of this Clause[15] he shall be entitled to refer the matter to the Engineer for his decision.[16,17,18]

1. SUPERVISORS—DEFINITIONS—APPOINTMENT—POWERS—APPEAL FROM DECISIONS. Under this very complicated clause the contractor is subject to control by no fewer than four categories of supervisor:

(a) One engineer. Appointed by the employer (cl. 1 (1) (c)). For powers and duties see chs. 13 and 14. The contractor's right of appeal from an engineer's decision is under cl. 66—back to the engineer himself and thence to an arbitrator provided a request for arbitration is made in time.

(b) One (see N. 10) engineer's representative. Appointed by the employer or engineer (cl. 1 (1) (d) and N. 2). His ordinary powers are to watch and supervise construction of both permanent and temporary works (sub-cl. (1) of this clause and N. 3, 4, 5 and 6), subject to extension by written delegation by the engineer under sub-cl. (3). Right of appeal by the contractor to the engineer under sub-cl. (3). Right of appeal by the contractor to the engineer under sub-cl. (4), appeal from the engineer's decision back to the engineer under cl. 66 and then to arbitration.

(c) Any number of assistants to the engineer's representative. Appointed by the engineer or the engineer's representative (sub-cl. (2)). Powers discussed in N. 7. Four tiers of appeal by the contractor—to the engineer's representative under sub-cl. (4), and then presumably to the engineer under that sub-clause, back to the engineer again under cl. 66 and finally to an arbitrator.

(d) Any other person responsible to the engineer to whom all or any of his powers are delegated by the engineer by written authorisation under sub-cl. (3). Discussed in N. 8 to 15. Appeal to the engineer as in (b).

Unless and until any decision of a supervisor is reversed on appeal, the decision generally must be obeyed by the contractor and employer. The employer's right of appeal is dealt with in N. 17. See also cl. 60 (7).

2. ENGINEER'S REPRESENTATIVE. For definition and written notification of

appointment to the contractor *see* cl. 1 (1) (d); for appointment by the engineer or employer *see* p. 385, N. 27. The representative may be a resident on site or assistant in the engineer's office.

3. ENGINEER'S REPRESENTATIVE'S ORDINARY DUTIES. The engineer's representative is appointed to continually supervise the construction of the works. By this clause he is merely the inspector and assistant of the engineer and has only negative powers, to condemn bad work or material. A contractor therefore acts at his peril on a representative's orders or approval:

> Under the terms of a contract the plans were subject to the approval in writing of the employer's principal engineer. The contractor carried out work on the basis of plans approved by the resident engineer, whose approval was held not to bind the employer.

o

For extension of the representative's powers *see* N. 9. *See also* cl. 17 on the employer's liability for incorrect setting out data supplied by a representative.

4. "NOR EXCEPT AS . . . PROVIDED HEREUNDER TO ORDER ANY WORK INVOLVING DELAY OR ANY EXTRA PAYMENT . . . TO MAKE ANY VARIATION OF OR IN THE WORKS". *See* N. 11 on variations. These words emphasise what is said in the last note: the contractor is not entitled to found a claim for extra payment or to extension of time on an order of the representative, unless there has been delegation under sub-cl. (3).

5. CONTROL OF TEMPORARY WORKS BY ENGINEER'S REPRESENTATIVE. As a result of the extended definition of *"Works"* in cl. 1 (1) (l), the representative's supervision now extends to all temporary works (p. 29).

6. TESTING OF MATERIALS is no longer included in the representative's ordinary duties, and apparently must be delegated under sub-cl. (3).

7. POWERS OF ASSISTANTS OF ENGINEER'S REPRESENTATIVE. The effect of this clause is that an assistant of the representative may issue instructions only if they are both within the functions allotted to him by the representative or engineer and notified to the contractor (which functions may be limited to a particular area or operation of the works) and are issued to ensure that work or materials are acceptable to the assistant as being in accordance with the *"Specification and Drawings"*. The contractor cannot recover payment for a variation on an assistant's order under this sub-clause; therefore he should not do work which he considers to be an enhancement of the specification or change in drawings at the behest of an assistant, without complying with cl. 51 (2).

Where the materials or workmanship required are not defined in the specification or drawings, for example in the case of contractor's own temporary works and items of permanent work of which the engineer's control is solely under cl. 13 (2), it appears that an assistant can have no function. And there is no reference to the assistant ensuring that the works are in accordance with instructions of the engineer unless embodied in drawings or amounting to a specification (compare cl. 26 (2) (a) and (b)).

(*o*) *Attorney-Gen.* v. *Briggs* (1855) 1 Jur. (N.S.) 1084.

Clearly, one function may be allotted to a number of assistants without division between them.

8. DELEGATION "FROM TIME TO TIME". That is, the engineer may delegate at any time during the contract, or at any time increase, change (for example during holidays or illness) or determine any delegation for the future. For written notification of delegation and changes *see* N. 13. The engineer has no power to alter these Conditions and therefore delegation binds the employer only if it is in writing as required by this sub-clause, unless he has given the engineer additional authority.

9. DELEGATION BY THE ENGINEER TO "THE ENGINEER'S REPRESENTATIVE OR ANY OTHER PERSON RESPONSIBLE TO THE ENGINEER". The limitation that delegation may only be to a person "*responsible to the Engineer*" is long in good intentions—that any person exercising the very important powers and judgments which the engineer may delegate must be responsible to him—but short in precision. Some relevant points:

(*a*) An employee of the engineer obviously is responsible to him and may receive delegated powers under this sub-clause (but *see* p. 384, N. 26, for the engineer's resulting responsibility for the delegate). An engineer who is a whole-time employee of a local or other public authority may presumably delegate functions to an assistant of his although they are fellow employees of the authority.

(*b*) Where a partnership is named as engineer, it seems that powers may be delegated to any one partner as a person responsible to the majority of the partners. But where one partner is appointed engineer he may not delegate power to another partner, since one partner is not "*responsible to*" another, in the sense of being bound to obey him.

(*c*) It is not unusual for the employer to employ direct a mechanical services consultant to deal with supply and installation of plant which is part of the construction contract. The engineer may wish to delegate some of his functions to such a consultant, but may not do so under this clause unless the consultant is employed by him (with attendant dangers, p. 384) and not direct by the employer, or some special arrangement is made ((*f*) below) by which the consultant is made responsible to the engineer.

(*d*) The engineer is specifically authorised to delegate powers to the engineer's representative, even though the representative may be appointed by and paid by the employer. The representative may be a long-term employee of a local authority employer, with corresponding duties and loyalties (and pension expectations).

(*e*) Unless their position is clarified by a special arrangement, it does not seem that the engineer may delegate to assistants of the representative who are employed direct by the employer (by sub-cl. (2) such persons are to "*assist the Engineer's Representative*" in the exercise of his functions "*under sub-clause* (1)"), but in any case they are unlikely to be of sufficiently high grade to justify delegation at least on major matters.

(*f*) It is implied that any person in the doubtful categories discussed above or any other person may be made responsible to the engineer without becoming his employee, presumably by a (preferably written) agreement to which he is a party with the engineer and his own employers providing that he will be responsible to the engineer in performing any delegated duties. There are problems as to how exactly such an agreement must be worded.

Clearly, the delegate must be required to obey the instructions of the engineer and not to obey any instructions from his employer or anyone else, and the engineer must have authority to end his delegated powers. Whether the employer may retain the power to dismiss the delegate from the works or from his employment generally is not clear. The fact that delegation is specifically allowed to the engineer's representative even if employed by the employer suggests that sole responsibility to the engineer is not required. The question of liability for the delegate, his errors or dishonesty, should be dealt with carefully in the agreement. The engineer may notwithstanding any agreement be liable to outsiders for the delegate and should make certain that his indemnity insurance covers the arrangement.

The contractor is protected to some extent against mistaken or improper decisions of delegates by the right of appeal to the engineer, as well as the right to arbitrate, unless the engineer is foolish enough to take the not uncommon attitude that he must support his colleagues and subordinates *vis-à-vis* the contractor even when they are wrong.

Delegates are clearly bound by the same duty of independence and impartiality as the engineer (ch. 14).

10. "THE ENGINEER'S REPRESENTATIVE OR ANY OTHER PERSON". It is reasonably clear that under this sub-clause the engineer may delegate his powers to one person only—either the representative or some other person responsible to him. This interpretation is strongly suggested by the contrast between the wording quoted at the head of this note and *"any number of persons"* in sub-cl. (2)—*see* p. 45. The context does not require *"person"* to be interpreted under cl. 1 (2) as including *"persons"*, because to allow the engineer to divide delegated functions amongst a number of persons, or even to give the same function to two or more concurrently, would produce considerable possibilities for confusion in the control of the works. If *"other person"* were interpreted to include the plural, logically so should *"Engineer"* and *"Engineer's Representative"*, which interpretation would make the contract unworkable.

It appears that the engineer may himself continue to perform functions which he has delegated, but he is bound by any decision of his delegate unless the contractor refers the decision back to him under sub-cl. (4) or the contractor or employer asks for his decision under cl. 66. The contractor should particularly act under one of those provisions to obtain the engineer's ruling in a case of conflicting instructions.

11. "ANY ACT OF ANY SUCH PERSON". *"act"*—not omission. For an omission to disapprove work *see* p. 127, N. 2. May a failure to contradict a confirmation of an oral variation order under cl. 51 be classed as an *"act"*?

12. DELEGATION BINDS EMPLOYER "FOR THE PURPOSES OF THE CONTRACT". This clause is, of course, purely for the contractor's protection under this contract and binds the employer in relation to the contractor only. The engineer cannot rely on the clause as a defence to liability to the employer

(p) In *Morren* v. *Swinton and Pendlebury B.C.* [1965] 2 All E.R. 349, a resident engineer appointed, paid and subject to dismissal by the local authority, but selected by and subject to the orders of the consulting engineer, was held to be an officer of the local authority.
(q) de Smith "Judicial Review of Administrative Action", p. 286: "The general rule is that an authority which delegates its powers does not divest itself of them."

for breach of his duty to supervise, if he delegates too freely to a representative (p. 384, N. 26), and the engineer may also be liable outside the contract to third parties for an act of a delegate.

13. NOTICE TO CONTRACTOR OF APPOINTMENT OF SUPERVISORS AND DELEGATION OF FUNCTIONS. The contractor is entitled to receive:

(a) From the engineer, written notice of the name of the person appointed engineer's representative (cl. 1 (1) (d)).

(b) From the engineer or the engineer's representative, notice (not specifically required to be in writing or to be prior notice as in (c) below) of the names and functions of the representative's assistants. This requirement appears to apply to all assistants, even inspectors who are not intended to give any instructions under sub-cl. (2).

(c) Prior written notice of any delegation of the engineer's functions under sub-cl. (3), specifying either the particular clauses of the contract in respect of which powers are being delegated or that the delegation is generally in respect of all the engineer's powers under the contract except those not delegable.

(d) Written notification of any change of engineer (cl. 1 (1) (c)) or of the engineer's representative (cl. 1 (1) (d)) and of change or determination of delegation under sub-cl. (3). Notice of determination of the powers of any assistant of the engineer's representative is not referred to (nor indeed is any right of determination specified). However, under the general law the contractor will be entitled to rely on the instructions of any such assistant until (but only until) he receives notice of determination of his powers in such a form and from such a source that a prudent contractor would rely on it.

The contractor should be written to with clear-cut notification of the appointment and functions of supervisors as soon as possible after acceptance of tender. Until he receives this notice the contractor should act only on orders from or confirmed by the engineer.

Despite the extreme particularity of this cl. 2, which aims to contribute to the practical administration of the contract by allowing the contractor to determine exactly where he stands in dealing with resident staff, difficulties have been reported in practice due to the engineer's refusal to follow this clause and to letters of delegation which fail to define delegated powers "*specifically in respect of particular Clauses of these Conditions*" as required by cl. 2 (3).

These clauses do not differentiate between minor and major variations and instructions, and particularly the absolute restriction on the powers of assistants to the representative (N. 7) may cause delays in practice while minor changes are confirmed.

There may be much to be said for a minuted meeting between the parties at the start of the works to devise a sensible and workable system of delegation of functions, under this clause and cl. 15 (2), and of co-operation between supervisors.

14. ENGINEER'S DECISIONS EXCLUDED FROM DELEGATION. The exclusion of cl. 12 (3) refers to action following notification of unforeseen physical conditions or obstructions, cl. 44 to extension of time, cl. 48 completion certificates, cl. 60 (3) the final certificate, cl. 61 the maintenance certificate, cl. 63 forfeiture, and cl. 66 a decision on referral back to the engineer of a dispute or difference.

Some important functions are not excluded from delegation, e.g. valuation of variations under cl. 52 and interim certificates. The engineer has no power under this clause of his own motion to alter a delegate's valuation or reverse a decision that work is an extra. The solution for the engineer is to advise the employer to refer the matter to him for a decision under cl. 66, but pending reversal of the delegate's decision the employer must pay certificates based on it. For correction of a certificate under cl. 60 (7) refer to p. 272.

15. "AUTHORISED BY THE ENGINEER UNDER SUB-CLAUSE (3)" appears to refer to "*other person*" and not to "*act*", so that there is a right of appeal to the engineer from acts of the engineer's representative whether done under sub-cl. (1) in his ordinary supervision of the works, or under sub-cl. (3) in performing delegated powers.

16. APPEAL BY THE CONTRACTOR TO THE ENGINEER FROM A SUPERVISOR'S DECISION. This right of appeal provides a useful alternative to referral back to the engineer under cl. 66. The time for claiming arbitration does not run from the decision under this paragraph and the contractor is left with a right to a further engineer's decision under cl. 66. The contractor particularly may apply for a review of a decision under this paragraph where he wishes to allow himself a further approach to the engineer when passions have cooled, but not of course if he wishes to go to arbitration as quickly as possible. For the scheme of appeals *see* N. 1.

17. APPEAL BY EMPLOYER FROM SUPERVISOR'S DECISIONS. The employer's only way of appeal from a decision (of the engineer, his delegate, the engineer's representative or his assistants) is to notify the contractor that a dispute exists and refer the dispute to the engineer under cl. 66, and then to arbitration provided he gives notice in time. The engineer should keep the employer advised of his right of appeal, and in particular should notify him of any doubtful decision made by a supervisor. For correction of a certificate refer to p. 272.

18. THE FORMER CLAUSE 2 (a) is moved to cl. 39 (3), and expanded (failure of supervisor to disapprove work or materials does not prejudice power subsequently to do so).

ASSIGNMENT

3.   The Contractor shall not assign the Contract or any part thereof[1] or any benefit or interest therein or thereunder[2] without the written consent of the Employer.[3]

SUB-LETTING

4.   The Contractor shall not sub-let the whole of the Works. Except where otherwise provided by the Contract the Contractor shall not sub-let any part of the Works without the written consent of the Engineer[4,5] and such consent if given shall not relieve the Contractor from any liability or obligation under the Contract and he shall be responsible for the acts defaults and neglects of any sub-contractor his agents servants or workmen as fully as if they were the acts defaults or neglects of the Contractor his agents servants or workmen.[6] Provided

always that the provision of labour on a piece-work basis shall not be deemed to be a sub-letting under this Clause.[7,8]

1. "THE CONTRACTOR SHALL NOT ASSIGN THE CONTRACT OR ANY PART THEREOF". This refers to an assignment by the contractor of liability for carrying out the contract so as to have another contractor take over his liability from him, and is the position even in the absence of a specific prohibition of this kind. For obvious reasons one party may not without the consent of the other rid himself of his duties under a contract simply by assigning them to someone else, who may be less able to perform them or pay damages. *See* as to successors cl. 1, N. 2. For sub-letting *see* N. 4.

If the contractor is a limited company there may be an assignment in fact although not in law where shares in the company are transferred and the directors are changed. The employer cannot object to this because in law the company is the party to the contract and is a legal entity quite distinct from, and not affected by any change in, shareholders or directors.

If the contractor attempts to assign without the necessary written consent, the employer has a right of forfeiture under cl. 63 (1).

If an assignment is allowed the bond must be altered—p. 321.

2. "THE CONTRACTOR SHALL NOT ASSIGN . . . ANY BENEFIT OR INTEREST" (IN THE CONTRACT). This requirement is to prevent the contractor assigning his right to contract payments, whether already due or not, which he may want to do as security for borrowing. Where there is no restriction in the contract the contractor is entitled to do so, and it now appears that this clause is legally valid to prevent assignment.

The pressure on the employer (presuming that this clause is valid) to agree to an assignment is that a contractor may reach the position that he cannot complete without raising a loan on the security of future payments, and if he does not complete forfeiture of the contract may, of course, involve the employer in loss. The dangers are that the contractor may not use the money raised to finance the works, and if the assignment covers the full contract price the assignee, having no interest in the contractor's reputation, may prevent the usual give-and-take settlement of accounts. A celebrated engineering action was brought and lost, at great cost to both parties, at the insistence of an assignee of the contract payments.

However, if it is possible that this clause will discourage tenderers, the tender form may be altered.

If he receives notice of a valid assignment the employer must pay the person to whom the assignment is made (assignee) direct; if he pays the contractor he may have to pay over again. The assignee, of course, takes no more than the contractor would have been entitled to—for example on forfeiture the contract payments only after deducting the employer's expenses and damages.

3. ". . . WITHOUT THE WRITTEN CONSENT OF THE EMPLOYER". Note that in these two cases (N. 1 and 2) it is the written consent of the employer and not merely of the engineer which is necessary. The employer's right to refuse

(r) *Helstan Securities Ltd.* v. *Hertfordshire C.C.* [1978] 3 All E.R. 262, considering earlier decisions that cast some doubt on the validity of a prohibition, and holding that this cl. 3 made void an assignment by contractors of sums alleged to be due to them by an employer under a contract incorporating these Conditions.

consent is absolute and the contractor has no right to challenge it either in the courts or in arbitration. As to waiver of written consent *see* cl. 47, N. 11.

4. "THE CONTRACTOR SHALL NOT SUB-LET THE WHOLE OF THE WORKS ... THE CONTRACTOR SHALL NOT SUB-LET ANY PART OF THE WORKS WITHOUT THE WRITTEN CONSENT OF THE ENGINEER". The position in the absence of a special term in the contract is that although he may not assign his liability so as to rid himself of it (*see* N. 1) a party ordinarily may sub-let the contract work, that is, have it carried out physically by someone else but remaining himself solely liable to the other party to the contract for the result. As the rest of this clause sets out, sub-letting and not assignment of liability is the basis of the sub-contracting system; the main contractor remains solely liable to the employer for the quality of all the work but, with consent where necessary, employs others to carry out parts or to supply material.

This clause requires consent to sub-letting and the main contractor will not be entitled to payment for work sub-let without consent, even though the sub-contractor's work is satisfactory. The employer has contracted to pay only for physical performance of the contract by the original contractor; if he does not get that it is not for him to prove in what way the work might have been better if he had. The analogy is with the case of an author employed to write a book, who is obviously not entitled to payment if without consent he has someone else write it for him, however good the result. The fact that the employer may necessarily keep the benefit of the work by the sub-contractor does not affect the legal position—*see* case pp. 266–7.

By cl. 63 (1) (e) the employer has a right of forfeiture in some cases of wrongful sub-letting. Where he does not wish to forfeit the whole contract, and it may be that because the contractor knows this the threat to do so has no effect, it should be enough to discourage sub-contracting if it is pointed out that neither the main contractor nor the sub-contractor (p. 223) will be entitled to recover payment for the sub-contractor's work.

It is clear on general principles that the written consent of the engineer must be given before a sub-letting is made, so that the arbitrator cannot validate a sub-letting made by the contractor without asking for consent— *see* p. 302, N. 13. If the contractor does ask for consent, an arbitrator may under cl. 66 "*review and revise ... (the Engineer's) decision*" to refuse consent. However, that remedy is not effective for the contractor. He is not entitled to arbitration before completion of the works unless the engineer refuses to certify for some payment because of the sub-letting (cl. 66(2)), and (as this clause does not require the engineer's consent to be reasonable) the arbitrator does not appear to have power eventually to award damages to the contractor, even if loss can be proved (p. 417).

In the absence of regulation in the construction contract, sub-contracting by the contractor without the employer's consent still in many cases will be a breach of contract. It will be a breach so far as the circumstances

(s) The many cases holding that where a contract requires a written order for variations the order must be given before execution of the varied work are relevant—e.g. *Lamprell* v. *Billericay Union* (1849) 3 Exch. 283. This clause says that "The Contractor shall not sub-let any part of the Works" without the necessary consent, and the sub-letting takes place when the sub-contract is made. Where the employer knows of and acquiesces in execution of work by a sub-contractor for whom consent has not been obtained, he may be held to have waived his right to object—p. 157, N. 11.

show that the exercise by the original contractor of his particular skill or judgment in relation to the construction of the works was to the employer a material consideration in entering into the contract with him.

The contractor will, of course, use employees, but there is a real difference between that and sub-letting. The contractor has full practical and legal powers to organise and control the work of his employees, but in the absence of special agreement only very limited control over independent sub-contractors. The problems which the engineer should therefore consider before agreeing to a sub-contract are dealt with on pp. 222–3.

For the engineer's power to order a sub-contractor or sub-contractor's employee to be removed from the works *see* p. 85, N. 6.

5. THE ENGINEER'S AUTHORITY TO CONSENT TO A SUB-CONTRACT. The engineer has by this clause apparent authority to consent to a sub-contract, so that his consent is generally effective so far as the contractor is concerned even if the employer did not authorise it, but the engineer may be liable to the employer—p. 399.

6. "CONTRACTOR ... RESPONSIBLE FOR ... ANY SUB-CONTRACTOR". *See* p. 221.

7. "PROVISION OF LABOUR ON A PIECE-WORK BASIS ... NOT ... SUB-LETTING". Apparently the provision of labour referred to is not restricted to the provision by a worker of his own labour. The intention appears to be to make it unnecessary for the contractor to obtain consent to a "labour only" sub-contract, despite the many problems created by that form of sub-contracting.

8. THIS CLAUSE HAS BECOME PARTLY MISLEADING because of the new cls. 59A and 59B about nominated sub-contractors.

DOCUMENTS MUTUALLY EXPLANATORY

5. The several documents forming the Contract are to be taken as mutually explanatory of one another and in case of ambiguities or discrepancies the same shall be explained and adjusted by the Engineer[1] who shall thereupon issue to the Contractor appropriate instructions in writing[2] which shall be regarded as instructions issued in accordance with Clause 13.[3]

1. "AMBIGUITIES OR DISCREPANCIES ... SHALL BE ... ADJUSTED BY THE ENGINEER". It follows from the principles of interpretation applied by the courts (pp. 5–6) that the engineer may only certify expenses under this clause if there is genuinely an ambiguity or discrepancy in the contract; if the contract documents are clear they must generally be applied even if they produce a result which the parties obviously did not intend. The only exceptions are:

(*a*) Where the parties agree verbally on the terms to be set down in a written contract but a mistake is made and the writing does not set out their

(*t*) For a form of labour-only sub-contract see Butterworth's "Encyclopaedia of Forms and Precedents" 4th ed., vol. 3, p. 439.

agreement accurately, the courts will correct the contract provided the prior agreement and the mistake are proved clearly:

> A contracted with B to remove rubble. There was a term in the written contract eventually signed for a payment, but the clause was ambiguous as to whether the payment was to be made by or to A.
> It was proved that the parties had, in fact, agreed that the terms of the contract should be that A would make the payment, and the written contract was rectified to make this clear.

The cases in which the courts will grant rectification are limited by this necessity of proving prior agreement by the parties on the particular point; most of the disputes about interpretation are on points which were never thought about by the parties or the draftsman when the contract was being made.

(b) In some cases the courts will read a term into a contract because it was obviously intended by the parties:

> The plaintiff contracted with a mining company to remove certain waste rock, provided it was not more than 50,000 tons. The company agreed in the contract to supply a crusher and did so, but supplied one capable of crushing only 3 tons an hour.
> Held: A term was to be implied in the contract that the crusher would be adequate. Since the plaintiff would have had to work the machine supplied for almost 24 hours a day for the whole period of the contract to do the job, there was a breach of this term.

This doctrine is not very adventurous—a term will only be implied if it is not inconsistent with the express terms of the contract and is quite obviously necessary to give reasonable business efficacy to the contract:

> A contract for a hospital was set out in three sets of R.I.B.A. standard conditions, each relating to one phase of the hospital. The contractors agreed to complete Phase I by April 30th, 1969. Phase III was to commence "six months after the Date of Issue of the Certificate of Practical Completion of Phase I" and to be completed by April 30th, 1972.
> There was a delay of 59 weeks in completion of Phase I, and the architect granted an extension of time of 47 weeks. As a result the certificate of practical completion of that phase was not issued until June 22nd, 1970. This delay had the effect of postponing the commencement date for Phase III until December 22nd and leaving 16 months only instead of the original 30 months for completion of that phase by the specified date of April 30th, 1972.
> The contractors alleged that they were prepared to complete Phase III in 16 months and, since the employers were not able to nominate sub-contractors who could complete in that time, the contractors claimed extra payment for having to carry out the phase over a longer period. The employers contended that the

(u) *Monaghan County Council* v. *Vaughan* [1948] Ir.R. 306. In *Kemp* v. *Rose* (1858) 114 R.R. 429, it was held that there could be no rectification where the date for completion was omitted. However, this was on the grounds that if the court inserted the date "penal" damages would run from that date, which is not consistent with modern decisions on the nature of a liquidated damages clause (*see* p. 149), and it is suggested that this decision would not be followed.

(v) *Kleinert* v. *Abosso Gold Mining Co. Ltd.* [1913] 58 S.J. 45. In *Trollope & Colls* v. *Atomic Power Construction Ltd.* [1963] 1 W.L.R. 333, sub-contractors were asked to start work by the main contractors before all the terms of the sub-contract were agreed, and to incorporate changes in the sub-contract work agreed after the submission of tender. Held: that a term was to be implied into the sub-contract that the variation clause in that contract applied retrospectively to the valuation of changes made before the contract became binding.

contract time for completion of Phase III should be extended by adding a period equal to the extension of time properly allowable for completion of Phase I. In this way there was the unusual situation that it was the employer who was seeking the extension of time, in order to prevent a disruption claim by the contractor.

Held: As the contract clearly and unambiguously fixed the completion date for Phase III as April 30th, 1972, and did not specifically give the architect any power to extend that date for delay in completion of Phase I as it might so easily have done if that was intended, there was no room for implication of any term extending the date for completion of Phase III.

When a term is implied it is as binding as if it were written out in the contract—a point of which it is sometimes difficult to persuade engineers and others who have the misconception that everything they need to know about contract law is to be found between the covers of the printed contract form.

(c) It may be proved that the written documents do not set out the whole agreement—see pp. 58–60.

(d) The courts will take notice of any reasonable trade, market or local usage or custom that can be proved satisfactorily, even if it gives an unusual meaning to the words used.

(e) Some leeway is given by the basic rule (to which the first sentence of this clause refers) that a contract is to be interpreted as a whole, so that the literal meaning of a word or sentence may be controlled by the rest of the contract:

Contract to build a factory for £3,500,000. The conditions of contract included a wide variation clause (p. 173, footnote (uu)), and there was a note in the bill of quantities that it was probable that further work to the value of approximately £500,000 would be ordered on a measured basis.

As a result of delay by the employers the parties entered into a Deed of Variation by which the contractors agreed to adopt uneconomic working to complete by the original contract date. The Deed specified that the contract payments would be the actual cost to the contractors plus a net remuneration of not less than £150,000 or more than £300,000. The Deed confirmed all the other terms of the original contract.

The employers ordered extra works so that the total cost of the works to the contractors was £6,683,056. The arbitrator found that the extra work was not different in character than that anticipated at the time of the Deed of Variation, but that at the time the Deed was made the contractors contemplated that the actual cost of the finished work would not exceed £5,000,000—made up of the original contract work, the probable extras mentioned of £500,000 and £1,000,000 for uneconomic working.

There was evidence that the contractors' minimum and maximum remuneration was based on that estimated cost of the work.

(w) *Trollope & Colls Ltd.* v. *North West Metropolitan Regional Hospital Board* [1973] 2 All E.R. 260, H.L. The principles on which terms will be implied have been considered recently in *Liverpool City Council* v. *Irwin* [1977] A.C. 239, H.L., and *Shell U.K. Ltd.* v. *Lostock Garage Ltd.* [1977] 1 All E.R. 481, C.A. It is possible that the courts in the future will be a little less self-effacing than In the past in implying terms, at least those reasonably incidental to the nature of well recognised types of contract such as construction or plant hire contracts. In the meantime parliament has become active in positively dictating the meaning of contracts, *see* p. 60 for the Unfair Contract Terms Act 1977, and p. 431 for the Misrepresentation Act 1967.

(x) There is a reference in cl. 49 (3) of the Conditions to such implied obligations.

(y) In *Patman & Fotheringham Ltd.* v. *Pilditch* (1904) Hudson "Building Contracts" 4th ed., vol. ii, 368, at p. 372, the custom was referred to that figured dimensions are to be preferred to scale.

Held: That to have put the contractors at the mercy of the employers in making them liable to do whatever extra work the employers required without any increase in their profits, would have been absurd. On the true construction of the two contracts taken together the power to order variations did not entitle the employers to require work materially in excess of £5,000,000, so that the contractors were entitled to be paid reasonable profit on work beyond that amount.

A non-lawyer may be forgiven for asking why the courts strained the literal words of the contract in order to do justice in this case, but not in the case cited on p. 5. A realistic answer must be that the former decision was one of exceptional judicial valour, and that the extent to which a judge will stretch the literal meaning of one part of a contract to make it consistent with the general intention of the parties, as shown by the rest of the contract and the surrounding circumstances, is largely a matter of temperament. As it has been put in a somewhat purple passage—"the whole matter ultimately turns on the impalpable and indefinable elements of judicial spirit and attitude".

The following rules have been developed by the courts to help in finding the meaning of a contract which is not clear:

(i)   Obvious clerical errors will be read as corrected, but as to figures *see* p. 12, N. 5. The words govern where there is a discrepancy between numbers given both written out and in figures. *See also* footnote (*v*) above.

(ii)   Where as here part of a contract is in a standard printed form, any alterations or additions written in for the particular contract (for example special conditions added to the I.C.E. form) will be given greater weight than any inconsistent standard clauses. It does not seem that this principle is negated by the opening of this cl. 5.

(iii)   Corrections and erasures are presumed to have been made before signature of the contract, and therefore to be valid; alterations proved to have been made after signature are not valid unless agreed to by both parties, and the party making the alterations cannot enforce the contract. It has been held that the courts may refer to a deletion made by the parties from a printed form of contract as an aid to interpreting what they have chosen to leave in. It is likely that the courts will do so cautiously; often one party agrees to a deletion only because he is satisfied that the words remaining have the same meaning despite it.

(iv)   There are a number of technical rules which the courts may apply. For example the *eiusdem generis* rule—that where there are words of a particular class followed by general words, the general words are construed as referring only to matters of the same class:

Extension of time clause applying where the works were "delayed by

(*z*) *Parkinson (Sir Lindsay) & Co. Ltd.* v. *Commissioners of Works* [1950] 1 All E.R. 208, C.A. discussed in *British Movietonews* v. *London & District Cinemas* [1951] 2 All E.R. 617, H.L.
(*aa*) C. K. Allen "Law in the Making" 7th ed., p. 529—dealing with interpretation of statutes.
(*bb*) See *English Industrial Estates* v. *Wimpey & Co. Ltd.* [1973] 1 Lloyd's Rep. 118, C.A. per Lord Denning M.R. at pp. 123, 124, for the general principle, and the case as a whole for the effect of a provision in the contract contrary to the principle (in that case the R.I.B.A. standard form cl. 12).
(*cc*) *Mottram Consultants Ltd.* v. *Bernard Sunley & Sons Ltd.* [1975] 2 Lloyd's Rep. 197, H.L. discussed below on p. 270 footnote (*j*).

reason of any alteration or addition ... or in case of combination of workmen, or strikes, or by default of the sub-contractors ... or any cause beyond the contractor's control". Held: that the final category was intended to refer to causes of the same class as the examples given, and did not include delay caused by the employer.

dd

There is also a slight presumption that a change of words implies a change of meaning, and that the same word or phrase is intended to have the same meaning throughout a contract.

These presumptions presuppose a perfect draftsman—it is for example very difficult to maintain complete consistency in a complicated contract—and are therefore applied by the courts with extreme caution.

(v)   An ambiguity will be interpreted in the way least favourable to the party who had control over the drafting, usually the employer but the contractor in the case of tender qualifications (p. 20) or method-related charges written in by him (p. 218).

ee

(vi)   Provisions for which no meaning can be discovered may be ignored, but this may in exceptional cases make the whole contract too uncertain to be enforced (p. 1 (*a*)).

ff

(vii)   A negative principle is that in construing a contract the courts are not entitled to take into account the conduct of the parties subsequent to the execution of the contract in deciding on the meaning to be given to it. Of course, consistent with the principles discussed on pp. 5–6, the courts will not hear evidence of what was said or done by the parties in negotiations before the contract was made as to its intended meaning, but they will hear general evidence on the circumstances surrounding the contract, the setting of the contract, so as to understand what it is about.

gg

2. "IN CASE OF AMBIGUITIES OR DISCREPANCIES ... THE ENGINEER SHALL ... ISSUE ... APPROPRIATE INSTRUCTIONS IN WRITING". The scope of the instructions which the engineer is entitled to issue in resolving an ambiguity or discrepancy in the contract is not altogether clearly expressed in the

(*dd*) *Wells* v. *Army & Navy Co-op. Society* (1902) Hudson "Building Contracts" 4th ed., vol. ii, 346, at p. 357, C.A.

(*ee*) However, in *Tersons Ltd.* v. *Stevenage Development Corp.* (1963) reported in 5.B.L.R. 58, 78, 79, C.A., Pearson L. J. pointed out that the I.C.E. general Conditions "are not a partisan document ... (but) a general form ... prepared and revised jointly by several representative bodies.... It would naturally be incorporated in a contract of this kind, and should have the same meaning whether the one party or the other happens to have made the first mention of it in the negotiations". In *County & District Property Ltd.* v. *C. Jenner & Son* (Q.B. 1974) 3 B.L.R. 38, it was held that the standard form of building sub-contract was not to be interpreted against the main contractor, even when he sent it to the sub-contractor or specified its use, because the form is negotiated between the Builders' Federation and the Sub-Contractors' & Specialists' Federation.

For the extreme lengths to which the courts have gone in interpreting an indemnity clause against the party seeking to escape liability by relying on it, see p. 96, N. 1.

(*ff*) *Nicolene* v. *Simmonds* [1953] 1 All E.R. 822, C.A.—sale subject to "the usual condition of acceptance"; as no usual conditions existed the phrase was ignored and the contract enforced without it. Apparently uncertain terms (possibly, for example, "P.C. sum" if it is not defined in the contract) may be given sufficient certainty by a trade custom or previous dealings between the parties. "The court will always struggle to give meaning to what the parties have said if it can. The conclusion that it is void for uncertainty is really a counsel of despair": *Nea Agrex S.A.* v. *Baltic Shipping Co. Ltd.* [1976] 2 All E.R. 842, 850.

(*gg*) *Schuler (L.) A.G.* v. *Wickman Machine Tool Sales Ltd.* [1973] 2 All E.R. 39, H.L.

previous edition of this clause. This amendment gives the engineer the broad power to issue "*appropriate instructions*", which are to be regarded as instructions under cl. 13 with a consequential liability to compensate the contractor in some cases.

As a result of this amendment, on resolving an ambiguity or discrepancy the engineer may give instructions not merely as to the "*manner (in which) the work is to be carried out*" as in the previous edition, but also, e.g., about the time in which the work is to be carried out, or the contents of any documents to be submitted by the contractor.

Nevertheless, two limitations stand from the 4th edition. The engineer may act under this clause only if there is genuinely an ambiguity or discrepancy in the contract; if the contract documents are clear they must usually be applied even if they produce a result which the parties obviously did not intend (N. 1). And the contractor still has no remedy under this clause for ambiguities the resolution of which cannot result in an "*instruction*", for example an ambiguity about the method of payment for a claim.

3. EXTRA PAYMENT UNDER CLAUSE 13 FOR AMBIGUITIES AND DISCREPANCIES. The right to extra payment under cl. 13 as incorporated into this clause is less extensive than the contractor's right to payment under cl. 6 of the previous edition.

Under cl. 13 the contractor is entitled only to compensation to the extent that the "*instructions ... involve the Contractor in delay or disrupt his arrangements or methods of construction*". The contractor is no longer entitled to extra merely because he has to do more work than he anticipated because of the ambiguity, e.g. where work is shown on one drawing and omitted from another or from the specification, except to the extent that the resolution of the ambiguity causes disruption or delay.

The only exception, specifically stated in this clause, is where the instruction requires a variation to the works. Therefore where the engineer gives an instruction involving work about which the contract documents are ambiguous, it will be necessary under this new wording for the engineer (or arbitrator or court ultimately) to decide as a matter of law the correct interpretation of the documents. If the legally correct interpretation is that the work included in the instruction is part of the original contract works, then the contractor has no remedy under this clause merely because he has been involved in cost "which by reason of any such ambiguity or discrepancy the Contractor did not and had reason not to anticipate" (as he had under the former cl. 6), but only under cl. 13 if there is any delay or disruption involved. If the correct interpretation of the contract is such that the instruction requires the contractor to carry out extra work not part of the original contract works, then the instruction will amount to a variation order with a right to valuation under cl. 52. Since "*The several documents forming the Contract are to be taken as mutually explanatory*", work shown e.g. on one drawing but not on another will usually be part of the original contract work and not a variation.

Thus the wording does not achieve what might be thought to be one purpose of a clause of this kind—that irrespective of the correct legal resolution of an ambiguity the contractor should be entitled to extra payment if he was misled by it as to the work to be done.

The engineer has a duty to resolve an ambiguity or discrepancy of his own motion whenever one comes to his attention, irrespective of any request by the contractor for an instruction.

If the contractor does not raise with the engineer an ambiguity or discrepancy of which he but not the engineer has become aware, so that delay or disruption is caused or aggravated, it is suggested that when the matter eventually has to be resolved by an instruction it may not be "*reasonable*" as required by cl. 13 for the engineer to award the contractor any of the extra cost resulting from the contractor's default.

The contractor may even have a general duty to notify ambiguities in the contract documents of which he becomes or possibly should become aware, with liability to the employer or third parties for failure to do so. For breach of that duty the contractor may have to bear the costs of remedial works necessary because the ambiguity was not dealt with in time (p. 396).

The incorporation of cl. 13 brings with it cl. 52 (4) about notice of a claim by the contractor for extra payment for an instruction under this clause, and inclusion of payment in interim and final certificates (subject to retention).

SUPPLY OF DOCUMENTS

6. Upon acceptance of the Tender[1] 2 copies of the drawings[2] referred to in the Specification and of the Conditions of Contract the Specification and (unpriced) Bill of Quantities shall be furnished to the Contractor free of charge.[3] Copyright of the Drawings and Specification and of the Bill of Quantities (except the pricing thereof) shall remain in the Engineer[4] but the Contractor may obtain or make at his own expense any further copies required by him.[5] At the completion of the Contract the Contractor shall return to the Engineer all Drawings and the Specification whether provided by the Engineer or obtained or made by the Contractor.[6]

FURTHER DRAWINGS AND INSTRUCTIONS

7. (1) The Engineer shall have full power and authority to supply and shall supply to the Contractor from time to time during the progress of the Works such modified or further drawings and instructions[7] as shall in the Engineer's opinion be necessary for the purpose of the proper and adequate construction completion and maintenance of the Works[8] and the Contractor shall carry out and be bound by the same.

NOTICE BY CONTRACTOR

(2) The Contractor shall give adequate notice in writing to the Engineer of any further drawing or specification[9] that the Contractor may require for the execution of the Works or otherwise under the Contract.[8]

DELAY IN ISSUE

(3) If by reason of any failure or inability of the Engineer to issue at a time reasonable in all the circumstances[10] drawings or instructions requested by the Contractor[11] and considered necessary by the Engineer in accordance with sub-clause (1) of this Clause the Contractor suffers delay or incurs cost then the Engineer shall take such delay into account in determining any extension of time to which the Contractor is entitled under Clause 44 and the Contractor shall subject to Clause 52 (4)[12] be paid in accordance with Clause 60[13] the amount of such cost as may be reasonable.[14] If such drawings or instructions require any

variation to any part of the Works the same shall be deemed to have been issued pursuant to Clause 51.[15]

ONE COPY OF DOCUMENTS TO BE KEPT ON SITE

(4) One copy of the Drawings and Specification furnished to the Contractor as aforesaid shall be kept by the Contractor on the Site[16] and the same shall at all reasonable times be available for inspection and use by the Engineer and the Engineer's Representative and by any other person authorised by the Engineer in writing.

1. COPIES OF SOME CONTRACT DOCUMENTS TO BE FURNISHED FREE OF CHARGE "UPON ACCEPTANCE OF THE TENDER". A useful addition to ensure that the contractor has these documents at an early stage. These words hardly bind the engineer to supply the documents on the very day on which the tender is accepted, but in the case of substantial delay the contractor could have a claim for any adverse effects on his planning (p. 364).

2. DRAWINGS. Definition cl. 1 (1) (g), p. 25.

3. COPIES NOT FURNISHED FREE OF CHARGE. The contractor is not entitled to free copies of the pricing of the bill, the tender, the written acceptance by the employer or of any contract agreement. Copies of the first two should be retained when tendering, the contractor will have the original of the acceptance, and the agreement should be executed in duplicate. There is no requirement in cl. 7 (1) that the contractor is supplied with more than the original of "*modified or further drawings and instructions*".

4. COPYRIGHT. *See* p. 402, N. 35. The statement that copyright shall "*remain in the Engineer*" is not completely accurate; copyright in the contract documents will belong to the employer where the engineer is a full-time employee of his, such as an engineer of a local authority.

For ownership of documents *see* p. 402.

5. "THE CONTRACTOR MAY ... MAKE ... ANY FURTHER COPIES REQUIRED BY HIM". Clearly, this permission is limited to copies required for the works, since the engineer owns the copyright—*see* the last note.

6. RETURN OF DOCUMENTS BY THE CONTRACTOR. The contractor is not required to return the bill of quantities.

Only "*Drawings*" and "*Specifications*" each with a capital letter have to be "*returned*" under this sub-clause, i.e. those furnished or approved in writing by the engineer within the definition in cl. 1 (1) (f) and (g), and not other drawings, etc., made by the contractor, e.g. for his own temporary works.

The documents are to be returned "*At the completion of the Contract*". That stage appears to be reached only with the issue of the final certificate under cl. 60(3) and not earlier with the maintenance certificate, particularly as the contractor may need the documents for preparing his final account.

7. "THE ENGINEER ... SHALL SUPPLY ... SUCH MODIFIED OR FURTHER DRAWINGS" ETC. *See* N. 11.

8. "NECESSARY FOR THE PURPOSE OF THE PROPER AND ADEQUATE CONSTRUCTION COMPLETION AND MAINTENANCE OF THE WORKS"—"REQUIRE FOR THE EXECUTION OF THE WORKS OR OTHERWISE UNDER THE CONTRACT". No reason for this variety of wording is apparent.

9. "THE CONTRACTOR SHALL GIVE ADEQUATE NOTICE IN WRITING" of drawings, etc., required. *See* N. 11.

10. CLAIMS FOR "FAILURE OR INABILITY OF THE ENGINEER TO ISSUE AT A TIME REASONABLE IN ALL THE CIRCUMSTANCES DRAWINGS OR INSTRUCTIONS". In view of the importance of disruption claims by contractors, this phrase is discussed separately in ch. 12 on disruption.

11. "DRAWINGS OR INSTRUCTIONS REQUESTED BY THE CONTRACTOR". This clause can hardly be said to be graced with a rational scheme. Sub-cl. (1) places the duty on the engineer to issue "*modified or further drawings*" as he considers necessary; nevertheless, the contractor is required by sub-cl. (2) to give "*adequate notice in writing*" of any "*further drawing or specification*" that he may require for the execution of the works. and by sub-cl. (3) is entitled to compensation only for delay in the issue of "*drawings or instructions requested*" and "*considered necessary by the Engineer in accordance with sub-clause* (1)".

In view of the ambiguity of the requirement that drawings and instructions must be "*requested*" to entitle the contractor to claim for delay (not, as could easily have been said if intended, "*requested by notice in accordance with sub-clause* (2)"), the initial duty placed on the engineer to supply drawings, etc., and the incidental mystery of the change from "*drawings and instructions*" in sub-cl. (1) to "*drawing or specification*" in sub-cl. (2) and back again to "*drawings or instructions*" in sub-cl. (3), it does not seem that "*requested*" means requested by the contractor by "*adequate notice in writing*" as specified in sub-cl. (2). Nor does it seem that the contractor is limited to claiming for a period of delay after a request has been made ("*at a time*", not "*within a time*"). Nevertheless, lateness of or lack of clarity or urgency in a request may be relevant to deciding what was a reasonable time for the engineer to provide the drawings or instructions (p. 365).

There remains also the very practical point that the contractor has a remedy under this clause for late drawings or instructions only if they have been "*requested*" by him at some time before receipt. This clause appears to be intended as a comprehensive provision dealing with the contractor's remedy for delayed instructions or drawings (unlike the equivalent provision of the J.C.T. Standard Forms of building contract, in which the contractor's common law rights are specifically preserved), so that there is no room for implication of any other term dealing with compensation for delay with drawings or instructions which have not been requested (p. 42). However, in certain circumstances the contractor's rights under other clauses may come to his rescue.

hh

ii

(*hh*) It has been accepted on behalf of the committee that produced the 5th edition that this change of wording is a drafting error, presumably soon to be corrected—(1973) 72 New Civil Engineer 33 at p. 34.
(*ii*) The forms issued by the Joint Contracts Tribunal which now officially have the above title were formerly and are still commonly known as the R.I.B.A. building contract.

The problems of delay and disruption claims are discussed at large in ch. 12, but the relationship of the various clauses in these Conditions can be summarised by saying that in so far as performing the work in instructions or drawings would have caused the delay whenever they were issued, then the contractor may have a remedy under cls. 13 or 51 but not under this clause (N. 15); in so far as the contractor suffers delay before instructions or drawings are issued in waiting for them, his only remedy for the cost of that delay is under this clause; if because of the time at which the instructions are issued the contractor has to delay the works after their issue (e.g. in order to pre-plan) he may have the useful alternative to a claim under this clause of claiming under cl. 13 or cl. 51, for instance if the engineer produces some delaying detail which the contractor did not expect and therefore did not request in advance as required by this clause.

In the interests of progress of the works as well as his contractual position if matters do go wrong, it is advisable for the contractor to have a regular office procedure by which in sending his programme he also notifies the dates by which he requires the full drawings and instructions for specified parts of the works. A programme under cl. 14 merely showing a date on which particular work is to be carried out is hardly by itself a sufficient implied request for the drawings and instructions necessary to execute that work so as to satisfy the requirements of this clause.

The contractor should also have a set procedure for giving further written notice in good time of all information he needs, allowing a reasonable period for the engineer to prepare and issue the information and for the contractor himself to do any necessary pre-planning, and recording in what cases and why delay in furnishing the information will disrupt his work. The importance of such records for both the engineer and the contractor is discussed again under the heading of "Claimsmanship" in ch. 17.

Only the engineer or his delegate specifically given all the engineer's functions or his functions under this clause appear to have power to receive the necessary request, not the engineer's representative or his assistants (cl. 2 (1)–(3)).

12. PAYMENT TO CONTRACTOR "SUBJECT TO CLAUSE 52 (4)"—dealing with notice of money claims.

13. PAYMENT "IN ACCORDANCE WITH CLAUSE 60"—i.e. included in interim and final certificates, and subject to retention.

14. PAYMENT TO CONTRACTOR OF "SUCH COST AS MAY BE REASONABLE". See p. 31, N. 18, as to overheads and exclusion of loss of profit. Under the previous edition the contractor's claim for delayed documents is mainly for breach of a term implied into the contract, and compensation for such breach of contract includes loss of profits (p. 427). This clause appears to be intended as a comprehensive provision dealing with the contractor's remedy for delayed instructions or drawings, so that there is no room for implication of any other term dealing with compensation for delay (p. 42) The clause therefore, by removing the right to loss of the profits he would have earned if his resources had not been kept on the site by the delay, seriously limits the contractor's remedy for delay or disruption due to late supply of drawings or instructions, but not, e.g., delay in inspecting works under cl. 38 or by other contractors employed direct by the employer (but as

to a suspension order *see* p. 131, N. 4). For disruption due to variations *see* the next note.

In view of this restriction on his rights, the contractor should keep in mind the one remnant of his rights under the ordinary law, that is the right to end the contract in the case of serious or indefinite delay and to recover full damages which may include loss of profit (p. 427). In the case of delay lasting four months the contractor's specific rights under cl. 40 (2) may be useful, including as they probably do a right to lost profits where the whole works are treated as abandoned because of suspension.

It is possible, although unlikely, that the Unfair Contract Terms Act 1977 may improve the contractor's right to compensation for delay—p. 432.

It is clearly not "*reasonable*" to award costs incurred because of the contractor's inefficiency, a problem discussed on p. 442. For another example of unreasonable costs *see* p. 82, N. 18.

15. DELAY WITH INSTRUCTIONS OR DRAWINGS CONSTITUTING A VARIATION, AND INSTRUCTIONS OR DRAWINGS REQUIRING A VARIATION. If delay in supplying instructions or drawings necessitates a change in any "*specified sequence method or timing of construction*" of the works, the contractor may be entitled to argue that the engineer must give a variation order under cl. 51, to be valued under cl. 52 including profit (p. 187). If the contents of an instruction or drawing when issued involve such a variation or a variation in the physical works, then, as this sub-clause says, again the variation must be priced under cl. 52 and such valuation will normally include a profit for the contractor, and compensation for loss of profit for any extra time on the site due to the variation.

16. THE DOCUMENTS TO BE KEPT BY THE CONTRACTOR ON SITE are extended to the Specification (defined in cl. 1 (1) (f)) as well as drawings. For no apparent reason the contractor is not required to keep on site written instructions other than specifications.

CONTRACTOR'S GENERAL RESPONSIBILITIES

8. (1) The Contractor shall subject to the provisions of the Contract[1] construct complete and maintain the Works and provide all labour materials Constructional Plant Temporary Works transport to and from and in or about the Site and everything whether of a temporary or permanent nature required in and for such construction completion and maintenance so far as the necessity for providing the same is specified in or reasonably to be inferred from the Contract.

CONTRACTOR RESPONSIBLE FOR SAFETY OF SITE OPERATIONS

(2) The Contractor shall take full responsibility for the adequacy stability and safety of all site operations and methods of construction[2] provided that the Contractor shall not be responsible for the design or specification of the Permanent Works (except as may be expressly provided in the Contract) or of any Temporary Works designed by the Engineer.[3,4]

1. "SUBJECT TO THE PROVISIONS OF THE CONTRACT". This addition recognises that by cl. 55 (2) the contractor is entitled to extra payment for items omitted from the bill of quantities, even if they are "*reasonably to be inferred from the Contract*" within the last line of this sub-clause (pp. 206–9).

2. "THE CONTRACTOR SHALL TAKE FULL RESPONSIBILITY FOR THE
ADEQUACY STABILITY AND SAFETY OF ALL SITE OPERATIONS AND METHODS OF
CONSTRUCTION"—RESPONSIBILITY FOR TEMPORARY WORKS. This is a
suitable place to deal with a matter on which clear guidance from the law is
of great practical importance, but unfortunately is lacking. The complex
question of responsibility for temporary works may be analysed under four
headings: (i) responsibility of the contractor to the employer; (ii)
responsibility of the engineer to his client; (iii) responsibility (or rather lack
of responsibility) of the employer via his engineer to the contractor as such;
and (iv) responsibility of the employer, engineer and contractor to
employees and members of the public.

(i) The contractor's responsibility to the employer is clear-cut. By this
clause the contractor is responsible for the "*adequacy stability and safety of
all site operations and methods of construction*", but not for the design of
temporary works designed by the engineer. If temporary works not
designed by the engineer (i.e. designed by the contractor or a sub-
contractor, including a nominated sub-contractor (p. 229)) are inadequate
or defective the contractor must supplement or rectify them in order to
perform his contract by completing the permanent works. If damage to the
permanent or temporary works does occur as a result of such deficiencies,
the contractor (or his insurers) are liable under cls. 20 and 21.

In the process of achieving satisfactory temporary works the contractor
may become entitled to extra payment (pp. 87 and 170), but the engineer's
approval of temporary works does not relieve the contractor of liability (cl.
14 (7)). For the engineer's other powers of control *see* cls. 13, 39, 40, 49 and
51.

(ii) The engineer undoubtedly has a duty to his client to ensure that the
completed permanent works will not be adversely affected by stresses
due to the contractor's temporary works, and that duty he carries out in the
first instance by a proper specification, by actually designing temporary
works where it would not be satisfactory to leave the design to the
contractor, and by exercising his powers of control, keeping in mind the
dangers of opening the way to claims (above). The engineer must also
ensure that temporary works are in fact built in accordance with his or the
contractor's design, at least in so far as necessary to avoid detriment to the
completed permanent works.

One of the problem areas is whether the engineer has any duty to his
client to see that temporary works are designed and built satisfactorily even
in respect of defects that will not have physical repercussions on the
completed permanent works. A relevant consideration is that the employer
seeks works finished on time, not a right to damages against the contractor,
and a serious failure of temporary works may delay completion of the
permanent works. In addition, even if he is entitled to an indemnity from
the contractor the employer scarcely will be happy to have injuries to life in
the course of works being constructed for him. Actual or threatened
damage to neighbouring property may halt the permanent works by way of
an injunction (p. 430). It is suggested that given the terms of cls. 8 (2) and 14
(3) and the protection obtained by the employer from the contractor's
liability (and insurance), and in the absence of any special term in the
engineer's service contract, the true position is that the engineer has a
limited duty. That duty (it is submitted) is to take steps to have remedied
any defects in the methods or results of constructing temporary works that
are apparent on the normal site inspections, but not to go out of his way to

prevent or search for such defects independently of his design and inspection of permanent work.

(iii) It is worth emphasising that the engineer.has no duty to the contractor as such to detect or prevent faults in temporary works (or the permanent works). The engineer is appointed to protect the employer, not the contractor. The argument often put forward in practice that it is somehow an excuse for faults in workmanship or materials that they were not objected to by the engineer or resident, is to imply that the employer is in a worse position if he engages engineers to supervise the contractor than if he does not. In particular the engineer has rights of control under cls. 8, 13 and 14, not duties, and refer to cl. 39 (3).

(iv) Responsibility to employees and to the public. The relevant grounds of liability, and the right of an injured party to sue all or any of the parties liable, are discussed in ch. 4. The contractor clearly is liable to employees of his and to third parties if he breaks his duty of care in designing or constructing temporary works. He is probably also liable if he follows a design of the engineer when he knew or should as a competent and careful contractor have known it was faulty.

The liability of the engineer to third parties in respect of temporary works is the most difficult to define:

"That case, in both courts, further establishes that an architect has no right to instruct a builder how his work is to be done or the safety precautions to be taken.

(*jj*) This opinion is supported to some extent by the dicta cited in footnotes (*kk*) (*oo*), defining the sphere of responsibility of the architect and engineer to the contractor and third parties, but with the warning in the last of those notes, and see also the excerpt from the *Florida* decision quoted on p. 391 of the text below.

(*kk*) "... it seems abundantly plain that the duty of care of an architect or of a consulting engineer in no way extends into the area of how the work is carried out. Not only has he no duty to instruct the builder how to do the work or what safety precautions to take but he has no right to do so, nor is he under any duty to the builder to detect faults during the progress of the works. The architect, in that respect, may be in breach of his duty to his client, the building owner, but this does not excuse the builder for faulty work": *Oldschool* v. *Gleeson (Construction) Ltd.* (1976) reported in 4 B.L.R. 105, 131. In that case H. H. Judge Stabb Q.C. did not accept the evidence of the defendant's expert that the consulting engineer was to be regarded "as being 'the father and mother of the job', whose duty it is to direct the contractors as to the manner in which the work is to be done, if he sees that the method which they are employing might endanger the safety of the works, and to stop the work if necessary" (p. 122). It was argued on behalf of the contractors that "when the consulting engineer knows or ought to know that the contractors are heading into danger whereby damage to property is likely to result, then he owes the contractor a duty of care to prevent such damage occurring ... I am not sure that the consulting engineer's duty extends quite that far, but, even if it does, I do not believe that he is under a duty to do more than warn the contractors to take the precautions necessary ..." (p. 124). The contractors sought an indemnity from the engineers for liability to neighbours of the building site when a party wall collapsed because of failure of clay beneath foundations, caused when the builders excavated a hoist pit below the level of the party wall without taking proper precautions to support the foundations.

In *Vonasack* v. *Hirsch* 221 N.W. 2d 815 (1974) contractors sued the architect for the cost of repairs to a building when steel roof joists with 100 ft span collapsed mainly because the contractor did not tie each member to the end wall or the previous member during erection. The Supreme Court of Wisconsin held that any construction hazards should have been known to the contractors as well as the architect and the architect had no duty to warn the contractors of special precautions which were generally known in the steel erection industry. "The contract does not make the ... (architect) a supervisor of the project in the sense that he was responsible for the procedures adopted by the contractor. .... To hold otherwise would make the architect a general safety supervisor of the site, a job which would require his continuous presence in disregard of the express language of his contract. In addition, it would fundamentally alter the relationship between the owner, architect and contractor....

See also *East Ham Borough Council* v. *Bernard Sunley & Sons Ltd.* [1965] 3 All E.R. 619, 636, 639, 640, H.L.

"It is the function and right of the builder to carry out his own building operations as he thinks fit."

ll

In the case referred to in that quotation:

A wall in which a chase was being cut fell on and injured a bricklayer. The bricklayer had suggested to the architect that it would be better to pull down and rebuild the wall. The architect decided, correctly according to the court, that the wall was safe. The wall fell down because the builders did not support it properly.

Held: That the architect was not liable to the bricklayer. It was the builders' and not the architect's duty to see that proper precautions were taken when cutting the chase, and the architect had no reason to believe that they would not do so.

mm

The result appears to be that as far as employees of the contractor and members of the public are concerned, the engineer is not bound to look for defects in temporary works. The fact that in some cases he may have a duty to his client to do so ((ii) above) cannot be relied on by these third parties to make the engineer liable to them. Nevertheless, the position is complicated if the engineer, from any inspection of drawings or of the physical temporary works he does make or from any other information that does come to his attention, recognises or should as a careful and competent engineer have recognised a danger of injury to the person or property of another. If he does not then take reasonable care to avoid the injury via some action which he has power to take, it may be that he will be liable:

The managing director of demolition contractors asked the architect whether a wall of a building which was being demolished could be left standing. The architect, without inspecting the wall, said that it could "if it is safe to do so" and the director said it was. The fact that the wall was dangerous would have been obvious on an inspection, which the architect had an opportunity to make.

Eventually the wall fell on a workman employed by building contractors who had come on to the site. It was held that the architect was 42 per cent liable for his injuries, because the workman was entitled to have relied on both the architect and demolition contractors to exercise reasonable care to leave the site safe for him.

nn

It seems that the above case goes to the limit of the engineer's liability, and as stated above it can hardly be that the engineer has a positive duty to take it on himself to inspect the drawings for or supervise the contractor's temporary works purely for the protection of the contractor's workmen.

oo

In some cases the employer may be liable to third parties for the default of

(*ll*) *A.M.F. International Ltd.* v. *Magnet Bowling* [1968] 2 All E.R. 789 at p. 809, per Mocatta J.

(*mm*) *Clayton* v. *Woodman & Son (Builders) Ltd.* [1962] 2 All E.R. 33, C.A. Reference is made in the course of the judgments (p. 41) to the "confusion of functions" that would result from any other view.

(*nn*) *Clay* v. *A. J. Crump & Sons Ltd.* [1963] 3 All E.R. 687, C.A. Pages 691–2 of the report show how strongly the peculiar facts of that case were against the architect. The decision was discussed in *Florida Hotels Pty. Ltd.* v. *Mayo* [1965] 113 C.L.R. 588 Aus., summarised in the text p. 391 below.

(*oo*) In the previous edition of this book it was said that it seemed "clear" that the last case went to the limit of the engineer's liability, but the encouragement being given by the courts to the growing tendency of injured parties to claim against everyone in sight means that little about the law of negligence can be said to be clear. The industry itself may also be blurring the distinction between the roles of the contractor and engineer—see the Final Report of the Advisory Committee on Falsework (1975) H.M.S.O., pp. 73–6.

the engineer. The right of contribution between several parties sued for the same injury or damage, and the particular rights of indemnity as between employer and contractor, are discussed in ch. 4. Design of or interference by the engineer with the contractor's temporary works may be an "*act*" of the engineer for liability arising from which the employer is bound to indemnify the contractor under cls. 22 and 24. Failure to inspect the contractor's design or execution of temporary works is not a "*default*" or "*neglect*" within those clauses so as to involve such liability, because the engineer has no duty to the contractor to do so.

3. "THE CONTRACTOR SHALL NOT BE RESPONSIBLE FOR THE DESIGN OR SPECIFICATION OF THE PERMANENT WORKS . . . OR OF ANY TEMPORARY WORKS DESIGNED BY THE ENGINEER". This form of contract binds the contractor to construct and maintain works in accordance with documents supplied to him. Ordinarily, the contractor's only duty is to do the work described in these documents; he takes no responsibility for the result. This sub-clause recognises this position and dovetails with the excepted risk in cl. 20 of the engineer's design. *See* the next note.

For the definitions of "*Permanent Works*" and "*Temporary Works*" see cl. 1 (1) (j) and (k).

4. "EXCEPT AS MAY BE EXPRESSLY PROVIDED IN THE CONTRACT":

(*a*) These Conditions are unsuitable for a wholly or partly design and construct contract without extensive amendment, which has not deterred employers from using the previous edition unchanged for package deals, with unfortunate results. Note that any design responsibility for permanent works must be "*expressly*" (*see* p. 215, footnote (*x'*)) imposed on the contractor. If the contract is silent as to some matter of choice of materials or other detailing the contractor should apply to the engineer for an instruction under cls. 5 or 13, with a possible right to extra payment. For the position of the contractor if he takes it on himself to make the choice *see* p. 179, N.2.

pp

(*b*) The contractor may nevertheless have some responsibility outside the contract, to warn of defective design. That is part of a large and developing area of the law, which is discussed on pp. 393 4.

(*c*) As to design by nominated sub-contractors *see* p. 227.

(*pp*) In *Brunswick Construction Ltd.* v. *Nowlan* (1977) 49 D.L.R. (3d) 93, the employer made a lump sum contract with a builder for construction of a house according to plans prepared by the owner's architect. There was no written specification. Where the plans were silent the builder supplied the specification. The architect did not supervise the works. Rotting was found later in the walls of the house, primarily because the architect's plans did not provide for ventilation although poor workmanship contributed. The Supreme Court of Canada held that the builder was jointly and severally liable with the architect for the owner's losses, for breach of a contractual duty to warn the owner of the danger inherent in executing the architect's plans.

Obviously the facts and contractual position in favour of exonerating the contractor were not at all as strong in that case as they would be in the case of works under these Conditions. The duty of the contractor was held to arise not outside of the contract for negligence (above) but by reason of an express undertaking to carry out work which would perform its function, although there is no indication in the judgments where such an express undertaking did in fact appear in the contract. There was a strong dissenting judgment.

CONTRACT AGREEMENT

9. The Contractor shall when called upon so to do enter into and execute a Contract Agreement (to be prepared at the cost of the Employer) in the form annexed.

See p. 22.

SURETIES

10. If the Tender shall contain an undertaking by the Contractor to provide when required 2 good and sufficient sureties or to obtain the guarantee of an Insurance Company or Bank[1] to be jointly and severally bound[2] with the Contractor in a sum not exceeding 10 per cent of the Tender Total[3] for the due performance of the Contract under the terms of a Bond the said sureties Insurance Company or Bank and the terms of the said Bond shall be such as shall be approved by the Employer[4] and the provision of such sureties or the obtaining of such guarantee and the cost of the Bond to be so entered into shall be at the expense in all respects of the Contractor unless the Contract otherwise provides.[5]

1. BOND. Where the contractor is a limited company the directors may also be asked to guarantee the contract personally, and in some cases an employer should be asked to provide a bond for payment.

Failure by the contractor to obtain a bond is generally sufficiently serious to entitle the employer to bring the whole contract to an end (ch. 16). For the engineer's duty to ensure that a bond is supplied at the outset, *see* p. 378. For the January 1979 revision to this clause *see* p. 322, N. 6.

2. "JOINTLY AND SEVERALLY BOUND". *See* p. 321, N. 2.

3. "10 PER CENT OF THE TENDER TOTAL". Definition cl. 1 (1) (h). If there are large increases in the works the employer may have to consider getting a further bond at his own cost.

4. "APPROVED BY THE EMPLOYER". The bond must be inspected by the engineer and any doubtful points brought to the employer's attention, for legal advice if necessary. *See* recommended form, p. 320. The form is not referred to in this clause, but by the Form of Tender the contractor undertakes to provide a bond in the form "*annexed to the Conditions of Contract*". It is important for the form actually to be included or incorporated (p. 25, N. 8) in the tender documents.

5. SUB-CONTRACT BONDS. *See* p. 321.

INSPECTION OF SITE

11. (1) The Contractor shall be deemed to have inspected and examined the Site and its surroundings and to have satisfied himself[1] before submitting his tender[2] as to the nature of the ground and sub-soil (so far as is practicable and having taken into account any information in connection therewith which may have been provided by or on behalf of the Employer)[3,4] the form and nature of the

qq

(qq) Roberts v. *Brett* (1865) 145 R.R. 223 and *Swartz & Son (Pty.) Ltd.* v. *Wolmaranstad. Town Council* (1960) S.A.L.R. 1.

Site[5] the extent and nature of the work and materials necessary for the completion of the Works the means of communication with[6] and access to the Site the accommodation he may require[7] and in general to have obtained for himself all necessary information (subject as above-mentioned) as to risks contingencies and all other circumstances influencing or affecting his tender.

SUFFICIENCY OF TENDER

(2) The Contractor shall be deemed to have satisfied himself before submitting his tender as to the correctness and sufficiency of the rates and prices stated by him[8] in the Priced Bill of Quantities[9] which shall (except in so far as it is otherwise provided in the Contract) cover all his obligations under the Contract.[10]

1. CONTRACTOR'S PRE-TENDER INVESTIGATIONS. Unfortunately it is not possible to say precisely what investigations a prudent contractor should make prior to tender, to ensure that he covers all his obligations under this clause in his tender price and will have a cl. 12 claim if the actual conditions differ from those foreseen.

A contrast is drawn in this clause between the required investigation of the site ("*Site*" is defined in cl. 1 (1) (n), but clearly in this context is not intended to include the sub-soil) and the "*nature of the ground and sub-soil*". The contractor is required to inspect the site but is not specifically bound to inspect the ground and sub-soil, only "*to have satisfied himself . . . (so far as is practicable)*" as to its nature. This distinction implies that the contractor may satisfy himself about the nature of sub-soil without any actual opening into and inspection of it—e.g. by inspecting excavations in the neighbourhood, enquiries from the local contractors and examination of geological and other records. It is important to preserve carefully the evidence that these investigations have been carried out.

Where there is not sufficient reliable information to be gathered in this way, it appears that the contractor is bound to satisfy himself as to the nature of the sub-soil by trial pits or boreholes, "*so far as is practicable*". The magnitude of the investigations which it is practicable for a contractor to carry out must be limited particularly by the time available for tender. An incidental argument often made by contractors is the impracticability of a number of tenderers digging up private lands or highways (often with no right to do so) and which may be in use. Employers should at least make a practice of notifying tenderers of the arrangements which have been made to give them access to the site to carry out investigations, and tenderers should be required to have insurance in force against any damage or injury caused in the course of investigations.

Special considerations which arise where the employer supplies site information are discussed below.

Unfortunately all that can be said on the legal position does not add up to anything like a clear code of good practice for pre-tender investigations. The guide in each case is what an experienced contractor would reasonably do to satisfy himself in accordance with his onerous obligations under this clause. For a further discussion, in the context of claims, refer to p. 436.

2. "BEFORE SUBMITTING HIS TENDER". It appears from this wording that changes in the physical conditions, etc., after the date of tender, even if known to the contractor, are to be disregarded in adjudicating on a cl. 12

claim. It may be argued that if the change in conditions became known to the contractor at a time when he was free to withdraw his tender (p. 3), then by entering into the contract he must be taken to have waived his rights to claim for the change. However, on balance it seems that the contractor is entitled to argue that he was under no duty to alter his tender, because of this wording.

The contractor has no right to claim merely on the grounds of a change in conditions or circumstances after the date of his tender, and before formation of the contract, even if unknown to him, unless he has a cl. 12 claim. However, if the employer has represented some matter to the contractor before tender, but before the contract is made owing to a change of circumstances the representation becomes false to the knowledge of the employer, or for the first time he learns that it was false when made or ceases to have reasonable grounds to believe it is true, then he is bound to notify the contractor of the change of circumstances so that the contractor may amend his tender. If the employer does not do so the contractor has a

rr remedy in damages.

3. CONTRACTOR'S REMEDIES FOR MISINFORMATION. The contractor, despite this clause, may have a remedy for misinformation given to him by the employer about ground conditions or other risks, in a number of cases:

(*a*) If the contractor can show that in the contract documents (*see*
ss F.I.D.I.C. International Conditions cl. 11) or before or at the time when the contract was made, the employer gave any definite information about site conditions, etc., whether verbally or in writing, in a form or in circumstances which implied particularly that the information might be accepted and acted on as correct by the contractor, then the employer may be liable if the information is not correct. The information may be binding either on the grounds that it is a term .of the construction contract—a warranty—that the information is correct, or that the employer and contractor have made a collateral contract about the information quite separate from the construction contract.

Whether or not a statement is intended to be binding as a warranty depends on the intention of the parties. Their intention is, however, judged objectively—if the form or circumstances of the statement are such that a reasonable person would believe that the employer intended to warrant the information the employer is bound, even though in his own mind he did not intend to do so. It is suggested that a statement about the nature of sub-soil made casually or in passing even in the contract documents does not amount to a warranty, particularly if it is practicable within cl. 11 for the contractor to find out the actual conditions, but that a definite and clear statement made to influence the contractor in pricing may do so, unless it is
tt specifically stated that the information is not guaranteed.

(*rr*) *With* v. *O'Flanagan* [1936] 1 All E.R. 727, *Davies* v. *London and Provincial Insurance Co.*
(1878) 8 Ch.D. 469, and the Misrepresentation Act, 1967 (p. 60).

(*ss*) Conditions of Contract (International) for Works of Civil Engineering Construction, 3rd ed. March 1977, approved by the Fédération Internationale des Ingénieurs' Conseils and others.

(*tt*) See *Bentley (Dick) Productions Ltd.* v. *Smith (Harold) (Motors) Ltd.* [1965] 2 All E.R. 65, C.A. and *Bank of Ireland* v. *Smith* (1968) 102 I.L.T.R. 69 at p. 75.

In *Bacal Construction (Midlands) Ltd.* v. *Northampton Development Corporation* (1975) now reported at 8 B.L.R. 91, tender documents for design and construction of a house included a statement that the general information was that the site was a mixture of Northamptonshire sand and upper lias clay, whereas in various areas of the site some surface

It is clear also that the statement in this cl. 11 that the contractor may take information supplied by the employer into account does not of itself amount to a warranty of the accuracy of that information, which is not made part of the contract and usually is expressly stated not to be guaranteed.

A collateral agreement by which the contractor agrees to enter into the construction contract on the employer's oral or written promise that certain information is correct need not be made in so many words but may be implied from the parties' statements and behaviour. Such agreement may be enforced even though it is not referred to in the contract documents and it seems even though it is inconsistent with the terms of the construction contract—e.g. with the usual statement that borehole records or similar information is not guaranteed:

> Conditions of sale at an auction set out that no verbal warranty of the quality of any animal being sold was to be effective unless it was written on the purchaser's account. A cow was put up for auction but its appearance was not impressive enough to produce any bid. The auctioneer then said that there was nothing wrong with the animal and that he would take her back if she turned out not to be as he said.
>
> Held: This verbal assurance was binding and overrode the written condition.   *uu*

If there is in this way a warranty or collateral contract between the parties that, e.g., site conditions are as stated, then the contractor has all the remedies for breach of contract (ch. 16) if they are not so, even if the employer had reasonable grounds for believing that the statement of the conditions was correct.

Although the employer may bind himself, the engineer as such has no apparent authority in relation to the contractor to bind the employer by any assurance outside the contract documents, e.g. as to feasibility of the design, the accuracy of the quantities or the conditions of the site. The   *vv*

strata or patches of assorted spongy material known as tufa were encountered. The contractors had been told in writing on behalf of the employer at the time of tender that their design was to assume the soil conditions disclosed at boreholes, which did not give any warning of the presence of tufa. Held that it was an implied term or warranty of the contract that the ground conditions would accord with the hypothesis on which the contractors were instructed to design the foundations. The contractors recovered compensation accordingly.

In *Cana Construction Co. Ltd.* v. *The Queen* (1973) 37 D.L.R. (3d) 418 Can., the employer was held liable for the inaccuracy of an "estimate" of the expected cost of installing equipment in a building given to a contractor for the building, who relied on the estimate in pricing in his tender his overheads, profit and supervision in connection with that special equipment which was to be supplied and installed by other contractors under a separate contract.

(*uu*) *Harling* v. *Eddy* [1951] 2 All E.R. 212, and see *Jameson* v. *Kinmell Bay Land Co. Ltd.* (1931) 47 T.L.R. 593, *City & Westminster Properties* (1934) *Ltd.* v. *Mudd* [1958] 2 All E.R. 733 and *J. Evans & Son (Portsmouth) Ltd.* v. *Andrea Merzario Ltd.* [1976] 2 All E.R. 930, C.A. In *Unit Construction Co. Ltd.* v. *Liverpool Corporation* (1972) 221 E.G. 459, it was held that letters between the parties prior to contract fell short of the "strict proof" and "clearly shown" intention necessary to constitute a collateral contract.

(*vv*) But an engineer who is also a full-time employee, e.g. of a local authority, may have wider authority. In *Carlton Contractors* v. *Bexley Corporation* (1962) 60 L.G.R. 331 it was held that a borough surveyor had actual and apparent authority (see p. 399, N.32) to agree with the contractor to correct discrepancies between contract documents before execution of the contract. It is, however, now common practice to state in instructions to tenderers or other tender documents that no agent or servant has any authority to make any representation or explanation as to any matter or thing so as to bind the employer. As a result, it is important for a tenderer to confirm direct to the employer before tender any explanations on which he is replying. See *Overbrooke Estates Ltd.* v. *Glencombe Properties Ltd.* [1974] 3 All E.R. 511.

employer will not therefore be bound if the engineer gives an assurance on his behalf without special authority, but the engineer may be liable to the contractor for breach of warranty of authority (p. 399).

(b) If a statement is made by the employer which does not become contractually binding under (a) the contractor will nevertheless have remedies if he was induced to make the contract in reliance on the statement and it was made fraudulently or recklessly.

A misrepresentation is fraudulent if it is made knowing that it is not true; reckless if it is made without knowing that it is untrue but "with a reckless indifference whether ... (it is) true or false", "a reckless disregard of the interests of the other contracting party".

ww
xx

A disclaimer of responsibility for representations will not exclude liability for fraud or recklessness:

> The engineer had shown a wall on the contract drawings in a position which he knew was not correct. Held: that the clause in the contract to the effect that the contractor would satisfy himself as to the dimensions, levels and nature of all existing works and that the employer did not hold himself responsible for the accuracy of information given, was no defence to liability to the contractor for fraud.

yy

(c) Formerly the remedies for an innocent misrepresentation, that is, a misrepresentation made without fraud or recklessness, were very limited. Now, under the Misrepresentation Act 1967, the remedies formerly restricted to cases of fraud or recklessness apply to all misrepresentations, unless the contracting party who made the representation can prove "that he had reasonable ground to believe and did believe up to the time the contract was made that the facts represented were true".

zz

As a result, the remedies for misrepresentation are damages in the case of a negligent or fraudulent misrepresentation, and rescission (i.e. ending of the contract) in the case of such a representation or even a blameless misrepresentation where the contracting party had reasonable grounds to believe that it was true. Obviously a contractor who finds that some soil conditions have been seriously misrepresented may prefer to end his contract rather than perform it at extra cost with the usual delay in recovering the damages to which he may be entitled. However, except in the case of a fraudulent misrepresentation, the remedy of rescission is in the discretion of the court, which may refuse the remedy and grant damages instead. Since no cases have yet been decided on the point, it remains to be seen what the attitude of the courts will be to granting rescission of a construction contract, although clearly a misrepresentation would have to be serious to justify that remedy.

The major restriction on the remedies under this important Act is that a term in a contract which would exclude or restrict any liability or remedy by reason of any misrepresentation made before a contract was made is of no effect *except* in so far as the term "shall have been a fair and reasonable one to be included having regard to the circumstances which were, or ought

(*ww*) *Pearson & Son Ltd.* v. *Dublin Corporation* [1907] A.C. 351, 353 per Lord Loreburn L.C.

(*xx*) See *Boyd & Forrest* v. *Glasgow & S.W. Ry. Co.* [1912] S.C. (H.L.) 93, at p. 104.

(*yy*) *Pearson & Son Ltd.* v. *Dublin Corporation* [1907] A.C. 351, applied in *Dublin Port and Docks Board* v. *Britannia Dredging Co. Ltd.* [1968] Ir.R. 136.

(*zz*) Misrepresentation Act 1967 section 3 as amended by the Unfair Contract Terms Act 1977 sections 8 and 11.

reasonably to have been, known to or in the contemplation of the parties when the contract was made".

Cl. 11 specifically entitles the contractor to take into account information supplied by the employer, and at most limits the contractor's right to complain of a misrepresentation in such information to cases where it was not practicable for the contractor to discover the error before tender.

The courts are obviously disinclined to allow a party to make a groundless misrepresentation without accepting liability for the consequences. But taking into account general considerations (p. 433) and the uncertainties of the science or art of soil and rock mechanics, this clause is hardly unreasonable in requiring the contractor to test information given to him by making his own inspections, examination and enquiries so far as practicable, provided what is practicable is decided realistically (p. 63). If it is the Act that is applied unrealistically, employers may refrain from giving information.

The engineer will be liable personally for a fraudulent or reckless misstatement, but it is not clear to what extent he may be personally liable

a'

(*a'*) For example, in *Howard Marine & Dredging Co. Ltd* v. *A. Ogden & Sons (Excavations) Ltd.* [1978] 2 All E.R. 1134, C.A. owners of a barge were held liable to contractors who had hired the barge for construction works on the faith of a misrepresentation of the barge's dead weight, although the charterparty stated that "Charterers' acceptance of handing over the vessel shall be conclusive that they have examined the vessel and found her to be in all respects ... fit for the intended and contemplated use by the Charterers and in every other way satisfactory to them". In that case the defendant's marine manager said at a meeting that the payload of the barge was 1,600 tonnes, whereas in fact it was only 1,055 tonnes. The misstatement was based on the manager's recollection of a figure given in Lloyd's Register that was incorrect. He had at some time seen shipping documents which gave a more correct figure that had not registered in his mind.

   Cremdean Properties Ltd. v. *Nash* (1977) 244 E.G. 547, C.A. the invitation to tender for purchase of property included a term attempting to exclude liability for any error or misdescription in particulars furnished by the seller and saying that the particulars were not guaranteed and that "Any intending purchaser ... must satisfy himself by inspection or otherwise as to the correctness of each of the statements contained in these particulars". The court commented that only Humpty Dumpty would have fallen for the defendants' argument that the clause nullified any representation in the documents so that as there had been no representation at all the Misrepresentation Act had no application.

   These decisions are obviously relevant to the rider that tenderers must check the information for themselves usually added to site information supplied by the employer. In that context there is a notable passage in the judgment of Lord Denning in the *Howard Marine* decision, in which he dissented from the majority conclusion that the charterers' remedy in misrepresentation was not barred by the special clause in the charterparty: "It seems to me that the clause itself was fair and reasonable. The parties here were commercial concerns and were of equal bargaining power. The clause was not foisted by one on the other in a standard printed form. It was contained in all the drafts which passed between them, and it was no doubt given close consideration by both sides, like all the other clauses, some of which were amended and others not. It was a clause common in charterparties of this kind; and is familiar in other commercial contracts, such as construction and engineering contracts; *see* for instance *S. Pearson & Son Ltd.* v. *Dublin Corpn.* and the useful observations in Hudson on Building Contracts. It is specially applicable in cases where the contractor has the opportunity of checking the position for himself. It tells him that he should do so; and that he should not rely on any information given beforehand, for it may be inaccurate. Thus it provides a valuable safeguard against the consequences of innocent misrepresentation" (at p. 1143).

   The *Pearson* decision is summarised in the text above on p. 60. The other reference in the above quotation is to pp. 39 and 48 of the 10th ed. of Hudson in which the implication is that the courts should uphold under the Misrepresentation Act disclaimers of liability by employers giving information about site conditions, etc. to tenderers to thwart "a builder who finds that, for reasons unconnected with the representation, he has underestimated on his pricing of the contract" and who is then "likely to fasten upon the description of the state of the site under the Act for a negligent misrepresentation. The employer will be liable for a misrepresentation by the engineer if the engineer had special authority to make the representation by giving information to tenderers, *see* p. 399.

It is relevant both under (*a*) and under this heading to determine the exact scope of a representation. For example, the wide scope of a statement that, e.g., "the soil is sand" is clear, but to say merely that boreholes were made by the X company and that the following are the results supplied by the company, is a representation that boreholes were in fact made by the particular company and that the results given to the contractors are the results furnished by the company—not that the results are an accurate representation of the soil in the boreholes, or that they are representative of the soil in the area in general. Again, a statement that "in the engineer's

b'

and the account of pre-contract investigations" provided by the employer's advisers, in order to found a claim.

Lord Denning does not discuss the difficult question of the extent to which the contractor does and does not have a realistic opportunity of verifying tender information, which at least where cl. 11 (1) of these Conditions is allowed to stand without any special disclaimer, is the difficult and important question. That problem like most in the construction industry, is not solved by a simplistic answer—refer to footnote (*d'*) and p. 436.

(*b'*) An employer who passes on site investigation information nevertheless may not be protected if he does so in a form that is misleading or if he negligently abbreviates or interprets the information and may not have "reasonable ground to believe" (within the Misrepresentation Act) that the information conveyed is accurate if he chose the investigators because they were the cheapest to be found although evidence was available that their competence was doubtful.

The contractor may also have a remedy where the employer at the time the information was supplied was in possession of other information obtained for the particular works or even in his archives that should have revealed to him the inaccuracy of the information supplied.

The crucial factor under both the Misrepresentation Act and liability for negligence (text, below) is the care it is reasonable to expect of the employer in putting forward information knowing of its importance to the contractor (footnote (*d'*)).

In *Boyd & Forrest* v. *Glasgow & S.W. Ry. Co.*[1912] S.C. (H.L.) 93, at p. 96, Lord Atkinson suggested, but expressed no conclusion on the point, that there might be a warranty that, e.g. a journal of bores supplied was prepared with "reasonable skill, care and accuracy", or that skilful people were appointed to do the boring, or that the documents submitted to the contractors should reasonably answer the description of a journal of bores. That decision was reversed ([1913] A.C. 404) but on another point. There were then later proceedings (reported in 1914 S.C. 472, Court of Session in Scotland) in which it was held that there had been misrepresentation to the contractor on several counts. What was described on behalf of the employer as a "journal of bores" was not a record kept by the borers, but a statement made up in the form of a journal in which the description of what was found in the bores contradicted information supplied by the borer himself, without any notification of the fact (the word "hard" had been removed from the description of strata in the report and "blaes" a soft material—substituted for "black ban", "rock", "appears to be rock" and "whinstone"). Certain check bores ordered were not supplied to the contractors so that the information given was not complete.

The employers were held to have misrepresented that the tenderers would see at the engineer's office the accurate and complete journal of all the bores, as reported by the borers and that all the bores taken were disclosed. The statements in the contract that the employers did not guarantee the accuracy of the bores and would not be liable in respect of any inaccuracy were held to give no protection to the employers from liability for the misrepresentation.

It was also held that the employers warranted that the journal of bores was a complete and accurate record of all the bores and that the employers should appoint or had appointed to do the work of boring skilled persons fully competent for that work (unknown to the contractors the boring had been placed in charge of the employer's superintendent of the permanent way who had no previous experience of making bores).

That second decision was also reversed on appeal ((1915) A.C. 526, H.L.) but only on the remedy of the contractor assuming that there had been misrepresentations.

opinion the soil is silt" is only a representation that the opinion is held and at most that he has reasonable grounds for holding the opinion.

(*d*) Concurrently with liability under the Misrepresentation Act, and rather confusingly, the courts have developed a remedy in damages for a negligent misstatement. This liability may give the contractor a remedy against the persons or company which actually carried out the site investigations, the engineer, or even the employer. The remedy is discussed on pp. 394 5.

(*e*) The fact that information provided by the employer was misleading may be one factor in enabling the contractor to establish a claim under cl. 12—*see* the next note.

(*f*) The contractor has independent rights if the actual site conditions result in variations within cl. 51, omissions or misdescriptions in the bill under cl. 55, or in changes in quantities within cl. 56.

4. "AND HAVING TAKEN INTO ACCOUNT ANY INFORMATION IN CONNECTION THEREWITH WHICH MAY HAVE BEEN PROVIDED BY OR ON BEHALF OF THE EMPLOYER". The remedies of the contractor where any such information is given fraudulently or negligently are dealt with in the previous note.

This addition is also relevant to the important problem of the significance to be given under cl. 12 to information provided by the employer, since the information that the contractor is entitled to take into account in tendering obviously determines the conditions and obstructions which he can reasonably foresee. The solution which the second edition of this book suggested is to be implied into the 4th edition of these Conditions is now written into this edition. Information provided by the employer may be "*taken into account*", but clearly only so far as reasonable and only as one relevant factor.

The more extensive the information given by the employer about the site, and the more it is based on detailed investigations, the more significance an experienced contractor will reasonably attach to it, and the less it will be practicable for a tenderer to test the information by his own investigations. The difficult question of right balance between supply of information by the employer and investigation by the contractor has already been mentioned and is discussed again in ch. 17 in the context of claims.

Note that the specific right to take into account information provided by

(*c'*) In *Smith* v. *Land & House Property Corpn.* (1884) 28 Ch. D7 a statement that a tenant known to be in arrear with rent was "a most desirable tenant" was held to amount to an actionable misrepresentation. That decision was followed in *Brown* v. *Raphael* [1958] 2 All E.R. 79, C.A., and see *Esso Petroleum Co. Ltd.* v. *Mardon*, footnote (*mm*) p. 396.

(*d'*) "The basic information in the site information document appears to have been the result of much highly technical effort on the part of the (employer). It was information which the (contractors) had neither the time nor the opportunity to obtain for themselves. It might even be doubted whether they could be expected to obtain it by their own efforts as a potential or actual tenderer." *Morrison-Knudsen Int.* v. *Commonwealth of Australia* [1972] 46 A.L.J.R. 265, per Barwick C.J. at p. 267. In *Boyd & Forrest* v. *Glasgow & S.W. Ry. Co.* (1914) S.C. 472, 482, it was said that because the works were great in quantity and tenderers had only a fortnight in which to tender "it was certain that, as regards all calculations as to cutting work, they could not inform themselves by any inspection of their own, or conduct any boring works to make their own tests as to the nature of the material to be taken out and removed. They could not have tendered at all without having some information, and this information (the employer) professed to supply by giving them access" (to site investigations). This case is also mentioned in footnote (*b'*). In *Bryant & Son Ltd.* v. *Birmingham Hospital Saturday Fund* [1938] 1 All E.R. 503 (p. 215 below) it was held that it was not reasonable to expect tenderers who had seen two trial holes to search a site overgrown with grass and find three more holes of which they were not aware, but which did show evidence of rock.

the employer and the phrase "*so far as is practicable*" apply only to the contractor's duty to investigate the "*nature of the ground and sub-soil*", not, e.g., the availability of material.

5. The contractor is no longer required to satisfy himself as to the QUANTITIES OF THE WORK—*see* p. 210.

6. "EXTENT . . . OF THE WORKS" and "COMMUNICATION WITH" the site are new, but add nothing to what is implied in law in any case.

7. "THE CONTRACTOR . . . DEEMED TO HAVE . . . SATISFIED HIMSELF . . . AS TO . . . ACCESS TO THE SITE THE ACCOMMODATION HE MAY REQUIRE". *See* cl. 42 (2).

8. RATES AND PRICES "STATED BY HIM" (THE CONTRACTOR) IN THE BILL. The words in quotations are new, to allow for provisional sums and other items already priced in the bill when issued to tenderers.

9. NO SCHEDULE OF RATES AND PRICES. The reference to this Schedule in the 4th edition has been omitted, because no function was assigned to the Schedule.

10. ITEMS OMITTED FROM THE BILL. There are two changes in this clause that are very important in strengthening the contractor's right to claim for items omitted from the bill. "*otherwise provided in the Contract*" is substituted for "*hereinafter otherwise provided*", and the provision omitted that the contractor's rates and prices cover "*all matters and things necessary for the proper completion and maintenance of the Works*". *See* fully pp. 206 9.

ADVERSE PHYSICAL CONDITIONS AND ARTIFICIAL OBSTRUCTIONS

12. (1)[1] If during the execution of the Works[2] the Contractor shall encounter physical conditions (other than weather conditions or conditions due to weather conditions) or artificial obstructions[3] which conditions or obstructions he considers could not reasonably have been foreseen by an experienced contractor[4] and the Contractor is of opinion that additional cost will be incurred[5] which would not have been incurred if the physical conditions or artificial obstructions had not been encountered he shall if he intends to make any claim for additional payment give notice to the Engineer pursuant to Clause 52 (4) and shall specify in such notice the physical conditions and/or artificial obstructions encountered[6] and with the notice if practicable or as soon as possible thereafter give details of the anticipated effects thereof the measures he is taking or is proposing to take[7] and the extent of the anticipated[5] delay in or interference with the execution of the Works.

MEASURES TO BE TAKEN

(2) Following receipt of a notice under sub-clause (1) of this Clause the Engineer may if he thinks fit[8] *inter alia*
  (a) require the Contractor to provide an estimate of the cost of the measures he is taking or is proposing to take;[9]
  (b) approve in writing such measures with or without modification;[10]
  (c) give written instructions as to how the physical conditions or artificial obstructions are to be dealt with;[11]
  (d) order a suspension under Clause 40[12] or a variation under Clause 51.[13,14]

1. GENERAL. This clause caps the change from the old practice of putting all the risk on the contractor. It is important, not only in a pure lump sum contract but also in a measure and value or quantities form, because the courts have applied the lump sum principle to engineering contracts as a whole and to individual rates (p. 27) without allowing for the fact that it is often not possible for the contractor to estimate the risks in advance.

The clause is, however, carefully limited, and it should not be read by the contractor, the engineer or an arbitrator as giving *carte blanche* to claim or award extra payment whenever the contractor loses out on a calculated risk (p. 436).

2. "DURING THE EXECUTION OF THE WORKS". It is arguable that this phrase does not cover the execution of maintenance work under cls. 49 and 50. Clearly the engineer may not act under cl. 39 or order extra work (p. 175) in the maintenance period, and a strong contrast is drawn between the execution or construction and the maintenance of the works in cls. 13, 15 and 62. *See also* the Tender and Agreement and cls. 16 and 18, but note cl. 7.

"*Works*" now include all temporary works, by the definition in cl. 1(1)(l), subject to the discussion on p. 29.

3. "PHYSICAL CONDITIONS ... OR ARTIFICIAL OBSTRUCTIONS". The contractor has a remedy for these types of unforeseen difficulties only, not, e.g., for unforeseen difficulty in getting labour or supplies (*see* second case, p. 283). It is hardly necessary to give examples of cl. 12 situations, since contractors do not seem to have difficulty finding cases in which to make cl. 12 claims.

There is nothing in this clause specifically restricting the remedy to physical conditions which are on the site. It may be argued that because the words "*so far as is practicable*" in cl. 11 only qualify the duty on the contractor to satisfy himself as to the nature of the site ground and sub-soil, this clause only applies to that ground and not, e.g., to an unforeseeable shortage of suitable material in off-site borrow pits. The argument is not compulsive. It is also argued in the other direction that the "*artificial obstructions*" need not even be physical—contractors may sometimes be heard murmuring that the clause should be applied to a certain class of obstructive resident engineer. However, the word "*obstructions*" and the context are against extending the clause to acts of will.

It is strongly suggested that cl. 20 takes precedence over this clause for damage to the works themselves due to unforeseen conditions, etc. (consequential loss is outside cl. 20, p. 100, N. 6). This opinion is based on the words used, with the very specific and limited excepted risks, and the fact that insurance under cl. 21 is to protect the employer as well as the contractor against what may be catastrophic loss due to damage to the works. Therefore in such a case all risks insurers are not entitled to claim cl. 12 compensation from the employer through the contractor to set off against their liability under a policy in joint names, as they sometimes do. For damage to other property *see* p. 104, N. 1.

4. "WHICH ... COULD NOT REASONABLY HAVE BEEN FORESEEN BY AN EXPERIENCED CONTRACTOR". The burden is clearly on the contractor to show that the "*conditions or obstructions ... could not reasonably have been foreseen*", but these words are ambiguous. Is a claim excluded only if an experienced contractor could have foreseen that the conditions or

obstruction must occur, or is it sufficient that he could have foreseen that
there was a possibility, however remote, that the conditions might occur?

The mere fact that some risk of meeting the conditions was foreseeable
can hardly be enough, since an experienced contractor will know that
anything can happen, particularly in work underground. It is suggested
that a claim is barred only if an experienced contractor could have foreseen
a substantial risk.

This view is supported to some extent by the conclusions reached by the
judges in developing the law of negligence (p. 93) by which there is liability
for a negligent act if it could *reasonably have been foreseen* that the act
would cause damage:

> The plaintiff was struck by a cricket ball which a batsman had hit out of the
> ground. Although the owner of the ground knew that this had happened before,
> the House of Lords held that the likelihood of injury to a person situated as was
> the plaintiff was so slight that the owner was not negligent in allowing cricket to
> be played without taking more precautions. The distance from the pitch to the
> edge of the ground, which sloped upwards to a 7 ft. fence, was about 78 yards.

It follows from this view that the mere fact that the odds are against meeting
particular conditions or obstructions is not enough to exonerate the
contractor, if there is a substantial risk. However, because of the different
context and since the problem is basically one of fact, the countless reported
cases on the law of negligence are unlikely to be of very much help in
deciding what an experienced contractor could have foreseen.

A frequent argument of contractors is that if the engineer's design shows
that he did not envisage particular physical conditions, then there is no
reason why an experienced contractor should have foreseen them. In
practice this argument may have force, but if it is shown that the engineer
did not in fact do his job properly, the contractor has no right to use the
engineer's failure to perform his duty to his client as an excuse for his own
failure to fulfil his independent duties under cl. 11. In many such cases the
design will have to be varied so that the contractor will be able to claim
under cl. 51 instead of under this clause.

Refer also to N. 23 on ground conditions that are better than were
foreseeable.

5. "WILL BE INCURRED"; "ANTICIPATED" DELAY. *See* the next note.

6. PROCEDURE AND RECOVERY OF COST INCURRED PRIOR TO NOTICE.
Contractors will breathe a sigh of relief that the unrealistic notice

---

(*e'*) In *C. J. Pearce & Co. Ltd.* v. *Hereford Corporation* (1968) 66 L.G.R. 647, contractors
knew before tender that a sewer at least 100 years old had to be crossed in the course of laying
a new sewer. What was described on the map as "the approximate line of the ... Sewer" was
shown on a map supplied to tenderers. The witnesses for both parties accepted that the word
"approximate" meant that the contractor would realise that the line of the old sewer might be
10 feet to 15 feet one side or the other of the line shown (p. 652). The old sewer fractured when
the contractors disturbed the surrounding soil within this area. Held: that the condition
could have been "reasonably foreseen", so that even if they had served the necessary notice
they would not have been entitled to extra payment under this clause for renewing the old
sewer, backfilling the excavation, backheading, etc.

(*f'*) *Bolton* v. *Stone* [1951] 1 All E.R. 1078, H.L.

(*g'*) For a general discussion of the law of negligence see "Winfield & Jolowicz on Tort" 10th
ed., and for cases p. 93, N.4, and p. 393, N.30B, and "The Modern Cases on Negligence" 3rd
ed. by R. Bingham. For an interesting discussion of a somewhat similar problem in another
branch of the law read *Czarnikow* v. *Koufos* [1969] 1 A.C. 350, H.L.

requirements of the 4th edition have been abandoned. The new scheme of this clause may be summarised as follows:

(*a*) The contractor encounters physical conditions or artificial obstructions.

(*b*) He considers that these conditions, etc., could not reasonably have been foreseen by an experienced contractor.

(*c*) The contractor must give notice under cl. 52 (4) "*as soon as reasonably possible after the happening of the events giving rise to the claim*" specifying the physical conditions or artificial obstructions encountered. There may be a time lag between (*a*), (*b*) and (*c*)—between the contractor encountering the conditions, realising that the cause of his problems falls within this clause and giving notice accordingly. It seems (despite the words quoted in N. 5 and 7 to this clause) that the contractor may nevertheless recover compensation for all the conditions or obstructions encountered (N. 17). In particular, in judging when notice was reasonably possible it appears relevant that the contractor could not have realised for some time that his difficulties were due to unforeseen conditions or obstructions, where that was the case.

(*d*) The contractor with the notice "*if practicable or as soon as possible thereafter (is to) give details of the anticipated effects (of the conditions or obstructions) the measures he is taking or is proposing to take and the extent of the anticipated delay in or interference with the execution of the Works*" (*see* N. 7).

(*e*) The engineer may require the contractor to provide an estimate of the cost of the measures "*he is taking or is proposing to take*", and may take various other steps—*see* N. 8–13.

(*f*) Cl. 52 (4) requires the contractor to furnish various other accounts.

7. "AND SHALL . . . WITH THE NOTICE . . . GIVE DETAILS . . . OF THE MEASURES HE IS TAKING OR PROPOSING TO TAKE". Note that it is the contractor who must decide what measures are necessary to deal with the difficulties—N. 8. The contractor is not bound to give details of any measures he has already completed, although apparently he may recover extra payment for them— N. 6 and 17.

The results under cl. 52 (4) of failure to give a notice do not appear to apply to absence of this information "*with the notice*". Under the general law it seems that failure to give the information does not automatically invalidate a claim, because this clause does not say that it does, but *see* N. 8. Failure to give the information also may make it difficult for the contractor to persuade the engineer or an arbitrator of the merits of his claim.

8. "FOLLOWING RECEIPT OF A NOTICE . . . THE ENGINEER MAY IF HE THINKS FIT". Since he has a general duty "*to complete the Works*", by cl. 3 of the Form of Agreement and cl. 8 (1) of these Conditions, for example, the contractor is bound in the first instance to determine what measures are necessary to achieve completion despite unforeseen conditions or obstructions, and to give details under sub-cl. (1), after which the engineer may take, or even be bound to take, a measure of control under this sub-cl. (2).

The ideal procedure under this clause is that as soon as he encounters the difficulties the contractor notifies the engineer (N. 6), giving details of the measures he proposes to take to deal with them (N. 7). The contractor will point out if a change of design is necessary to cope with the difficulties at a reasonable cost and within a reasonable time and will draw the engineer's attention to the consequential necessity or desirability of a variation order under sub-cl. (2), and will also draw the engineer's attention to any other action required under that sub-clause. The contractor will also seek the approval of the engineer under para. (b) before proceeding, to minimise the risk of the engineer or arbitrator holding that cost incurred was unreasonable. The functions of the engineer are dealt with more specifically in the following six notes.

Unfortunately the symmetry of this procedure may be upset because the notice by the contractor may not be given until the unforeseen conditions or obstructions have been dealt with by him for a time (N.6). The engineer need not wait for such notice to take any of the steps mentioned in paras. (b)–(d) of this sub-clause if he knows what is happening: he is at all times during the progress of the works entitled to give an instruction or suspension or variation order and he may intimate that measures do or do not have his approval under cl. 13 (2). If he does not know what is happening the engineer will be at a disadvantage. For example, he may lose the opportunity to change design to reduce the extra cost due to the conditions or obstructions. That is one reason why an arbitrator should enforce cls. 12 (1) and 52 (4) (d) about notices and particulars, and if the contractor does breach those lax requirements resulting in such a lost opportunity, the employer may counter-claim for his losses against the contractor's claim for extra cost under this clause.

The words "*if he thinks fit*" are peculiar to this clause and cl. 44 (2), but in this context do not appear to be different in effect to the many references in the Conditions to the engineer deciding according to his own opinion. The engineer hardly could be entitled to refuse approval for satisfactory and proper measures proposed by the contractor, and as to variations and suspension orders *see* specifically p. 169, N.3. and p. 131, N.2.

9. "THE ENGINEER MAY ... REQUIRE THE CONTRACTOR TO PROVIDE AN ESTIMATE OF THE COST OF THE MEASURES HE IS TAKING OR IS PROPOSING TO TAKE". The purpose of this whole sub-clause is to give the engineer some measure of control over the additional work, etc., in view of the employer's liability for costs. Unfortunately no effective sanction is provided for failure by the contractor to supply an estimate, apart from the largely theoretical right of forfeiture under cl. 63. If a negligently low estimate is furnished and as a result the engineer is dissuaded from making an alternative design change that in the event would have been cheaper than the measures proposed, the employer may have a right to compensation from the contractor—p. 396.

The engineer is not entitled to an estimate of the cost of measures already taken, although apparently the contractor may be entitled to payment for them—*see* N. 6 and 17. The engineer is entitled to interim accounts by cl. 52 (4).

An estimate of cost may be taken into account as some evidence of what is "*reasonable*" payment under sub-cl. (3). With his client's authority the engineer may negotiate with the contractor a collateral agreement that the amount of the estimate shall constitute the compensation payable to the contractor whatever his actual costs.

10. "THE ENGINEER MAY . . . APPROVE IN WRITING SUCH MEASURES WITH OR WITHOUT MODIFICATION". Note that the responsibility is on the contractor to propose in the first instance and, unless the engineer acts under this clause, decide on the measures to be taken to cope with the unforeseen difficulties—N. 8.

Under cl. 13 (2) the whole of the works are subject to the engineer's approval, but not necessarily in writing. Obviously it is more likely to avoid arguments if the engineer puts his views in writing. If the contractor obtains the engineer's approval, it will reduce the burden of proving in arbitration that the measures he has taken were reasonable. Oddly, there is no provision in this clause that the contractor automatically loses payment for work done contrary to the engineer's requirements, but the engineer or an arbitrator may refuse such payment if they are satisfied that the work was unnecessary or unsatisfactory. If the contractor refuses to carry out modifications required by the engineer, there may be forfeiture under cl. 63.

11. "THE ENGINEER MAY . . . GIVE WRITTEN INSTRUCTIONS". Although sub-cl. (4) does not say so specifically, as it does in the case of any variation ordered, it is conceivable that the contractor may have a remedy under cl. 13 (3) for any delay or disruption due to an instruction, even though eventually it is decided that he has no claim under this clause. The engineer normally will be wise to act cautiously in giving instructions in a potential claim situation—see p. 75.

12. "THE ENGINEER MAY . . . ORDER A SUSPENSION UNDER CLAUSE 40". A suspension order gives the contractor a number of rights—see p. 130. The contractor may be entitled to those rights for suspension, even though eventually it is decided that he is not entitled to a claim under this clause (although this is not said specifically in sub-cl. (4)). The engineer normally will be wise to act cautiously in giving a suspension order in a potential claim situation under this clause.

13. "THE ENGINEER MAY . . . ORDER A . . . VARIATION", for which the contractor will be entitled to payment even though eventually it is decided that he is not entitled to claim under this clause. See sub-cl. (4) and, for dangers, p. 180.

The contractor, of course, is entitled to payment only if the variation order is valid, and the employer is entitled to challenge under cl. 66 the validity of an order. Generally the only case in which the engineer may validly give a variation order is to change the design of the works, for example where the difficulties make the original design unstable or where redesign will avoid or reduce the cost of the work causing the difficulty. A variation order is not appropriate merely because a contractor has found rock more difficult to excavate than could have been anticipated, for example—the contract work defined in cl. 8 (1) is not changed, and this is a pure cl. 12 (1) claim.

14. ARBITRATION BEFORE COMPLETION UNDER THIS SUB-CLAUSE—is dealt with in N. 22.

Delay and Extra Cost

12. (3) To the extent that the Engineer shall decide that the whole or some part of the said physical conditions or artificial obstructions could not reasonably have been foreseen by an experienced contractor the Engineer shall take any delay suffered by the Contractor as a result of such conditions or obstructions into account in determining any extension of time to which the Contractor is entitled under Clause 44 and the Contractor shall subject to Clause 52 (4) (notwithstanding that the Engineer may not have given any instructions or orders pursuant to sub-clause (2) of this Clause)[15] be paid in accordance with Clause 60[16] such sum as represents the reasonable cost of carrying out any additional work done and additional Constructional Plant used which would not have been done or used had such conditions or obstructions or such part thereof as the case may be not been encountered[17] together with a reasonable percentage addition thereto in respect of profit[18] and the reasonable costs incurred by the Contractor by reason of any unavoidable delay or disruption of working[19] suffered as a consequence of encountering the said conditions or obstructions or such part thereof.

Conditions Reasonably Foreseeable

(4) If the Engineer shall decide that the physical conditions or artificial obstructions could in whole or in part have been reasonably foreseen by an experienced contractor he shall so inform the Contractor in writing as soon as he shall have reached that decision but the value of any variation previously ordered by him pursuant to sub-clause (2) (d) of this Clause shall be ascertained in accordance with Clause 52 and included in the Contract Price.[20,23]

15. "(NOTWITHSTANDING THAT THE ENGINEER MAY NOT HAVE GIVEN ANY INSTRUCTIONS)". *See* p. 69.

16. CONTRACTOR SHALL "BE PAID IN ACCORDANCE WITH CLAUSE 60"— i.e. the payment is included in interim and final certificates, and subject to retention.

17. "SUBJECT TO CLAUSE 52 (4) . . . (THE CONTRACTOR SHALL) BE PAID . . . SUCH SUM AS REPRESENTS THE REASONABLE COST OF CARRYING OUT ANY ADDITIONAL WORK DONE AND ADDITIONAL CONSTRUCTIONAL PLANT USED WHICH WOULD NOT HAVE BEEN DONE OR USED HAD SUCH CONDITIONS OR OBSTRUCTIONS . . . NOT BEEN ENCOUNTERED". There is nothing in this clause to limit the costs for which payment may become due to those incurred after notice has been given. It appears therefore that a defect in the previous edition is cured, by permitting the contractor to recover additional costs incurred before notice, particularly those incurred at a time when it was not possible to appreciate that they were due to conditions or obstructions within this clause. The only circumstance in which the contractor will lose rights is under cl. 52 (4) where the contractor does not give notice as soon as reasonably possible "*after . . . the events giving rise to the claim*" and the engineer is prejudiced in investigating the claim by such failure. Cl. 12 (1) implies that such events are to be regarded as having taken place even though the cost which is the subject of the claim has not been incurred (contrast the other cases mentioned on pp. 192–3). It cannot be said, however, that the clause is perfectly drafted, and in particular it is unfortunate that the contractor is not bound to give details of past work in his notice (N. 6 and 9).

18. "A REASONABLE PERCENTAGE ADDITION . . . IN RESPECT OF PROFIT" ON COST OF WORK OR PLANT. The authors of the form have abrogated their duty by leaving to dispute the important question of· the amount of the percentage addition. It is unfortunate that agreement could not have been reached on some necessarily compromise figure for all claims. Presumably the contractor's levels of profit on the whole original job and on any particularly comparable work included in it, and the normal market profit (if there is such a thing) on work of the particular kind and size, are relevant. It is impossible to generalise as to how these factors should be balanced, but since the percentage is applied to the contractor's actual costs, no allowance for risks or contingencies should be included.

19. "THE REASONABLE COSTS INCURRED . . . BY REASON OF ANY UNAVOIDABLE DELAY OR DISRUPTION OF WORKING". For delay or disruption of working the contractor is not entitled to any payment in respect of profit, as he is for the additional work. This dovetails with cl. 7, which largely removes the contractor's right to loss of profit for delay attributable to the employer. The contractor is entitled to profit only on the cost of "*carrying out . . . additional work . . . and additional Constructional Plant*", not on the additional cost of consequential delay to the remainder of the works. Demarcation problems may arise. For example, if the additional work holds up completion, involving extended watching, lighting and supervision costs, then it is suggested that a proportion of those costs, based on the proportion which the volume of the additional work bears to the volume of all the work executed in the extended period, is part of the "*cost of carrying out . . . (the) additional work done*" rather than of "*delay or disruption of working*". Plant retained on or brought specially to site to carry out the additional work itself attracts the percentage for profit; plant retained on site to carry out other work delayed as a result of that additional work does not.

20. PAYMENTS NOTWITHSTANDING REFUSAL OF CLAUSE 12 CLAIM. *See* N. 11, 12 and 19.

21. "THE ENGINEER . . . SHALL SO INFORM THE CONTRACTOR IN WRITING AS SOON AS HE SHALL HAVE REACHED THAT DECISION" (that there is no claim). Presumably it is intended that the engineer shall make his decision within a reasonable time. The advantage to the contractor of being told that the engineer is not allowing a claim is that he may then decide whether or not to go to arbitration before completion (next note). Exercise of the right to require a decision from the engineer under cl. 66 and to go to arbitration if necessary is the only remedy of a contractor where the engineer is loath to make up his mind. Whether or not he agrees with the engineer's decision the contractor is generally bound to surmount the unforeseen difficulties and complete the works in the meantime at his own cost (N. 8).

22. ARBITRATION ON CLAUSE 12 CLAIMS BEFORE COMPLETION OF THE WORKS. By cl. 66 (2) either party is entitled to arbitration before completion of the works "*in the case of any dispute or difference as to any matter arising under Clause 12*". An arbitrable dispute within these words may be raised by referral back to the engineer under cl. 66 if he acts or fails (presumably within a reasonable time) to act under sub-cl. (2), or allows or (N. 21) refuses

a claim, including refusal by failing to include a claim in an interim certificate (p. 292, N. 5).

23. No REVERSE CLAUSE 12. The contractor does not have to give back money to the employer if he encounters conditions that are less onerous than foreseeable at the time of tender. But then the contractor is always entitled to take as pessimistic a view of risks as he thinks fit in his tender, or indeed merely to allow for a large profit, subject only to the pressures of competitive tendering. The contractor does not represent to the employer that his rates are not more than cost plus a reasonable profit on the works as they actually have to be constructed.

At the same time, for example, some piles or parts of a length of sewer taken by themselves may be harder to construct than the average foreseeable, due to physical conditions or artificial obstructions, and some easier. The engineer may particularly be entitled to treat all pile driving or at least driving of a related group of piles and the length of sewer as a single operation. He may hold that variation of conditions above and below the average could have been foreseen so that the contractor overall has no claim under this clause.

WORK TO BE TO SATISFACTION OF ENGINEER

13.   (1) Save in so far as it is legally or physically impossible[1] the Contractor shall construct complete and maintain the Works in strict accordance with the Contract to the satisfaction of the Engineer[2] and shall comply with and adhere strictly to the Engineer's instructions and directions on any matter connected therewith (whether mentioned in the Contract or not).[3,4] The Contractor shall take instructions and directions only from the Engineer or (subject to the limitations referred to in Clause 2) from the Engineer's Representative.

MODE AND MANNER OF CONSTRUCTION

(2) The whole of the materials plant and labour to be provided by the Contractor under Clause 8 and the mode manner and speed of construction and maintenance of the Works are to be of a kind and conducted in a manner approved of by the Engineer.[5]

DELAY AND EXTRA COST

(3) If in pursuance of Clause 5 or sub-clause (1) of this Clause the Engineer shall issue instructions or directions which involve the Contractor in delay or disrupt his arrangements or methods of construction so as to cause him to incur cost beyond that reasonably to have been foreseen by an experienced contractor[6] at the time of tender[7,8] then the Engineer shall take such delay into account in determining any extension of time to which the Contractor is entitled under Clause 44 and the Contractor shall subject to Clause 52 (4) be paid in accordance with Clause 60[9] the amount of such cost as may be reasonable.[10] If such instructions or directions require any variation to any part of the Works the same shall be deemed to have been given pursuant to Clause 51.[11]

1. CONTRACTOR TO CARRY OUT THE CONTRACT WORKS "SAVE IN SO FAR AS ... LEGALLY OR PHYSICALLY IMPOSSIBLE". That is, the contractor may fail to

carry out work specified in the contract if it is legally or physically impossible, without being liable to pay damages for breach of contract.

There is some confusion abroad about this clause. If the contractor does work described in the bill he is normally entitled to payment even though the work does not achieve the result intended, e.g. if he welds but the specified material is such that the weld is liable to break (p. 55). But if the contractor cannot carry out the work described at all, e.g. a weld will not take, the employer is not liable to pay the contractor for trying to do so, unless the contractor has a cl. 12 claim. The general principle which applies is that the employer does not guarantee that the works can be completed in accordance with the contract (p. 28).

The result is that the contractor should avoid fruitless efforts to do work which is impossible, and instead require a properly ordered variation to avoid the impossibility.

There is also, of course, a difference between work which is impossible and work which is more difficult or requires more plant or temporary works than the contractor anticipated—as to which *see* cl. 12.

For impossibility due to events occurring after the contract is made *see* cl. 64.

2. "IN STRICT ACCORDANCE WITH THE CONTRACT TO THE SATISFACTION OF THE ENGINEER". The engineer has no power to alter the contract—*see* cl. 39, N. 2, p. 127, pp. 157–8, and the next note: For expedition of completion ordered by the engineer *see* p. 371.

3. "AND SHALL COMPLY . . . WITH THE ENGINEER'S INSTRUCTIONS . . . ON ANY MATTER CONNECTED THEREWITH (WHETHER MENTIONED IN THE CONTRACT OR NOT)", but not any instruction positively contrary to the contract, *see* the references in the previous note. For the engineer's control over the contractor's method of working and temporary works *see* also cl. 14. For written instructions necessary and extra payment in some cases *see* ch. 11.

"*connected therewith*" is new. "*therewith*" appears to refer to "*the Works*", and not "*the Contract*".

4. LIABILITY OF THE ENGINEER FOR INJURY DUE TO INSTRUCTIONS. *See* pp. 53–4.

5. "MODE MANNER AND SPEED OF CONSTRUCTION AND MAINTENANCE OF THE WORKS APPROVED OF BY THE ENGINEER". For temporary works *see* p. 29, and for maintenance work p. 165, N. 11. For the advantages of controlling the contractor's work under this sub-clause instead of sub-cl. (3) of this clause or cl. 14 *see* the next note and p. 83, N. 21.

6. RECOVERY BY CONTRACTOR OF COSTS DUE TO INSTRUCTIONS OR DIRECTIONS. To try to define the practical scope of this, possibly the most important provision in these Conditions, it is necessary to consider

---

(*h'*) For example, if machines or materials which are protected by a patent (*see* cl. 28) are specified, but the person who is entitled to the benefit of the protection will not supply or consent to use of the protected item at all (not if he merely requires larger payment than the contractor anticipated), then use of the item without consent would be illegal. It appears to follow that the contractor is not bound to comply with the specification and is entitled to a variation order.

separately the four ingredients specified for a claim by the contractor: (a) "*instructions or directions*", and (b) "*in pursuance of Clause 5 or sub-clause* (1) *of this Clause*", and (c) "*which involve the Contractor in delay or disrupt his arrangements or methods of construction*", (d) "*so as to cause him to incur cost beyond that reasonably to have been foreseen by an experienced contractor at the time of tender*". None of these requirements is free from difficulty.

(a) To give the contractor a right to compensation the instruction or direction need not be in writing, or confirmed by the contractor in writing. Notice of any claim to extra payment is required under cl. 52 (4) but only "*as soon as reasonably possible after the happening of the events giving rise to the claim*", which is the incurring of extra cost by the contractor, not the receipt of the instruction. Thus the engineer may receive notice of a claim for extra money founded on some misunderstanding or misinterpretation of an instruction or much larger than he expected, when it is too late for him to clarify or alter the instruction involved.

No distinction is intended between an instruction or direction and an order ("*instructions including the ordering*"—cl. 26 (2) (b) and *see* cl. 40 (1) and N. 11).

Possibly a requirement of the engineer authorised by the Conditions (e.g. cls. 14 (2), 16, 19 and 31, and *see* cls. 49 and 50) is distinct from an instruction or direction, and does not bring this sub-clause into effect (but see the description of what is "*required*" by the engineer under cls. 49 (2) and 50 as "*work ordered*" in cl. 60 (5) (c)). For cl. 20 (2) refer to p. 100, N. 6.

The engineer may avoid a claim under this clause by avoiding instructions and directions. For example, if the specification says that the contractor may not use explosives without the engineer's consent, then the engineer may prohibit explosives where necessary without having to instruct the contractor not to use them. The engineer also has a general wide power of refusing approval under sub-clause (2) of this clause. He will also have to avoid later "instructing" the contractor to stop work for which he has refused consent or approval, and instead merely point out that the method of working has not been approved.

It does not appear that in such a case the contractor is entitled to argue that the refusal of approval amounts to an instruction, or claim merely on the grounds that the engineer's refusal of consent or approval was unreasonable, although he will have a claim if the engineer is not acting on correct principles in good faith (p. 416). The argument that cls. 51 and 52 may entitle the contractor to extra payment where refusal of approval leads to changes in temporary works is discussed on p. 170, N. 4. Whether positive action by the engineer following disapproval, under cls. 39 or 40, entitles the contractor to claim under this clause is discussed in the next part of this note. The engineer as a last resort may give a certificate for forfeiture under cl. 63 where his disapproval is being flouted. By persisting with doubtful temporary works or methods the contractor also takes the risk of liability for failure or damage to the temporary or permanent works or for injury or damage to the person or property of third parties (p. 52, N. 2).

It is a strange result that the engineer is in a position very much to restrict the scope of this clause in so far as he can direct the works by stating in the specification what the contractor is not to do without his consent, or even rely on cl. 13 (2), rather than positively instructing the contractor during the contract.

(b) If an instruction or direction from the engineer is provided for specifically in another clause of the Conditions, the instruction or direction normally would be said to be issued in pursuance of that clause, and not in pursuance of sub-cl. (1). This interpretation is strengthened by the specific statement in cl. 5 that an instruction under that clause is to be regarded as an instruction issued in accordance with cl. 13 and the separate reference here to an instruction in pursuance of cl. 5, both unnecessary if every instruction or direction by the engineer within the contract is to be deemed to be given "*in pursuance of . . . sub-clause* (1) *of this Clause*". Again, in contrast to, e.g., cls., 26 (2) (b) and 48 (1), cl. 71 (2) (a) says that the engineer may "*instruct the Contractor pursuant to Clause* 13". The reference to variations (N. 11) and the words in brackets in cl. 12 (3), perhaps pointing the other way, increase the confusion.

If there is this distinction that the right to extra payment under this clause does not apply to instructions given under the terms of some other clause of the Conditions, the reason for it, if there is a reason, is presumably that the contractor can allow in his tender for the possibility of delay or disruption due to exercise of the engineer's power to give instructions mentioned in other clauses of the contract, but not under the wide and general power in this clause. Unfortunately, the practical results of the distinction are distinctly odd. The contractor has a specific right to payment for disruption due to an instruction under cl. 5, but not to disruption due to an order under cls. 38 or 39 to remove or uncover work previously approved, or under cl. 36 if a test instructed causes delay or disruption. The contractor may have a claim due to exercise of any of the engineer's powers arising only out of this cl. 13 (1), but what of instructions empowered by the specification?

On the other hand, if the wider interpretation is intended, that the contractor has a remedy under this sub-clause for delay or disruption due to any instructions or directions whether mentioned elsewhere or not, it would have been easy to say so by leaving out "*in pursuance*" to and including the second "*Clause*" in the opening line of this sub-clause.

Unfortunately the arguments are so evenly balanced that it would be rash to give an opinion as to the solution of this conundrum, which will have to be found by the courts, or by an amendment to these Conditions.

(c) The draftsman must have searched hard and long to discover a word so wide and vague in meaning as "*arrangements*". Arrangements by the contractor with his suppliers and sub-contractors, internal staff arrangements, arrangements with his labour—all appear to be included, however private, peculiar or unreasonable they may be and unrevealed to the engineer at the time the tender is accepted or when he gives his instruction or direction. But the engineer will have some help if he obtains as soon as possible, as he should, "*a general description of the arrangements and methods of construction which the Contractor intends to adopt*", to which he is entitled under cl. 14, within 21 days after acceptance of the tender. Presumably the arrangements affected must relate to the works for which the claim is made, not to other contracts which the contractor happens to be carrying out at the same time.

(d) It is the cost which must be beyond that reasonably to have been foreseen, not the instruction or direction. An experienced contractor must be taken to foresee that the engineer will give him the necessary instruction to correct any breach of the contract by the contractor, but even in that case the strict wording of this clause produces the strange result that the contractor may recover if the cost of delay or disruption due to making the correction exceeds the costs which he would have reasonably foreseen. An example of the type of claim with which the engineer may be harassed is a situation where an instruction to make good failure to fence the site to safeguard the public has to be carried out immediately and disrupts the contractor's arrangements or causes delay with other work. May the contractor claim that owing to the particular time at which he had to carry out the instruction, the costs of delay were "*beyond that reasonably to have been foreseen by an experienced contractor at the time of tender*"?

h''

Note also the different and, it seems, less stringent wording compared with cl. 12—"*beyond that reasonably to have been foreseen*" instead of "*could not reasonably have been foreseen*". If a substantial risk of extra cost is foreseeable it will not be recoverable under cl. 12 (p. 65); under this clause any cost beyond that which is the likely foreseeable cost appears to be recoverable.

This clause is more conducive to chaos than to good order in contract administration and management. At the least, clarification of the meaning and restriction of extra payments to instructions given or confirmed in writing are essential, and should be written into the special conditions under cl. 72. It is hoped that official amendments will be made soon.

For the relationship of this clause to cl. 7, dealing with cost due to delay in issuing drawings or instructions, *see* p. 49, N. 11.

7. "AT THE TIME OF TENDER". *See* p. 57, N. 2.

8. INSTRUCTIONS AND DIRECTIONS BY ENGINEER'S AIDES. Instructions by the engineer's delegates and representative's assistants are included — they are deemed to be instructions of the engineer and the engineer's representative respectively, by cl. 2 (2) and (3).

9. PAYMENT "SUBJECT TO CLAUSE 52 (4) . . . IN ACCORDANCE WITH CLAUSE 60", i.e. notice of money claims, and inclusion of payments in interim and the final payment certificate, subject to retention.

(*h''*) Some light is thrown on this issue by the following comment made by counsel for the contractor in a leading case referring to the Standard Form of building contract: "An instruction to postpone work (under cl. 21 (2)) leading to a suspension of the works can be disastrous for the employer. The contractor may be able to determine (the contract). See clause 26 ... In any event he will usually have a claim to loss and/or expense under clause 24 (1) (e). Can the contractor rely on such an instruction when it arose out of a defect in the works, or other matter for which he is responsible? In *Gloucestershire County Council* v. *Richardson* it was conceded in the Court of Appeal that he could not. The concession was made after some forceful expressions of view during argument by the members of the Court. When the case went to the House of Lords the concession was maintained but it appeared in argument that some of their Lordships were not satisfied that it was necessarily correct. The point must be regarded as open, although, having regard to the care with which the courts approach determination clauses it may well be that the concession was correct" (D. Keating "Building Contracts", 4th ed., pp. 344 5).

Of course this cl. 13 (3) is not a determination clause, and in the case posited in the text above it is the particular circumstances of the instruction that are the effective cause of the unforeseen cost claimed. In the *Gloucestershire* case (p. 226 below) the contractor actually was held entitled to determine his own employment on the ground that it was the architect's instruction that was the cause of the delay for the purpose of the clause, notwithstanding that the ultimate cause was faulty columns which compelled the architect to give the instruction and notwithstanding that the contractor agreed with the instruction and would have felt bound to act similarly on his own account.

10. PAYMENT TO CONTRACTOR OF "COST AS MAY BE REASONABLE". *See* p. 50.

11. "IF SUCH INSTRUCTIONS OR DIRECTIONS REQUIRE ANY VARIATION ... SHALL BE DEEMED TO HAVE BEEN GIVEN PURSUANT TO CLAUSE 51". Placed here, "*such instructions or directions*" logically means "*instructions or directions which involve the Contractor in delay or disrupt his arrangements or methods*" etc. only, and this wording emphasises that disruption is to be allowed for in valuing variations (p. 176). For the relevance of this sentence to the difficult problem of the meaning of this sub-clause *see* N. 6.

PROGRAMME TO BE FURNISHED

14. (1)[1] Within 21 days after the acceptance of his Tender the Contractor shall submit to the Engineer for his approval a programme showing the order of procedure[2] in which he proposes to carry out the Works and thereafter shall furnish such further details and information as the Engineer may reasonably require in regard thereto.[3] The Contractor shall at the same time also provide in writing for the information of the Engineer a general description of the arrangements and methods of construction which the Contractor proposes to adopt for the carrying out of the Works.[4]

REVISION OF PROGRAMME

(2) Should it appear to the Engineer at any time that the actual progress of the Works does not conform with the approved programme[5] referred to in sub-clause (1) of this Clause the Engineer shall be entitled to require the Contractor to produce a revised programme showing the modifications to the original programme necessary to ensure completion of the Works or any Section within the time for completion as defined in Clause 43 or extended time granted pursuant to Clause 44 (2).[5a]

METHODS OF CONSTRUCTION

(3) If requested by the Engineer the Contractor shall submit at such times and in such detail as the Engineer may reasonably require[6] such information pertaining to the methods of construction (including Temporary Works and the use of Constructional Plant) which the Contractor proposes to adopt or use and such calculations of stresses strains and deflections that will arise in the Permanent Works or any parts thereof during construction from the use of such methods as will enable the Engineer to decide whether if these methods are adhered to the Works can be executed in accordance with the Drawings and Specification[7] and without detriment to the Permanent Works when completed.[8,9]

ENGINEER'S CONSENT

(4) The Engineer shall inform the Contractor in writing within a reasonable period after receipt of the information[10] submitted in accordance with sub-clause (3) of this Clause either:
  (a) that the Contractor's proposed methods have the consent of the Engineer; or
  (b) in what respects in the opinion of the Engineer they fail to meet the requirements of the Drawings or Specification or will be detrimental to the Permanent Works.[11]

In the latter event the Contractor shall take such steps or make such changes in the said methods[12] as may be necessary to meet the Engineer's requirements and to obtain his consent. The Contractor shall not change the methods which have received the Engineer's consent without the further consent in writing of the Engineer which shall not be unreasonably withheld.[13]

DESIGN CRITERIA

(5) The Engineer shall provide to the Contractor such design criteria relevant to the Permanent Works or any Temporary Works designed by the Engineer as may be necessary to enable the Contractor to comply[14] with sub-clauses (3) and (4) of this Clause.

DELAY AND EXTRA COST

(6) If the Engineer's consent to the proposed methods of construction shall be unreasonably delayed[15] or if the requirements of the Engineer pursuant to sub-clause (4) of this Clause or any limitations imposed by any of the design criteria supplied by the Engineer pursuant to sub-clause (5) of this Clause could not reasonably have been foreseen by an experienced contractor[16] at the time of tender[17] and if in consequence of any of the aforesaid the Contractor unavoidably incurs delay or cost[18] the Engineer shall take such delay into account in determining any extension of time to which the Contractor is entitled under Clause 44 and the Contractor shall subject to Clause 52 (4) be paid in accordance with Clause 60[19] such sum in respect of the cost incurred as the Engineer considers fair in all the circumstances.[20,21]

RESPONSIBILITY UNAFFECTED BY APPROVAL

(7) Approval by the Engineer of the Contractor's programme in accordance with sub-clauses (1) and (2) of this Clause and the consent of the Engineer to the Contractor's proposed methods of construction in accordance with sub-clause (4) of this Clause shall not relieve the Contractor of any of his duties or responsibilities under the Contract.

1. INFORMATION TO BE FURNISHED BY THE CONTRACTOR TO THE ENGINEER, according to requirements distributed throughout this clause, may be summarised as follows:

(a) Within 21 days after acceptance of the tender a programme showing the order of procedure in which the contractor proposes to carry out the works (including all temporary works, cl. 1 (1) (l)) (discussed N. 2).

(b) At the same time as the programme a general description of the arrangements and methods of construction which the contractor proposes for the carrying out of the works (as before including all temporary works) (N. 4).

(c) Such further details and information as the engineer may reasonably require in regard to the order of procedure (N. 3).

(d) Revised programmes as may be required by the engineer (N. 5).

(e) Such information in such detail as the engineer may reasonably require pertaining to the methods of construction (including temporary works and use of constructional plant) and calculations of stresses, strains and deflections that will arise in permanent works from the use of such methods (N. 6–9). The engineer is to provide the contractor with such design criteria relevant to permanent works or any temporary works designed by the engineer as may be necessary for this purpose (N. 14).

An habitual question in the industry is whether or not a programme or other information given by the contractor is part of the contract. The question is meaningless. The programme, for example, is not contractual in the same sense as the specification, since neither the contractor nor the employer is bound by it. The programme is what it is—a document indicating the intention of the contractor at the time he furnishes it as to how he intends to programme the works, and may be used in evidence against or (subject to serious limitations, pp. 366–7) for him.

For the importance, and difficulty, of enforcing the contractor's duty to give information, refer to p. 441 on "Claimsmanship".

The possible liability of the contractor for negligent information is discussed on p. 396.

2. "WITHIN 21 DAYS AFTER THE ACCEPTANCE OF HIS TENDER THE CONTRACTOR SHALL SUBMIT ... A PROGRAMME SHOWING THE ORDER OF PROCEDURE". This is a useful requirement to ensure that the engineer will have a programme from the contractor at an early stage. A prudent engineer will already have obtained an outline programme with the tender (for reasons discussed on p. 441).

"*order of procedure*" is a quaint phrase retained from the 4th edition. The programme must certainly show the sequence of operations and, it is suggested, the duration of each operation. This clause may be amplified by special conditions requiring, e.g., network analyses.

There is a discussion of "Programmemanship" in relation to claims in ch. 17.

3. THE CONTRACTOR TO FURNISH "FURTHER DETAILS AND INFORMATION AS THE ENGINEER MAY REASONABLY REQUIRE". If the engineer's requirements are unreasonable the contractor may refuse to supply the information, and if he complies may be entitled to extra payment (p. 194, N. 4).

4. THE CONTRACTOR TO PROVIDE IN WRITING "A GENERAL DESCRIPTION OF THE ARRANGEMENTS AND METHODS OF CONSTRUCTION". These words are extremely imprecise, perhaps necessarily so. The operative words are "*general description*". Unfortunately the engineer is given a right to the information once only, not to revised and up-to-date or further information as in the case of the programme itself.

It may be vitally important for the engineer to obtain as much information as he can as soon as he can, because under cl. 13 the contractor has a right to compensation if the engineer's instructions or directions disrupt his "*arrangements or methods of construction*", words which are identical to the words from this clause quoted at the head of this note. The engineer may be able to deal with improper or exaggerated claims under cl. 13 if he obtained full details from the contractor under this clause at an early stage. Conversely, the fact that they were disclosed at an early stage may help the contractor to establish a claim for later disruption of his arrangements.

The problem of information, in relation to claims, is discussed fully in ch. 17.

5. REVISED PROGRAMME IF "THE ACTUAL PROGRESS OF THE WORKS DOES NOT CONFORM WITH THE APPROVED PROGRAMME"—whether because the permanent or temporary works are ahead of or behind the programme, or have departed from the programmed sequence. In view of the sundry rights óf the contractor to claim compensation for delay and disruption, it is most important that the engineer should exercise this right to obtain a revised programme so that the programme to which the contractor is actually working is in the engineer's hands at all times.

For "Programmemanship" *see* p. 442. The engineer is not given any specific right to require a programme to be revised because he believes that it is unrealistic—that the future progress of the contractor is unlikely to conform to it. But it is suggested that he can refuse to accept such a programme on the grounds that it does not genuinely represent the contractor's plans as it is required to do by sub-cl. (1). *See also* next note.

5(a). "EXTENDED TIME GRANTED PURSUANT TO CLAUSE 44(2)". Read literally the right to "*modifications to the original programme necessary to ensure completion ... within the time for completion ... in clause 43 or extended time ...*" does not entitle the engineer to require a programme showing the contractor's actual plans to minimise late completion, where late completion is inevitable. A programme that is not actually a plan of what is intended to be done is a contradiction in terms, and the engineer may be able to make some use of his right to "*further details and information*" under sub-cl. (1) to obtain realistic information. When approving a programme showing late completion, the engineer will make it clear that he is not granting an extension of time.

It is not clear why cl. 44 (3) is not mentioned here.

6. "AT SUCH TIMES AND IN SUCH DETAIL AS THE ENGINEER MAY REASONABLY REQUIRE". *See* p. 418 for the contractor's remedy if the engineer is unreasonable.

7. "INFORMATION PERTAINING TO THE METHODS OF CONSTRUCTION (INCLUDING TEMPORARY WORKS AND THE USE OF CONSTRUCTIONAL PLANT) ... CALCULATIONS OF STRESSES STRAINS ... AS WILL ENABLE THE ENGINEER TO DECIDE WHETHER ... THE WORKS CAN BE EXECUTED IN ACCORDANCE WITH THE DRAWINGS AND SPECIFICATION". "*Works*" includes all temporary works (cl. 1 (1) (l)).

Note the absence of any reference to the works being capable of execution in accordance with engineer's instructions not embodied in a drawing or specification (compare cls. 26 (2) (a) and (b) and 20 (2)).

8. "AND WITHOUT DETRIMENT TO THE PERMANENT WORKS WHEN COMPLETED". It is suggested that this phrase includes cases where the detriment to the permanent works consists of latent deficiencies that will not produce collapse, settlement or other actual damage for a time. Whether the possibility of future trouble is sufficient must depend on the degree of likelihood of the trouble eventuating and the time it will take to appear, the seriousness of the defect, and the intended life of the works. The words "*when completed*" are not repeated in sub-cl. (4) (b).

9. THE LIMITED SCOPE OF THIS SUB-CLAUSE is discussed in N. 21.

10. "THE ENGINEER SHALL INFORM THE CONTRACTOR IN WRITING WITHIN A REASONABLE PERIOD AFTER RECEIPT OF THE INFORMATION". *See* p. 365 on the circumstances relevant to calculating a "*reasonable period*".

11. "IN WHAT RESPECTS . . . (THE CONTRACTOR'S PROPOSED METHODS) FAIL TO MEET THE REQUIREMENTS OF THE DRAWINGS OR SPECIFICATION OR WILL BE DETRIMENTAL TO THE PERMANENT WORKS". These two are the only grounds on which the engineer may refuse consent to the contractor's methods of construction or use of constructional plant under this clause. They are discussed above in N. 7 and 8 and in N. 21.

12. "THE CONTRACTOR SHALL TAKE SUCH STEPS OR MAKE SUCH CHANGES . . . TO MEET THE ENGINEER'S REQUIREMENTS". Under para. (b) the engineer tells the contractor in what respects the contractor's proposed methods fail to meet the relevant requirements (N. 11), but the contractor chooses the steps to be taken and the changes to be made to satisfy the requirements and by implication reapplies for consent. If the engineer lays down positive requirements in instructions, it is possible that the contractor may have a claim under cl. 13 (p. 73, N. 6) apart from his rights under sub-cl. (6).

13. "THE CONTRACTOR SHALL NOT CHANGE THE METHODS WHICH HAVE . . . THE ENGINEER'S CONSENT WITHOUT THE FURTHER CONSENT IN WRITING OF THE ENGINEER WHICH SHALL NOT BE UNREASONABLY WITHHELD". The engineer may reasonably refuse consent only if as a result of the change the temporary works would fail to meet the requirements of the drawings, etc., as set out in para. (b) of this sub-clause. Refusal of consent to change approved methods appears to imply "*requirements*" of the engineer, giving the contractor a right to compensation under sub-cl. (6).

14. THE ENGINEER SHALL PROVIDE "DESIGN CRITERIA . . . AS MAY BE NECESSARY TO ENABLE THE CONTRACTOR TO COMPLY". A prudent engineer will supply these criteria with the tender documents, to minimise claims under sub-cl. (6).

If the engineer negligently misstates the actual design criteria the contractor nevertheless appears to be liable for damage to the works resulting from design of temporary works based on the criteria stated, since the excepted risk in cl. 20 (3) of a design fault is not worded so as to apply in that case (p. 97). The contractor (or his insurers by subrogation — p. 98, footnote (q)) may then have a remedy against the engineer outside of the contract to recover the cost of making good the damage, and the contractor may similarly have a remedy where the engineer's negligence causes him to construct unnecessarily expensive temporary works. This important topic of liability for negligence outside the terms of the construction contract is discussed on p. 393.

15. "ENGINEER'S CONSENT TO THE PROPOSED METHODS . . . UNREASONABLY DELAYED". *See* p. 365 on what constitutes unreasonable delay.

This provision covers delay with the original consent, delay in giving consent following the contractor taking steps or making changes to meet the engineer's requirements, and apparently also delay in giving consent to a change in methods which have already been approved, within sub-cl. (4).

16. EXTRA PAYMENT WHERE "THE REQUIREMENTS OF THE ENGINEER ... OR ANY LIMITATIONS ... COULD NOT REASONABLY HAVE BEEN FORESEEN BY AN EXPERIENCED CONTRACTOR". The requirements of the engineer as enshrined in the drawings and specification are of course known to the contractor at the date of tender (unless there is a variation under cl. 51—*see* N. 4, p. 170). This right to extra payment therefore will take effect only in relation to an unreasonable application of standards left to the discretion of the engineer by the specification (e.g. "as the Engineer shall require") or engineer's requirements designed to avoid detriment to the permanent works after completion. It would hardly be a valid argument in law that the contractor did not foresee that the engineer would fully enforce detailed requirements of a specification, despite the normal practice not to "apply the book" rigidly (discussed on p. 445).

i'

The effect of this clause is to give the contractor some (N. 21) protection against unreasonableness on the part of the engineer in relation to temporary works. The engineer may be wise in order to minimise claims under this clause to include in the specification detailed requirements for methods of construction, materials and workmanship of all temporary works, including a required factor of safety. To do so is not unfair to the contractor, who will know at the time of tender what the engineer's requirements for temporary works are and will have an opportunity to price accordingly.

The hallowed phrase "*could not reasonably have been foreseen*" is discussed in N. 4, p. 65.

17. "AT THE TIME OF TENDER". *See* p. 57, N. 2.

18. "THE CONTRACTOR UNAVOIDABLY INCURS DELAY OR COST". Why is "*unavoidably*" slipped in here, although not in cls. 12, 31 or 44? Why more strict than "*could not reasonably avoid*" in cl. 59A (3) (b)? And *see* cl. 59B (4) (b). Very often delay and cost are not both unavoidable, but alternatives. The wording of this clause invites the absurdity of an engineer arguing in such a case that delay was avoidable by more expenditure by the contractor, and that cost could have been avoided by taking more time to do the work, so that the contractor loses under both headings.

Obviously the test must be reasonableness. It is suggested that if the contractor chooses to avoid or reduce delay by uneconomic working, the engineer may not be bound to award the contractor's resulting costs, particularly if he had warned the contractor that he will not do so and given an appropriate extension of time. The engineer similarly may refuse a full extension of time claimed by the contractor so far as the delay is due to use of inadequate resources by the contractor.

19. PAYMENT "SUBJECT TO CLAUSE 52 (4) . . . IN ACCORDANCE WITH CLAUSE 60"—dealing with notice of money claims and inclusion in interim and the final payment certificates, subject to retention.

20. PAYMENT OF "SUCH SUM IN RESPECT OF THE COST INCURRED AS THE ENGINEER CONSIDERS FAIR IN ALL THE CIRCUMSTANCES". A further addition to the disparate galaxy of phrases used in these conditions to describe

---

(*i'*) Reasonable tolerance may however be implied in the light of trade usage, if not inconsistent with the words of the specification (p. 43).

additional payment to which the contractor may become entitled. Presumably since the sum is "*in respect of the cost incurred*", profit is excluded. Presumably also the contractor may be paid less than his actual costs where the costs have been increased by inefficiency, but may he be awarded less for any other reason? One possibility is mentioned in N. 18.

21. LIMITATIONS ON ENGINEER'S CONTROL UNDER THIS SUB-CLAUSE AND ALTERNATIVE CONTROL. The engineer has no power under this sub-clause to require the contractor to give information about temporary works except as relevant to the considerations discussed in two previous notes, and his right to refuse consent under this sub-clause is similarly limited (N. 11). For example, the engineer is not specifically entitled to obtain information or refuse consent to ensure that temporary works will not cause damage to neighbouring property, or because temporary works may delay completion (without actually affecting the permanent works when completed), or may fail and cause injury to workmen. Therefore the engineer has rights under this sub-clause in respect of such dangers only in order to enforce requirements that are written into the specification or the drawings. It follows that a comprehensive specification is wise, demanding temporary works that are safe and satisfactory for all purposes. (The effect of the content of the specification on claims is discussed in N. 16.)

In any case it seems that the engineer, even if he has embarked on the procedure under this sub-clause, may supplement his control of temporary works by refusing approval under cl. 13 (2) to works that do not fully meet the contractor's responsibility under cl. 8 (2). It is possible that the engineer has an implied right to information necessary to enable him to decide whether or not to give such approval. Otherwise he may obtain the information at the tender stage, or from the contractor's method statement under sub-cl. (1) of this clause, or on the initiative of the contractor or from site inspection.

The possibility of a claim by the contractor under this cl. 14(6) only arises if the engineer starts the ball rolling by requesting information about the contractor's methods of construction, etc. for the purpose specified in sub-cl. (3). The request may be written or oral and casual during a site inspection, but if there is no such request at all this clause does not operate. In particular, in so far as the engineer obtains sufficient information and controls temporary works by way of refusal of approval under cl. 13 (2) (apparently whether or not for the purpose specified in this cl. 14 (3)), leaving it to the contractor to decide on the changes necessary to obtain approval, the contractor has no claim to extra payment under this clause. The rights of the parties under other clauses of the Conditions are discussed on p. 170 and obviously this negative control of the contractor's methods will not always be satisfactory to protect the permanent works, but it may be useful if the engineer finds himself harassed by false claims.

CONTRACTOR'S SUPERINTENDENCE

15. (1) The Contractor shall give or provide all necessary superintendence during the execution of the Works and as long thereafter[1] as the Engineer may consider necessary. Such superintendence shall be given by sufficient persons having adequate knowledge of the operations to be carried out[2] (including the methods and techniques required the hazards likely to be encountered and methods of preventing accidents) as may be requisite for the satisfactory construction of the Works.[3]

CONTRACTOR'S AGENTS

(2) The Contractor or a competent and authorised agent or representative approved of in writing by the Engineer (which approval may at any time be withdrawn) is to be constantly on the Works and shall give his whole time to the superintendence of the same. Such authorised agent or representative shall be in full charge of the Works[4] and shall receive on behalf of the Contractor directions and instructions[5] from the Engineer or (subject to the limitations of Clause 2) the Engineer's Representative.[6] The Contractor or such authorised agent or representative shall be responsible for the safety of all operations.[7]

1. "AND AS LONG THEREAFTER", i.e. as necessary during the maintenance period—see p. 65, N. 2.

2. "SUPERINTENDENCE ... BY SUFFICIENT PERSONS HAVING ADEQUATE KNOWLEDGE". Makes explicit what was implied in the 4th edition of these Conditions.

3. "FOR THE SATISFACTORY CONSTRUCTION OF THE WORKS" should as elsewhere read "construction and maintenance".

4. AGENT "IN FULL CHARGE OF THE WORKS". A contractor's agent is normally subject to control by supervision of his superiors from head office, and may have no authority to order plant or materials or make decisions involving more than a specified cost. In ordinary language he is in charge of the works subject to certain limitations, not in "full charge". As a result of this clause the engineer need not accept as a reason for delay in obeying his instructions the situation which does sometimes arise, where superiors (often in a different country and with no great knowledge of the site) must be consulted by the agent on even minor matters.

The engineer may withdraw approval of an agent if he finds that he is not "in full charge". If there is persistent failure to obey this clause, at least in theory the contract may be forfeited under cl. 63 (1) (d).

Unlike the engineer, the agent is given no specific power to delegate his duties. He is nevertheless entitled to delegate subsidiary functions as long as he remains "in full charge" and may send any "qualified agent" to assist in measurement under cl. 56 (3).

5. "SUCH ... REPRESENTATIVE SHALL ... RECEIVE ON BEHALF OF THE CONTRACTOR DIRECTIONS AND INSTRUCTIONS". Immediately the contractor's representative receives instructions or directions they take effect as if they were given direct to the contractor. The representative has power to receive directions and instructions only, not notices required to be given by the general conditions—see cl. 68. Neither is it required that the representative should have power to make agreements binding the contractor. Therefore the engineer should have a representative's authority to bind the contractor confirmed before agreeing with him, e.g., rates or a final account.

Although the agent apparently must be available to receive instructions

(j') It is conceivable that these words mean only that the agent is to be fully responsible for the care of the works, but, e.g., "In my view the words 'in charge of' in Sec. 15 of the (Road Traffic Act, 1930) mean being responsible for the control ... of the car." *Crichton* v. *Burrell* [1951] S.L.T. 365, 367 per Lord Keith.

and directions if the engineer insists, the agent may notify the engineer that others have authority on behalf of the contractor to substitute for him. The contractor will not then be entitled later to deny the effectiveness of any instruction or direction received by such substitute.

6. DIRECTIONS AND INSTRUCTIONS OF ENGINEER'S REPRESENTATIVE, ASSISTANTS, ETC. *See* p. 33, N. 1.

7. SAFETY. This addition is in keeping with the emphasis on safety in the next clause and cl. 19.

REMOVAL OF CONTRACTOR'S EMPLOYEES

16.   The Contractor shall employ or cause to be employed[1] in and about the execution of the Works[2] and in the superintendence thereof[3] only such persons as are careful skilled and experienced in their several trades and callings and the Engineer shall be at liberty to object to and require the Contractor to remove from the Works[4] any person employed by the Contractor in or about the execution of the Works who in the opinion of the Engineer misconducts himself or is incompetent or negligent in the performance of his duties[5,6] or fails to conform with any particular provisions with regard to safety which may be set out in the Specification or persists in any conduct which is prejudicial to safety or health[7] and such persons shall not be again employed upon the Works without the permission of the Engineer.

1. "OR CAUSE TO BE EMPLOYED". A clarification of the previous edition, to include sub-contractor's employees. The change is not carried through in the reference later on in the clause to *"any person employed by the Contractor"*.

2. "IN AND ABOUT THE EXECUTION OF THE WORKS". *See* p. 65, N. 2. But these words may more easily than *"during the execution of the works"* be interpreted to include work in the maintenance period.

3. "THE SUPERINTENDENCE THEREOF". A clarification making clear tnat supervisors are included.

4. REMOVAL OF EMPLOYEES EMPLOYED AWAY FROM THE SITE. The inclusion of persons employed *"about the execution of the Works"* suggests that the engineer may order persons employed away from the site to be removed *"from the Works"*.

5. REMEDIES FOR WRONGFUL ORDER TO REMOVE EMPLOYEES. If the engineer without justification orders an employee to be removed, the contractor may disobey the order and contest forfeiture if the engineer acts under cl. 63. Alternatively he may claim damages, but apart from other difficulties (pp. 417–18) it may be difficult to prove tangible loss beyond the wages of a substitute (and that only if the contractor cannot make full use elsewhere of the services of the employee dismissed), however valuable the employee may be to the contractor's organisation.

It is conceivable, but doubtful, that the contractor may have a remedy under cl. 13 for any resulting delay or disruption to the contractor's arrangements—p. 75.

The man dismissed from the site (apart from any rights he may have against his employer, which are not relevant here) will have a right of action for defamation against the engineer, since the order implies that he has misconducted himself or been incompetent or negligent, if the engineer acted maliciously, i.e. out of spite or other ulterior motive, but not if the engineer was merely mistaken.

6. REMOVAL OF PARTNER, SUB-CONTRACTOR, DIRECTOR. The engineer may have power under this clause to order removal from the works of a partner in a contracting firm, or of a sub-contractor himself, although neither is a servant of the main contractor, if "*employ*" is to be read in the wide sense of "*make use of*". Nominated sub-contractors are dealt with fully in ch. 6. A director whether or not an employee of a contracting company may also be removable under this clause, as may an independent consultant employed *k'* by the contractor in or about the execution of the works.

7. SAFETY. This specific reference to safety is new, and ties in with the new cl. 19. The case of a workman who is careless only of his own safety is included.

If dismissal of a worker in the interests of safety causes a strike, the contractor may be entitled to an extension of time under cl. 44, given the irrational attitude of unions to justified safety measures.

SETTING-OUT

17. The Contractor shall be responsible for the true and proper setting-out of the Works and for the correctness of the position levels dimensions and alignment of all the parts of the Works and for the provision of all necessary instruments appliances and labour in connection therewith. If at any time during the progress of the Works[1] any error shall appear or arise in the position levels dimensions or alignment of any part of the Works the Contractor on being required so to do by the Engineer shall at his own cost rectify such error to the satisfaction of the Engineer unless such error is based on incorrect data supplied in writing by the Engineer or the Engineer's Representative[2] in which case the cost[3] of rectifying the same shall be borne by the Employer. The checking of any setting-out or of any line or level by the Engineer or the Engineer's Representative shall not in any way relieve the Contractor of his responsibility for the correctness thereof[4] and the Contractor shall carefully protect and preserve all bench-marks sight rails pegs and other things used in setting out the Works.

1. ERROR IN SETTING-OUT APPEARING "DURING THE PROGRESS OF THE WORKS". Some of the problems in interpreting the Contract forms may be illustrated by reference to the contractor's liability if an error in setting-out is only found during the maintenance period:

(*a*) Is the contractor liable to make good the error under this clause, although it refers to the error appearing or arising "*during the progress of the Works*"? *See* p. 65, N. 2.

(*k'*) "The use of the verb '*employ*' in both these sections (of an Act) is clearly in the sense of performing work" *Matthews* v. *Auckland Farmers Freezing Co. Ltd.* [1965] N.Z.L.R. 1110, 1112. "For instance, a solicitor who is engaged by a client to do certain work for him is employed by him for that purpose, as is a doctor who gives his professional skill to a patient ..." *Carter* v. *Gt. West Lumber Co.* [1919] 3 W.W.R. 901, 902 Can.

(*b*) If he is not, does this work fall within cl. 49 (2), or has the employer a remedy at common law in damages? *See* p. 164, N. 9.

(*c*) May the engineer vary the works in the maintenance period, by altering the position of the works although they are situated in accordance with the drawings? *See* p. 175, N. 9.

2. "ERROR BASED ON INCORRECT DATA SUPPLIED IN WRITING BY THE ENGINEER OR THE ENGINEER'S REPRESENTATIVE". On the wording of this clause the employer is liable for the cost of an error based on such data even if the contractor should have noticed that the data were incorrect, but, it is suggested, not if he did notice it since it is the contractor's action rather than the original mistake in the data that is the direct cause of the erroneous setting out. And even in the former case the contractor may have liability outside of the contract—p. 396.

The contractor should ensure that the written order or confirmation and notices of claim under cls. 51 and 52 are given for any intentional change by the engineer in the dimensions, levels, etc., of the works.

The contractor's right to extra payment applies to data supplied by the engineer's representative apparently whether or not power to give the data was delegated to the representative in writing under cl. 2 (3).

3. "COST . . . BORNE BY THE EMPLOYER". *See* p. 31, N. 18.

4. APPROVAL NOT BINDING. *See* the case set out on p. 399.

BOREHOLES AND EXPLORATORY EXCAVATION

18. If at any time during the execution of the Works[1] the Engineer shall require the Contractor to make boreholes or to carry out exploratory excavation such requirement shall be ordered in writing and shall be deemed to be a variation ordered under Clause 51 unless a Provisional Sum or Prime Cost Item in respect of such anticipated work shall have been included in the Bill of Quantities.[2]

1. "DURING THE EXECUTION OF THE WORKS". *See* cl. 12, N. 2, but for the engineer's powers in the maintenance period, *see* cl. 50.

2. "BOREHOLES OR . . . EXPLORATORY EXCAVATION . . . TO BE A VARIATION . . . UNLESS", ETC. But *see* cl. 38 (2) and cl. 50.

SAFETY AND SECURITY

19. (1) The Contractor shall throughout the progress of the Works[1] have full regard for the safety of all persons entitled to be upon the Site[2] and shall keep the Site (so far as the same is under his control) and the Works (so far as the same are not completed or occupied by the employer) in an orderly state appropriate to the avoidance of danger to such persons and shall *inter alia* in connection with the Works provide and maintain at his own cost all lights guards fencing warning signs[3] and watching when and where necessary[4] or required by the Engineer or by any competent statutory or other authority[5] for the protection of the Works or for the safety and convenience of the public or others.

EMPLOYER'S RESPONSIBILITIES

(2) If under Clause 31 the Employer shall carry out work on the Site with his own workmen he shall in respect of such work:
   (a) have full regard to the safety of all persons entitled to be upon the Site; and
   (b) keep the Site in an orderly state appropriate to the avoidance of danger to such persons.

If under Clause 31 the Employer shall employ other contractors on the Site he shall require them to have the same regard for safety and avoidance of danger.[6]

1. "THROUGHOUT THE PROGRESS OF THE WORKS". See p. 65, N. 2.

2. CONTRACTOR TO HAVE REGARD FOR "THE SAFETY OF ALL PERSONS ENTITLED TO BE UPON THE SITE". The contractor has some duty of care even to persons who are not entitled to be upon the site (p. 93).

It is hoped that the new emphasis on safety will pass from paper into practice.

3. "WARNING SIGNS" is new.

4. "THE CONTRACTOR SHALL . . . PROVIDE . . . ALL LIGHTS . . . FENCING . . . WHERE NECESSARY". For a decided case relevant to this duty, see p. 93.

5. "OR REQUIRED . . . BY ANY . . . STATUTORY OR OTHER AUTHORITY", ETC. The Highways Act, 1959, Sec. 144, authorises a local authority by notice to the owner or occupier of land beside a road or passage to order enclosure, etc., to prevent danger from works on the land. For public nuisance generally see pp. 420-1.

By Sec. 8 (1) of the Public Utilities Street Works Act, 1950, undertakers executing work regulated by the Act are bound to secure that the street is adequately fenced and guarded, and lighted in such manner as to give proper warning to the public during the hours of darkness, so long as the street is open or broken up.

6. LIABILITY FOR DAMAGE, ETC., DUE TO WORK ON THE SITE BY THE EMPLOYER OR HIS OTHER CONTRACTORS. Liability and insurance are the subject of ch. 4.

The extreme importance of checking and if necessary regularising insurance before the employer makes any use of the site is noted on p. 98, and the danger of disruption claims by the contractor if others are working on the site for the employer is discussed on p. 371.

(1') For the Public Utilities Street Works Act, 1950, see cl. 27. Infringement of Sec. 8 of the Act does not give a member of the public injured as a result any right to damages unless the undertaker has been negligent. *Keating* v. *Elvan Reinforced Concrete Co. Ltd.* & *Anor.* [1967] 3 All E.R. 611.

CHAPTER 4

Liability and Insurance: Conditions Clauses 20–25

These complicated insurance and liability clauses are dealt with by a general commentary, followed by detailed notes on the changes in the 5th edition, and completed by a key on pp. 360 3 which it is hoped will be useful as a check list in arranging or approving insurance cover.

CARE OF THE WORKS

20. (1) The Contractor shall take full responsibility for the care of the Works[1] from the date of the commencement thereof until 14 days after the Engineer shall have issued a Certificate of Completion for the whole of the Works pursuant to Clause 48.[2] Provided that if the Engineer shall issue a Certificate of Completion in respect of any Section or part of the Permanent Works before he shall issue a Certificate of Completion in respect of the whole of the Works the Contractor shall cease to be responsible for the care of that Section or part of the Permanent Works 14 days after the Engineer shall have issued the Certificate of Completion in respect of that Section or part and the responsibility for the care thereof shall thereupon pass to the Employer.[3] Provided further that the Contractor shall take full responsibility for the care of any outstanding work which he shall have undertaken to finish during the Period of Maintenance until such outstanding work is complete.[4]

RESPONSIBILITY FOR REINSTATEMENT

(2) In case any damage loss or injury from any cause whatsoever (save and except the Excepted Risks as defined in sub-clause (3) of this Clause) shall happen to the Works or any part thereof while the Contractor shall be responsible for the care thereof the Contractor shall at his own cost repair and make good the same so that at completion the Permanent Works shall be in good order and condition and in conformity in every respect with the requirements of the Contract and the Engineer's instructions. To the extent that any such damage loss or injury arises from any of the Excepted Risks[5] the Contractor shall if required by the Engineer repair and make good the same as aforesaid at the expense of the Employer.[6,6a] The Contractor shall also be liable for any damage to the Works occasioned by him in the course of any operations carried out by him for the purpose of completing any outstanding work or of complying with his obligations under Clauses 49 and 50.[7]

EXCEPTED RISKS

(3) The "Excepted Risks" are riot war invasion act of foreign enemies hostilities (whether war be declared or not) civil war rebellion revolution

89

insurrection or military or usurped power[8] ionising radiations or contamination by radio-activity from any nuclear fuel or from any nuclear waste from the combustion of nuclear fuel radioactive toxic explosive or other hazardous properties of any explosive nuclear assembly or nuclear component thereof pressure waves caused by aircraft or other aerial devices travelling at sonic or supersonic speeds[9] or a cause due to use or occupation by the Employer his agents servants or other contractors (not being employed by the Contractor) of any part of the Permanent Works[10] or to fault defect error or omission in the design of the Works[11] (other than a design provided by the Contractor pursuant to his obligations under the Contract).[12]

For detailed notes see p. 96.

INSURANCE OF WORKS, ETC.

21. Without limiting his obligations and responsibilities under Clause 20 the Contractor shall insure in the joint names of the Employer and the Contractor:

    (a) the Permanent Works and the Temporary Works (including for the purposes of this Clause any unfixed materials or other things delivered to the Site for incorporation[1] therein) to their full value;[2]

    (b) the Constructional Plant to its full value;

against all loss or damage from whatever cause arising (other than the Excepted Risks) for which he is responsible under the terms of the Contract and in such manner that the Employer and Contractor are covered for the period stipulated in Clause 20 (1)[3] and are also covered for loss or damage arising during the Period of Maintenance from such cause occurring prior to the commencement of the Period of Maintenance and for any loss or damage occasioned by the Contractor in the course of any operation carried out by him for the purpose of complying with his obligations under Clauses 49 and 50.[4]

    Provided that without limiting his obligations and responsibilities as aforesaid nothing in this Clause contained shall render the Contractor liable to insure against the necessity for the repair or reconstruction of any work constructed with materials and workmanship not in accordance with the requirements of the Contract unless the Bill of Quantities shall provide a special item for this insurance.

    Such insurances shall be effected with an insurer and in terms approved by the Employer (which approval shall not be unreasonably withheld)[5] and the Contractor shall whenever required produce to the Employer the policy or policies of insurance and the receipts for payment of the current premiums.

For detailed notes see p. 103.

DAMAGE TO PERSONS AND PROPERTY

22. (1) The Contractor shall (except if and so far as the Contract otherwise provides) indemnify and keep indemnified the Employer against all losses[1] and claims for injuries or damage to any person or property whatsoever (other than the Works for which insurance is required under Clause 21[2] but including surface or other damage to land being the Site[3] suffered by any persons in beneficial occupation of such land) which may arise out of or in consequence of the construction and maintenance of the Works and against all claims demands proceedings damages costs charges and expenses whatsoever in respect thereof or in relation thereto. Provided always that:[4]

    (a) the Contractor's liability to indemnify the Employer as aforesaid shall be reduced proportionately to the extent that the act or neglect of the

Employer his servants or agents may have contributed to the said loss injury or damage;[4]

(b) nothing herein contained shall be deemed to render the Contractor liable for in respect of or to indemnify the Employer against any compensation or damages for or with respect to:[4]

   (i) damage to crops being on the Site[5] (save in so far as possession has not been given to the Contractor);

   (ii) the use or occupation of land (which has been provided by the Employer) by the Works or any part thereof or for the purpose of constructing completing and maintaining the Works (including consequent losses of crops)[5] or interference whether temporary or permanent with any right of way light air or water or other easement or quasi easement which are the unavoidable result of the construction of the Works in accordance with the Contract;[5(a)]

   (iii) the right of the Employer to construct the works or any part thereof on over under in or through any land;

   (iv) damage which is the unavoidable result of the construction of the Works in accordance with the Contract;[6]

   (v) injuries or damage to persons or property resulting from any act or neglect or breach of statutory duty done or committed by the Engineer[7] or the Employer his agents servants or other contractors (not being employed by the Contractor) or for or in respect of any claims demands proceedings damages costs charges and expenses in respect thereof or in relation thereto.[4,8]

INDEMNITY BY EMPLOYER

(2) The Employer will save harmless and indemnify the Contractor from and against all claims demands proceedings damages costs charges and expenses in respect of the matters referred to in the proviso to sub-clause (1) of this Clause. Provided always that the Employer's liability to indemnify the Contractor under paragraph (v) of proviso (b) to sub-clause (1) of this Clause shall be reduced proportionately to the extent that the act or neglect of the Contractor or his sub-contractors servants or agents may have contributed to the said injury or damage.[4]

For detailed notes see p. 104.

INSURANCE AGAINST DAMAGE TO PERSONS AND PROPERTY

23. (1) Throughout the execution of the Works[1] the Contractor (but without limiting his obligations and responsibilities under Clause 22) shall insure against any damage loss or injury which may occur to any property or to any person by or arising out of the execution of the Works or in the carrying out of the Contract otherwise than due to the matters referred to in proviso (b) to Clause 22 (1).

AMOUNT AND TERMS OF INSURANCE

(2) Such insurance shall be effected with an insurer and in terms approved by the Employer (which approval shall not be unreasonably withheld)[2] and for at least the amount stated in the Appendix to the Form of Tender. The terms shall include a provision whereby in the event of any claim in respect of which the Contractor would be entitled to receive indemnity under the policy being brought or made against the Employer the insurer will indemnify the Employer

against such claims and any costs charges and expenses in respect thereof.[3] The Contractor shall whenever required produce to the Employer the policy or policies of insurance and the receipts for payment of the current premiums.

For detailed notes *see* p. 107.

ACCIDENT OR INJURY TO WORKMEN

24. The Employer shall not be liable for or in respect of any damages or compensation payable at law in respect or in consequence of any accident or injury to any workman or other person in the employment of the Contractor or any sub-contractor save and except to the extent that such accident or injury results from or is contributed to by any act or default of the Employer his agents or servants[1] and the Contractor shall indemnify and keep indemnified the Employer against all such damages and compensation (save and except as aforesaid) and against all claims demands proceedings costs charges and expenses whatsoever in respect thereof or in relation thereto.[2]

For detailed notes *see* p. 107.

REMEDY ON CONTRACTOR'S FAILURE TO INSURE

25. If the Contractor shall fail upon request to produce to the Employer satisfactory evidence[1] that there is in force the insurance referred to in Clauses 21 and 23 or any other insurance which he may be required to effect under the terms of the Contract then and in any such case the Employer may effect and keep in force any such insurance and pay such premium or premiums as may be necessary for that purpose and from time to time deduct the amount so paid by the Employer as aforesaid from any monies due or which may become due to the Contractor or recover the same as a debt due from the Contractor.[2]

For detailed notes *see* p. 108.

General Commentary cls. 20–25:
The above clauses 20–25 settle liability as between the contractor and employer for various risks incidental to the works and provide for insurance:

(*a*) For damage to the works themselves, etc., while they are being built, e.g. by fire or flood—dealt with in the notes to cls. 20 and 21.

(*b*) For damage to other property or injury to persons.

(*c*) For injury to employees.

Liability under (*b*) may be for:

1. TRESPASS (*see* cl. 22 (1) (b) (ii) and (iii)), e.g. by entering even by mistake on land or buildings or beneath or in the air space above land in possession of another without his consent, and it is not necessary for the other party to prove that he has been caused any actual loss. It is also a trespass to place any object in contact with land or buildings:

Injunction granted to stop a jobber storing building material against a boundary wall which belonged to his neighbour.

a

(*a*) *Westripp* v. *Baldock* [1939] 1 All E.R. 279, C.A. In *Woollerton and Wilson Ltd.* v. *Richard Costain Ltd.* [1970] 1 All E.R. 483 a claim was made for trespass by a tower crane into air space.

2. NUISANCE, ETC.—ch. 15.

3. DANGEROUS PREMISES. The occupier must take reasonable care to see that any person who enters land or buildings lawfully will be reasonably safe in using the premises for the purpose for which he is invited or permitted to be there. A warning of danger is only effective if in all the circumstances it is sufficient to enable the person to be reasonably safe. The contractor will usually be the occupier of the site, but the employer may be a joint occupier if he has a degree of control from presence on and use of the site or works in course of construction.

An occupier even has some duty to a trespasser. His liability is to do what in the circumstances a conscientious humane man, with his knowledge, skill and resources, would do to prevent injury:

> Workmen of demolition contractors lit a bonfire to burn rubbish. The site was next to a public park. The men failed to keep a look-out for children coming on to the site although they had taken down the hoardings. A five-year old boy, who had been chased off the site repeatedly, came back to see the fire. The contractors were held liable to pay compensation for his severe burns.

4. NEGLIGENCE. There is in most cases liability for not taking reasonable care to avoid acts or omissions which a "reasonable man" would foresee would be likely to cause injury or damage to the person or property of another:

> A pedestrian was injured when he fell into a trench excavated along the pavement in a popular part of London. The contractors had placed warning notices at both ends of the trench and a hammer with a long handle raised and sloping across the pavement. The pedestrian injured, a blind man who missed the handle with his stick, recovered damages from the contractors on the grounds that they should have foreseen the possibility of blind people using the pavement, and taken special precautions.

Employer's liability under (c) above. An employer is very widely liable for the safety of his employees (that is, the contractor for his labour under the contract, not the "employer"). He is bound to see that reasonable care is taken to supply them with and maintain proper plant and appliances and material, and to see that they have a safe place of work and a safe system of work, and he is also liable for any injury caused to an employee by the negligence of any other employee of his:

> A, an employee at an electrical sub-station, was injured while making a test because he removed a screen between the dead and live parts of the switchboard.
> A had learned to do this from a fellow employee and had then pointed out the dangers, but had been told that if no risks were taken nothing would be done, and, in fact, the usual practice in the station was to remove the screen. A had later been appointed to do dangerous work and had been given a copy of the regulations, which forbade removal of the screen, and told to make himself familiar with them.
> Held: A's employers were liable for his injuries; they had not provided a safe

(b) Occupier's Liability Act 1957, and *see* the Unfair Contract Terms Act 1977 (p. 431 below).
(c) *British Railways Board* v. *Herrington* [1972] 1 All E.R. 749, H.L., and see *Southern Portland Cement Ltd.* v. *Cooper* [1974] 1 All E.R. 87, P.C.
(d) *Pannett* v. *P. McGuiness & Co. Ltd.* [1972] 3 All E.R. 137, C.A.
(e) *Haley* v. *London Electricity Board* [1964] 3 All E.R. 185, H.L. For important extensions of the law of negligence refer to pp. 393–7. For special protection against defective goods *see* Consumer Safety Act 1978.

system of work simply by telling him to follow these regulations, and even if they had originally supplied a safe system they had allowed it to be ignored. A was not himself guilty of contributory negligence, because he had followed the example
f   of his superiors.

To this is added the employer's liability for penalties and to pay compensation for injury due to failure to see that the safety, health and welfare regulations in the Factories Act 1961 and the Health and Safety at
g   Work Act 1974, and the regulations under the Acts are carried out.

Finally, by recent legislation the employer is liable for any injury to an employee in consequence of a defect in equipment provided by the employer even though the defect is due to the fault of a third party (e.g. the manufacturer) and could not reasonably have been detected by the employer. "Equipment" includes any plant and machinery, vehicle, aircraft
h   and clothing.

Under these headings an employee is entitled to compensation by a lump sum to cover all loss of earnings, pain and suffering, disability, etc., but if he was negligent himself he may lose all or part of the compensation:

> An experienced employee was killed when he fell from a roof on which he was doing an unusually awkward job.
>
> Held: His employers were liable for breach of statutory duty in not supplying him with proper crawling boards as required by the Building (Safety, etc.) Regulations, 1948, and for negligence in not drawing his attention to the regulations or to the necessity for a proper system of work.
>
> But as the workman was partly to blame in not using scaffolding boards which had been supplied, his widow was held entitled only to two-thirds of the full
i   damages.

An employee who cannot prove liability under these headings may still claim under the National Insurance (Industrial Injuries) Acts 1965–74. In that case he has only to prove that his injury was caused by an accident arising out of or in the course of his employment or by an industrial disease; it is not necessary for him to prove any negligence or breach of duty by the employer, and he is generally entitled to full compensation even though he was himself negligent or disobeyed orders. Compensation is usually by weekly payments subject to relatively small limits whatever the loss.

Dependants also have similar rights to compensation in the case of fatal
j   accidents.

The wide legal liability of an employer, which goes far beyond cases

(*f*) *Barcock* v. *Brighton Corp.* [1949] 1 All E.R. 257   a case which goes unusually far in holding the employer fully liable, but may be taken as a warning of how careful a prudent employer will be to protect his workers.

(*g*) The most important regulations which apply to civil engineering works are the Construction (General Provisions) Regulations 1961 (S.I. 1961 No. 1580); the Construction (Lifting Operations) Regulations 1961 (S.I. 1961 No. 1581); the Construction (Working Places) Regulations 1966 (S.I. 1966 No. 94); and the Construction (Health and Welfare) Regulations 1966 and 1974 (S.I. Nos. 95 and 209). In addition there are special regulations   e.g. the Electricity (Factories) Act Regulations 1908–1944 (S.I. 1312 and 739). The Offices, Shops and Railway Premises Act 1963, and regulations made under the Act generally apply to site offices which are to remain for longer than six months. The changes in practice that will occur as the Health and Safety at Work Act 1974 takes effect are outside the scope of this book.

(*h*) Employer's Liability (Defective Equipment) Act 1969.

(*i*) *Jenner* v. *Allen West & Co. Ltd.* [1959] 2 All E.R. 115, C.A.

(*j*) The Fatal Accidents Acts 1846, 1959, and the Law Reform (Miscellaneous Provisions) Act 1934.

where he is morally to blame, is justified on the grounds that it is the complexity and pressure of modern industrial work which makes workmen accident-prone. The employer passes the cost of compensation or insurance on to the public in his prices, and it is felt right that the public, who ultimately get the benefit of the work, should bear the financial loss from accidents, and not the individual workmen injured.

Division of liability—indemnity. There are, of course, at least three parties who may be liable under these headings—the employer, the engineer and the contractor—and two or more of them may be liable in law for the same damage, e.g. the employer with the contractor in some cases of nuisance (p. 420, second case, and case p. 391).

In these cases the injured party is entitled to recover the damages which he has suffered wholly from one or partly from each of the parties liable and may sue one or more of them as he thinks fit. These cls. 22 and 24, therefore, define the position clearly by specifying, very roughly, that the contractor must make good to the employer all liabilities which he incurs to third parties due to the contractor's fault and *vice versa*.

Even where there is no specific agreement to indemnify, e.g. as between the engineer and contractor, a party who pays more than his just and equitable share of the compensation having regard to his responsibility for the damage may by statute recover a contribution or complete indemnity from any other person liable (p. 404). In neither case, of course, is the right of the injured third party to recover all his damages from one or more of the parties liable affected.

The Unfair Contract Terms Act 1977 now may affect indemnity clauses—p. 431.

Insurance. As an added protection to the employer the contractor is bound to insure against his liability. Insurance is for the benefit of the contractor, because his liability to indemnify the employer under cls. 20, 22 and 24 remains whether or not he is insured, and for the benefit of the employer to avoid the danger of having to try to enforce a right of indemnity against an insolvent contractor.

The contractor's insurance usually will be set out in more than one policy or in several sections in one policy, and there must be no gaps. The fact that a policy is called "Contractors' All Risk" does not in the insurance world mean that all risks are covered, and the policy must be considered carefully. It is common to see policies issued to contractors which do not comply with these clauses. Exclusions from cover constantly give trouble; they are not always in the "Exclusions" part of the policy, but may be hidden in the

---

(*k*) As far as liability to workers is concerned the contractor's main interest will be to prevent accidents and to collect the facts of those that occur as soon as possible. The actual negotiation and litigation of claims will normally be taken over by the contractor's insurers. That is why the topic has been dealt with very briefly here; for more reading see J. Munkman "Employer's Liability", 8th ed.; "Winfield and Jolowicz on Tort", 10th ed.

(*l*) Law Reform (Married Women and Tortfeasors) Act, 1935, Sec. 6, and the Civil Liability (Contribution) Act 1978.

(*m*) On insurance for construction "The Contractors' Insurance Compendium" prepared by the National Federation of Building Trades Employers in collaboration with W. L. Tunnicliffe is very useful. Reference may be made also to Hagart "Conditions of Contract and Insurance", Eaglestone "The R.I.B.A. Contract and the Insurance Market", 3rd ed. Madge "Liability Policy Wordings and Cover", 2nd ed. and "Construction and Erection Insurance" Insurance Institute of London, Advanced Study Group 208 (1978).

"Conditions" section or, e.g., in the limitation to accidental damage (p. 106, N. 6).

The key on pp. 360–3 tries to set out the insurance requirements in a way that will help the contractor to arrange cover and the engineer to check both the contractor's and employer's policies. However, it may be very difficult to be sure that the pieces for what is often an insurance jigsaw are all present and dovetail together precisely. The engineer is not bound to be an expert on insurance, and should have any doubtful points clarified in writing direct by insurers or brought to the employer's notice for legal advice if necessary.

It has indeed been argued that, particularly as these clauses require approval of policies by "*the Employer*", the engineer has no duty to play any role at all in connection with insurance. But the engineer is no more an expert on legal matters than he is on insurance matters, yet there are many situations in which it is undoubtedly his duty to take preliminary precautions on behalf of the employer, subject to having any difficult points finally dealt with by a lawyer (p. 390). In particular the engineer is no less qualified to require production of policies by the contractor and to check any departure in policies from the requirements of these clauses than to advise on the preparation of contracts, as he is specifically required to do by cl. 2C of the A.C.E. service agreement (p. 375). Indeed if the engineer does not have a reasonable knowledge of insurance matters, is he competent to recommend the employer to accept and include unaltered in the main contract the terms of these insurance clauses?

If there are any special risks attached to particular works or anyone has doubts at any time as to whether a particular risk is covered, the parties should confirm the cover with insurers in writing or take out a special policy, and argue later about who is liable for any extra premium.

Notes to Clause 20:

1. CONTRACTOR'S RESPONSIBILITY FOR THE WORKS. By cl. 20 and his duty to hand over completed works to the employer, the contractor is bound to make good at his own cost (irrespective of whether he is insured) any damage to the works before completion. This clause confirms the liability of the contractor to make good any such damage to the works (and "*Works*" now includes all temporary works by cl. 1 (1) (1)) from "*any cause*

(n) The A.C.E. service agreement cl. 2C (ch. 13 below) places on the engineer at the construction stage general "administration of the Contract" as well as the "technical control of the construction of the Works". The contract can hardly be fully and properly administered without the engineer taking preliminary action to verify that full cover exists and is extended during the course of the works as necessary (e.g. cl. 54, N. 2 and 5, pp. 204 5), although as stated in the text he is entitled to pass over to others the decision on any points that are at all doubtful. In deciding what is doubtful the engineer will be wise to keep in mind any features of the works that may extend the cover necessary or nullify cover, and to read the policy very critically indeed, for example for any departure in wording, however microscopic, from cl. 20(3). It is safer for the engineer to leave it to the employer to choose his other advisers and to employ and consult them direct, warning him to rely only on brokers and lawyers who are versed in the peculiarities of construction insurance.

The engineer must make sure that his indemnity insurers are informed of the activities about insurance he does in fact engage in, and accept that they are part of the duties they are insuring.

(o) In *Charon* (*Finchley*) *Ltd.* v. *Singer Sewing Machine Co. Ltd.* (1968) 112 S.J. 536, a builder was held not entitled to payment for repairs carried out at the request of the employer, where damage to the works had been caused by vandals prior to completion.

whatsoever", with the relief provided by this clause that the contractor is not liable in respect of the excepted risks defined in sub-cl. (3).

Until recently it seemed clear that the phrase just quoted included damage to the works due even to the negligence of the employer. The law has become less certain as a result of a recent decision. Nevertheless interpreting cls. 20 and 21 as a whole and taking into account that the specific excepted risk of faulty design, which will usually although not always be due to the negligence of the employer's agent, implies that negligence of the employer and his agents is covered unless specifically excluded, it seems that the intention of the clauses will not be frustrated by the courts. The manifest intention is that the contractor is responsible for the overall insurance of the works for the benefit of both himself and the employer, and ultimately at the employer's expense, save for the risks expressly excluded. But there is an element of uncertainty that cannot be tolerated in a clause as important as this, so that the words "and including any negligence or default of the Employer his servants or agents" should be added after the words "*of this Clause*" within the brackets at the opening of sub-cl. (2). Even that alteration does not produce absolute safety, because of the Unfair Contract Terms Act 1977, but for the reasons given on p. 433 it is suggested that these cls. 20 and 21 clearly pass the test of reasonableness applied by the Act.

p

p'

2. **Contractor responsible for the Works** "until 14 days after the Engineer shall have issued a Certificate of Completion for the whole of the Works". This change avoids any problem where the engineer backdates his certificate of completion or the arbitrator holds that the certificate should have been given earlier. It is the actual date of issue of the certificate that is relevant.

The employer will have 14 days from the issue of the certificate to make his own insurance arrangements, and the engineer should warn him (in writing) to do so. The insurers should be informed that the contractor will still be on the site, but is liable for any damage he causes (N. 7).

The requirement in sub-cl. (1) of this clause that the contractor shall take responsibility for the care of the works until "14 *days after*" certified completion is clear enough not to be affected by the drafting peculiarity that although sub-cl. (2) refers to damage to the works "*while the Contractor shall be responsible for the care thereof*" it also says that the contractor shall repair such damage so that "*at completion*" the permanent works shall be in good order and condition. Presumably the contractor must make good immediately any damage occurring in the 14 day extra period after

(*p*) *Smith* v. *South Wales Switchgear Ltd.* [1978] 1 All E.R. 18, H. L. holding that for a clause effectively to require one party to indemnify another against the results of his own negligence the clause must either contain an express provision using the word 'negligence' or some synonym for 'negligence' or the words of the clause in their ordinary meaning must be wide enough to cover negligence, and that reference to any injury or damage "whatsoever" was not necessarily wide enough. Several previous decisions were disapproved.

(*p'*) It would be irrational of the courts to apply the hostility to standard contract forms imposed by one party, which engendered this decision, to these cls. 20 and 21 negotiated by representatives of employers and well known to employers generally (as already recognised by the courts—p. 45 above, footnote (*ee*)), where the purpose of the clause is to facilitate insurance, and where restrictions on the operation of the clause will only benefit insurers. The clause and circumstances of the *Smith* decision (above) differed greatly from these clauses and the circumstances to which they relate, and it was emphasised in the decision that the relevant clause must be read as a whole.

completion. *See* the next note for a possible insurance problem where the employer takes possession of the works within the 14 day period, unless that is covered by the original policy as it should be.

3. EMPLOYER RESPONSIBLE FOR THE CARE OF ANY SECTION OR PART OF THE PERMANENT WORKS CERTIFIED COMPLETE. The employer is here made liable for damage from any cause to any part of the works certified complete. By cl. 20 (3) the employer is also liable for damage, loss or injury to the works to the extent that it arises from "*a cause due to use or occupation by the Employer his agents servants or other contractors ... of any part of the Permanent Works*" whether or not that part is certified complete.

Moreover, a contractor's All Risks insurance policy is intended for works in the course of construction. The insurers may be entitled to take the view that the works are no longer only a structure in course of construction if they are also being used as a store or otherwise by the employer. On that basis the cover may be invalidated for the whole works by such use.

The insurance position therefore should be reviewed very carefully in the interests of both employer and contractor before the employer is allowed to take occupation of or use any part of the works, however temporary or trivial the occupation or use may be. In any case in which it is doubtful which party bears liability the insurance should cover any liability of both the contractor and the employer; otherwise, for example, the contractor's insurers who pay up may have a right to claim back the payment from the employer if he is the party actually responsible for the damage under the construction contract. At the least the parties and the engineer may become involved in time-consuming litigation.

The dangers are illustrated by the following case:

Employers allowed lessees of a factory to install equipment and store a number of reels of paper in part of a new extension to a factory being built by the defendant contractors. A disastrous fire occurred in the extension. It was held that the contractors were liable to the employers for the damage caused even to the parts so used by the employers, although the R.I.B.A. conditions of contract which applied say that any part of the works of which the employer takes possession is at the sole risk of the employer as regards fire.

Under this clause the engineer must warn the employer to take out his own insurance within 14 days of issue of a completion certificate for a part or section. In view of the changeover of liability it is important that any section to be taken over early is carefully defined in the appendix to tender, and that any part being certified complete is carefully defined in the certificate of completion.

For the other danger, of a disruption claim, where the employer uses part of the works before completion *see* p. 161.

For damage to a completed part or section caused by the contractor *see* N. 7.

(q) "The right of subrogation is the right of an insurer who has paid the insurance moneys to receive the benefit of all rights of the assured against third parties, which if satisfied, will extinguish or diminish the ultimate loss sustained." "H. MacGillivray on Insurance", 5th ed. by Denis Brown, paras. 1882 and 1889. Other aspects of subrogation are mentioned on p. 107 of the text, below.

(r) *English Industrial Estates Corp.* v. *G. Wimpey & Co. Ltd.* [1973] 1 Lloyd's Rep. 118 C.A.

4. "THE CONTRACTOR SHALL TAKE FULL RESPONSIBILITY FOR THE CARE OF ANY OUTSTANDING WORK WHICH HE SHALL HAVE UNDERTAKEN TO FINISH DURING THE PERIOD OF MAINTENANCE UNTIL SUCH OUTSTANDING WORK IS COMPLETE". This addition appears to mean that the contractor is liable for each item of outstanding work included in an undertaking under cl. 48 until that particular item of work in the undertaking (not every item in the undertaking) is complete. Once an item is dealt with it is no longer "*outstanding*" work within these words.

It may be extremely difficult to determine what the "*outstanding work*" is, where defects are to be made good. If the work consists of patching defects in a concrete slab, presumably the "*outstanding work*" for which the contractor remains liable is only the defective areas and not the whole slab. The engineer should require items of outstanding work to be defined precisely in the contractor's undertaking under cl. 48, and if necessary in any major case clarify the question of liability by agreement and check insurance cover.

"*complete*" in this context implies absolute completion. Unfortunately there is no procedure specified for determining when completion takes place.

The contractor should make sure that this liability is covered by his insurance.

See N. 7 for the contractor's liability for damage caused in completing outstanding work.

5. EMPLOYER LIABLE "TO THE EXTENT THAT . . . DAMAGE (TO THE WORKS) . . . ARISES FROM ANY OF THE EXCEPTED RISKS". The burden of proof is on the contractor to prove on the balance of probabilities that damage arose wholly or partly from an excepted risk. In a case where damage is caused partly by an excepted risk and partly by an event for which the contractor is responsible, it appears on general principles that if there was one "dominant or effective" cause of the occurrence, that alone will be considered in deciding whether the employer or contractor bears the loss.

> Insured in the course of a fit fell on a railway line and was run over. His representatives recovered payment under an insurance policy which covered accidental injuries provided they were "the direct and sole cause of death".

> Under a contract with a factory owner contractors installed electrically operated equipment in his factory. The equipment was completely unsuitable for its purpose and a potential fire hazard. When the equipment had been installed an employee of the contractors switched it on, although it had not yet been tested, and left it unattended throughout the night. As a result a fire broke out and damaged the factory.
> Held: That of the two causes of the damage, the dangerous nature of the equipment and the conduct of the employee, the former was the dominant or effective cause. Therefore insurers were not liable under a policy which excluded cover for any damage caused by the nature or condition of any goods supplied by the contractors.

If there are two effective causes one only of which is an excepted risk, for example if collapse of work due to a combination of defective design and

(s) *Lawrence* v. *Accidental Insurance* (1881) 7 Q.B.D. 216.
(t) *Wayne Tank & Pump Co. Ltd.* v. *The Employers' Liability Assurance Corp. Ltd.* [1973] 3 All E.R. 825 C.A.

workmanship would not have happened from either cause alone, it seems that an apportionment of the cost of making good must be made under this clause, although it may be very difficult to find a basis for determining "*the extent that . . . such damage*" arose from each cause:

> "But for my part I do not consider that the Court should strain to find a dominant cause if . . . there are two causes both of which can properly be described as effective causes of the loss. Counsel for the plaintiffs recognised that if there are two causes which are approximately equal in effectiveness, then it is impossible to call one rather than the other the dominant cause."

u

The mere fact that one cause is nearer to the accident in time than the other, does not make it the effective cause.

For the contractor's right to expenses, abandonment of the contract, etc., for suspension due to an excepted risk *see* cl. 40.

6. "IF REQUIRED BY THE ENGINEER REPAIR AND MAKE GOOD THE SAME AT THE EXPENSE OF THE EMPLOYER": CONSEQUENTIAL LOSS. The contractor is entitled to reasonable charges for the repair, including profit (p. 32).

Under the words of this clause the contractor is entitled only to payment for rectifying the damage caused by the excepted risk, and not for his consequential standing time and other loss due to delay to the rest of the works whilst the damage is made good. If the damage was caused by negligence or breach of contract by or on behalf of the employer, the contractor may have a remedy for consequential loss under the general law (discussed at p. 396): for consequential loss from damage due to unforeseen conditions or obstructions he may have a cl. 12 claim (p. 65): he may conceivably have a claim under cl. 13 where the engineer's requirements for repair of damage due to an excepted risk involve unforeseeable cost of delay or disruption (p. 74).

6a. EXTENSION OF TIME FOR DAMAGE TO THE WORKS. The contractor normally will be entitled to an extension of time under cl. 44 for damage to the works, but he may not be "*fairly*" entitled to any or to a full extension for delay due to damage wholly or partly the result of his own or a sub-contractor's negligence or breach of contract. The employer may insure against delay for which an extension deprives him of the right to liquidated damages—p. 363.

7. "CONTRACTOR . . . LIABLE FOR ANY DAMAGE TO THE WORKS OCCASIONED . . . IN THE COURSE OF ANY OPERATIONS . . . FOR . . . COMPLETING ANY OUTSTANDING WORK OR . . . UNDER CLAUSES 49 AND 50". Two defects in the previous edition are cured. The contractor should make sure that this liability is covered by his insurance. For example, if his public liability policy excludes damage to property on which the contractor is or has been working, the liability must be picked up in his All Risks cover.

For the (possibly incorrect) implication that cl. 50 applies only in the maintenance period, *see* p. 168, N. 2.

8. DEFINITIONS OF EXCEPTED RISKS:
"*riot*" is a tumultous disturbance of the peace by three or more persons

---

(*u*) *Wayne* case above, per Cairns L. J. at p. 831. On this most difficult problem of causation refer to Colinvaux "The Law of Insurance" 3rd ed., and Hardy Ivamy "General Principles of Insurance Law" 3rd ed., ch. 38.

who assemble together, without lawful authority, with an intent mutually to assist one another, by force if necessary, against any who shall oppose them in the execution of a common purpose and who actually execute, or begin to execute, that purpose in a violent manner displayed not merely by demolishing property but in such a manner as to alarm "at least one person of reasonable firmness and courage".

"*war*" is "the state or condition of governments contending by force". Where the word is used in a private document the question of whether there is a war or not is a question of fact. It is not necessary that the war is recognised by Her Majesty's Government, although a court may be bound to accept a statement to that effect by the Government.

The meaning of "*invasion*" is self-evident.

"*act of foreign enemies*" implies the existence of a war between the state and a foreign state.

"*hostilities (whether war be declared or not)*" means "hostile acts by persons acting as the agents of sovereign powers, or of such organised and considerable forces as are entitled to the dignified name of rebels as compared to mobs or rioters, and does not cover the act of a mere private individual acting entirely on his own initiative, however hostile his action may be".

"*civil war*" is a contest carried on by arms between parties who are citizens of the same state.

"*rebellion*". One definition is the taking-up of arms traitorously against the Crown whether by natural subjects or others when subdued. It also means disobedience to the process of the courts.

"*revolution*" and "*insurrection*" are similar. The latter has been defined as a rising of the people in open resistance against established authority with the object of supplanting it.

"*military or usurped power*". "Without using words of rigorous accuracy, military and usurped power suggests something more in the nature of war and civil war than riot and tumult . . . nor can it be properly contended that the words 'military power' do not refer to military power of a government lawfully exercised. The disjunctive 'or' is used between and contrasting the words 'military' and 'usurped'. The words are not 'usurped military power'."

All the above excepted risks follow exclusions required by the insurance market. Taken together they include most acts of organised violence, but not acts of malicious damage not involving "tumultuous" disturbance of the peace.

9. "IONISING RADIATIONS . . . AIRCRAFT AT . . . SUPERSONIC SPEEDS". The wording of these excepted risks follows exclusions which are required by the insurance market. Radiation from instruments brought on site by the contractor is not excluded.

(*v*) 10 Halsbury's Laws (3rd ed.) 587.
(*w*) *Pesquerias y Secaderos de Bacalao de España S.A.* v. *Beer* [1949] 1 All E.R. 845, 847.
(*x*) *Drinkwater* v. *London Assurance Corp.* (1767) 95 E.R. 863.
(*y*) *Atlantic Mutual Insurance Co.* v. *King* [1919] 1 K.B. 307, 310.
(*z*) *Lindsay and Pirie* v. *General Accident etc. Corp. Ltd.* [1914] App. D. 574.
(*aa*) Jowitt "The Dictionary of English Law".
(*bb*) Both these quotations are from *Rogers* v. *Whittaker* [1917] 1 K.B. 942, 944, 945. An interesting illustration of the excepted risk is the decision of the Supreme Court of West Pakistan in *Jilani* v. *The Government of the Punjab* (1972) P.L.D. vol. XXIV, no. 6, p. 139, that the regime of General Yahya Khan was based on usurpation of power.

10. "CAUSE DUE TO USE OR OCCUPATION BY THE EMPLOYER . . . OF ANY PART OF THE PERMANENT WORKS". This excepted risk again represents an exclusion common in All Risks insurance policies. It applies however temporary or minor the use may be, and whether or not the part of the works is certified complete. If the part of the works is certified complete the employer takes the risk of damage to that part from any cause, even if not due to his use (cl. 20 (1)). Despite these protections it is unwise from the point of view of the contractor as well as the employer for the employer to occupy or use the works without specially seeing to the insurance position N. 3.

To fall on the employer, damage, etc., need no longer be "solely" due to this excepted risk as it must in the 4th edition—N. 5.

See also cl. 31.

11. "FAULT DEFECT ERROR OR OMISSION IN THE DESIGN OF THE WORKS". The concept of design of the works in itself is quite far-reaching in scope. In a recent case:

> Counsel for the employer conceded that if the arbitrator concluded that settlement of a sewer was not due to bad workmanship on the part of the contractor, it followed by simple process of elimination that the engineer's design was the sole cause of a settlement that had taken place, in that ground conditions had rendered the engineer's design unsuitable.

In this edition of the Conditions the limitation to "*fault defect error or*

(cc) *Hughes (Norman) & Co. Ltd.* v. *Ruthin Borough Council* (1971) 222 E.G. 163. In *C. J. Pearce & Co. Ltd.* v. *Hereford Corp.* (1968) 66 L.G.R. 647 it was said: "The word 'design' of course means . . . that documents of the nature of plans, and so forth, are handed to the contractor, showing the precise detail of the work the contractor is to carry out. In other words the word 'design' deals with how the work is to be carried out and not what work is to be carried out" (at p. 650). The learned Judge held that in this case (discussed in the text, p. 66) "there was no evidence . . . as to any design by the engineer". It is respectfully suggested that, as admitted in the *Hughes* case, the suitability of the works for the chosen site is a matter of design.

In *Pentagon Construction* (1969) *Co. Ltd.* v. *United States Fidelity & Guarantee Co. Ltd.* [1978] 1 Lloyd's Rep. 93, Can., the plans and specifications for a concrete tank in a sewage treatment plant required the ends of steel struts laid across the top of the tank to be welded to a plate let into the concrete wall beneath it. The function of the struts was to strengthen the tank by holding the sides together, as well as to carry equipment. The contract required the contractors to test the tank, which they did by pouring water into it before the ends of the struts had been welded in place. One of the sides bulged. Insurers denied liability under the contractors' policy, which excluded "Loss or damage caused by . . . faulty or improper material or . . . faulty or improper workmanship or . . . faulty or improper design".

Held that the exclusion of faulty workmanship applied. One member of the court also held that the exclusion of faulty design did not apply on the grounds that detailed instructions on how work or construction is to be carried out is not part of the design, so that the lack of instruction as to the order in which the welding and the testing were to be done did not amount to faulty or improper design—design as used in the policy meant only the concept of the finished structure to be constructed under the contract which finds its expression in the plans and specifications (at p. 97). The other judge who considered the point held that design includes not only structural calculations, shape and location of materials but their choice, as well as the choice of particular work processes. "In other words in sophisticated contracts the design includes the specification as well as the drawings". He held that the design in this case was improper or faulty due to omission of the required instruction that the testing was not to be done until the beams had been welded in place (at p. 95).

This decision is obviously noteworthy also as a cautionary tale on the dangers of exclusions in contractor's insurance policies—text p. 95.

omission" in design has been added, but it is not clear that this change will confine the exception to negligent design:

> Railway bridge being built to replace bridge built in 1897, which had been swept away by flood waters. Prismatic piers (similar to the original piers, but strengthened) specified in the design were overturned by a flood after exceptionally heavy rains.
>
> Held: The damage was not covered by insurance which excluded "loss or damage arising from faulty design". Faulty design did not involve any element of blameworthiness or negligence. The effective cause of the loss was the inadequacy of the piers to withstand the flood and it was irrelevant that the design was satisfactory according to the state of engineering knowledge at the time it was made. *dd*

However, the words of this excepted risk follow precisely the normal exclusion in insurance policies, so that the contractor should never have to pay for making good damage to the works due to the engineer's design out of his own pocket; he should be entitled to recover either from his own insurers or from the employer for an excepted risk. A contractor nevertheless may be out of pocket for consequential losses, for which he may seek a remedy elsewhere (N. 6).

If this excepted risk does extend to cases where there has been no negligence by the engineer, the employer has no remedy against anyone for damage in such a case—not against the engineer (or his indemnity insurers) nor the contractor. For special insurance by the employer *see* p. 363.

The relevance of the similar excepted risk in the 4th edition has not always been appreciated, for example in cases of damage to the works caused by corrosion due to the atmosphere and other cases of damage not due to some sudden accident.

It is of course important to notify insurers immediately of any possible claim.

In the case of negligent design, the engineer will be liable to the employer for the extra expense under this clause—p. 386.

To fall on the employer, damage need no longer be "solely" due to this excepted risk, as it must in the 4th edition (N. 5).

12. "OTHER THAN A DESIGN PROVIDED BY THE CONTRACTOR PURSUANT TO HIS OBLIGATIONS UNDER THE CONTRACT". The complications where the contractor takes on himself or is requested (he cannot be ordered) by the engineer to submit a design for part of the works which the engineer is bound to design himself are discussed at length in N. 2 on p. 179.

Notes to Clause 21:

1. INSURANCE OF "ANY UNFIXED MATERIALS OR OTHER THINGS DELIVERED TO THE SITE FOR INCORPORATION" IN THE WORKS OR TEMPORARY WORKS. A more precise definition than the "*materials . . . and other things brought on to the Site*" in the 4th edition.

2. "TO THEIR FULL VALUE" replaces the previous "*to the full value of such works executed from time to time*". Refer to p. 360.

3. "THE PERIOD STIPULATED IN CLAUSE 20 (1)". INSURANCE IN RESPECT OF OUTSTANDING WORK UNDER CLAUSE 48. It is problematical whether the

(dd) *Manufacturer's Mutual Insurance* v. *Queensland Gov. Ry.* [1969] 1 Lloyd's Rep. 214 Aus.

words in quotations are sufficiently clear to bind the contractor to insure his liability for the care of outstanding work which he has undertaken to complete under cl. 48 (p. 99, N. 4). The contractor certainly should insure for such liability, and for damage to the works caused in completing the outstanding work for which he is made liable by cl. 20 (2) (next note).

4. "ANY LOSS OR DAMAGE OCCASIONED BY THE CONTRACTOR IN THE COURSE OF ANY OPERATION . . . UNDER CLAUSES 49 AND 50". The reference to 50 is a necessary addition to the words of the previous edition. Cl. 49 refers to outstanding work under cl. 48, as well as maintenance work, so any damage caused by the contractor in completing such work must be covered by his insurance under this clause. As to damage to the outstanding work itself see the last note.

5. APPROVAL OF INSURER AND TERMS OF REFERENCE "SHALL NOT BE UNREASONABLY WITHHELD" BY THE EMPLOYER . . . The contractor has no right to arbitrate before completion of the works so as to have refusal of approval reversed. His remedy is to do what is necessary to obtain the employer's approval, and to claim damages for any extra premium or other cost resulting from the employer's breach of contract in acting unreasonably.

Notes to Clause 22:

1. "ALL LOSSES". This duty on the contractor to indemnify the employer against losses principally covers damage to the employer's property (other than the works themselves—next note). At the same time it may have wider application. For example, if the contractor becomes entitled to extra payment under cl. 12 for artificial obstruction by property which the contractor damages and has to make good in order to complete the contract works, the contractor may be bound under this clause to pay back to the employer any payment recovered under cl. 12 for the cost of making good the damage to the property (but not cost received under cl. 12 for consequential delay to the works). It is proper that this clause should override cl. 12, because the contractor should be insured against this liability.

ee

2. CONTRACTOR'S LIABILITY FOR DAMAGE TO PROPERTY "OTHER THAN THE WORKS FOR WHICH INSURANCE IS REQUIRED UNDER CLAUSE 21". This new exception clears up a possible muddle between cls. 20 and 21 in the 4th edition of these Conditions.

ff

3. "SURFACE OR OTHER DAMAGE TO LAND BEING THE SITE". Refer to N. 5.

4. DIVISION OF LIABILITY UNDER THIS CLAUSE. A third party who suffers injury or damage may proceed against either or both employer or contractor, but under this clause if the employer is sued he has a right of indemnity from the contractor "*against all losses and claims for injuries or damage to any person or property whatsoever . . .*", except in the cases set out in para. (b). If the employer is sued in any case falling within para. (b) (i) to (iv) he must pay the compensation without any right of indemnity from the contractor.

(*ee*) See *C. J. Pearce & Co. Ltd.* v. *Hereford Corp.* (1968) 66 L.G.R. 647, 658.
(*ff*) *Pearce* case, above.

Unfortunately the position in the most important case of liability resulting partly from an act or neglect or breach of statutory duty of the employer and partly from the act or neglect of the contractor is expressed in an extremely confused way. Para. (a) implies that the contractor indemnifies the employer proportionately, by saying that the contractor's liability to indemnify the employer is *"reduced proportionately to the extent that the act or neglect of the Employer ... may have contributed to the said loss, injury or damage"*. Para. (b) on the other hand says that the contractor has no duty at all to indemnify the employer against *"any compensation or damages for or with respect to ... (v) injuries or damage ... resulting from any act or neglect or breach of statutory duty ... by the Engineer or the Employer"*, etc. The expected explanation that para. (v) only applies where the employer's act, etc., is the sole cause of the injury or damage is not open because of sub-cl. (2). However, the opening words of para. (b)—*"nothing herein contained shall be deemed to render the Contractor liable ... to indemnify the Employer"*—at least do not take away the statutory right to a contribution from the contractor in the case where the contractor is partly responsible for injury or damage (p. 95).

If it is the contractor who is sued by the third party, in any case falling under para. (b) the employer has the duty to indemnify him against any compensation awarded, subject under para. (2) to a proportionate reduction in the indemnity for any contributory act or neglect of the contractor.

There are other difficulties about the detailed drafting of this clause in respect of division of liability. Sub-cl. (1) (a) mentions *"loss"* but not *"breach of statutory duty"*, but the reverse is the case in para. (b) (v) and sub-cl. (2). As to recovery by the employer of losses *see* N. 1. The words *"to the extent neglect ... of the Employer ... contributed to"* injury or damage, etc., vary from the statutory words which allow a contribution in the case of damage jointly caused so far as may be "just and equitable having regard to the extent of that person's responsibility for the damage" (*see* p. 95 above). It is difficult to see that this whole elaborate clause as it now stands produces any improvement on the division of liability that would be made by statute if this clause were left out altogether.

Claims for injuries or damages will be brought by third parties against the employer or contractor or both in the courts, but disputes between the employer and contractor about apportionment of liability under this clause are subject to arbitration under cl. 66. It is likely that in appropriate cases the courts will refuse to enforce the arbitration clause and have the rights of all the parties decided by a court at one hearing (p. 404, N. 42).

5. CROPS. This para. (i) and a change to para. (ii) recognise certain difficulties about placing liability for damage to crops on the site on the contractor. That liability is now placed on the employer. Despite the fact

(gg) Apart from the contrast drawn in this clause itself, it has been held that liability for "any act or neglect" does not cover liability for breach of statutory duty, in *Hosking* v. *De Havilland Aircraft Co. Ltd.* [1949] 1 All E.R. 540, and see *Murfin* v. *United Steel Co. Ltd.* [1957] 1 W.L.R. 104 C.A. and *Smith* v. *South Wales Switchgear Ltd.* [1978] 1 All E.R. 18, 28, H.L.

According to the decision in *City of Manchester* v. *Fram Gerrard Ltd.* (1974) 6 B.L.R. words similar to *"Contractor or his sub-contractor servants or agents"* as in this cl. 22 (2) do not include sub-sub-contractors. The American expression "sub-contractors of any tier" is useful if wider cover is intended.

that the second sentence of sub-cl. (2) is not stated to apply to the case of damage to crops, it appears that the employer will have a statutory right of contribution (p. 95) from the contractor in any case where the damage is due to the contractor's negligence, e.g. in using greater working space than reasonably necessary. Unfortunately the position is not altogether clear; it might be argued against such a reading that it makes para. (i) unnecessary because the employer's liability is then covered by para. (iv), but on balance that does not seem to be fatal to the argument since there is other overlapping in paras. (i) to (v).

5(a). INTERFERENCE WITH EASEMENTS, ETC.—is discussed in ch. 15. Liability for interference will not normally be covered in fact by the contractor's public liability policy, which will be restricted to material damage.

6. UNAVOIDABLE DAMAGE. A large, but just, new limit on the contractor's liability. Normally a contractor can obtain public liability cover for *hh* accidental damage only, and damage which is the unavoidable result of constructing the works in accordance with the contract is not accidental. There is no reason why the contractor should bear the cost of such damage out of his own pocket.

This exception may be extremely important, e.g. for piling in a heavily built-up neighbourhood, damage by traffic to pavements where the work necessarily obstructs roads, etc. The exception by its wording applies not only where it was or should have been foreseen when the original design was being prepared that damage was unavoidable, but also where, for example, unexpected ground conditions render damage unavoidable from a design that would have been perfectly satisfactory in the ground conditions foreseen at the time of contract.

The relief from liability given to the contractor by this paragraph applies only to liability for "*damage*" and does not extend to injury to persons that is the unavoidable result of the construction of the works. As stated, it is difficult to obtain such cover in a public liability policy, although an employer's liability policy commonly is not restricted to accidental injury. Refer also to N. 8.

7. "THE ENGINEER". The honour afforded to the engineer of separate mention in this paragraph (but inconsistently not in sub-cl. 1 (a)) is otiose. The engineer is already included as an agent of the employer in making the design and supervising construction of the works:

> Employer held liable to indemnify a contractor under the paragraph of the 4th edition I.C.E. conditions similar to but narrower than this paragraph, but which does not specifically mention the engineer, against liability for subsidence of a shop neighbouring the works. The subsidence was due to a change by variation order in the line of a sewer. The contractor had carried out properly the close sheeting required by the engineer, who had given no instructions to shore the neighbouring building.

ii

(hh) The meaning of "accidental" in an insurance policy is discussed in *Marcel Beller Ltd.* v. *Hayden* [1978] 3 All E.R. 111. Stated that the "running of danger (by) . . . a conscious act of volition" prevents the mishap of which the danger was foreseen being accidental.
(ii) *Brighton* v. *A. R. Cleghorn & Co. Ltd.* Mocatta J., unreported, Norfolk Assizes, April 7th, 1967.

An employer who has to bear a loss or third party claim under any of these cls. 20–24 is likely to have to do so as a result of negligence by the engineer in design or in the course of supervision, and either he or his insurers may pursue the engineer for an indemnity (p. 98 on subrogation). The effect of the relaxation of the contractor's indemnity and insurance liabilities in this edition therefore is to transfer many risks from the contractor's insurance on to the engineer's indemnity insurance. Such professional indemnity cover for the engineer is essential, for his own protection and that of the employer and others to whom he may now be liable (p. 386 ff.).

8. The limitation "DURING THE CURRENCY OF THE CONTRACT" in the previous edition disappears from this paragraph. By that change and the new para. (iv) of this clause (N. 6) (and with cl. 24) the contractor is relieved from liability for claims due to negligence of the engineer in the original design of the works as well as in the design of variations after the contract has been made.

Notes to Clause 23:

1. "THROUGHOUT THE EXECUTION OF THE WORKS". These words suggest that the duty to maintain Public Liability insurance under this clause ends with substantial completion of the whole works. Nevertheless it is most important for a contractor to keep in force at all times a general Public Liability policy for his business, because this clause does not affect the rights of a third party (including the employer) to claim for damage to property or injury due to negligence by the contractor. However many years it may take works to fall down or cause harm from defects, the contractor is liable for the personal injury or damage to property caused if the failure or defects are due to his negligence (p. 430). For the contractor's continued liability to the employer for the defective work itself *see* p. 274, N. 2.

As to insurance of the works for damage due to maintenance operations, etc., *see* cl. 21.

2. INDEMNITY TO PRINCIPALS CLAUSE. The change in this paragraph has been made because insurance in joint names as required by the previous edition may create difficulty.

The clause now here required in the policy has the effect that the employer is entitled to an indemnity from the insurers where an injured party sues the employer direct instead of proceeding against the contractor, in any case in which the contractor would have been entitled to recover under his policy if he had been sued.

Notes to Clause 24:

1. "SAVE AND EXCEPT TO THE EXTENT THAT SUCH ACCIDENT OR INJURY RESULTS FROM OR IS CONTRIBUTED TO BY ANY ACT OR DEFAULT OF THE EMPLOYER". There is no mention here, as there is in cl. 22, of relief to the contractor from liability where there is a breach of statutory duty by the

---

(*ii*) *See* the opening of cls. 50 (1) and 62, and compare "*in the execution of the Contract*" in cl. 34 (1). Any other interpretation would mean that insurance cover could be put on and off by the contractor as he happened actually to execute work during the maintenance period. In practice the period of cover under the Public Liability policy taken out by the contractor for the works usually is stated to include the maintenance period.

employer (p. 94). Although cl. 22 (2) is worded widely enough to cover injury to the contractor's employees, clearly in such a case it is intended to be superseded by this clause, and the contractor is fully liable despite breach of statutory duty by the employer.

There is no equivalent in this clause of cl. 22 (2) by which the employer gives an indemnity to the contractor against liability contributed to by the employer's acts or neglects, but the contractor may recover from the employer under statute (p. 95).

2. COMPULSORY INSURANCE. The sub-cl. (2) of the equivalent of this clause in the 4th edition, requiring the contractor to insure, is now *kk* unnecessary because such insurance is compulsory by statute.

Notes to Clause 25:

1. CONTRACTOR TO PRODUCE "SATISFACTORY EVIDENCE THAT THERE IS IN FORCE THE INSURANCE". The evidence may be the original policy and premium receipt or, it is suggested, a photostatic copy. If the insurers will issue a certificate that the insurance required by these clauses is in effect, this may be accepted, but insurers are reluctant to issue certificates because all policies have detailed exclusions and conditions.

2. DEDUCTIONS. *See* p. 269. N. 33.

(*kk*) Employers' Liability (Compulsory Insurance) Act, 1969, requiring the contractor to insure against liability to his employees and sub-contractors to insure their own employees. The contractor's liability to employees of sub-contractors is ordinary third party liability which will be covered by his Public Liability policy under cl. 23.

CHAPTER 5

Conditions Clauses 26–57

26. (1) The Contractor shall save as provided in Clause 27 give all notices and pay all fees[1] required to be given or paid by any Act of Parliament or any Regulation or Bye-law of any local or other statutory authority in relation to the execution of the Works and by the rules and regulations of all public bodies and companies whose property or rights are or may be affected in any way by the Works. The Employer shall repay or allow to the Contractor all such sums as the Engineer shall certify to have been properly payable and paid by the Contractor in respect of such fees[2] and also all rates and taxes paid by the Contractor in respect of the Site or any part thereof or anything constructed or erected thereon or on any part thereof or any temporary structures situate elsewhere but used exclusively for the purposes of the Works or any structures used temporarily and exclusively for the purposes of the Works.[3]

CONTRACTOR TO CONFORM WITH STATUTES, ETC.

(2) The Contractor shall ascertain and[4] conform in all respects with the provisions of any general or local Act of Parliament and the Regulations and Bye-laws of any local or other statutory authority which may be applicable to the Works[5] and with such rules and regulations of public bodies and companies as aforesaid and shall keep the Employer indemnified[6] against all penalties and liability of every kind for breach of any such Act Regulation or Bye-law. Provided always that:

   (a) the Contractor shall not be required to indemnify the Employer against the consequences of any such breach which is the unavoidable result of complying with the Drawings Specification or instructions of the Engineer;[7]
   (b) if the Drawings Specification or instructions of the Engineer shall at any time be found not to be in conformity with any such Act Regulation or Bye-law the Engineer shall issue such instructions including the ordering of a variation under Clause 51 as may be necessary to ensure conformity with such Act Regulation or Bye-law;[7]
   (c) the Contractor shall not be responsible for obtaining any planning permission which may be necessary in respect of the Permanent Works or any Temporary Works specified[8] or designed by the Engineer and the Employer hereby warrants that all the said permissions have been or will in due time be obtained.[9]

1. "GIVE ALL NOTICES AND PAY ALL FEES". *See*, e.g., the Public Health Acts, 1936–61, and the appropriate building regulations, the Street Works Act, 1950 (cl. 27 below), the Highways Act, 1959 (e.g. Sec. 146, consent to temporary deposit of building materials on the highway). *See also* ch. 15 on

a   statutory controls of pollution and other nuisances and for planning control N. 9.

2. FEES PAYABLE BY RULES, ETC., OF "PUBLIC BODIES AND COMPANIES ... AFFECTED IN ANY WAY BY THE WORKS. THE EMPLOYER SHALL REPAY ... SUMS ... IN RESPECT OF SUCH FEES". The employer must repay such fees in respect of the contractor's own temporary works, as a result of the new definition of "*Works*" in cl. 1 (1) (l). By cl. 60 the fees are repaid in interim certificates, less retention.

3. EMPLOYER'S LIABILITY TO REPAY CONTRACTOR'S RATES AND TAXES. By cl. 1 (1) (l) "*Works*" means "*the Permanent Works together with the Temporary Works*". Cl. 1 (1) (n) defines "*Site*" to mean "*the lands and other places on under in or through which the Works are to be executed ...*". If that definition includes places where temporary works alone (not being executed there "*together with*" permanent works) are executed in fact at the choice of the contractor then this clause gives the contractor very wide relief against rates and taxes. An employer would not readily be able to gauge his potential liability at the time of tender. That unsatisfactory result supports restriction of the words "*are to be executed*" in cl. 1 (1) (n) to places in which the works are reasonably required to be executed in order to perform the contract. It is certainly implied in this clause that the relief against rates and taxes is restricted to lands or buildings, temporary structures and structures used temporarily that are reasonably required for the works; that the contractor may not save rates by occupying unnecessarily for the works places for which he has no other use.

4. The new words "ASCERTAIN AND" clarify but do not add to the effect of the previous wording. Despite these words, the contractor bears any additional burdens affecting the construction of the works that are due to legislation (or judge made law—p. 7) after the date of tender or contract, subject to the rest of this clause and to the possibility that the changed law may lead to one of the other grounds for extra listed in ch. 11, such as an increase in a price fluctuation index.

5. LEGISLATION—ILLEGALITY. Some relevant legislation is the Highways Act, 1971 (Secs. 31 and 32 on builders' skips on the highway, Sec. 36 providing penalties for building operations affecting public safety, and Sec. 37 on precautions to be taken by persons executing works in a street) and the Deposit of Poisonous Waste Act, 1972. *See also* N. 1.

A contract which contravenes a statute, bye-law or statutory regulation is illegal. The parties to such a contract do not necessarily commit a crime, but the contract is tainted in the eyes of the civil courts, which as a general rule will refuse to have anything to do with enforcing it:

> The courts have refused to enforce claims by contractors for the price of works done without the building licence required by war-time legislation, even where
b   > the employer did not wish to rely on the illegality as a defence.

(a) General reading: Riche "Municipal Law for the Engineer"; Wikeley "Municipal Engineering Law and Administration"; Heap "An Outline of Planning Law", 5th ed.; Whyte and Powell-Smith "The Building Regulations Explained and Illustrated", 4th ed.; Lewis "Administrative Law for the Construction Industry".

(b) *McIlvenna* v. *Ferris & Green* [1955] I.R. 318.

This rule normally applies even where the party wishing to enforce the contract did not realise when he made it that it was illegal—on the general principle that ignorance of the law is no excuse. But where only the use to be made of a building is contrary to bye-laws or involves planning consent, the contractor may enforce the contract if he did not know of the intended infringement or genuinely believed that the employer would get the necessary consent.

For the position of the contractor where the employer actually promises to obtain necessary authorisation and for planning permission *see* N. 9.

6. INDEMNITY. This indemnity is itself illegal (N. 5) and unenforceable if the employer is a party to the contractor breaking an Act or bye-law.

7. BREACH OF STATUTE, BYE-LAW OR REGULATION "WHICH IS THE UNAVOIDABLE RESULT OF COMPLYING WITH THE DRAWINGS SPECIFICATION OR INSTRUCTIONS OF THE ENGINEER". The previous edition did not deal specifically with this case. By this clause a duty is placed on the engineer to issue instructions, including the ordering of a variation, to ensure conformity with the applicable legislation. The contractor is entitled under cl. 7 to extra payment for delay in giving instructions or orders, and under cl. 52 for any variation order. The contractor is possibly also entitled to claim under cl. 13 for any delay or disruption caused by instructions the practical purpose of this new sub-clause, which is clearly intended to give protection to the contractor against losses due to drawings, etc. that do not conform to legislation, requires that the contractor should have that right of recovery and appears to imply the wider interpretation of cl. 13 discussed on p. 75.

The clause does not place any duty on the contractor to notify the engineer if and when the contractor becomes aware that the design involves an infringement. Therefore, if the engineer does not give instructions in time, it appears that as far as the employer is concerned the contractor may proceed with the works and refuse any indemnity to the employer under the specific terms of sub-cl. (a). However, it is legally unsafe as well as morally wrong for the contractor to do so because he may be liable directly for a penalty, and although by this clause he is not obliged to indemnify the employer, neither is the employer bound to indemnify him against a penalty. In addition, the contractor's right (if any) to recover under cl. 13 any extra (reasonable) cost due to the delay may be adversely affected.

8. "SPECIFIED OR DESIGNED BY THE ENGINEER". *See* p. 102, N. 11, for definition of "*design*". There is no discernible reason for "*specified or*" here, and not in cl. 8 (2).

9. "THE EMPLOYER HEREBY WARRANTS THAT ALL ... (PLANNING) PERMISSIONS HAVE BEEN OR WILL IN DUE TIME BE OBTAINED". If the employer does not obtain necessary planning permission the contractor may not be entitled to recover the contract payments as such (N. 5). Nevertheless it seems that he is entitled to damages from the employer for breach of this warranty equal to the payments lost and his loss of profits on work stopped,

(c) *Townsends Ltd.* v. *Cinema News* [1959] 1 W.L.R. 119 and *Best* v. *Glenville* [1960] 1 W.L.R. 1198.

provided he was not "guilty of culpable negligence" in failing to become
d   aware that the employer had no permission.

The new reference to planning permissions being obtained "*in due time*" covers the duty to obtain planning permission for a variation decided on during the works.

Planning permission is not necessary for the usual contractor's board if it is not more than 20 sq. feet on each road frontage for each contractor and
e   sub-contractor.

Public Utilities Street Works Act 1950—Definitions

27.   (1) For the purposes of this Clause:
   (a) the expression "the Act" shall mean and include the Public Utilities Street Works Act 1950[1] and any statutory modification or re-enactment thereof for the time being in force;
   (b) all other expressions common to the Act and to this Clause shall have the same meaning as that assigned to them by the Act.

Notifications by Employer to Contractor

(2) The Employer shall before the commencement of the Works notify the Contractor in writing:
   (a) whether the Works or any parts thereof (and if so which parts) are Emergency Works; and
   (b) which (if any) parts of the Works are to be carried out in Controlled Land or in a Prospectively Maintainable Highway.

If any duly authorised variation of the Works shall involve the execution thereof in a Street or in Controlled Land or in a Prospectively Maintainable Highway or are Emergency Works the Employer shall notify the Contractor in writing accordingly at the time such variation is ordered.

Service of Notices by Employer

(3) The Employer shall (subject to the obligations of the Contractor under sub-clause (4) of this Clause) serve all such notices as may from time to time whether before or during the course of or after completion of the Works be required to be served under the Act.

Notices by Contractor to Employer

(4) The Contractor shall in relation to any part of the Works (other than Emergency Works) and subject to the compliance by the Employer with sub-clause (2) of this Clause give not less than 21 days' notice in writing to the Employer before:
   (a) commencing any part of the Works in a Street (as defined by Sections 1 (3) and 38 (1) of the Act); or

(d) *Strongman* (1945) v. *Sincock* [1955] 2 Q.B. 525, 536. In that case the employer, who was an architect, broke an oral promise made to the builder that he would obtain the licence then necessary under Defence Regulations. The builder failed to recover payment under the building contract, as it was illegal because the work was done without licence, but he was awarded compensation equal to the payment, for breach by the employer of his promise. Although the judgments in this case are not clear, it seems that such a promise is enforceable even though contained in and not made outside of the construction contract.
(e) Town and Country Planning (Control of Advertisements) Regulations 1969, Reg. 12(S.I. 1969 No. 1532).

(b) commencing any part of the Works in Controlled Land or in a Prospectively Maintainable Highway; or

(c) commencing in a Street or in Controlled Land or in a Prospectively Maintainable Highway any part of the Works which is likely to affect the apparatus of any Owning Undertaker (within the meaning of Section 26 of the Act).

Such notice shall state the date on which and the place at which the Contractor intends to commence the execution of the work referred to therein.

FAILURE TO COMMENCE STREET WORKS

(5) If the Contractor having given any such notice as is required by sub-clause (4) of this Clause shall not commence the part of the Works to which such notice relates within 2 months after the date when such notice is given such notice shall be treated as invalid and compliance with the said sub-clause (4) shall be requisite as if such notice had not been given.

DELAYS ATTRIBUTABLE TO VARIATIONS

(6) In the event of such a variation of the Works[2] as is referred to in sub-clause (2) of this Clause being ordered by or on behalf of the Employer and resulting in delay in the execution of the Works by reason of the necessity of compliance by the Contractor with sub-clause (4) of this Clause the Engineer shall take such delay into account in determining any extension of time to which the Contractor is entitled under Clause 44 and the Contractor shall subject to Clause 52 be paid in accordance with Clause 60 such additional cost as the Engineer shall consider to have been reasonably attributable to such delay.[3]

CONTRACTOR TO COMPLY WITH OTHER OBLIGATIONS OF ACT

(7) Except as otherwise provided by this Clause where in relation to the carrying out of the Works the Act imposes any requirements or obligations upon the Employer the Contractor shall subject to Clause 49 (5) comply with such requirements and obligations and shall (subject as aforesaid) indemnify the Employer against any liability which the Employer may incur in consequence of any failure to comply with the said requirements and obligations.

1. PUBLIC UTILITIES STREET WORKS ACT 1950. The bones of this complicated Act are:

(a) The undertaker—that is, an employer with statutory power to place, repair, etc., apparatus in a street—must give notice with a plan and section (or a description may be accepted) before doing major street works (Sec. 3). But the street works code in the Act does not apply to railway works or work for road purposes (Sec. 1 (1) and (2)), and notice is not necessary for maintenance or repair work, specified work on service pipes or lines or for temporary works, and in the case of emergency works a plan and section must be supplied only as soon as reasonably practicable (Sec. 3 (2) and (3)).

The notice is to be to the street authority or manager and, where their property is affected, to the transport, bridge or sewer authorities (Sec. 2).

Street is defined as any length of a highway, road, lane, footway, alley or passage, any square or court, and any length of land laid out as a way,

_f_

(f) Reading: T. U. Wilson and I. V. Paterson "The Public Utilities Street Works Act 1950".

whether formed as a way or not, and whether a thoroughfare or not (Sec. 1). For definitions of the other terms in this clause of the general conditions *see* below and Sec. 39 (1) of the Act.

(*b*) Agreement must be reached between these interested authorities and the undertaker before the works are started. Disputes to be settled by arbitration (Secs. 4 and 5).

(*c*) Sec. 6 deals with the further notices to be given before the work is actually begun. The authorities must be given seven days' notice (three days in the case of works relating to service pipes or lines or overhead telegraphic lines). In the case of emergency work notice and the reason for any delay in giving it must be served as soon as reasonably practicable. The notice lapses and a fresh notice must be given if the work is not substantially begun within two months, unless the authorities agree to extend the time.

Other undertakers whose apparatus is likely to be affected by the works (the "Owning Undertakers" referred to in (4) (c) of this clause) must also generally be given three days' notice before work is started (Sec. 26 (1)).

(*d*) The work is to be done with all reasonable despatch. No greater width or length of the street is to be open or broken up and there is to be no greater obstruction of traffic or normal use of controlled land ((*l*) below) than is reasonably necessary (Secs. 8 and 11 (2)).

(*e*) Any transport authority affected by the works is entitled to supervise the work (Sec. 7 (1)), or may elect to do part of the works at the undertaker's cost in certain cases, and may recover the cost of stabilising a bridge, etc., necessary because of the undertaker's work (Sec. 10). A sewer authority may require the undertaker to do work to prevent interruption of drainage, and if the works involve breaking up or opening a public sewer the sewer authority is entitled to supervise that work or to elect to do it at the undertaker's cost (Sec. 12).

(*f*) For reinstatement *see* cl. 49 (5), p. 166 below.

(*g*) The undertaker is liable for lighting (and *see* Sec. 11 (1)), fencing and guarding the works and for signalling and controlling traffic (Secs. 7 (3) (b) and 8).

(*h*) By the Highways Act, 1959, Sec. 63 (repealing Sec. 27 of this Act), if use of a highway is prohibited or restricted because of the works so that traffic has to use as an alternative a highway of lower classification—e.g. to go from a trunk to a class 1—the person doing the works is liable to pay to the appropriate authority the cost of strengthening or making good any damage to the alternative road by diverted traffic.

(*i*) The undertaker is liable for damage to the property of any street, bridge or transport authority due to the execution of the works or by explosion, discharge of gas, etc. (Secs. 18 and 19).

(*j*) By the Highways Act, 1959, Secs. 136–138 (repealing Sec. 28 of this Act), to avoid too frequent openings of the highway undertakers may not do street works within 12 months of major works by the highway authority, of which they are given three months' notice, subject to emergency work and certain other exceptions. In the London Traffic Area the Minister of Transport has power to settle a scheme so that road maintenance, etc., and undertaker's work may, as far as possible, be done at the same time, and undertakers may not do work within 12 months of maintenance work in the scheme without the consent of the Minister.

(*g*) Highways Act, 1959, Sec. 138, is amended by Sec. 18 of the Road Traffic and Roads Improvement Act, 1960.

(*k*) Sec. 26 regulates the liability of an undertaker doing work for interference, damage to the apparatus, etc., of other undertakers.

(*l*) A street authority may authorise undertakers to carry out future work in controlled land, in which case the undertakers must give notice as for works in a street and also to the occupier of the land (First Schedule). The authority may also, when given notice of works, require them to be done in controlled land instead of in the street itself (Sec. 5).

Controlled land is in effect land bordering a street which is a highway maintainable by the public or prospectively a maintainable highway held or intended to be taken over for road purposes, and which land the street authority already owns or in which it is otherwise in a position to authorise the works (First Schedule, para. 1). The object of these powers is to enable the authority to have apparatus placed in a suitable position having regard to what will be the eventual layout of the street.

A street is prospectively a maintainable highway when it is registered by the local authority in the register of local land charges as likely to become maintainable.

(*m*) The Act in Part II provides a code regulating the position where undertaker's apparatus is affected by road, bridge or transport works.

The Act is amended for pipelines by the Pipelines Act, 1962.

The scheme in this clause is to have the employer serve the initial notice referred to in (*a*) above. The contractor must then give notice to the employer (for service *see* cl. 68 below) 21 days before starting any work within the Act, unless it is emergency work, so that the employer may give notice under (*c*). The contractor is entitled to be notified by the employer if work is emergency work or is to be done in controlled land or in a prospectively maintainable highway, so that he knows whether to give this notice—in other cases the fact that the works are street works will be obvious. In the case of variations the contractor is entitled to an extension of time and additional costs—*see* cl. 12, N. 13—for delay caused by having to give this 21 days' notice.

The contractor is bound to indemnify the employer (*see* p. 95) against all obligations on the undertaker under the Act "*in relation to the carrying out of the Works*". This covers (*d*), (*e*), (*g*), (*i*) and (*k*) above. Liability under the last two headings and for the cost of stabilising a bridge damaged by the works—(*e*)—is covered by insurance under cl. 23.

Liability under (*h*) is not shifted to the employer under this clause, and the contractor may have to allow for it in his tender. Alternatively, cl. 30 may be altered to cover it, since it is difficult to estimate in advance.

2. References to "THE WORKS" now include temporary works by the new definition in cl. 1 (1) (*l*).

3. The wording about EXTENSION OF TIME and COSTS for the contractor has been changed to fit the new cls. 44 (extension of time), 52 (4) (notice of money claims) and 60 (inclusion in interim certificates and final payment certificate, subject to retention).

PATENT RIGHTS

28. (1) The Contractor shall save harmless and indemnify[1] the Employer from and against all claims and proceedings for or on account of infringement of any patent rights design trade-mark or name[2] or other protected rights in respect of any Constructional Plant machine work or material used for or in connection with the Works[3] and from and against all claims demands proceedings damages costs charges and expenses whatsoever in respect thereof or in relation thereto.

ROYALTIES

(2) Except where otherwise specified the Contractor shall pay all tonnage and other royalties rent and other payments or compensation (if any) for getting stone sand gravel clay or other materials required for the Works.

1. INDEMNITY. *See* p. 95.

2. "PATENT RIGHTS DESIGN TRADE-MARK OR NAME". For illegality *see* cl. 13, footnote (*h'*).

3. "WORKS" now includes temporary works by the definition in cl. 1 (1') (l) (p. 29).

INTERFERENCE WITH TRAFFIC AND ADJOINING PROPERTIES

29. (1) All operations necessary for the execution of the Works[1] shall so far as compliance with the requirements of the Contract permits be carried on so as not to interfere unnecessarily or improperly with the public convenience or the access to or use or occupation of public or private roads and foot-paths or to or of properties whether in the possession of the Employer or of any other person and the Contractor shall save harmless and indemnify the Employer in respect of all claims demands proceedings damages costs charges and expenses whatsoever arising out of or in relation to any such matters.[2]

NOISE AND DISTURBANCE

(2)[3] All work shall be carried out without unreasonable noise and disturbance. The Contractor shall indemnify the Employer from and against any liability for damages on account of noise or other disturbance created while or in carrying out the work and from and against all claims demands proceedings damages costs charges and expenses whatsoever in regard or in relation to such liability.

1. "WORKS" now includes all temporary works by the definition in cl. 1 (1) (l).

2. INTERFERENCE WITH THE PUBLIC, ETC. *See* p. 420. This indemnity is already covered by cl. 22.

3. SUB-CLAUSE (2) reproduces the last two sentences of cl. 46 of the 4th edition, but applying the restriction to all work and not merely work at night as formerly.

(*h*) For a general outline of patent law see P. Meinhardt "Inventions, Patents and Monopoly", 2nd ed.

Avoidance of Damage to Highways, etc.

30. (1) The Contractor shall use every reasonable means to prevent any of the highways or bridges communicating with or on the routes to the Site from being subjected to extraordinary traffic within the meaning of the Highways Act 1959 or in Scotland the Road Traffic Act 1930[1] or any statutory modification or re-enactment thereof by any traffic of the Contractor or any of his sub-contractors and in particular shall select routes and use vehicles and restrict and distribute loads so that any such extraordinary traffic as will inevitably arise from the moving of Constructional Plant and materials or manufactured or fabricated articles from and to the Site shall be limited as far as reasonably possible and so that no unnecessary damage or injury may be occasioned to such highways and bridges.

Transport of Constructional Plant

(2) Save insofar as the Contract otherwise provides[2] the Contractor shall be responsible for and shall pay the cost of strengthening any bridges or altering or improving any highway communicating with the Site[3] to facilitate the movement of Constructional Plant equipment or Temporary Works required in the execution of the Works and the Contractor shall indemnify and keep indemnified the Employer against all claims for damage to any highway or bridge communicating with the Site caused by such movement[4] including such claims as may be made by any competent authority directly against the Employer[5] pursuant to any Act of Parliament or other Statutory Instrument and shall negotiate and pay all claims arising solely out of such damage.[6]

Transport of Materials

(3) If notwithstanding sub-clause (1)[7] of this Clause any damage shall occur to any bridge or highway communicating with the Site arising from the transport of materials or manufactured or fabricated articles in the execution of the Works[8] the Contractor shall notify the Engineer as soon as he becomes aware of such damage or as soon as he receives any claim from the authority entitled to make such claim. Where under any Act of Parliament or other Statutory Instrument the haulier of such materials or manufactured or fabricated articles is required to indemnify the highway authority against damage the Employer shall not be liable for any costs charges or expenses in respect thereof or in relation thereto. In other cases the Employer shall negotiate the settlement of and pay all sums due in respect of such claim and shall indemnify the Contractor in respect thereof and in respect of all claims demands proceedings damages costs charges and expenses in relation thereto. Provided always that if and so far as any such claim or part thereof shall in the opinion of the Engineer be due to any failure on the part of the Contractor to observe and perform his obligations under sub-clause (1) of this Clause then the amount certified by the Engineer to be due to such failure shall be paid by the Contractor to the Employer or deducted from any sum due or which may become due to the Contractor.[9]

1. Extraordinary traffic. Sec. 62 of the Highways Act, 1959 applies, briefly, where it appears to a highway authority that extraordinary expenses, having regard to the average expense of repairing the highway or other similar highways in the neighbourhood, have been or will be incurred by the authority in repairs to a highway because of damage caused by excessive weight on it or other extraordinary traffic. The highway authority may then recover from any person "by or in consequence of whose order"

the traffic has been run so much of the expenses as may be proved to the
court to have been, or to be likely to be, incurred as a result of damage
arising from the extraordinary traffic. If liability is admitted before the
traffic starts, the authority may agree a payment to cover it in advance or a
figure may be fixed in advance by arbitration. There is a time limit for
proceedings for these expenses of 12 months from the time the damage was
done or six months from the completion of any building contract or work
extending over a long period which produced the traffic.

Whether or not traffic is extraordinary is a question of fact and the
definition is necessarily not very helpful—"traffic is extraordinary which in
weight, character or volume substantially increases the burden placed by
ordinary traffic on the highway so as to cause damage and expense beyond
what is reasonable". But it follows that a road authority must have regard to
modern traffic requirements and must make reasonable provision for
ordinary motor traffic.

2. CONTRACTOR RESPONSIBLE "SAVE INSOFAR AS THE CONTRACT
OTHERWISE PROVIDES", e.g. in the specification or the special conditions
provided for in cl. 72—the general conditions do not so provide.

3. "COST OF STRENGTHENING ANY BRIDGES OR ALTERING OR IMPROVING
ANY HIGHWAY". The 4th edition required the contractor in some
circumstances to carry out works of protection or strengthening at the cost
of the employer. That requirement created certain difficulties, particularly
because the contractor might not be allowed by a public authority
responsible for the highway or bridge to carry out works directly. This
clause now deals only with the cost of strengthening, which is shifted on to
the contractor in the cases explained in the next note.

A reference as in sub-cl. (1) to highways or bridges "*on the routes to the
Site*" additionally to those "*communicating with ... the Site*", is missing
here.

4. "CONSTRUCTIONAL PLANT EQUIPMENT OR TEMPORARY WORKS REQUIRED
IN THE EXECUTION OF THE WORKS". SCHEME OF THIS CLAUSE. The scheme of
this Clause is:

(*a*) By this sub-cl. (2) the contractor is liable for the cost of strengthening
any bridge or altering or improving any highway and for extraordinary
traffic claims caused by passage of "*Constructional Plant equipment or
Temporary Works*" (even if the temporary works are designed by the
engineer and however much care the contractor may take to avoid damage).
It is reasonably clear from the context and sub-cl. (3) that equipment means
the contractor's equipment, and not equipment for installation in the
permanent works (although this interpretation involves a duplication with
the reference to "*Constructional Plant*" as defined in cl. 1 (1) (o)).

(*b*) Insofar as the contractor takes reasonable care to avoid
extraordinary traffic it is the employer who is liable to pay and indemnify
the contractor against claims in respect of "*materials or manufactured or
fabricated articles*", by implication from sub-cl. (2) only if they are for the
permanent works (see in particular the definition in cl. 1 (1) (o) of the
"*Constructional Plant*" referred to in sub-cl. (2)), but the drafting is bad—
N. 8.

(*i*) *Hill* v. *Thomas* [1893] 2 Q.B. 333.

(*c*) Unless the haulier is liable, the contractor is liable for extraordinary traffic even if caused by transport of materials, etc., for the permanent work, insofar as the claim is due to the contractor's failure to use every reasonable means to prevent extraordinary traffic.

5. "INCLUDING SUCH CLAIMS AS MAY BE MADE . . . DIRECTLY AGAINST THE EMPLOYER". A gap in the previous edition is closed.

6. "ARISING SOLELY OUT OF SUCH DAMAGE". *See* p. 99, N. 5.

7. "IF NOTWITHSTANDING SUB-CLAUSE (1)". Inelegant drafting, which means "*notwithstanding compliance by the Contractor with sub-clause* (1)", and in any case duplicates the last five lines of this sub-clause.

8. "MATERIALS OR MANUFACTURED OR FABRICATED ARTICLES IN THE EXECUTION OF THE WORKS". This phrase appears to be intended to mean materials or articles for the permanent works, but the words (with the definition of "*Works*" in cl. 1 (1) (l)) are wide enough to cover extraordinary traffic arising out of transport of manufactured articles or materials for temporary works. It is to be hoped that despite the drafting the courts will give the phrase the intended meaning so as to give effect to the contractor's liability under sub-cl. (2). Reference to materials, articles, etc., for incorporation in the permanent works would have made the meaning clear.

9. DEDUCTION BY THE EMPLOYER. *See* N. 33, p. 269.

FACILITIES FOR OTHER CONTRACTORS

31. (1) The Contractor shall in accordance with the requirements of the Engineer afford all reasonable facilities for any other contractors employed by the Employer and their workmen and for the workmen of the Employer and of any other properly authorised authorities or statutory bodies who may be employed in the execution on or near the Site of any work not in the Contract or of any contract which the Employer may enter into in connection with or ancillary to the Works.[1]

DELAY AND EXTRA COST

(2) If compliance with sub-clause (1) of this Clause shall involve the Contractor in delay or cost beyond that reasonably to be foreseen by an experienced contractor[2] at the time of tender then the Engineer shall take such delay into account in determining any extension of time to which the Contractor is entitled under Clause 44 and the Contractor shall subject to Clause 52 (4) be paid in accordance with Clause 60 the amount of such cost as may be reasonable.[3]

1. PAYMENT FOR FACILITIES FOR OTHER CONTRACTORS AND AUTHORITIES. One object of this clause is to make it clear that the contractor is not entitled to exclusive possession of the site. "*afford . . . facilities*" indicates allowing other contractors to use, e.g., haul roads built by the contractor for his own purpose, not building roads or supplying equipment specially for them.

It seems clear also that facilities which would cause serious disruption to the contractor's programme are not "*reasonable*", provided the programme is itself reasonable in the light of the work to be done by other contractors, etc., as disclosed in the contract documents.

If the contractor is ordered to afford facilities beyond what is reasonable or to provide special facilities, despite sub-cl. (2) (next note) he is entitled to refuse absolutely to do so or agree only if his charge is accepted in advance. unless the facilities fall within the definition of variation in cl. 51 as extra work or a change in timing, etc. Alternatively he may provide the facilities and claim for extra payment under cl. 51 or sub-cl. (2), or under cl. 40 claim a suspension and expenses for delay.

In many cases it should be possible for the engineer to detail in the tender documents the facilities that will be required, so as to allow the contractor to price them and at least minimise (N. 2) the possibility of claims.

Cl. 19 deals with the employer's duties in respect of safety and the orderly state of the site where direct contractors, workmen or authorities carry out work on the site under this clause.

The run of the words at the end of this sub-clause does not clearly produce the sensible result that the contractor is bound to provide reasonable facilities for others "*employed in the execution ... of any work not in the Contract*" only if their work is "*in connection with or ancillary to the Works*".

If the contractor does not afford facilities in accordance with this sub-clause he is in breach of contract and liable to the employer. The extent to which the liability will include reimbursement of compensation payable by the employer to the others deprived of the facilities, for their extra work or disruption, will be decided by the ordinary tests for remoteness of damages (p. 428), so that the more information the contractor is given at the time of tender about the employer's arrangements with other contractors and authorities the stronger any such later claim will be. If the employer is delayed in using the works because, although they themselves are finished. the lack of facilities causes delay to ancillary works without which they cannot be used effectively, the employer's losses are outside the liquidated damages cl. 47 and therefore he may be entitled to recover general damages from the contractor for loss of use, depending again on the ordinary tests.

2. UNFORESEEABLE COST OR DELAY. As pointed out in the last note. irrespective of this right to extra payment the contractor is not bound at all to afford unreasonable facilities for other contractors or authorities.

This sub-clause entitles the contractor to extra payment for cost due to delay by statutory undertakers which makes it necessary for him to extend unreasonably or unforeseeably the time at which he has to afford facilities to them. That is, it will do so if employers restrain themselves from adding the special clauses so often used in the past in an unfair effort to put these risks on the contractor (*see* p. 438 on this aspect of "Tendermanship"). Under the words used the contractor has a right to unforeseen cost even if it is the result of affording reasonable and foreseeable facilities—p. 75, N. 6.

For the definition of "*cost*" *see* p. 31, N. 18.

3. DAMAGE, ETC., BY OTHER CONTRACTORS AND AUTHORITIES. Damage to temporary or permanent works by the other contractors or authorities on site is covered by the contractor's insurance under cl. 21, except that

damage due to any use or occupation of the permanent works themselves by other contractors or authorities is an excepted risk under cl. 20 (3). Damage to other property or injury to persons by such parties is the responsibility of the employer under cl. 22 (2).

FOSSILS, ETC.

32. All fossils coins articles of value or antiquity and structures or other remains or things of geological or archaeological interest discovered on the Site[1] shall as between the Employer and the Contractor be deemed to be the absolute property of the Employer[2] and the Contractor shall take reasonable precautions to prevent his workmen or any other persons from removing or damaging any such article or thing and shall immediately upon discovery thereof and before removal acquaint the Engineer of such discovery and carry out at the expense of the Employer[3] the Engineer's orders as to the disposal of the same.

1. "ON THE SITE". For definition *see* cl. 1 (1) (n).

2. ARTICLES FOUND. It is a criminal offence to hide the discovery of gold or silver, coin, plate or bullion hidden (not abandoned altogether or lost) in the earth or any other secret place the owner of which is unknown—which belong to the Crown as treasure trove.

In the absence of a clause of this kind the employer is entitled to everything found under or fixed in any way to his land which has been lost or abandoned by the owner, but it is not clear who, as between the owner of land or buildings and the finder, has the right to articles, etc., found lying on the surface.

3. "AT THE EXPENSE OF THE EMPLOYER". This phrase implies that the employer pays the contractor's costs plus a reasonable profit. The contractor may also have a remedy under cls. 12 or 40, or a right to extension of time under cl. 44, for any interference by the fossils, etc., with the works.

CLEARANCE OF SITE ON COMPLETION

33. On the completion of the Works the Contractor shall clear away and remove from the Site all Constructional Plant surplus material rubbish and Temporary Works of every kind and leave the whole of the Site and Permanent Works clean and in a workmanlike condition to the satisfaction of the Engineer.

RATES OF WAGES/HOURS AND CONDITIONS OF LABOUR

34. (1) The Contractor shall in the execution of the Contract observe and fulfil the obligations upon contractors specified in the Fair Wages Resolution passed

(j) In *City of London Corporation* v. *Appleyard* [1963] 2 All E.R. 834 it was held that a safe found built into an old wall and the contents of the safe—a wooden box containing £5,728 in current notes—were within a clause similar to cl. 32, which referred to "Every relic or article of antiquity, rarity or value." See also *Moffatt* v. *Kazana* [1968] 3 All E.R. 271.

by the House of Commons on the 14 October 1946[1] of which the following is an extract:

EXTRACT FROM FAIR WAGES RESOLUTION

"1 (a)   The contractor shall pay rates of wages and observe hours and conditions of labour not less favourable than those established for the trade or industry in the district where the work is carried out by machinery of negotiation or arbitration to which the parties are organisations of employers and trade unions representative respectively of substantial proportions of the employers and workers engaged in the trade or industry in the district.

" (b)   In the absence of any rates of wages, hours or conditions of labour so established the contractor shall pay rates of wages and observe hours and conditions of labour which are not less favourable than the general level of wages, hours and conditions observed by other employers whose general circumstances in the trade or industry in which the contractor is engaged are similar.

"2   The contractor shall in respect of all persons employed by him (whether in execution of the contract or otherwise) in every factory workshop or place occupied or used by him for the execution of the contract comply with the general conditions required by this Resolution.

"3   In the event of any question arising as to whether the requirements of this Resolution are being observed, the question shall, if not otherwise disposed of, be referred by the Minister of Labour and National Service to an independent Tribunal for decision.

"4   The contractor shall recognise the freedom of his workpeople to be members of Trade Unions.

"5   The contractor shall at all times during the continuance of a contract display, for the information of his workpeople, in every factory, workshop or place occupied or used by him for the execution of the contract a copy of this Resolution.

"6   The contractor shall be responsible for the observance of this Resolution by sub-contractors employed in the execution of the contract."

CIVIL ENGINEERING CONSTRUCTION CONCILIATION BOARD

(2) The wages hours and conditions of employment above referred to shall be those prescribed for the time being by the Civil Engineering Construction Conciliation Board for Great Britain save that the rates of wages payable to any class of labour in respect of which the said Board does not prescribe a rate shall be governed by the provisions of sub-clause (1) of this Clause.

1. FAIR WAGES RESOLUTION. Employees of the contractor, of course, cannot sue him directly under the contract for breaking this clause, since they are not parties to the contract (p. 221). The employer will have a right to nominal damages and may have a right of forfeiture under cl. 63 (1) (d) or in an exceptional case to end the contract under the general law (p. 425). Most important, the contractor will not be entitled to an extension of time for completing, or to plead frustration of the contract (cl. 64), because of a strike of his, or a sub-contractor's employees which can be proved to be due to failure to carry out his duties under this clause.

k

(*k*) In *Kelly* v. *Winnipeg City* (1908) 18 Man.L.R. 269; 9 W.L.R. 310 Can. it was held that the employers were not entitled to keep back out of an interim certificate the amount of the wages which the contractors had underpaid, in breach of a clause similar to this. There is no right under these conditions to withhold an interim certificate for breach of this clause.

The Fair Wages Resolution requires disputes about observance of the Resolution to be referred by the Minister of Labour (now Secretary of State for Employment) to an independent tribunal.

The form of tender includes a certificate by the contractor that he has complied with the Resolution for the three months immediately preceding the date of this tender. The effect of this certificate is discussed on p. 21.

RETURNS OF LABOUR AND PLANT

35. The Contractor shall if required by the Engineer deliver to the Engineer or at his office a return in such form and at such intervals as the Engineer may prescribe showing in detail the numbers of the several classes of labour from time to time employed by the Contractor on the Site and such information respecting Constructional Plant as the Engineer may require.[1] The Contractor shall require his sub-contractors to observe the provisions of this Clause.[2]

1. IMPORTANCE OF LABOUR RETURNS. For the importance of requiring returns, in case the information is necessary to check claims, refer to p. 442 ff.

2. SUB-CONTRACTOR'S RETURNS. This specific reference to sub-contractors is new. The words *"his sub-contractors"* do not imply that nominated sub-contractors are excluded. The main contractor must be careful to incorporate this clause in every sub-contract.

QUALITY OF MATERIALS AND WORKMANSHIP AND TESTS

36. (1) All materials and workmanship shall be of the respective kinds described in the Contract and in accordance with the Engineer's instructions[1,2] and shall be subjected from time to time to such tests as the Engineer may direct[2] at the place of manufacture or fabrication or on the Site or such other place or places as may be specified in the Contract.[3] The Contractor shall provide such assistance instruments machines labour and materials as are normally required for examining measuring and testing any work and the quality weight or quantity of any materials used and shall supply samples of materials before incorporation in the Works for testing as may be selected and required by the Engineer.

COST OF SAMPLES

(2) All samples shall be supplied by the Contractor at his own cost if the supply thereof is clearly intended by or provided for in the Contract but if not then at the cost of the Employer.[4]

COST OF TESTS

(3) The cost of making any test shall be borne by the Contractor if such test is clearly intended by or provided for in the Contract and (in the cases only of a test under load or of a test to ascertain whether the design of any finished or partially finished work is appropriate for the purposes which it was intended to fulfil) is particularised in the Specification or Bill of Quantities in sufficient detail

(*l*) For a discussion of the duties of the contractor under the Fair Wages Resolution see Sir. D. Walker-Smith and H. A. Close "The Standard Forms of Building Contract" at pp. 65–69.

to enable the Contractor to have priced or allowed for the same in his Tender. If any test is ordered by the Engineer which is either:

(a) not so intended by or provided for; or

(b) (in the cases above mentioned) is not so particularised;

then the cost of such test shall be borne by the Contractor if the test shows the workmanship or materials not to be in accordance with the provisions of the Contract or the Engineer's instructions but otherwise by the Employer.[5.6]

1. "DESCRIBED IN THE CONTRACT AND IN ACCORDANCE WITH THE ENGINEER'S INSTRUCTIONS". *See* cl. 13.

If the engineer instructs the contractor that work or material is in future to equal the results of tests or a sample which are in fact below what is specified in the contract, the contractor if feasible should protect himself by confirming the instruction as a variation—p. 127, N. 2.

2. DELAY BY THE ENGINEER IN DIRECTING TESTS AND DELAY AND DISRUPTION DUE TO TESTS. For the contractor's remedies *see* ch. 12.

3. TESTS "AT . . . SUCH OTHER PLACE OR PLACES AS MAY BE SPECIFIED IN THE CONTRACT". This addition at the end of the first sentence of sub-cl. (1), coupled with deletion of paragraph (c) in sub-cl. (4) of the previous edition, has a number of effects:

(*a*) The engineer may direct a test at a place other than the place of manufacture or fabrication or on the site (e.g. at a commercial testing laboratory), provided not merely the test but also the other place is specified in the contract (normally in the specification).

(*b*) Since the place at which such a test is to be carried out is to be specified in the contract, the contractor has as much data to enable him to estimate for it as he has for a test on site or at the place of manufacture. Therefore the contractor now is required to carry out the test without extra payment, although the previous edition entitled him to extra where the test showed that the workmanship and materials were in accordance with the contract. Where unusual tests may or may not be found necessary, the obvious procedure in the interests of the employer (so that he does not pay in the tender rates for tests which are not ordered), and in fairness to the contractor, is to include a provisional sum for the tests.

(*c*) The contractor is not bound under cl. 37 to obtain for the engineer access to any such place where a test is to be carried out in accordance with this addition. The contractor should be required in the specification of the test to obtain access for the engineer, or the engineer should confirm access with the intended tester before nominating his testing place in the contract.

Cl. 50 also refers to tests.

4. SAMPLES, TESTS, AT THE COST OF THE EMPLOYER. *See* p. 31, N. 18 and N. 2 above.

5. COST OF TEST BORNE BY THE CONTRACTOR "IF THE TEST SHOWS THE WORKMANSHIP OR MATERIALS NOT TO BE IN ACCORDANCE WITH . . . THE CONTRACT", ETC. There may be practical difficulties in applying this clause, where, for example, tests of many expansion joints show that one only is faulty, or several tests over a long length of sewer show that only a small section is faulty. It is suggested that this clause must be applied

separately to each individual test and the part of the works it was designed to test.

Particularly where a test is unsuccessful, when the rectification work is carried out the engineer will normally order a further test of the remedied work. Since such a test should show the work to be in accordance with the contract, it is important that repeat tests are provided for initially in the specification so that under this clause the cost is always borne by the contractor.

See also the reference to tests in cl. 50, p. 168, N. 2.

6. EXCAVATIONS AND EMPLOYER'S MATERIALS. If necessary, a clause should be added dealing with materials on the site.

The ordinary position is that the contractor is not entitled to use existing materials in or on the site, which in law belong to the employer. By note 3 to class D on demolition and site clearance in the new standard method of measurement "Item descriptions for work from which the materials arising remain the property of the Employer shall so state". Where the method applies under cl. 57 of these Conditions it seems that failure to so state implies that the ordinary legal position is being changed so that the materials referred to pass into the ownership of the contractor (*see* generally p. 213 on the method). On that basis the engineer is not entitled to deduct a credit for such materials if used in the works, and the contractor may sell the materials or use them elsewhere. *See also* cl. 33.

There are serious dangers in the employer supplying materials: the contractor will be entitled to an extension of time and possibly to suspension of the works or damages if there is any delay by the employer in making them available (p. 365), and if they are faulty the contractor will be entitled to a variation order for any extra work or compensation for any other expense the fault throws on him. Because the employer in this way normally will be held to warrant by implication that materials supplied by him will be suitable for their intended use on the works, the practice is growing of adding a special term by which the contractor is bound to inspect such materials with the resident engineer before taking them over, and stating that the contractor is deemed then to accept the materials and to have no remedy for any defects not notified at the time of the inspection. Any attempt to deprive the contractor of a remedy even for latent defects that could not reasonably be discovered on an inspection may not be effective (p. 432). The employer may have an adequate remedy against the supplier to recover any payments to the contractor and other losses due to defective goods or late supply, particularly if the supplier was or should have been aware of the purpose for which the goods were required by the employer (p. 428).

m

ACCESS TO SITE

37.   The Engineer and any person authorised by him shall at all times have access to the Works and to the Site and to all workshops and places where work is being prepared or whence materials manufactured articles and machinery are being obtained for the Works and the Contractor shall afford every facility for and every assistance in or in obtaining the right to such access.

(m) *MacIntosh* v. *Midland Counties Ry*. (1845) 14 M. & W. 548, and see *W. H. Gaze & Sons Ltd.* v. *Corporation of Port Talbot* (1929) 93 J.P. 89.

ACCESS FOR TESTING: *See* p. 124, N. 3 (*c*).

EXAMINATION OF WORK BEFORE COVERING UP

38. (1) No work shall be covered up or put out of view without the approval of the Engineer and the Contractor shall afford full opportunity for the Engineer to examine and measure any work which is about to be covered up or put out of view and to examine foundations before permanent work is placed thereon. The Contractor shall give due notice to the Engineer whenever any such work or foundations is or are ready or about to be ready for examination and the Engineer shall without unreasonable delay unless he considers it unnecessary and advises the Contractor accordingly attend for the purpose of examining and measuring such work or of examining such foundations.[1]

UNCOVERING AND MAKING OPENINGS

(2) The Contractor shall uncover any part or parts of the Works or make openings in or through the same as the Engineer may from time to time direct and shall reinstate and make good such part or parts to the satisfaction of the Engineer. If any such part or parts have been covered up or put out of view after compliance with the requirements of sub-clause (1) of this Clause and are found to be executed in accordance with the Contract the cost of uncovering making openings in or through reinstating and making good the same shall be borne by the Employer[2] but in any other case all such cost shall be borne by the Contractor.[3,4]

1. DELAY BY THE ENGINEER IN EXAMINING WORK. In view of the first line of this clause, if the engineer delays unreasonably in inspecting or notifying the contractor that it is not necessary the contractor should not cover the work, but he will be entitled to an extension of time for completing and possibly to compensation—ch. 12.

2. "COST ... BORNE BY THE EMPLOYER". It is suggested that these words mean that the contractor is entitled to payment of reasonable charges for the work and materials involved, and not merely his own "costs" (p. 32).

3. UNCOVERING WORK PREVIOUSLY APPROVED BY THE ENGINEER. *See* p. 127, N. 2.

4. DELAY OR DISRUPTION DUE TO UNCOVERING. Apart from the right to the cost of the uncovering itself, does the contractor have a right under cl. 13 to the cost of consequential delay and disruption due to an engineer's direction to uncover any part of the works—if the work was previously approved or if not previously approved, if found defective, if not found defective? *See* pp. 75 and 128.

REMOVAL OF IMPROPER WORK AND MATERIALS

39. (1) The Engineer shall during the progress of the Works[1] have power to order in writing:
(a) the removal from the Site within such time or times as may be specified

in the order of any materials which in the opinion of the Engineer are not in accordance with the Contract;

(b) the substitution of proper and suitable materials; and

(c) the removal and proper re-execution (notwithstanding any previous test thereof or interim payment therefor)[2] of any work which in respect of materials or workmanship is not in the opinion of the Engineer in accordance with the Contract.[3,4]

DEFAULT OF CONTRACTOR IN COMPLIANCE

(2) In case of default on the part of the Contractor in carrying out such order the Employer shall be entitled to employ and pay other persons to carry out the same[5] and all expenses consequent thereon or incidental thereto shall be borne by the Contractor and shall be recoverable from him by the Employer or may be deducted by the Employer from any monies due or which may become due to the Contractor.[6]

FAILURE TO DISAPPROVE

(3) Failure of the Engineer or any person acting under him pursuant to Clause 2 to disapprove any work or materials shall not prejudice the power of the Engineer or any of them subsequently to disapprove such work or materials.[7]

1. "DURING THE PROGRESS OF THE WORKS". It is suggested that a specific right to exercise the powers in this clause in the maintenance period should have been added here—p. 65, N. 2.

2. ENGINEER'S CHANGE OF MIND. It has been suggested by the courts that once an architect or engineer approves work or material he cannot later go back on that approval. But it seems to be quite clear from cl. 38 (2) and the reference to previous tests, etc., here that the engineer's powers are not normally affected merely by a previous approval by him. On general principles, too, it does not seem that the engineer has any power to alter the contract requirements by giving a binding approval of work which infringes a specification (p. 73, N. 2 and p. 157 on waiver). In any case, the contractor may eventually have to re-do bad work under the maintenance clause 49.

The contractor may confirm an engineer's approval of work not up to specification as a variation only if there was an oral "order" from the engineer before the variation was made (cl. 51 (2)). For the possibility of confirming the result of a test or sample as a variation for the future *see* p. 124, N. 1.

Quite apart from the engineer's powers to change his decision on his own motion, the employer has a right to dispute the engineer's approval of work under cl. 66, in which case the engineer must reconsider the matter and clearly may change his mind.

(n) *Adcock's Trustees* v. *Bridge R.D.C.* (1911) 75 J.P. 241. The architect approved of a sample of brick. The bricks used were up to that sample. Held: that they could not be condemned under a power to reject material during the currency of the works, so that the architect's only power was to require their removal under the maintenance clause. However, that decision was clearly based on the peculiar wording of the contract, and the judge stated that the sample brick in fact conformed to the specification which required that bricks should be hard, square, free from cracks, etc.

If the engineer reverses approval, the contractor, of course, has a remedy in arbitration if he thinks that the final disapproval is wrong. If it was the original approval which was wrong it follows from these clauses (subject to what is said below) that the contractor has no claim for the cost of work done in reliance on it, as is stated specifically in cl. 38 in the case of uncovering, etc. However, if the contractor claims arbitration when the engineer changes his mind the employer may allow the work to remain without prejudice to a claim for damages, rather than risk liability for the cost of having it re-done if he loses in arbitration. If the arbitrator holds that the work is, in fact, bad he may award the employer damages to cover only the reduction in value of the works because of the defect and not the full cost of having the defect made good. He will generally do so if the cost of making good is disproportionately high and the defect is not serious. See also N. 4.

o

This position may perhaps be unfair to the contractor, particularly if the employer changes an incompetent engineer and the new engineer goes back on his predecessor's approvals. Yet it seems to be clearly intended by the Conditions to place the contractor under an independent duty to see that the work is up to contract standard, and that he should not be entitled to place the onus of discovering when the contract has been broken entirely on the engineer—*see also* cls. 14 (7), 17 and 60 (7).

Of course, where the description of materials required in the specification is followed by "or other approved" or words to that effect or the *only* requirement is that particular work is to be done to the engineer's approval, the specification requirements are fulfilled when materials or work are approved by the engineer (specifically, or by implication by failing to disapprove with knowledge of the condition of the materials, etc.). No question of waiver by the engineer of a breach of specification arises since no breach has taken place, and the engineer has no power later to disapprove of materials or work of his own motion. It is suggested that where there is no detailed specification for particular materials cl. 13 (2) applies—"*The whole of the materials ... are to be of a kind ... approved of by the Engineer*"—so that on approval the contract requirements are fulfilled.

p

In addition the contractor now conceivably may have a remedy on the grounds that an order under this cl. 39 (1) amounts to an instruction pursuant to cl. 13, and that in requiring him to undo work done on the faith of an approval, the instruction involves delay or disruption to the contractor's arrangements, etc., and causes him to incur cost not reasonably foreseeable at the time of tender (p. 75, N. 6). For mere notice of condemnation, as an alternative to an order under this clause, *see* cl. 63 (1) (c).

The contractor also may be entitled to an extension of time under cl. 44 if the engineer's change of mind causes delay which would not have been caused by disapproval in the first place.

(*o*) *See* Hudson "Building and Engineering Contracts", 10th ed. by I. N. Duncan Wallace, pp. 587–590, and see *Olive Ackland (Canterbury) Ltd.* v. *Gedge* [1972] 224 E.G. 2019, footnote (*k*), p. 429 below.

(*p*) The example is given at p. 384 of Hudson "Building and Engineering Contracts", 10th ed., of approval of a sample of timber which the specification requires to be reasonably free from knots and approved by the architect before incorporation in the works. It is arguable that even under this clause such approval will prevent the engineer later disapproving timber up to that sample, on the grounds that his approval determines what is reasonable.

Cases on approval by a final certificate which is conclusive and not open to arbitration—collected in Hudson, pp. 425–31—do not seem to be relevant to this clause.

Finally, the employer himself of course at any time may agree to alter the contract he has made with the contractor. If he agrees or represents to the contractor that defective work may remain in place, or authorises the engineer to do so, the employer may be bound if the contractor gave consideration (p. 3), by agreeing to expedite the works, for example, or acted to his detriment on the representation, however informally the representation was made (p. 157, N. 11).

3. TIME FOR RE-EXECUTION OF BAD WORK. There should have been added here *"within such time or times as may be specified in the order"* to correspond with sub-cl. (a).

4. AMBIGUITIES—EXTRA PAYMENT, ETC. The contractor may be entitled to an extension of time under cl. 44 for re-doing work, if he gives the necessary notice, and possibly to expenses under cl. 5, where he was misled by an ambiguity in the specification, etc., as to the quality of work or materials required.

5. EMPLOYER'S RIGHTS ON DEFAULT BY THE CONTRACTOR. This clause supplies a useful alternative to a full-blown forfeiture under cl. 63. The contractor has no specific right to immediate arbitration as he has on full forfeiture—but *see* cl. 66, N. 19. For disadvantages *see* N. 6 below, and as to use of the contractor's plant, etc., p. 201, N. 9 and 12.

It is clear that the employer may claim liquidated damages for delay in completing even where it is work that has been taken out of the contractor's hands under this clause which overruns the completion date. q

The contractor should be given a reasonable time to carry out the order, but if he makes it clear that he has no intention of obeying it the rights under this clause may be used immediately.

There are provisions similar to this in cls. 49 (4) and 62, which might be extended, e.g. to cl. 19, where the work will generally be urgent.

As this clause stands the engineer has no power unless both parties agree to allow nominal defects to remain and to certify a reasonable deduction from the contract price—he may not treat bad work as a variation and deduct for that, since there must be at least an oral order by him before a variation is made (cl. 51 (2)). This means that if the engineer insists on having work re-done because of nominal defects the arbitrator is not entitled to reverse his decision and award the contractor extra payment. If the contractor claims arbitration on an order to re-do work and the employer does allow the work to remain without prejudice to a claim for damages, the arbitrator may award the employer damages to cover only the reduction in value of the works because of the defect, and not the full cost of having the defect made good. r

(q) In *British Glanzstoff Manufacturing Co. Ltd.* v. *General Accident, etc. Insurance Corporation Ltd.* [1912] S.C. 591 and [1913] A.C. 143, it was held that liquidated damages could not be claimed for a period when the whole works were in another contractor's hands, after the contract had been ended under the general law for breach by the contractor. That is clearly distinguishable from the position under this clause. By cl. 47 (1) liquidated damages are payable *"for every week ... which shall elapse between the ... prescribed time ... and the date of completion of the ... Works"*, and there is no specific reference to completion by the original contractor only. It would be a strange result if the contractor's default were to deprive the employer of liquidated damages. See further p. 281.

(r) *See* p. 127, footnote (n).

6. "DEDUCTED ... FROM ANY MONIES DUE OR ... BECOME DUE". In this edition the engineer no longer has power to withold certificates so that he will have money in hand to pay another contractor employed under this clause—*see* cl. 60, N. 35.

· Where there is not sufficient retention money in hand, in advising the employer to act under this clause in reliance on the right to deduct the cost from money to become due to the contractor, the engineer should consider whether there is any danger that it may become necessary to forfeit the whole contract before the money is earned by the contractor. If there is, it may be preferable to try again to induce the contractor to do the work, so as to reduce any loss on eventual forfeiture, or to forfeit the whole contract immediately, since it may be cheaper to have a substituted contractor come on the site only once to complete the whole works.

The law on deductions by an employer is discussed on pp. 268–73.

7. ENGINEER'S POWERS NOT AFFECTED BY "FAILURE ... TO DISAPPROVE ANY WORK OR MATERIALS". This new sub-clause is an expansion of cl. 2 (a) of the previous edition, now worded to include failure by the engineer as well as the engineer's representative and assistants, etc., to disapprove any work or materials. For the reasons set out fully on pp. 127–9 it does not appear that there is any difference in effect between failure to disapprove and a positive approval of work or materials.

SUSPENSION OF WORK

40. (1) The Contractor shall on the written order of the Engineer suspend the progress of the Works[1] or any part thereof for such time or times and in such manner as the Engineer may consider necessary[2] and shall during such suspension properly protect and secure the work so far as is necessary in the opinion of the Engineer. Subject to Clause 52 (4) the Contractor shall be paid in accordance with Clause 60[3] the extra cost[4] (if any) incurred in giving effect to the Engineer's instructions under this Clause except to the extent that[5] such suspension is:

  (a) otherwise provided for in the Contract; or
  (b) necessary by reason of weather conditions or by some default on the part of the Contractor; or
  (c) necessary for the proper execution of the work or for the safety of the Works or any part thereof[6] inasmuch as such necessity does not arise from any act or default of the Engineer or the Employer[7] or from any of the Excepted Risks defined in Clause 20.[8]

The Engineer shall take any delay occasioned by a suspension ordered under this Clause (including that arising from any act or default of the Engineer or the Employer) into account in determining any extension of time to which the Contractor is entitled under Clause 44 except when such suspension is otherwise provided for in the Contract or is necessary by reason of some default on the part of the Contractor.[9,9a]

SUSPENSION LASTING MORE THAN THREE MONTHS

(2) If the progress of the Works or any part thereof is suspended on the written order of the Engineer and if permission to resume work is not given by the Engineer within a period of 3 months from[10] the date of suspension then the Contractor may unless such suspension is otherwise provided for in the

Contract or continues to be necessary by reason of some default on the part of the Contractor[11,12] serve a written notice on the Engineer requiring permission within 28 days from the receipt[13] of such notice to proceed with the Works or that part thereof in regard to which progress is suspended. If within the said 28 days the Engineer does not grant such permission the Contractor by a further written notice so served may (but is not bound to) elect to treat the suspension where it affects part only of the Works as an omission of such part under Clause 51 or where it affects the whole Works as an abandonment of the Contract by the Employer.[14]

1. "THE CONTRACTOR SHALL ON THE WRITTEN ORDER OF THE ENGINEER SUSPEND THE PROGRESS OF THE WORKS". *See* as to maintenance work p. 65, N. 2, and p. 165, N. 10, but these words may more easily than "*during the execution of the Works*" be interpreted so as to include work in the maintenance period.

"*Works*" now include temporary works by the definition in cl. 1 (1) (l).

2. "AS THE ENGINEER MAY CONSIDER NECESSARY". It is not clear whether the engineer is entitled to act only if he considers a suspension necessary for engineering reasons connected with the construction of the works, or may suspend the works merely for the convenience of the employer, e.g. because the employer has temporarily run short of money. Probably the engineer's power is limited, but if a suspension is necessary for the proper construction of the works he may order the suspension even if that necessity has arisen due to the default of the employer (para. (c) of this sub-clause).

On disruption claims generally, refer to ch. 12.

3. "SUBJECT TO CLAUSE 52 (4) ... IN ACCORDANCE WITH CLAUSE 60". These clauses deal with notice of claim and inclusion of payment in interim and the final certificate, subject to retention.

4. "EXTRA COST ... INCURRED". *See* p. 31, N. 18, as to overheads. Cost incurred in doing the work eventually at a later date than planned is included—disruption and price, etc., increases not covered by any price variation clause in the contract.

For the conceivable implications of the Unfair Contract Terms Act 1977 refer to p. 432.

5. "EXCEPT TO THE EXTENT THAT". These words now replace "*unless*" and have the effect that if the suspension is only partly due to the matters set out in paras. (a), (b) and (c), the contractor is entitled to a proportionate part of his costs. Where there are two causes of delay, one falling within these paragraphs and one not, the division is straightforward if they are successive. If they are concurrent the apportionment may be a difficult task for the engineer or arbitrator, and indeed usually only one will be the effective cause of the delay to be taken into consideration—p. 99, N. 5, and p. 138, N. 1.

6. "NECESSARY BY REASON OF WEATHER CONDITIONS ... FOR THE PROPER EXECUTION OF THE WORK ... THE SAFETY OF THE WORKS OR ANY PART". *See* N. 9 and 12.

7. "NECESSARY FOR THE PROPER EXECUTION OF THE WORK ... INASMUCH AS

SUCH NECESSITY DOES NOT ARISE FROM ANY ACT OR DEFAULT OF THE ENGINEER OR THE EMPLOYER". This addition removes an ambiguity in the previous edition. "*act or default of the Engineer*" includes failure to supply drawings or instructions where necessary. The contractor is entitled at least to costs for suspension for the convenience of the employer and not "*necessary for the proper execution of the work*", and such suspension may even be invalid because it is outside the proper use of the engineer's powers (N. 2) so that the contractor may refuse to accept the order and claim full damages or even end the contract for breach if the stoppage is insisted on by the employer (ch. 16).

Suspension due to the design of the works is covered separately as an excepted risk (next note).

8. "OR FROM ANY OF THE EXCEPTED RISKS DEFINED IN CLAUSE 20". A new right is conferred on the contractor to costs of a suspension due to excepted risks, which would not otherwise be the responsibility of the employer. This change is reasonable since even the insurance market normally will not accept these risks.

For definitions of the excepted risks *see* pp. 100-1.

9. EXTENSION OF TIME—SUSPENSION AFFECTED BY DEFAULT OF THE CONTRACTOR—WEATHER CONDITIONS. Whereas the right to payment for suspension is reduced "*to the extent that*" it is due to some default on the part of the contractor, the right to an extension of time is stated to be affected only when the suspension "*is necessary by reason of*" the contractor's default, not specifically for default of the contractor which extends a suspension initially necessary for some other reason. Nevertheless the engineer may be entitled to award a reduced extension on the grounds that the prolongation of the original suspension is to be classed as a separate suspension "*necessary by reason of* ... (the Contractor's default)", or under the "*fairly to entitle ... to an extension*" words of cl. 44, e.g. where the contractor does not act reasonably to minimise the suspension necessary.

Suspension for default by a nominated sub-contractor is counted as due to default by the contractor (p. 242, N. 15).

If the engineer suspends the works because the contractor carries on working in weather that will harm the permanent works and expresses an intention to continue to do so, then it is arguable that the suspension is necessitated by the contractor's default, so that he is not entitled to an extension of time. Since this clause says only that the engineer shall take delay due to suspension for weather "*into account*" in determining an extension of time under cl. 44 and since under that clause the right to an extension is confined to exceptional adverse weather conditions, the contractor is not entitled to an extension if in tendering he should reasonably have allowed for the suspension as a normal seasonal interruption. *See also* N. 12.

10. "WITHIN A PERIOD OF 3 MONTHS FROM", i.e. expiring at midnight of the last day of the three calendar month period, not counting the day on which the suspension is ordered. For example, in the case of a suspension ordered on 15th May the period ends at midnight on 15th August.

11. "UNLESS SUCH SUSPENSION ... CONTINUES TO BE NECESSARY BY REASON OF SOME DEFAULT ON THE PART OF THE CONTRACTOR". A necessary addition

to the previous edition, which apparently allowed the contractor to act under this sub-clause even if the suspension was due to his own fault.

The wording is a little strange—taken literally the contractor may act under this sub-clause if a suspension for two months is necessary by reason of default by the contractor, but is continued for a third month for some other reason. Where possible the engineer should end the suspension due to the contractor's default and start a separate suspension for the new cause.

12. ABANDONMENT, ETC. FOR SUSPENSION DUE TO WEATHER CONDITIONS OR NECESSARY FOR THE PROPER EXECUTION OR SAFETY OF THE WORKS. Since the right is not negatived in this sub-clause, the contractor may treat the contract as abandoned or part of the works as omitted for a suspension due to weather conditions or necessary for the proper execution or safety or the works (even if not due to any act or default of the engineer or employer) if it lasts for the specified period. This is the case even though under sub-cl. (1) the contractor is not entitled to his costs in the period of suspension.

It does not seem that the engineer is bound to act under this clause where the works are in fact held up due to weather conditions which impede, e.g., earth-moving. The engineer may have to act if the contractor insists on continuing in unsuitable conditions detrimental to the works, or in order to have the works protected under this clause. Should a contractor become entitled to substantial damages as a result (N. 14), or the employer have to do without his works, or pay another contractor extra or bargain with the existing contractor to do work at renegotiated prices, the engineer or any lawyer who permitted the employer to enter into these Conditions would have much explaining to do and possibly an action for negligence to defend. That is, unless the clause was carefully explained to and approved by the employer before the contract (*see* p. 376). The argument suggested in the last paragraph of N. 9 may apply to avoid this anomaly, even on the different words of this sub-cl. (2). Alternatively, advantage may be taken of the exception of suspension which is "*otherwise provided for in the Contract*" to write into cl. 72 a special term definitely negativing this result.

13. "WITHIN 28 DAYS FROM THE RECEIPT". The day on which the notice is received is not included, since the law does not take account of parts of a day. In a time limit "*days*" includes holidays and Sundays unless "working days" are specified.

14. "MAY . . . TREAT THE SUSPENSION . . . (OF) PART . . . OF THE WORKS AS AN OMISSION . . . OR . . . (OF) THE WHOLE WORKS AS AN ABANDONMENT OF THE CONTRACT BY THE EMPLOYER". Abandonment of the contract by the employer generally entitles the contractor to full damages (p. 425). If the contractor treats the suspension as "*an omission . . . under Clause 51*", then provided the necessary notice is served he may claim a variation of rates under cl. 52 (2), but will not be entitled to damages since he is treating the omission as properly made under cl. 51.

Independently of this clause the contractor may have a right under the

___

(s) There is no provision in the Conditions for adjusting payment to the contractor for unfinished work, etc. (as there is in cl. 65 (5), and cl. 26 of the J.C.T. Standard Form of building contract), where he treats a suspension as an abandonment, which supports the view that the contractor's general rights for breach of contract are intended to apply.

general law to treat the contract as abandoned for suspension by the employer lasting less than three months, if it shows that the employer does not intend to be bound by the contract (pp. 425–6).

For the time for arbitration where the contractor ends the contract under this clause *see* p. 307, N. 22.

COMMENCEMENT OF WORKS

41. The Contractor shall commence the Works on or as soon as is reasonably possible after the Date for Commencement of the Works[1] to be notified by the Engineer in writing which date shall be within a reasonable time after the date of acceptance of the Tender.[2] Thereafter the Contractor shall proceed with the Works with due expedition and without delay[3] in accordance with the Contract.

1. "THE CONTRACTOR SHALL COMMENCE THE WORKS ON OR AS SOON AS IS REASONABLY POSSIBLE AFTER THE DATE FOR COMMENCEMENT OF THE WORKS". Fairly equivalent to "*as soon as practicable*", for which *see* p. 163, N. 3.

This change substitutes uncertainty for certainty in respect of the time for commencement, which may be so crucial to timely completion of the works. By the previous version of this clause the contractor is bound to commence the works within fourteen days of receipt of the engineer's order to commence.

By cl. 43 the time for completion runs from the date of commencement notified by the engineer under this clause, not from the date thereafter when commencement is reasonably possible.

The requirement to "*commence the Works*" is necessarily a little vague. It is suggested that only a real, substantial commencement satisfies this clause, although such commencement may conceivably take place off site. The engineer should require the contractor to furnish with his tender a programme showing the period for and details of commencement. This programme will be evidence of what is a reasonable time to commence and may be helpful in establishing what is necessary to amount to commencement.

2. "WHICH DATE (OF COMMENCEMENT) SHALL BE WITHIN A REASONABLE TIME AFTER THE DATE OF ACCEPTANCE OF THE TENDER" is implied in any case. The employer is ordinarily liable to pay full damages for unreasonable delay. However, under this form the engineer generally may deal with delay by giving an order to commence on time and an extension of time for completion to cover any delay in giving possession of the site, in which case the contractor is entitled only to the cost caused by the delay (p. 135, N. 1). For the contractor's right to end the contract in exceptional cases of delay *see* p. 425.

Unfortunately a contractor has little protection in a related situation, of an employer who seeks tenders and then delays in making up his mind and announcing the successful tenderer. In the meantime all tenderers may be inhibited from taking on other contracts, or the successful tenderer may find himself over-committed. In most cases a tenderer is free to withdraw his tender at any time up to acceptance (p. 3), but for commercial reasons tenderers are reluctant to do so. If there is a specific time limit during which tenders are to remain open stated in the invitation to tender or the tender itself, although the tenderer generally is not bound to keep his tender open

(p. 4) the time limit does have the effect that at the end of the period the tender lapses automatically and may not validly be accepted by the employer unless it is renewed. If there is no such specific time limit the tender lapses after a reasonable time, and as usual all that can be said about what is reasonable in law is that it must depend on the circumstances of the case.

3. "PROCEED WITH ... DUE EXPEDITION AND WITHOUT DELAY IN ACCORDANCE WITH THE CONTRACT" replaces "*except as may be expressly sanctioned or ordered by the Engineer or be wholly beyond the Contractor's control*". The change may have some repercussion on the interpretation of cl. 44 in relaxing by implication the conditions for an extension of time.

Before forfeiting the contractor's employment for failure to proceed with the works with due diligence, the engineer must give written warnings under cl. 63 (1) (d).

Refer to p. 311 for the possible relevance of the words at the head of this note to a claim by the contractor under the tax fluctuations clause for increased costs in a period of his own delay.

POSSESSION OF SITE

42. (1) Save in so far as the Contract may prescribe the extent of portions of the Site of which the Contractor is to be given possession from time to time and the order in which such portions shall be made available to him and subject to any requirement in the Contract as to the order in which the Works shall be executed the Employer will at the Date for Commencement of the Works notified under Clause 41 give to the Contractor possession of so much of the Site[1] as may be required to enable the Contractor to commence and proceed with the construction of the Works in accordance with the programme referred to in Clause 14[2] and will from time to time as the Works proceed give to the Contractor possession of such further portions of the Site as may be required to enable the Contractor to proceed with the construction of the Works with due despatch in accordance with the said programme. If the Contractor suffers delay or incurs cost from failure on the part of the Employer to give possession in accordance with the terms of this Clause then the Engineer shall take such delay into account in determining any extension of time to which the Contractor is entitled under Clause 44[3,4] and the Contractor shall subject to Clause 52 (4)[5] be paid in accordance with Clause 60[6] the amount of such cost as may be reasonable.[7]

WAYLEAVES, ETC.

(2) The Contractor shall bear all expenses and charges for special or temporary wayleaves required by him in connection with access to the Site. The Contractor shall also provide at his own cost any additional accommodation outside the Site required by him for the purposes of the Works.[8]

1. DELAY BY THE EMPLOYER IN GIVING POSSESSION OF THE SITE. The ordinary position is that if the employer causes delay the completion date fixed by the contract ceases to hold good and the contractor has a reasonable time to complete—"If in the contract one finds the time limited within which the builder is to do the work, that means not only that he is to do it within the time, but it means also that he is to have that time within

(*t*) *Wells* v. *Army and Navy Co-op. Society* (1902), Hudson "Building Contracts", 4th ed., vol. ii, p. 346, at p. 354.

which to do it". The courts will not fix a new completion date allowing for the employer's delay. And since liquidated damages are stated to run from the completion date fixed by the contract (cl. 47), if it goes the right to liquidated damages for delay goes also. The power given to the engineer in this clause to fix a new completion date, from which liquidated damages will run, is therefore for the employer's benefit. Irrespective of this clause the employer's delay may in some cases entitle the contractor to bring the whole contract to an end and to claim full damages as a result (ch. 16), or there may be frustration of the contract by delay outside the parties' control (cl. 64).

See also cl. 12 on underground services. For wide definition of "*Site*" *see* cl. 1 (l) (n).

2. "IN ACCORDANCE WITH THE PROGRAMME REFERRED TO IN CLAUSE 14". In this edition cl. 14 refers both to an initial contract programme and also revised programmes. Clearly this clause must be read so that the contractor's right to cost, etc., under the clause applies even if the contractor revises his programme because of foreseen delay by the employer in giving possession of the site.

By this clause possession of so much of the site as may be necessary in accordance with the contractor's programme is to be given at the date for commencement of the works, but by cl. 14 the contractor has 21 days from acceptance of his tender to submit his initial programme. In any case, the latter time limit may have to be shortened where commencement is very urgent, and indeed where the employer can only give possession of parts of the site from time to time the engineer should require the contractor to include his programme with his tender, so that he can check that the partial handovers will meet the contractor's requirements.

3. "THE ENGINEER SHALL TAKE SUCH DELAY INTO ACCOUNT IN DETERMINING ANY EXTENSION OF TIME ... UNDER CLAUSE 44" NOTICES. It is clear from the words of cl. 44 that the requirements of that clause about delivery of particulars by the contractor now apply to a claim under this clause for delayed possession of the site.

4. TIME FOR GRANTING EXTENSION OF TIME—ACCELERATION CLAIMS. Cl. 44 also now governs the important question of the times at which the engineer must deal with claims to extension of time—p. 138, N. 1. For acceleration claims *see* ch. 12.

5. PAYMENT TO CONTRACTOR "SUBJECT TO CLAUSE 52 (4)" dealing with notice of money claims.

6. "IN ACCORDANCE WITH CLAUSE 60", i.e. included in interim certificates and the final payment certificate, and subject to retention.

7. "THE AMOUNT OF SUCH COST AS MAY BE REASONABLE". *See* p. 31, N. 18, on the inclusion of overheads. It does not seem that the contractor may recover loss of profit by claiming under the general law (p. 50, and *see* p. 431 on the Unfair Contract Terms Act 1977).

8. RATES AND TAXES ON ACCOMMODATION. *See* cl. 26 for reimbursement by the employer.

TIME FOR COMPLETION

43. The whole of the Works and any Section required to be completed within a particular time[1] as stated in the Appendix to the Form of Tender shall be completed within the time so stated (or such extended time as may be allowed under Clause 44) calculated from the Date for Commencement of the Works[2] notified under Clause 41.

1. "ANY SECTION REQUIRED TO BE COMPLETED WITHIN A PARTICULAR TIME". *See* cl. 48.

2. "COMPLETED WITHIN THE TIME ... CALCULATED FROM THE DATE FOR COMMENCEMENT", not calculated from the date "*as soon as reasonably possible*" thereafter when actual commencement is due by cl. 41. As the period is stated to run "*from*" the date for commencement, that date is not included. The period ends at midnight of the last day, and all days whether working days or not are included.

The contractor is bound to finish the works "*within*" the time stated, and is therefore entitled to finish early even though this may upset the employer's budget arrangements for paying him. Where the employer's flow of finance is such that more certainty about his commitment is necessary, it may be necessary to specify some form of equal interim instalments in place of cl. 60. All such plans may of course be upset by unforeseen difficulties and variations leading to claims, so that full preparation of drawings before invitation of tenders and a stricter form of contract may be necessary if the employer requires greater certainty that his budget will not be exceeded (p. 439 on "Tendermanship").

For disruption claims where the contractor intends to complete early and requires early supply of drawings and instructions *see* p. 366.

EXTENSION OF TIME FOR COMPLETION

44. (1)[1,(a)] Should any variation ordered under Clause 51 (1)[2] or increased quantities referred to in Clause 51 (3) or any other cause of delay referred to in these Conditions[3] or exceptional adverse weather conditions[4] or other special circumstances of any kind whatsoever[5,6] which may occur be such as fairly to entitle the Contractor to an extension of time for the completion of the Works or (where different periods for completion of different Sections are provided for in the Appendix to the Form of Tender) of the relevant Section[7] the Contractor shall within 28 days after the cause of the delay has arisen or as soon thereafter as is reasonable in all the circumstances deliver to the Engineer full and detailed particulars of any claim to extension of time to which he may consider himself entitled in order that such claim may be investigated at the time.[8]

INTERIM ASSESSMENT OF EXTENSION

(2) The Engineer shall upon receipt of such particulars or if he thinks fit in the absence of any such claim[9] consider all the circumstances known to him at that time[10] and make an assessment of the extension of time (if any) to which he considers the Contractor entitled for the completion of the Works or relevant Section and shall by notice in writing to the Contractor grant such extension of time for completion. In the event that the Contractor shall have made a claim for an extension of time but the Engineer considers the Contractor not entitled thereto the Engineer shall so inform the Contractor.

ASSESSMENT AT DUE DATE FOR COMPLETION

(3) The Engineer shall at or as soon as possible after the due date or extended date for completion[11] (and whether or not the Contractor shall have made any claim for an extension of time)[12] consider all the circumstances known to him at that time[10] and take action similar to that provided for in sub-clause (2) of this Clause. Should the Engineer consider that the Contractor is not entitled to an extension of time he shall so notify the Employer and the Contractor.[13]

FINAL DETERMINATION OF EXTENSION

(4) The Engineer shall upon the issue of the Certificate of Completion of the Works or of the relevant Section review[14,15] all the circumstances of the kind referred to in sub-clause (1) of this Clause and shall finally determine and certify to the Contractor the overall extension of time (if any) to which he considers the Contractor entitled in respect of the Works or any relevant Section. No such final review of the circumstances shall result in a decrease in any extension of time already granted by the Engineer pursuant to sub-clauses (2) or (3) of this Clause.[16]

1. GENERAL. This clause is a new and complicated version of the traditional clause entitling the contractor to receive from the engineer an extension of the time for completion if the works are delayed by a cause outside the contractor's control. The complications are intended to ensure that the contractor knows as soon as possible whether or not he is entitled to an extension, so that he may plan his progress accordingly.

The only duty placed on the contractor by this clause is to deliver to the engineer "*full and detailed particulars*" of his claim to extension "*within 28 days after the cause of the delay has arisen or as soon thereafter as is reasonable in all the circumstances*" (*see* N. 8). The particulars are stated specifically to be required "*in order that such claim may be investigated at the time*", but nevertheless the engineer eventually is under an independent duty to assess an extension of time even if they are never given. If the contractor is claiming money for delay as well as an extension (N. 6) he must, of course, comply with any notice, etc. terms applicable, such as cl. 52 (4).

On the other hand the engineer has numerous duties under this clause which will present themselves as follows:

(*a*) Without waiting for particulars from the contractor the engineer may (but is not bound to) "*consider all the circumstances known to him at the time*" and grant any extension he considers is due (N. 9 and 10).

(*b*) Upon receipt of particulars he must make an assessment of any extension due, whether or not he has previously made an assessment (N. 10).

(*c*) If and as often as the current due date for completion is reached without substantial completion of the works having been achieved, the engineer must as soon as possible assess any extension due to the contractor (N. 11–13).

(*d*) "*Upon the issue of the Certificate of Completion*" the engineer must review the contractor's right to an extension and make a final assessment which may not decrease any extension already granted (N. 14–16).

(*e*) At each of these stages (but *see* N. 11) including certified completion of a section of the works, the engineer must consider separately the contractor's right to an extension for any section for which a separate time for completion is stated in the form of tender, as well as the assessment for the whole works.

(*f*) The engineer has certain duties to notify the results of his deliberations. He is, of course, bound to notify the contractor whenever he grants an extension, and he should also notify the employer. He is specifically bound to notify the contractor if he decides that he is not entitled to an extension in response to a claim made by the contractor, or if he decides that he is not entitled to an extension on a review after the due date for completion, but not so bound by this clause if he decides that no further extension is due on the final review. However, the engineer when he considers that the contractor is not entitled to an extension of time on any review following the due date for completion must notify the employer and the contractor so that the employer may then start deducting liquidated damages (p. 155, N. 7).

(*g*) The engineer or an arbitrator may also have to review an extension on a dispute raised under cl. 66 (N. 16).

The engineer will keep in mind at all times the possibility of using his preventative powers under cl. 46 (*see* particularly N. 2 to that clause).

It does not seem that the contractor has an acceleration claim merely because the engineer increases an earlier extension of time, or (even though the contractor has no right to arbitration before completion on any claim merely to an extension, although he may have on a related money claim (p. 305)) merely because the extension is increased in arbitration. However, because of his right to notification of the engineer's decisions the contractor will know if the engineer has not merely made a wrong or unreasonable decision about extension but has failed to administer this clause properly by failing to consider at all at the required times the contractor's rights, in which case he may have a claim. Acceleration claims are dealt with generally on p. 371.

In deciding whether or not there is a case for an extension of time, the two crucial questions are whether the contractor has in fact been held up by delay within this clause, and whether he is "*fairly*" entitled to an extension. The actual facts on site must be considered to determine whether the occurrence affected any operation critical to the contractor's completion time. It is not enough for the contractor to show that, according to his plans as set out in a programme, delay fell on his critical path. It is his actual not his planned progress which is relevant.

1(a). CONCURRENT DELAYS. The situation where there are concurrent delays, only one of which is outside the contractor's control, is most difficult. The case may arise where the contractor due to his own deficiencies is late in reaching a position to start some programmed activity, but in fact could not have started the activity earlier even if he had been ready because of delay by the engineer with some necessary drawings. It is suggested that in this sort of situation the net point is that the contractor has not in fact been held up by "delay" outside his control, and it is immaterial that if his progress had been different he would have been so held up. The late drawings are not an actual "*cause of delay*" within this clause. The contractor therefore is entitled to an extension of time only so far as the drawings are withheld past the date on which he in fact became ready for them.

The above conclusion does have the perhaps unfair result that the employer may be entitled to recover liquidated damages from the contractor for delayed completion even though the employer was not in a position to allow the contractor to complete earlier, but any other principle could lead to much confusion in substituting for an examination of whether the contractor actually was delayed by a cause beyond his control a wide ranging examination into all events that could have caused delay had the contractor's progress been different. Of course, the contractor will be entitled to an extension if he can show that he was in a position to be ready earlier for the drawings, but delayed his progress because of advance notice that they would be late—in such a case the contractor would be wise to give notice at an early stage of his decision to take that step.

Alternatively, the contractor may say that if the employer's concurrent delay had not occurred, he would have been able, for example, to increase his resources or bring pressure on a recalcitrant sub-contractor so as to overcome the delay for which he is being held responsible. It does not seem that the mere existence of that abstract possibility is sufficient. Unless the contractor raises the issue at the time and gives evidence of readiness and ability in fact, a later argument that his delay would have been eliminated or shortened but for the employer's concurrent delay is unlikely to be believed by the engineer or an arbitrator on a claim to extension. Further discussion of this almost philosophical problem of concurrent delay will be found on p. 370 in connection with disruption claims.

2. EXTENSION FOR EXTRA WORK, AND OMISSIONS. The contractor is obviously entitled to an extension only if extra work was authorised properly—see p. 169.

In deciding whether the amount of extra or additional work *"fairly entitle(s) the Contractor to an extension of time"* the engineer (or arbitrator) may certainly allow for any omissions, but he is given no power to reduce the completion time when there are more omissions than extras. Even if there have been substantial omissions the engineer must consider only the original completion date in deciding whether to forfeit the contract for lack of due diligence under cl. 63, and in calculating liquidated damages for delay.

In addition, the new code requiring the engineer to consider extensions of time at various stages may in practice make it difficult for the engineer to reflect omissions in the final extension given—N. 16.

(u) This point has been discussed in two South African decisions. In *Chaffer and Tassie* v. *Richards* (1905) 26 N.L.R. 207 it was held that no extension of time was due where the arbitrator found that omissions could fairly be put against extras so that the balance being within the sum allowed in the contract for extras to be completed within the contract time, no allowance of extra time was due to the contractor. In *Kenny and Hingles' Trustees* v. *Union Government* (1928) T.P.D. 272, 289 it was said that if the extension of time clause had been worded to give the engineer jurisdiction to assess delay in ordering extras "he might, perhaps, reasonably take into account in deciding as to allowances for such delay the effect of other orders requiring omissions". Cases will vary from the omission of contract work and substitution of new work for it, where obviously a balance has to be struck in calculating extension of time, to cases where the omission is so removed from the addition that in fact there is no counter-balancing effect on the contractor's progress.

Logically there is no reason why the contractor should gain the advantage of any events outside his control that reduce the time necessary for completion, but be entitled to pass delays on to the employer by having an extension of time assessed for each delay without reference to countervailing factors.

A contractor may seek an extension for extra work ordered, even though delay to the progress of the works could be avoided by bringing on additional resources to carry out the variation. It is hardly a valid argument that a contractor is entitled to limit the resources he provides to those necessary to carry out the original contract works: for example, where an extra length of trench is ordered, to insist on doing it after the contract length, although physically it could be done simultaneously, rather than supply such extra workmen and plant as are economical to execute the length of trench involved. The contractor has undertaken to perform any properly ordered extra work "*with due expedition*" (cl. 41), and is not "*fairly*" entitled to an extension of time if he behaves unreasonably. What additional resources the contractor is reasonably bound to provide for extra work must depend on the level of resources necessary for the original contract work, judged by reference to the extent of that work and the contract time for completion. If the extra work will cause delay even though he meets that resource level for the extra work, the contractor is entitled to an extension of time, and if he is requested to do the extra work to an accelerated programme and to forfeit his right to an extension, then the element of expedition should be allowed for in valuing the variation (p. 372).

3. EXTENSION FOR "ANY OTHER CAUSE OF DELAY REFERRED TO IN THESE CONDITIONS". Delay for which the employer is responsible is specifically included—e.g. under cls. 7, 13, 40 and 42. Thus the argument raised on the wording of the 4th edition, that the engineer had no power to give an extension for delay by the employer, and that as a consequence any such delay invalidated the liquidated damages provision, is no longer open in most cases. The argument can still be raised in a case of delay not "*referred to in these Conditions*", e.g. possibly delay in examination of work before covering up under cl. 38, and if cl. 13 is given a narrow interpretation (p. 75). However, it was suggested in the second edition of this book that this argument is in any case a bad one.

For delay by nominated sub-contractors *see* p. 227.

4. EXTENSION FOR "EXCEPTIONAL ADVERSE WEATHER CONDITIONS". Adverse weather conditions may be exceptional either in their intensity, e.g. a storm which disrupts the contractor's work, or in their duration, e.g. an abnormal number of rainy days in the place and season(s) of the contract.

(*v*) Pages 95–96 of the second edition of this book. The recent overruling of some decisions mentioned there (*see* p. 96, N. 1, above) was in a quite different context and for reasons that do not apply to this clause. Two recent cases have, however, been cited in support of the argument. *Peak Construction (Liverpool) Ltd.* v. *McKinney Foundations Ltd.* (1970) reported in 1 B.L.R. 114, C.A. is one of the cases, but the words in the extension of time clause referred to "*strikes*" (etc.) ... or *other unavoidable circumstances*", and it was pointed out that the circumstances were not "unavoidable" because they could have been avoided by the employer. In the other case, *Perini Pacific Ltd.* v. *Greater Vancouver Sewerage & Drainage District* (1966) 57 D.L.R. (2d) 307 (British Columbia Court of Appeal), the wording was "*alterations, strikes, subcontractors or other causes beyond the contractor's control*".

Fortunately the courts have not raised to a fetish the principle of reading an extension of time clause against the employer. In the *Peak* case the rule was stated to be that an extension of time clause which "*expressly or by necessary inference*" covers an extension on account of fault or breach on the part of the employer is valid to preserve liquidated damages (at p. 121).

In the latter case it appears that the engineer is entitled to look at the contract weather as a whole (N. 2), subject to practical difficulties discussed in N. 16.

The fact that special heating or protection measures are specified in the contract may be relevant to deciding whether or not the contractor is "*fairly*" entitled to an extension.

For suspension of the works for weather conditions *see* pp. 132, N. 9 and 133, N. 12.

5. EXTENSION OF TIME FOR PROVISIONAL SUMS, P.C. ITEMS AND CONTINGENCIES. In the case of P.C. items (even though by cl. 58 (1) they only "*may be used*") and provisional sums, whether for work which has not been specified in detail or for work to be executed by a nominated sub-contractor, ordering of work to the value in the bill hardly constitutes "*special circumstances*" within cl. 44. It is therefore suggested that the contractor is not entitled to any extension of time for work up to the value in the bill. That is, unless the nature and extent of the work are not sufficiently indicated to permit the contractor at the tender stage to calculate an allowance for it in his programme, or the work has been altered without any increase in the price in such a way as to make it more time-consuming or to move it for the first time on to the contractor's critical path. Since there is no certainty that a contingency sum (now a species of provisional sum) will be used at all or for what type of work it will be used, it is suggested that the contractor is not bound to try to include for the work in his programme. On that basis he will be entitled to an extension of time for any work ordered under the sum which affects the time of completion.

If the amount of a P.C. item or provisional sum that otherwise would not entitle the contractor to an extension is exceeded, then it will depend on all the circumstances whether or not the contractor is "*fairly*" entitled to an extension of time in respect of the excess. If the increase is due to inflation without any change in the work covered by the sum or item as indicated to the contractor at the time of tender, then no extension will be due. If the work indicated is added to or changed so as to affect the contractor's critical path, then an extension is due.

6. EXTENSION OF TIME AND EXTRA PAYMENT. Two related misconceptions are widespread. The first is that an extension of time automatically entitles a contractor to a *pro rata* addition to his preliminaries, and the second is that if the contractor does not require an extension of time he is not entitled to such an addition or to other payment for delay.

The first misconception is evidence that those who administer contracts do not always take the precaution of reading them. This clause does not mention extra payment following an extension of time, and therefore the contractor must found a right to such extra payment elsewhere—e.g. on cl. 12 or on some delay for which the employer is responsible. Delay claims are discussed fully in ch. 12.

Conversely, the fact that a contractor does not need an extension of time because he is able to finish the work within the completion time, despite a delay caused by the employer, does not deprive the contractor of his right to compensation for that delay. The completion time in the contract is a maximum time for completion; there is no minimum time and the contractor is free to complete as early as he can. This aspect is discussed further on p. 366 in relation to late drawings and instructions from the engineer.

7. EXTENSIONS WHERE THE TENDER PROVIDES FOR "DIFFERENT PERIODS FOR COMPLETION OF DIFFERENT SECTIONS OF THE WORKS". *See* p. 10.

A cause for delay may affect one or more sections, with or without the overall completion, depending on the contractor's critical path.

8. PERIOD FOR DELIVERING PARTICULARS OF EXTENSION CLAIMED. The 28-day period is retained from the previous edition, but *"or as soon thereafter as is practicable"* is relaxed to *"or as is reasonable in all the circumstances"* and the requirement of particulars has less significance (next note and N. 12).

The contractor's duty is to deliver *"full and detailed particulars"* of his claim, and it may of course be some time before such particulars can reasonably be prepared. This clause might well have placed on the contractor a duty at all times to give whatever particulars he can reasonably produce. Normally it will be in the contractor's interest to draw the engineer's attention to any facts which entitle him to an extension, to try to clarify his programme by inducing the engineer to act under sub-cl. (2) by giving a minimum extension.

9. "THE ENGINEER SHALL . . . . IF HE THINKS FIT IN THE ABSENCE OF ANY SUCH CLAIM . . . GRANT . . . EXTENSION". If it is clear that some extension of time is due, but it is not yet possible for the contractor to give full and detailed particulars, it may be reasonable for the engineer to exercise this power to give a minimum extension, so that the contractor has some idea of where he stands and may plan the works accordingly. In exercising this power the engineer will keep in mind the restrictions on subsequently reducing any extension given (N. 16).

In theory an arbitrator under cl. 66 may reverse a decision by the engineer that he will not give an extension before receipt of full particulars from the contractor, but such reversal does not seem to have any practical effect. What matters as far as liquidated damages are concerned is the eventual final extension of time given by the engineer or fixed by the arbitrator. The contractor will not be entitled to arbitration before completion unless the cause of delay also entitles the contractor to extra payment (p. 305, N. 19), and will not have any claim in arbitration for additional costs merely because he expedited the works as a result of the engineer's decision not to exercise his power under this sub-clause (p. 371).

The engineer eventually becomes bound to consider an extension, even if the contractor never makes any claim at all (N. 12).

10. "THE ENGINEER SHALL . . . CONSIDER ALL THE CIRCUMSTANCES KNOWN TO HIM AT THAT TIME". Even if the engineer later discovers circumstances which deprive the contractor of the right to an extension, he is not entitled effectively to reduce the extension given under this sub-clause, but *see fully* N. 16.

The engineer shall keep records of any consideration he gives at any time to an extension of time, and of the reasons for his decision. It may be reasonable for him to notify the contractor of his conclusions so that the contractor may draw his attention to any factors he has overlooked.

11. **REVIEW OF EXTENSION "AS SOON AS POSSIBLE AFTER THE DUE DATE OR EXTENDED DATE FOR COMPLETION".** The "*extended date*" is of course the "*due date*". Precise drafting would refer to the original or extended date for completion, and would say whether completion of the whole works only is meant, or also any relevant section as in sub-cl. (4).

The first occasion for the engineer to consider an extension under this sub-clause will be the expiration of the original contract date as extended by any time granted under sub-cl. (2). If he grants an extension at that time, he will create a new "*due date or extended date for completion*", and apparently under this sub-clause will be required at that date to consider whether any further extension is due, for example where a new cause of delay has occurred since his last decision. (Cl. 1 (2)—singular importing plural has some relevance.) If he does grant an extension the process will then have to be repeated at the expiration of that extension, and so on until the engineer decides on making a review under this sub-clause that no further extension is due, when he has a breathing space until he grants a certificate of actual completion and his duty finally to review the extensions arises under sub-cl. (4).

12. **"WHETHER OR NOT THE CONTRACTOR SHALL HAVE MADE ANY CLAIM".** It is difficult to see why the contractor is not placed under a duty at all times to give whatever particulars he reasonably can produce. Normally it will be in the contractor's interest to draw the engineer's attention to any facts which entitle him to an extension.

The phrase at the head of this note appears in sub-cl. (3) but not sub-cl. (4). Although the drafting of these Conditions is such that it cannot be said with any assurance whether or not the omission is intended to be significant, it would be a reasonable interpretation that the contractor is bound to make a claim (presumably with "*full and detailed particulars of . . . (the) claim*" under sub-cl. (1)) before the engineer is bound to make the final assessment upon the issue of the relevant certificate of completion. Otherwise the engineer might have to give a final extension even though the contractor is holding back some relevant information known to him and not to the engineer or is delaying in making a promised submission.

13. **"SHOULD THE ENGINEER CONSIDER THAT THE CONTRACTOR IS NOT ENTITLED TO AN EXTENSION . . . HE SHALL SO NOTIFY THE EMPLOYER AND THE CONTRACTOR".** The importance of notification is to enable the employer to know of and exercise his right to deduct liquidated damages for delay, under cl. 47 (p. 155, N. 7). On waiver *see* p. 157, N. 11. Notice to the contractor allows him to plan the work accordingly.

14. **REVIEW OF EXTENSION OF TIME "UPON THE ISSUE OF THE CERTIFICATE OF COMPLETION . . . OF THE RELEVANT SECTION".** It is clear that upon the issue of a certificate for a section the engineer only reviews the extension of time for that section.

It does not seem that the contractor is entitled to any compensation merely because the engineer increases his own previous extension, even if he moves the completion date beyond the date of actual completion achieved by the contractor in response to the engineer's previous decision. Such acceleration claims are dealt with on pp. 371–2. To enable the employer to recover liquidated damages it is important that the engineer reviews the extension of time at the latest at this stage (p. 155, N. 7).

15. REVIEW "UPON THE ISSUE OF THE CERTIFICATE OF COMPLETION"—not "*as soon as possible after*" as in sub-cl. (3), although a cause of delay may end only a short time before completion. *See also* N. 12.

Under cl. 66 the contractor is entitled to immediate arbitration on his right to an extension if the certificate of completion which has been issued relates to the whole works and on any claim to certification of extra payment for the delay the subject of the claim.

16. "NO SUCH FINAL REVIEW . . . SHALL RESULT IN A DECREASE IN ANY EXTENSION . . . ALREADY GRANTED . . . PURSUANT TO SUB-CLAUSES (2) OR (3)". This restriction on the final review is broadly reasonable; it would hardly be fair if a contractor who completed on the faith of the engineer's decisions were to find himself liable nevertheless for liquidated damages. because of a later reduction in an extension of time already given.

A side effect of this provision may be that engineers will be wary in granting initial extensions, particularly in exercising the power to do so before full particulars have been received from the contractor. An engineer might well feel unhappy if he were to give an extension for "*exceptional adverse weather conditions*" before completion of the works, which he was then not free to reduce although the balance of the works was favoured with exceptionally good weather (*see* N. 4), or if he were to be misled by the contractor into giving too long an extension. Undue wariness would be unfortunate, because failure to operate this clause may result in unfair loss to the contractor and possibly cost to the employer (p. 371).

If it can be proved that the contractor deliberately, recklessly or negligently (p. 60) misled the engineer, the employer will be entitled to claim damages from the contractor for all losses (e.g. liquidated damages not recovered) due to the overlong extension given as a result of the contractor's action.

Although this review is called "*final*", the employer also has a right to raise a dispute under cl. 66 on any decision by the engineer under this clause. There is no time limit on referring such a dispute back to the engineer, and apparently the employer may wait to test an extension given by the engineer under sub-cl. (2) or (3) until after the works are completed and all the facts relating to the contractor's entitlement are known fully. Although in theory it seems that the engineer (or arbitrator after completion) in giving a decision under cl. 66 should not take into account circumstances not known at the time the engineer gave the original decision being appealed from, it is doubtful if that restriction will always be adhered to in practice.

Thus an employer apparently may wait until the engineer has given his final extension under sub-cl. (4) and apply to the engineer or arbitrator under cl. 66 for a reduction in the extension, if necessary also claiming a reduction in a prior extension already given under sub-cl. (2) or (3). Particularly where the engineer has been misled by the contractor or some facts have been overlooked in giving the extension, it may be necessary for the engineer to bring to the employer's attention his right to seek in this way a reduction of an extension. It is to be expected that an arbitrator in deciding whether to make or uphold a reduction in an extension of time after completion will keep in mind that it may be unfair that a contractor who completes on the faith of an extension then finds the extension reduced with resulting liability for liquidated damages.

NIGHT AND SUNDAY WORK

45.   Subject to any provision to the contrary contained in the Contract none of the Works[1] shall be executed during the night[2] or on Sundays without the permission in writing of the Engineer save when the work is unavoidable or absolutely necessary for the saving of life or property or for the safety of the Works in which case the Contractor shall immediately advise the Engineer or the Engineer's Representative. Provided always that this Clause shall not be applicable in the case of any work which it is customary to carry out outside normal working hours or by rotary or double shifts.[3]

1. RESTRICTION ON NIGHT AND SUNDAY WORK. "*Works*" replaces "*permanent work*" in the previous edition, producing a major extension of this restriction to all temporary works by the definition in cl. 1 (1) (l). Work on bank holidays is not restricted by this clause.

2. NIGHT WORK. *See also* cl. 46. Occasionally "*night*" is defined in the specification as 2000–0700 hours. In the absence of a definition this period may be applicable on the basis of the custom of the industry (p. 43 (*d*)), although the position is far from clear.

3. "NOT BE APPLICABLE ... (TO) WORK WHICH IT IS CUSTOMARY TO CARRY OUT OUTSIDE NORMAL WORKING HOURS OR BY ROTARY OR DOUBLE SHIFTS". The first part of this phrase is new. In this context "*customary*" implies a general usage in operation for a substantial period of time.

RATE OF PROGRESS

46.   If for any reason which does not entitle the Contractor to an extension of time[1] the rate of progress of the Works or any Section[2] is at any time in the opinion of the Engineer too slow to ensure completion by the prescribed time or extended time for completion the Engineer shall so notify the Contractor in writing[3] and the Contractor shall thereupon take such steps as are necessary and the Engineer may approve[4] to expedite progress so as to complete the Works or such Section by the prescribed time or extended time. The Contractor shall not be entitled to any additional payment for taking such steps.[5] If as a result of any notice given by the Engineer under this Clause the Contractor shall seek the Engineer's permission to do any work at night or on Sundays such permission shall not be unreasonably refused.[6]

1. "IF FOR ANY REASON WHICH DOES NOT ENTITLE THE CONTRACTOR TO AN EXTENSION OF TIME"—ACCELERATION CLAIMS. The relationship between this clause and cl. 44 is not clear. It appears that the engineer must consider whether there are grounds for an extension of time before giving a notice under this clause, even though the next occasion on which he is bound under cl. 44 to give an extension for the delay is some time ahead.

(*w*) Usage appears to be more relevant in this context than the criminal law, which for the crime of burglary defines night as sunset to sunrise. In *R.* v. *National Insurance Commissioner*, The Times, July 5th, 1974, "night" was given a commonsense meaning, in another context.

If the engineer decides that the reason for the delay does not entitle the contractor to an extension and that decision is later found to be wrong by the engineer himself on any review or under cl. 66 by the engineer or arbitrator, the alternative interpretations of this clause are that the notice is valid nevertheless or that the notice is invalid because there was in fact a "*reason which does . . . entitle the Contractor to an extension of time*" within the opening of this clause. (Whereas cl. 44 throughout refers to the engineer giving the extension he "*considers*" due, the opening of this clause does not.) However, even if the latter rather legalistic view is accepted the only consequence is that the contractor may disregard the notice; the contractor can have no claim against the employer for acceleration on foot of an invalid notice that was outside the engineer's powers under this clause. There is a claim to acceleration only if the employer authorised the engineer to disregard the contractor's rights to an extension in giving notice, or the engineer fails to administer this clause by considering those rights at all, and the contractor may have to try to safeguard his position accordingly (pp. 371–2).

2. "SECTION". *See* cl. 48.

3. "THE ENGINEER SHALL SO NOTIFY THE CONTRACTOR IN WRITING": PREVENTION. Such notification is important in case the engineer eventually has to forfeit the contractor's employment under cl. 63 (1) (d). More important, the preventive use of this clause should not be overlooked. The employer usually wants his works on time not liquidated damages, and the engineer is entitled to bring pressure on the contractor to increase his resources in good time where he is not proceeding with "*due expedition*" within cl. 41. The engineer's moral and legal authority to do so will be stronger if he has meticulously administered cl. 44 on extensions of time (N. 1).

4. "THE CONTRACTOR SHALL . . . TAKE SUCH STEPS AS ARE NECESSARY AND THE ENGINEER MAY APPROVE". The contractor must propose the steps; the engineer merely notifies and approves under this clause, and if he is wise carefully refrains from any instruction which might attract a claim under cl. 13.

5. "THE CONTRACTOR SHALL NOT BE ENTITLED TO ANY ADDITIONAL PAYMENT FOR TAKING SUCH STEPS". Not stated in the previous edition, but implied. For acceleration claims refer to N. 1.

6. PERMISSION FOR WORK AT NIGHT OR ON SUNDAYS NOT TO BE UNREASONABLY REFUSED. One change in this sentence from the previous edition extends the right to permission to Sunday as well as night work. In respect of the circumstances in which this permission must be granted a potential unfairness to the employer in the 4th edition is also removed, and the contractor gains too. If refusal of permission is unreasonable the contractor not only will be entitled to an extension of time and to have the decision reversed in arbitration as in the 4th edition (this reversal will rarely be in time to enable the contractor to work at night since the contractor generally has no right to arbitration until after completion), but more important it appears that he will now be entitled to compensation for the unreasonable refusal. Such compensation will be to cover any extra cost of —

alternative measures to accelerate taken as a result of the refusal of permission (p. 418).

LIQUIDATED DAMAGES FOR WHOLE OF WORKS

47. (1) (a) In the Appendix to the Form of Tender under the heading "Liquidated Damages for Delay" there is stated in column 1 the sum which represents the Employer's genuine pre-estimate (expressed as a rate per week or per day as the case may be) of the damages likely to be suffered[1] by him in the event that the whole of the Works shall not be completed[2,3] within the time prescribed by Clause 43.

Provided that in lieu of such sum there may be stated such lesser sum as represents the limit of the Contractor's liability for damages[4] for failure to complete the whole of the Works within the time for completion therefore or any extension thereof granted under Clause 44.

(b) If the Contractor should fail to complete the whole of the Works[3] within the prescribed time or any extension thereof granted under Clause 44 the Contractor shall pay to the Employer for such default the sum stated in column 1 aforesaid for every week or day as the case may be which shall elapse between the date on which the prescribed time or any extension thereof expired and the date of completion of the whole of the Works. Provided that if any part of the Works not being a Section or part of a Section shall be certified as complete pursuant to Clause 48 before completion of the whole of the Works the sum stated in column 1 shall be reduced by the proportion which the value of the part completed bears to the value of the whole of the Works.[5]

LIQUIDATED DAMAGES FOR SECTIONS

(2) (a) In cases where any Section shall be required to be completed within a particular time as stated in the Appendix to the Form of Tender there shall also be stated in the said Appendix under the heading "Liquidated Damages for Delay" in column 2 the sum by which the damages stated in column 1 or the limit of the Contractor's said liability[4] as the case may be shall be reduced upon completion of each such Section and in column 3 the sum which represents the Employer's genuine pre-estimate (expressed as aforesaid) of any specific damage likely to be suffered by him in the event that such Section shall not be completed within that time:

Provided that there may be stated in column 3 in lieu of such sum such lesser sum as represents the limit of the Contractor's liability[4] for failure to complete the relevant Section within the relevant time.[5]

(b)[6] If the Contractor should fail to complete any Section within the relevant time for completion or any extension thereof granted under Clause 44 the Contractor shall pay to the Employer for such default the sum stated in column 3 aforesaid for every week or day as the case may be which shall elapse between the date on which the relevant time or any extension thereof expired and the date of completion of the relevant Section. Provided that:

(i) if completion of a Section shall be delayed beyond the due date for completion of the whole of the Works the damages payable under sub-clauses (1) and (2) of this Clause until completion of that Section shall be the sum stated in column 1 plus in respect of that Section the sum stated in column 3 less the sum stated in column 2;

(ii) if any part of a Section shall be certified as complete pursuant to Clause 48 before completion of the whole thereof the sums stated in columns 2 and 3 in respect of that Section shall be reduced by the proportion which the value of the part bears to the value of the Section and the sum stated in column 1 shall be reduced by the same amount as the sum in column 2 is reduced; and

(iii) upon completion of any such Section the sum stated in column 1 shall be reduced by the sum stated in column 2 in respect of that Section at the date of such completion.

Damages not a Penalty

(3) All sums payable by the Contractor to the Employer pursuant to this Clause shall be paid as liquidated damages for delay and not as a penalty.[1]

Deduction of Liquidated Damages

(4) If the Engineer shall under Clause 44 (3) or (4) have determined and certified any extension of time to which he considers the Contractor entitled and shall have notified the Employer and the Contractor that he is of the opinion that the Contractor is not entitled to any or any further extension of time[7] the Employer may deduct and retain from any sum otherwise payable by the Employer to the Contractor hereunder the amount which in the event that the Engineer's said opinion should not be subsequently revised would be the amount of the liquidated damages payable by the Contractor under this Clause.[8]

Reimbursement of Liquidated Damages

(5) If upon a subsequent or final review of the circumstances causing delay the Engineer shall grant an extension or further extension of time or if an arbitrator appointed under Clause 66 shall decide that the Engineer should have granted such an extension or further extension of time[9] the Employer shall no longer be entitled to liquidated damages in respect of the period of such extension of time. Any sums in respect of such period which may have been recovered pursuant to sub-clause (3) of this Clause shall be reimbursable forthwith to the Contractor together with interest at the rate provided for in Clause 60 (6) from the date on which such liquidated damages were recovered from the Contractor.[10,11,12]

1. LIQUIDATED DAMAGES AND PENALTIES. The courts recognise that the parties to a contract may be wise to agree in advance the amount of compensation to be paid for any breach, rather than leave it to the courts to assess damages in the ordinary way, because it may be that, "although as a result of a particular breach a party will undoubtedly suffer damage, the nature of the damage may be such that proof of it is extremely complex, difficult and expensive". But, obviously, unfair advantage may be taken of a party anxious to get a contract, who often will not allow for the possibility

(x) *Clydebank Engineering Co.* v. *Yzquierdo-y-Castaneda Don Jose Ramos* [1905] A.C. 6, at p. 11.

that he may have to break it, and may agree to pay large damages for a small breach.

A party must pay compensation, but may not be punished for breaking a contract. The rule is therefore that a clause in a contract settling the amount of damages in advance will be enforced only if the amount fixed is a genuine pre-estimate of the loss likely to be suffered by the other party from a breach (called liquidated damages), and not if it is in the nature of a threat held over a party attempting to penalise him if he does not carry out his contract (a penalty). If the amount fixed is classified as liquidated damages, the injured party will be entitled to no less nor more than that amount, whatever his actual loss or even if in the event he suffers no loss at all from the breach, e.g. where some machinery essential to the use of the works and to be supplied by another direct contractor is also held up. Any other rule would defeat the whole purpose of agreeing the sum payable, since the injured party would have to prove that he actually suffered loss to the amount stated, and therefore would be in no better position than if the amount for damages had not been agreed in advance. If the sum is construed as a penalty, it will have no effect and damages will be assessed by the courts in the ordinary way.

The name given to a clause by the parties is not conclusive, nor are the several statements in this clause that the sums are a genuine pre-estimate of the employer's losses. A clause will be a penalty if the damages specified were extravagant and unconscionable, judged in the light of the circumstances when the contract was made not when it was broken, in comparison with the greatest loss that could then be expected to follow from a breach:

> A building contract provided that in the event of unsatisfactory progress the employer might forfeit the contract and should then become owner of the contractor's tools and material at the works.
> The contract did not require the employer to account to the contractor for the balance of the value of the tools and materials after deducting the actual loss he had suffered by the contractor's default and the clause was therefore held void as a penalty.

y

> In the same way a clause stating that the employer shall be entitled to keep all the retention money on forfeiture, and not merely enough to cover his loss, is void as a penalty. The retention money bears no relation to the employer's likely loss—the later in the progress of the works the employer forfeits the contract the less his loss will be, but the larger the retention money (but *see* cl. 60, p. 266, N. 27).

z

> A hire purchase agreement specified that if instalments were not paid the owners should be entitled to re-take machinery, and recover immediately the amount by which the original hire purchase price and their expenses exceeded any instalments already paid plus the price realised by them on sale of the machinery.
> Held: That this clause was void as a penalty, since it applied whether default took place at the beginning or end of the hire purchase term, despite the fact that the original price included a substantial amount for interest on the basis that payment would be spread over the term.

aa

It may not be easy to classify a particular clause, but there is a

(*y*) *Ranger* v. *G. W. Ry.* (1854) 5 H.L.C. 72.
(*z*) *Public Works Commissioner* v. *Hills* [1906] A.C. 368.
(*aa*) *Anglo-Auto Finance Co. Ltd.* v. *James* [1963] 1 W.L.R. 1042, affirmed [1963] 1 W.L.R. 1049. *See* the Consumer Credit Act, 1974.

presumption that it is a penalty if the same amount is fixed as compensation for breach of a contract in several different ways, some of which will cause serious and others only trivial damage. Where a damages clause is principally intended to guard against a particular type of breach it should not therefore be widened to cover all breaches of the contract. If a party yields to the temptation to do this, the result may be that, since some of the possible breaches may be trivial, the clause will be completely void, even in relation to major breaches for which the amount stated would have been reasonable.

A clause of this kind will particularly be enforced where it is difficult to estimate the likely damage in advance. In a leading case:

> The Spanish Government contracted for the supply of four torpedo boats which were eventually delivered several months late.
> Held: That a term in the contract for compensation at the rate of £500 a week for each vessel was valid. It would have been almost impossible to calculate in advance the actual damage, the sum was payable for one type of breach only and it was not exorbitant.

_bb_

The actual legal position therefore is exactly contrary to the widespread view that a public authority may not enforce an agreed damages clause for delay with public works where it is impossible for the authority to prove any actual money loss from the delay. This misconception must have relieved many dilatory contractors from the damages for which they were properly liable, and should finally be ended by the following quotation:

> "If . . . the loss accruing to the plaintiff from . . . the . . . breaches cannot, at the time when the contract was made, be accurately or even reasonably calculated in money, it becomes less easy to classify the sum to be paid on breach as extravagant and unconscionable. . . . The last hundred years have produced a number of decisions on building contracts in which there have been clauses stipulating the amount to be paid by the builder should he fail to complete construction upon the due date. The contracts have variously been for the erection of buildings, ships, railways, sewerage works and industrial plant; in most of them the stipulated amount has been held to be liquidated damages (and therefore enforceable). . . . The exceptions are (two cases where the amount of the sum payable was not related to the period of the delay)."

_cc_

There is also no rule, as there is often thought to be, that a liquidated damages clause for delay is not valid unless there is a provision for an equivalent bonus (N. 12) to the contractor for early completion. But the fact that there is a bonus clause in the contract is relevant as evidence of the value of time to the employer.

Where it is quite clear that a clause is intended to limit the amount of damages it will be enforced:

> The actual loss by one party to a contract as a result of delay by the other was £5,850. By a clause in the contract only £600 damages were payable for the delay and it was proved that the parties must have known that the actual loss would be greater.
> Held: That only £600 could be recovered.

_dd_

This clause can only be invalidated if the amount specified is exorbitant, since it meets all the other requirements for a valid liquidated damages

(_bb_) _Clydebank Engineering Co. etc._ (above).
(_cc_) "McGregor on Damages" 13th ed., paras. 350 and 367.
(_dd_) _Cellulose Acetate Silk Co._ v. _Widnes Foundry_ (1925) _Ltd._ [1933] A.C. 20.

clause. The rate of damages should never be chosen at random without careful investigation of the likely financial cost of delay to the employer. The net loss of business profits may be used as the basis for calculation in the case of a commercial structure which the employer is to occupy, or the net profit rental which will be lost where the property is to be let (not the gross profit, save in so far as overheads will be incurred even though the building is not complete). In the case of public works where delay will not cause any direct loss of revenue to the employer, the current rate of interest on the capital invested is often taken, plus the extra supervision costs.

For complete protection any liquidated damages in a sub-contract for delay by a sub-contractor who may hold up the whole works may be higher than the liquidated damages payable by the main contractor, to cover loss to the contractor in having plant idle, etc. *See* p. 428 on a sub-contractor's liability for main contract liquidated damages in the absence of equivalent damages in the sub-contract.

The engineer should carefully advise the employer on the calculation of liquidated damages and the papers showing that the damages were calculated and not chosen at random should be preserved.

It is important to appreciate that even if a contractor succeeds in invalidating an agreed damages clause on the grounds that it is a penalty, that does not mean he escapes scot-free for any delay, merely that the employer has to prove his loss in the ordinary way. It is conceivable that an employer's actual provable loss may be more than the agreed damages, and that the contractor will lose by invalidating the liquidated damages clause. However, in the case of public works, where it may be very difficult for the employer to prove any tangible money loss due to delay in completion, a liquidated damages clause is a very important protection to the employer to put the contractor under pressure to complete on time (above).

There are several possible defences to a claim for liquidated damages, apart from the defence that the clause is void as a penalty:

(*a*) That a time for completion is not stated in the contract, unless a time was, in fact, agreed on so that the contract may be rectified (p. 41).

(*b*) That the completion date no longer applies—p. 155, N. 7.

(*c*) Waiver—N. 11.

(*d*) Conclusive final certificate—p. 302, N. 13.

ee   (*e*) Frustration—cl. 64; or change in the whole works (p. 175).

2. "COMPLETION OF THE WORKS" clearly means substantial completion—*see* para. (b) of this sub-clause. The contractor is, of course, entitled to arbitration on any dispute about the time of completion.

Unless specially agreed, the employer has no right to take possession of any part of the works before the whole works are completed. This means that if the employer wants such possession the contractor may insist on the

---

(*ee*) In *Robophone* v. *Blank* [1966] 3 All E.R. 128, at p. 142, Diplock L. J. gave a warning against taking damages clauses too lightly—"the Court should not be astute to descry a 'penalty clause' in every provision of a contract which stipulates a sum to be payable by one party to the other in the event of a breach by the former". Although this case did not involve a construction contract, the warning might well be heeded by those contractors who work on the basis that it is always possible to find some way out of paying liquidated damages for delay.

engineer first giving a certificate under cl. 48, and he is then relieved of the whole or part of his liability for liquidated damages.

3. LIQUIDATED DAMAGES—THE TAX FLUCTUATIONS CLAUSE AND BREACH BY THE CONTRACTOR IN THE MAINTENANCE PERIOD. The fact that liquidated damages cover only a breach by the contractor consisting of failure to complete on time, so that the employer is entitled to general damages for any other breach, may be relevant to a claim by the employer for the contractor's failure to proceed with due expedition causing the employer to pay him extra under the tax fluctuations clause (p. 311) or for loss of use of the works due to defects in the maintenance period (p. 165).

4. "SUCH LESSER SUM AS REPRESENTS THE LIMIT OF THE CONTRACTOR'S LIABILITY FOR DAMAGES". This clause recognises that it may be necessary for the employer to agree to limit the damages for which the contractor will be liable for delay in completion, because contractors will not tender or the tender price will be increased unduly if liability is imposed for the full foreseeable cost to the employer of delay.

It is a serious step to insert damages less than a pre-estimate of the employer's full losses, which the engineer should not take without explaining the dangers to and obtaining the written authority of his client. If liquidated damages are low the employer may find himself suffering a running loss from delay which is irrecoverable, or even at the mercy of a contractor who finds it cheaper to pay the damages than incur the expense necessary to complete on time, with forfeiture under cl. 63 impracticable because of the expense and delay of bringing another contractor on the site.

For the relevance of the Unfair Contract Terms Act 1977 where contract documents with low liquidated damages emanate from the contractor, *see* p. 434.

5. REDUCTION OF LIQUIDATED DAMAGES ON PARTIAL COMPLETION. Such reduction is provided for, where any section of the works for which a separate completion time is stated in the tender is certified complete, where part of a section is certified complete, and where any other part of the works is certified complete. The procedures for filling in the columns for liquidated damages and recovering the damages are summarised in the next note.

6. COMPLETION OF THE "LIQUIDATED DAMAGES FOR DELAY" COLUMNS IN THE FORM OF TENDER AND CALCULATION OF LIQUIDATED DAMAGES. In completing the liquidated damages columns in the form of tender the engineer proceeds in this way:

(*a*) In consultation with the employer he determines the liquidated damages to be recovered for delay with the whole works (N. 1), and inserts that figure in column 1.

(*b*) He decides whether there is any benefit to the employer in specifying in the tender early completion of a section, calculates that benefit in money and inserts the figure in column 3.

(*ff*) If the employer insists on taking possession prematurely the courts may possibly even grant the contractor an injunction to prevent wrongful revocation of the contractor's licence to keep possession of the site (p. 306). In any ease the employer will be liable for damages for breach of contract.

(*c*) The engineer preserves the records and evidence showing how these figures were calculated (N. 1).

(*d*) If liquidated damages are recoverable for delay in completing the whole works and also a portion of those damages recoverable for delay in completing a section, then if the section overruns the completion date for the whole works there is duplication of damages. The contractor is liable to pay the full liquidated damages specified for the whole works plus for a second time the portion of those damages specified for the section.

This duplication is removed by the use of column 2. If the whole or part of the benefit obtained by completion of a section on time is merely a part of the benefit which will be obtained from completion of the whole works (e.g. a proportion of the profit to be earned from the works), the damages specified for that benefit in column 3 are also inserted in column 2. If a section overruns the completion date for the whole works the sum in column 2 is then deducted from the totals of columns 1 and 3.

(*e*) Where the whole or part of the loss that will be suffered by delay in completing a section is additional to the loss provided for in column 1 for delay with the whole works, i.e. where some use is intended of the section (either by the employer or other contractors of his) independent of the profitable use intended for the whole works, then the figure in column 2 will be "Nil" or reduced accordingly below the figure in column 3 (as in the examples below).

The statement in sub-cl. (2) (a) above that any "*specific*" damage likely to be suffered for delay with a section is to be included in column 3 is puzzling. It is suggested that "*specific*" means only that a proportion of the liquidated damages for the whole works is not to be inserted automatically, only if the employer will in fact lose that proportion from delay with the section. The word can hardly have the result of preventing the employer effectively inserting a proportion of general liquidated damages for public works (N. 1), where the section of the public works can be used separately before completion of the whole. Indeed such an interpretation would be inconsistent with the use designated for column 2.

Two examples may clarify the above procedure:

(i) Contract to build a jetty. A section of the jetty may be used separately for ships, and therefore an early completion date is specified in the tender for that section. The employer estimates that he will make a net profit of £15,000 per week when he has the whole jetty, and £5,000 per week when he has the section. If the section is delayed he will be liable to pay an estimated £2,000 per week to a following-on oil pipeline contractor.

Liquidated damages to cover the employer fully for delay in completing the whole works will be stated in column 1 as £15,000 per week. In column 2 a figure of £5,000 will be stated as the reduction on completion of the separate section. In column 3 £7,000 will be inserted to cover the weekly liability to the following-on contractor and the loss of profit from the section. Alternatively the equivalent daily rates should be inserted, if the employer's losses will be reduced *pro rata* for any part of a week in which the works are complete.

(ii) Contract to build a factory. The tender specifies early completion of a section, which cannot be used for production until the whole factory is completed but can be used for storage of plant and equipment. The employer estimates that he will make a net profit of £12,000 per week when he has the whole factory. If completion of the section is delayed the employer will have to rent storage at a cost of £1,000 per week.

Liquidated damages to cover the employer fully for delay in completing the whole works will be stated in column 1 as £12,000 per week. In column 2 a figure of "Nil" will be stated as the reduction on completion of the separate section. In column 3 the figure of £1,000 will be inserted to cover the cost of storage if the section is not completed on time.

The procedure at the other end, when it comes to enforcing liquidated damages, is as follows:

(*a*) When any section overruns the specified completion date the engineer first ensures that he has complied with the conditions for enforcing liquidated damages by deduction (N. 7) and the employer is then entitled to deduct the liquidated damages in column 3 and should be so informed by the engineer:

(*b*) As soon as the section is certified complete, the right to the liquidated damages in column 3 ceases, and the engineer should tell the employer to cease deduction.

(*c*) If the whole works overrun the final contract completion date, subject again to the engineer fulfilling the necessary conditions, the employer becomes entitled to deduct the damages specified in column 1 for the whole works. If a section is still incomplete the employer continues to recover the damages under column 3 as well, but with the total of columns 1 and 3 subject to deduction of any sum specified in column 2.

(*d*) Reduction in damages for part completion is provided for where part of a section is certified complete, and where any other part of the works is certified complete. The system is that if any part of the works not being a section or part of a section is certified complete under cl. 48, a proportionate reduction is made in the total liquidated damages in column 1. Where part of a section is certified complete, a reduction is made in the sums in respect of that section in columns 2 and 3 and the sum in column 1 is reduced by the same amount as the sum in column 2 has been reduced.

(*e*) Unfortunately no procedure is provided for certification by the engineer of the amount of a reduction for part completion. Nevertheless the engineer should calculate the adjustment and tell the parties his calculation. The reduction is to be in accordance with the proportion which the value of the part certified complete bears to the value of the relevant section or the whole works. Any dispute about the proportion would fall to be decided under cl. 66.

(*f*) Where the works or a section overrun the completion date the employer also has the right to sue the contractor for payment of liquidated damages, apart from the right to deduct the damages from any sums due by him to the contractor as specified in sub-cl. (4). This alternative is discussed in the next note.

7. THE TWO PRE-CONDITIONS FOR DEDUCTION OR RECOVERY OF LIQUIDATED DAMAGES are that the engineer "*shall under Clause* 44 (3) *or* (4) *have determined and certified any extension of time to which he considers the Contractor entitled*" and that the engineer "*shall have notified the Employer and the Contractor* (writing is not specified) *that he is of the opinion that the Contractor is not entitled to any or any further extension*".

It is noticeable that it is not a condition that the engineer has considered   *ff'*

(*ff'*) For contracts let under the January 1979 revision of these Conditions, published at proof stage of this book, the engineer only has either to certify any extension he considers due "*or*" (in place of "*and*" in the 2nd line of sub-cl. (4) above) notify the employer and contractor that no extension or no further extension is due, not both.

an extension at the time specified in cl. 44 (2), and sufficient if the engineer considers an extension under either sub-cl. (3) or (4). Therefore, even if the engineer does not consider an extension until the issue of the certificate of completion, only then makes under cl. 44 (4) any extension he decides is due and notifies the employer and contractor that he does not consider any further extension due, the employer may recover liquidated damages.

However, the engineer has an abstract duty to act under cl. 44 (2) to (4). It is also in the employer's interests that liquidated damages are deducted as soon as the contractor is late with completion. For that reason the engineer should consider an extension of time under cl. 44 (3) *"at or as soon as possible after the due date or extended date for completion"* and (despite his duty under sub-cl. (4) to make a further review on actual completion) may then certify that he considers no further extension is due, so that the employer may immediately start deducting liquidated damages. *See* the next note for the position where the engineer later changes his mind, or an arbitrator changes it for him.

The requirements set out at the head of this note are stated to be a condition only for deduction of liquidated damages, and not specifically to the employer's right to claim liquidated damages from the contractor in proceedings, where the employer does not hold any money from which they can be deducted. By this clause the contractor is required to *"pay to the Employer"* liquidated damages where the works or a section are not completed *"within the prescribed time or any extension ... granted under Clause 44"* (sub-cl. (1) (b); there are similar words in sub-cl. (2) (b)). It is suggested that if the engineer does not administer cl. 44 by considering the contractor's right to an extension of time on right principles at the proper times, at least under either cl. 44 (3) or (4) as required under this cl. 49 (4) to entitle the employer to deduct liquidated damages, or acts in bad faith by failing to grant the extension he does consider due, the employer is in breach of contract and not entitled to recover liquidated damages from the original completion date by proceeding against the contractor (or by a counter-claim if sued by the contractor for a certified payment) any more than by deduction. On this aspect of breach of contract *see* p. 418, and such a breach may entitle the contractor to an acceleration claim—p. 371. Instead of liability for liquidated damages from the contract completion date, after such a breach that date will cease to apply and the employer will be entitled to general damages if the contractor does not complete within a *ff"* reasonable time.

8. DEDUCTION OF LIQUIDATED DAMAGES. Note that the engineer does not deduct liquidated damages in his interim certificates; it is for the employer to deduct the damages from the total certified. The engineer should notify the employer of his right to deduct, and set out for the employer his calculation of the damages due. The damages are allowed for in calculating the balance on the final payment certificate (p. 264, N. 18), and a dispute about liquidated damages at any time is subject to cl. 66 (p. 290, N. 1).

9. "SUBSEQUENT OR FINAL REVIEW" BY ENGINEER OR BY ARBITRATOR AND RECOVERY BY CONTRACTOR OF LIQUIDATED DAMAGES. For the review procedure under cl. 44, *see* p. 138, N. 1.

(*ff"*) Refer to *Miller* v. *London,C.C.* (1934) 151 L.T. 425, and *Perini Corp* v. *Commonwealth of Australia* [1969] 2 N.S.W.R. 530.

The reference here to an arbitrator is a little out of place. If an arbitrator believes that the engineer should have given the contractor a longer extension of time, normally he will not say so specifically but simply award the contractor the amount of the liquidated damages which in his view has been wrongly deducted by the employer, with interest. If the arbitrator does in response to this clause state in his award that the contractor is entitled to an extension of time not allowed by the engineer, he should be careful to make clear whether he has allowed for reimbursement of liquidated damages in the money award; otherwise the contractor may claim reimbursement under this clause as well as the sum awarded by the arbitrator.

For reduction by the arbitrator of an extension granted by the engineer *'e* p. 145, N. 16.

10. INTEREST. *See* p. 268, N. 30.

11. WAIVER. If the employer leads the contractor to believe that he does not require the work to be finished by the completion date, and because of this the contractor does not give notice of claims for extensions of time or slows down the work, may the employer later change his mind and claim liquidated damages (or forfeit the contract—cl. 63) from the original completion date?

The difficulty in law, of course, is that the contractor has given no consideration for any agreement by the employer to release him from the original date in the contract. But despite the general rule that consideration is essential before the courts will enforce an agreement (p. 3 (*b*)), they have developed the doctrine of waiver, which may enable a party to defend himself against an unfair change of attitude.

> The defendant ordered a body for a Rolls-Royce chassis. The date for delivery was March 20, 1948. The body was not completed on that date, but the defendant continued to press for delivery.
>
> Held: That the defendant had lost his right to refuse to take the body and to leave it on the manufacturers' hands because it was not completed on March 20. He had waived the date for completion by continuing to press for delivery after that date, and the manufacturers had continued to do work on the car as a result of the representation by this conduct that the defendant would not rely on the original date, so that it would have been unjust to allow him to go back on that representation. *gg*

This doctrine does not only apply where one party deliberately misleads the other (that would be fraud and the other party would have a remedy in any case); it is sufficient if he unintentionally conducts himself so that the other reasonably believes that he is waiving his strict rights. Where the doctrine applies those rights may not be lost completely, but the other party may only be given an opportunity to put himself back in the position in which he would have been had he not relied on the representation, e.g. in the case referred to in the opening of this note by extending the time for completion.

The doctrine is subject to a number of limitations which need not be discussed here, except the point that the engineer has no more implied

(gg) *Rickards (Charles) Ltd.* v. *Oppenheim* [1950] 1 K.B. 616. This case is also discussed on pp. 425–6 of the text, below.

authority to bind his employer by a waiver of this kind than he has to change the construction contract expressly, so that the contractor is only entitled to rely on a representation by the engineer if he can prove that the engineer had special authority from the employer or that the employer impliedly authorised it by knowing of the conduct of the engineer (p. 399).

Failing to forfeit the contract for delay in completion or to deduct the damages as they become due does not, of course, by itself waive the right to
hh   claim liquidated damages for delay.

12. BONUS. A carrot may be more effective than a stick to persuade the contractor to complete on time, but there are complications about a bonus clause:

(*a*) The employer may not be pleased if he receives the works late but nevertheless has to pay a bonus because the contractor is entitled to an extension of time for completion.

The bonus clause therefore may specify either that the original contract date for completion is absolutely fixed for the purpose of calculating the bonus (which may be unfair) or give the contractor only a limited right to extension for that purpose. For example, the clause may say that the contractor is not to be entitled to an extension for strikes, or even for any delay unless it is caused by the employer.

(*b*) Whatever limit is placed on the contractor's right to an extension of time, if the contractor finishes late because of delay caused by the employer or engineer the contractor may be entitled to compensation for the lost bonus, under cl. 7 or as damages for the employer's breach of contract (ch. 16).

(*c*) A bonus specified in the contract is subject to adjustment under the price fluctuations formula (p. 314).

CERTIFICATE OF COMPLETION OF WORKS

48. (1) When the Contractor shall consider that the whole of the Works has been substantially completed and has satisfactorily passed any final test that may be prescribed by the Contract he may give a notice to that effect to the Engineer or to the Engineer's Representative accompanied by an undertaking to finish any outstanding work during the Period of Maintenance.[1,2] Such notice and undertaking shall be in writing and shall be deemed to be a request by the Contractor for the Engineer to issue a Certificate of Completion in respect of the Works and the Engineer shall within 21 days[3] of the date of delivery of such notice either issue to the Contractor (with a copy to the Employer) a Certificate of Completion stating the date on which in his opinion the Works were substantially completed in accordance with the Contract or else give instructions[4] in writing to the Contractor specifying all the work which in the Engineer's opinion requires to be done by the Contractor before the issue of such certificate. If the Engineer shall give such instructions the Contractor shall be entitled to receive such Certificate of Completion within 21 days[3] of completion to the satisfaction of the Engineer of the work specified by the said instructions.[5]

(*hh*) The term "waiver" is used generally in this note because it is more revealing as to the nature of the doctrine to a non-lawyer than the, in some cases, more correct legal title of promissory estoppel. Developments in this area of the law may be expected. "The whole sequence of cases based on promissory estoppel since the war ... may need to be reviewed and reduced to a coherent body of doctrine by the courts. I do not mean to say that any are to be regarded with suspicion." *Woodhouse Ltd.* v. *Nigerian Produce Ltd.* [1972] 2 All E.R. 271, 282 per Hailsham L.C.

COMPLETION OF SECTIONS AND OCCUPIED PARTS

(2) Similarly in accordance with the procedure set out in sub-clause (1) of this Clause the Contractor may request and the Engineer shall issue a Certificate of Completion in respect of:

    (a) any Section in respect of which a separate time for completion is provided in the Appendix to the Form of Tender; and

    (b) any substantial part of the Works which has been both completed to the satisfaction of the Engineer and occupied or used by the Employer.[6,7]

COMPLETION OF OTHER PARTS OF WORKS

(3) If the Engineer shall be of the opinion that any part of the Works shall have been substantially completed and shall have satisfactorily passed any final test that may be prescribed by the Contract he may issue a Certificate of Completion in respect of that part of the Works before completion of the whole of the Works and upon the issue of such certificate the Contractor shall be deemed to have undertaken to complete any outstanding work in that part of the Works during the Period of Maintenance.[7,8]

REINSTATEMENT OF GROUND

(4) Provided always that a Certificate of Completion given in respect of any Section or part of the Works before completion of the whole shall not be deemed to certify completion of any ground or surfaces requiring reinstatement unless such certificate shall expressly so state.

1. NOTICE OF COMPLETION AND UNDERTAKING BY THE CONTRACTOR. This clause introduces a procedure by which the contractor may serve notice on the engineer when the works are complete and any final test passed, in response to which the engineer must within 21 days either issue a certificate of completion or give written instructions "*specifying all the work ... to be done ... before issue of such certificate*". In the latter case the engineer must issue the certificate within 21 days of completion to his satisfaction of the specified work.

A similar procedure is laid down for any section of the works required by the contract to be completed early, and any substantial part of the works both completed and occupied or used by the employer.

There is no limitation on the number of notices which the contractor may give, or to protect the engineer from harassment by premature or repeated notice. Nevertheless if the lack of completion in fact is such as to establish that a notice is not bona fide, it is suggested that it may be ignored by the engineer.

There is no duty on the engineer to certify completion unless and until the contractor serves notice. Indeed, the engineer has no right to certify completion of substantially the whole works until the contractor chooses to serve a notice, although he is given power to certify completion of part of the works on his own initiative (N. 7). But should a contractor postpone notice in an attempt to extend the time for which he will recover compensation for any disruption for which the employer is liable (p. 364)

(ii) In *Meyer* v. *Gilmer* (1899) 18 N.Z.L.R. 129 an oral certificate of satisfaction was held sufficient where writing was not specifically required by the contract. Note that cl. 48 does not specify a written certificate but writing appears to be implied by the reference to a copy of a certificate, at least in sub-cls. (1) and (2).

his stratagem will fail; he will not be entitled to costs that are due to his failure to mitigate his losses by obtaining a certificate as soon as possible and deploying his resources on other works (p. 429).

If the engineer does not abide by the procedure in this clause, arbitration is an ineffective remedy to compel the engineer to specify the work to be done to reach completion, since no step may be taken in arbitration until the completion certificate is due. A remedy may arise in damages (p. 418).

In this edition the engineer is given greater control over the time of fulfilment of this undertaking by the contractor, who is bound to finish the outstanding work "*as soon as may be practicable*" (p. 163, N. 3), and the contractor's liability for damage to or done in executing the work included in the undertaking is clarified—p. 99, N. 4, and p. 100, N. 7.

There is still no extended period of maintenance for work made good after completion on foot of the undertaking, so that it is important for the engineer to see that the work is done as soon as possible.

The engineer has the powers he had before the certificate of completion in relation to work included in an undertaking (cl. 49 (2)) except that it is not clear whether he has power to vary such work, since the contractor's duty is to "*finish any outstanding work*". No price fluctuations are allowable on such work—p. 315, para. (c) (ii).

2. SUBSTANTIAL COMPLETION. The *Concise Oxford Dictionary* equates "substantial" with "virtual" which is defined as "that is such for practical purposes though not in name or according to strict definition". It is at least clear on the one hand that the fact that the works are or are capable of being used by the employer does not automatically mean that they are substantially complete ("*any substantial part of the Works which has both been completed . . . and occupied or used*") and on the other hand that the engineer may not postpone his certificate under this clause until the works are absolutely completed and free of all defects. The many reported cases on the question of "substantial" completion in relation to payment under an entire contract, a different legal problem, are of doubtful relevance. Obviously both the nature and extent of the uncompleted work or defects are relevant, and to say that substantial completion allows for minor deficiencies that can be readily remedied and which do not impair the structure as a whole is probably an accurate summary of what is a question of fact in each case.

The contractor's remedy if he alleges substantial completion is immediate arbitration—cl. 66, N. 17.

3. "WITHIN 21 DAYS". The engineer need not take the full 21 days in all cases. If the works or the work specified in instructions is completed when the notice is given he should certify as soon as the necessary checking has been done.

(*jj*) *Dakin* v. *Lee* [1916] 1 K.B. 566, C.A. (cost of remedying defects £55, contract price £750, held substantial completion); *Kiely & Sons Ltd.* v. *Medcraft* (1965) 109 S.J. 829 (contract to decorate house for £520, substantially complete although it would cost £200 to remedy the defects); *North American Wall Paper Co.* v. *Jackson Court Co., Inc.*, 167 App. Div. 779, 153 N.Y. Supp. 204; *Laundry* v. *Benjamin*, 141 N.Y.S. 2d 710 (14% and 28% respectively in value of contract work not done, no substantial completion). *See also Hoenig* v. *Isaacs* [1952] 2 All E.R. 176, C.A.; *Lawrence* v. *Kern* (1910) 14 W.L.R. 337, 352 Can.; *Webber* v. *Havill* (1964) 47 D.L.R. (2d) 36 Can.

(*kk*) *See Jacobs & Younger, Inc.* v. *Kent*, 230 N.Y. 239, 129 N.E. 889. Latent defects do not affect the validity of a completion certificate—*City of Westminster* v. *Jarvis* [1970] 1 All E.R. 943, H.L.

4. "GIVE INSTRUCTIONS SPECIFYING . . . WORK". It is conceivable that the contractor may be entitled to extra payments under cl. 13 for unforeseen costs of delay or disruption arising out of these instructions (p. 75).

5. "SPECIFYING ALL THE WORK WHICH . . . REQUIRES TO BE DONE . . . BEFORE THE ISSUE OF SUCH CERTIFICATE . . . THE CONTRACTOR SHALL BE ENTITLED TO RECEIVE SUCH CERTIFICATE . . . WITHIN 21 DAYS OF COMPLETION . . . OF THE WORK SPECIFIED". It is suggested that in the case of defects a direction by the engineer to the contractor to remedy a specified defect without telling him how, would be held to meet the requirement to specify "*the work . . . to be done*". It is not generally considered to be the engineer's duty to tell the contractor how to do his job.

The engineer should be careful to include in any such instructions the repair, replacement and making good of all defects that may appear before the issue of the completion certificate. It is suggested that this clause authorises such a requirement, although unfortunately again the phrase set out at the head of this note, requiring the work to be done to be specified, is not at all clear. If the engineer does not include this requirement the defects (and any outstanding work overlooked by the engineer) will be covered by the maintenance clause (p. 163, N. 4) but apparently the completion certificate must be given and half the retention money will have to be released and liquidated damages will cease to run after completion of the work in the instructions even if the works have collapsed in the meantime.

6. "ANY SUBSTANTIAL PART OF THE WORKS WHICH HAS BEEN BOTH COMPLETED . . . AND OCCUPIED OR USED BY THE EMPLOYER". There is room for much dispute about what is a "*substantial part*" sufficient to require separate certification under this provision, and both the quantity and usefulness of the part obviously must be taken into account.

"*Substantially*" does not appear before "*completed*" in this place. It is reasonably clear from the "*Similarly*", introducing this sub-clause, that it is nevertheless implied.

Apart from this right to apply for certification of part of the works which are complete and in fact already occupied by the employer, whatever the state of the works the contractor ordinarily may rely on his right to possession under cl. 42 (which is subject only to cl. 31) and refuse to give the employer occupation of any part unless the engineer first gives him a certificate of completion for that part. The engineer may be reluctant to do so unless the works are in fact substantially complete, because the employer will suffer a reduction in liquidated damages, the maintenance period will start for that part and a portion of the first half of the retention money must be released. To avoid such an impasse, it may be important for the engineer to specify in the contract documents that the employer will be entitled to occupy or use the whole or part of the works before completion, spelling out what is to happen about liquidated damages, defects liability, retention money and, most important, insurance of the works (p. 98).

The contractor may make a disruption claim if the employer's occupation or use of part of the works impedes the completion of the remainder. It is suggested that the right given to the engineer in this clause to certify completion of part of the works, and the implied right of the employer to use that part, protects the employer from a disruption claim in respect of any use that is normal having regard to the intended purpose of the works known to the contractor at the time of contract. A disruption claim would appear to be open for the effects of any extraordinary use. See ch. 12 on disruption claims generally. It may be wise to clarify the position by a special clause in any case where substantial use by the employer is envisaged, or occupation by other follow-on contractors of the employer.

7. COMPLETION CERTIFICATE FOR PART OF THE WORKS FOR WHICH SEPARATE COMPLETION TIME IS NOT SPECIFIED AND WHICH IS NOT OCCUPIED OR USED BY THE EMPLOYER. In this case the engineer has a discretion, which it seems he should exercise in favour of the contractor only if the employer has some immediate need for the part of the works, since the employer suffers a reduction in the liquidated damages, a portion of the first half of the retention money must be released, and the maintenance period commences for that part. Because the clause says that the engineer "*may issue*" a certificate of partial completion in this case, and does not bind him to do so when desirable in his personal opinion (as in the case of some other powers—p. 409), it seems that he may consult with the employer before doing so, and it is suggested that because of his duty to the employer as his client and the consequences for the employer, he should obtain the employer's prior approval. The engineer may exercise this power without any prior application or consent from the contractor.

It appears that the engineer may from time to time give certificates of partial completion of several parts of the works (by cl. 1 (2) the singular may include the plural). But as by this sub-clause he may certify completion of part of the works only "*before completion of the whole of the Works*", he must leave a substantial and not trivial last part of the works remaining for certification until he receives a notice from the contractor under sub-cl. (1).

8. THE DEFINITION OF THE PART FOR WHICH COMPLETION IS CERTIFIED should be set out very carefully in the certificate, in view of the changeover of liability for damage to that part—p. 98, N. 3.

DEFINITION OF "PERIOD OF MAINTENANCE"

49. (1)[1] In these Conditions the expression "Period of Maintenance" shall mean the period of maintenance named in the Appendix to the Form of Tender calculated from the date of completion of the Works or any Section or part thereof certified[2] by the Engineer in accordance with Clause 48 as the case may be.

EXECUTION OF WORK OF REPAIR, ETC.

(2) To the intent that the Works and each Section and part thereof shall at or as soon as practicable[3] after the expiration of the relevant Period of Maintenance be delivered up to the Employer in the condition required by the Contract[4] (fair wear and tear excepted) to the satisfaction of the Engineer the Contractor shall finish the work (if any) outstanding at the date of completion as certified under Clause 48 as soon as may be practicable after such date and shall execute all such work of repair amendment reconstruction rectification and making good of defects imperfections shrinkages or other faults[5] as may during the Period of Maintenance or within 14 days after its expiration be required of the Contractor in writing[6] by the Engineer as a result of an inspection made by or on behalf of the Engineer prior to its expiration.[7,8]

COST OF EXECUTION OF WORK OF REPAIR, ETC.

(3) All such work shall be carried out by the Contractor at his own expense if the necessity thereof shall in the opinion of the Engineer be due to the use of materials or workmanship not in accordance with the Contract or to neglect or failure on the part of the Contractor to comply with any obligation expressed or implied on the Contractor's part under the Contract.[9] If in the opinion of the Engineer such necessity shall be due to any other cause the value of such work shall be ascertained and paid for as if it were additional work.

REMEDY ON CONTRACTOR'S FAILURE TO CARRY OUT WORK REQUIRED

(4) If the Contractor shall fail to do any such work as aforesaid required by the Engineer[10,11] the Employer shall be entitled to carry out such work by his own workmen or by other contractors and if such work is work which the Contractor should have carried out at the Contractor's own cost shall be entitled to recover from the Contractor the cost thereof or may deduct the same from any monies due or that become due to the Contractor.[12]

1. GENERAL. Because it is likely to cost more to have another contractor do repairs alone, the contractor is required by this clause to do all necessary repairs for a specified time after completion, which will generally cover the teething period of the works, even if the defects, etc., are not due to his fault.

But the contractor bears the cost of maintenance work (and of searching for the cause of defects—cl. 50) only where the work is necessary as a result of his breach of contract (sub-cl. (3)). The contractor's duties under this clause are in addition to, not substitution for, his lengthy liability under the general law for defective workmanship or materials—p. 430.

There is no further maintenance period or retention for work made good under this clause, so that special supervision may be necessary.

2. CALCULATING THE PERIOD. The day on which the certificate of completion is given is not included in calculating the period, which ends on midnight of the last day.

3. "AS SOON AS PRACTICABLE AFTER THE EXPIRATION OF THE RELEVANT PERIOD OF MAINTENANCE BE DELIVERED UP".

A in July contracted to make machinery for delivery at the end of August and B contracted with him to make a part of the machinery "as soon as possible". B knew that A's delivery date was August, but did not complete his part of the machine until the end of September, and A refused to accept it.

The delay by B was due to not having at the time of his agreement a foreman competent to make necessary parts.

Held: B was liable—"as soon as possible" meant that, although he was not bound to leave aside all other work, he was to do the work in the shortest time reasonably possible given the resources which A was entitled to expect him to have.[ll]

4. "IN THE CONDITION REQUIRED BY THE CONTRACT". This new wording makes clear that under this clause the contractor may be ordered to make good defects existing but overlooked at the time of certification to substantial completion.

(ll) Hydraulic Engineering Co. v. McHaffie (1878) 4 Q.B.D. 670.

5. "REPAIR . . . RECONSTRUCTION", ETC. It seems, despite the reference to a *"maintenance"* rather than to a "defects liability" period and the opening of this sub-clause, that the duty to repair and reconstruct is qualified by the words "*of defects imperfections . . .*", etc. The contractor is not, therefore, liable to repair accidental damage to the works (*see also* cl. 20).

6. WRITTEN NOTICE TO THE CONTRACTOR. The contractor should be given as specific a notice as possible of work to be done. Even if he knows of the defects, etc., before the works may be put in other hands (N. 12) he must be given notice that the employer intends to rely on his rights. If notice is not given the contractor will not be liable for profit or any other additional sum paid to the substitute contractor for making good which would not have been incurred by the original contractor in curing the defects. That extra cost is paid only as a result of the employer's failure to respect the right, as well as duty, which the contractor has under this clause to make good defects himself. However, the remainder of the cost may be recoverable from the contractor, on the grounds that liability under the ordinary law for breach of contract in creating the defects is not superseded by the maintenance clause with its requirement of notice (N. 11).

7. "MAKING GOOD OF DEFECTS . . . (REQUIRED) DURING THE PERIOD . . . AS A RESULT OF AN INSPECTION . . . PRIOR TO ITS EXPIRATION". The contractor is only liable under this clause to make good defects which (but not necessarily the cause of which) actually appear during the maintenance period, so that this inspection is important:

> During a defects liability period defects developed in a road as a result of the use of concrete below the specified quality.
> Held: Discovery during the period that the concrete was bad did not make the contractor liable for other defects due to the same cause which appeared only
mm   after the period had ended.

The contractor is also liable to repair at his own (or rather his insurer's) cost any damage to outstanding work undertaken under cl. 48 to be finished in the period, and to the works caused by maintenance operations—the last sentences of cl. 20 (1) and (2).

The contractor is not bound to do more by way of maintenance than put the works back to their original standard even if that standard is
nn   unsatisfactory due to design.

As to the employer's remedy under the ordinary law for defects *see* N. 11.

8. THE EXTENT OF THE ENGINEER'S POWERS IN RELATION TO THE ACTUAL EXECUTION OF MAINTENANCE WORK is doubtful. *See* cl. 12, N. 2, cl. 39, N. 1, cl. 51, N. 9, cl. 63, N. 2, and N. 10 and 11 below.

9. MAINTENANCE WORK AT THE CONTRACTOR'S EXPENSE. BURDEN OF PROOF AND TECHNICAL BREACHES OF CONTRACT. The contractor is bound to remedy defects at his own expense only "*if the necessity thereof shall in the opinion of the Engineer be due to the use of materials or workmanship not in accordance*

with the Contract . . .", etc. To place the cost of repairs on the contractor the engineer must have evidence to justify forming an opinion to that effect. If he forms an opinion contrary to the evidence or where it is impossible to establish the cause of failure his view should be overruled by an arbitrator. In law the burden is on the employer to prove, on the balance of probabilities, that the defect was caused by the contractor's breach.

It is possible also that "*defects imperfections*", etc., means actual defects manifesting themselves in the works and rendering them less satisfactory for their purpose and not mere technical breaches of specification, such as use of material not specified but as satisfactory for its purpose as that specified. The contractor certainly remains liable for damages under the general law for any such breach, but the damages awarded are likely to be nominal—p. 429.

The possibility of a claim by the contractor under cl. 13 for disruption due to maintenance work is discussed on p. 75.

No price fluctuation is allowable on maintenance work—p. 315, para. (c) (ii).

10. THE TIME FOR DOING MAINTENANCE AND OUTSTANDING WORK. All that this clause says is that maintenance work and outstanding work in an undertaking under cl. 48 are to be completed "*as soon as practicable*" after the end of the period (*see* p. 163, N. 3), and the employer may hold back part of the retention money until the work is done (cl. 60 (5)). It is probably implied that particular items must be done within a reasonable time from the engineer's order. Refer also to the next note.

11. INTERFERENCE WITH USE OF THE WORKS BY MAINTENANCE WORK. It is doubtful whether the engineer has power under cl. 40 to suspend maintenance works for the employer's convenience (p. 131, N. 1 and 2), and if that clause does apply the contractor is entitled to the extra cost. If the engineer gives a specific instruction about the time for carrying out maintenance work the contractor also may have a claim, under cl. 13. But the engineer has alternative, if limited, control under cl. 13 (2), by which the mode and speed of maintenance of the works is subject to his approval. In exercising this right of approval the engineer must act fairly to the contractor (p. 409) and is not entitled, e.g., to take into consideration the fact that the employer does not have enough money at the moment to pay for maintenance work to be done at his expense, but presumably may take into account reasonable wishes of the employer to minimise the disruption to his use of the works. In addition the employer may be entitled to damage for any loss of use of the works while defects due to the contractor's workmanship or materials in breach of contract are being made good in the maintenance period.

Defective work amounting to a breach of contract normally entitles the employer to compensation for loss suffered, including loss of use of the works whilst the defects are being made good (p. 428), and it is very arguable that this right under the general law is not superseded by this maintenance cl. 49. The employer may even be entitled to damages *oo*

(*oo*) In *P. & M. Kaye Ltd.* v. *Hosier & Dickinson Ltd.* [1972] 1 All E.R. 121, H.L., employers claimed under the R.I.B.A. contract form very substantial loss of profits resulting from relaying by contractors of a floor in a warehouse, necessary because of defects which became apparent after the warehouse was substantially complete. There was no decision on the merits of claim.

exceeding the liquidated damages in the contract, which are not relevant since they cover only delay in achieving substantial completion and latent defects do not prevent the work being substantially complete (p. 160, footnote (*kk*)). The odd result is that the level of damages payable by the contractor for defects which delay or interfere with use of the works may depend on whether or not the defects come to light before or after substantial completion, and it may suit the contractor to argue that the works were not substantially complete when the engineer says they were.

This right to damages will largely be confined to commercial structures, since in the case of public works it will be very difficult for the employers to prove any tangible loss due to maintenance operations.

Of course the contractor is not liable to pay compensation for necessary disturbance in executing maintenance work not due to his defective materials or workmanship, which under this clause he is bound to execute at the employer's expense.

12. EMPLOYER'S RIGHTS ON CONTRACTOR'S DEFAULT, DEDUCTION OF COST. *See* p. 130.

This clause does not refer to the employer's right to recover any extra cost involved in having another contractor carry out maintenance work which the contractor should have done at the contract rates, but under the general law the employer has a right to set off the extra cost against any money due or which may become due to the contractor—p. 269, N. 33, and *see* p. 265, N. 26, on retention money.

TEMPORARY REINSTATEMENT

49. (5) Provided always that if in the course or for the purposes of the execution of the Works or any part thereof any highway or other road or way shall have been broken into then notwithstanding anything herein contained:

(a) If the permanent reinstatement of such highway or other road or way is to be carried out by the appropriate Highway Authority or by some person other than the Contractor (or any sub-contractor to him) the Contractor shall at his own cost and independently of any requirement of or notice from the Engineer be responsible for the making good of any subsidence or shrinkage or other defect imperfection or fault in the temporary reinstatement of such highway or other road or way and for the execution of any necessary repair or amendment thereof from whatever cause the necessity arises until the end of the Period of Maintenance in respect of the works beneath such highway or other road or way or until the Highway Authority or other person as aforesaid shall have taken possession of the Site for the purpose of carrying out permanent reinstatement (whichever is the earlier) and shall indemnify and save harmless the Employer against and from any damage or injury to the Employer or to third parties arising out or in consequence of any neglect or failure of the Contractor to comply with foregoing obligations or any of them and against and from all claims demands proceedings damages costs charges and expenses whatsoever in respect thereof or in relation thereto. As from the end of such Period of Maintenance or the taking of possession as aforesaid (whichever shall first happen) the Employer shall indemnify and save harmless the Contractor against and from any damage or injury as aforesaid arising out or in consequence of or in connection with the said permanent reinstatement or any defect imperfection or failure of or in such work of permanent reinstatement and against and from all claims demands proceedings damages costs charges and expenses whatsoever in respect or in relation thereof.

(b) Where the Highway Authority or other person as aforesaid shall take possession of the Site as aforesaid in sections or lengths the responsibility of the Contractor under paragraph (a) of this sub-clause shall cease in regard to any such section or length at the time possession thereof is so taken but shall during the continuance of the said Period of Maintenance continue in regard to any length of which possession has not been so taken and the indemnities given by the Contractor and the Employer respectively under the said paragraph shall be construed and have effect accordingly.

REINSTATEMENT. The Public Utilities Street Works Act, 1950, deals with reinstatement after work which involves opening, boring or tunnelling under a street or controlled land. The Act and the various technical terms used in this note are dealt with generally in cl. 27 above.

By Sec. 7 and the Third Schedule of the Act the employer/undertaker is bound:

(a) To begin reinstatement as soon after completion of any part of the works as is reasonably practicable without hindering the rest of the works; to allow each of the interested authorities to supervise reinstatement-and-to carry out their reasonable requirements; to pay the cost of supervision, and of traffic control by the transport authority; to reinstate up to surface levels unless the street authority or managers elect to do this reinstatement.

(b) The street authority may elect to do (at the undertaker's cost) the permanent reinstatement of the upper levels of a street that is a maintainable highway or controlled land. The election must be either by a specific notice given without avoidable delay after the authority first learns of the undertaker's intention to do the street works and generally within eight days of the settlement of the plan and section, or by a general notice to the undertaker that the authority will reinstate after all or a particular class of work by the undertaker. But for the safety of apparatus the authority may not do work within 12 inches of the undertaker's apparatus without special arrangement. The undertaker remains liable for interim reinstatement from the time reinstatement becomes necessary until notice that the authority intends to start permanent reinstatement, which it must do as soon after completion of the works by the undertaker as is prudent and practicable.

(c) The undertaker is bound to pay the cost of making good any subsidence within six months of reinstatement, unless due to faulty reinstatement of upper levels by the street authority, and of making good deterioration generally within the same period if shown to be due to the undertaker's faulty work or materials. The undertaker is entitled to notice and to inspect defects before the authority has them made good at his expense.

Under this clause where the street authority elects to reinstate at upper levels the contractor takes over the liability for interim reinstatement from the undertaker/employer until the end of the maintenance period or until the street authority takes possession of the site, whichever is earlier. He is also liable until then for injury to the employer or third parties, but this is covered in practice by insurance under cl. 23. From then on the employer indemnifies the contractor against any liability, damages, etc., in connection with permanent reinstatement, and should insure to cover this liability.

This clause does not deal expressly with liability under this section of the Act for defects in the contractor's reinstatement of lower levels appearing after the authority takes possession of the site for permanent reinstatement, or liability for subsidence or deterioration where the contractor does the permanent reinstatement at upper levels. The liability in both cases is to pay the authority the cost of making good the defects and so may not be covered by cl. 49, which only refers to cases where the contractor has an opportunity of making good defects himself, but it appears to be covered by cl. 26.

This clause also does not refer to reinstatement of controlled land, which is included in this section of the Act.

CONTRACTOR TO SEARCH

50. The Contractor shall if required by the Engineer in writing carry out such searches tests or trials as may be necessary to determine the cause of any defect imperfection or fault under the directions of the Engineer. Unless such defect imperfection or fault shall be one for which the Contractor is liable under the Contract the cost of the work carried out by the Contractor as aforesaid shall be borne by the Employer.[1] But if such defect imperfection or fault shall be one for which the Contractor is liable the cost of the work carried out as aforesaid shall be borne by the Contractor and he shall in such case repair rectify and make good such defect imperfection or fault at his own expense in accordance with Clause 49.[2]

1. "COST ... BORNE BY THE EMPLOYER". *See* p. 31, N. 18.

2. RECOVERY BY CONTRACTOR OF COST OF DELAY OR DISRUPTION DUE TO SEARCHES, TESTS, ETC., REQUIRED BY ENGINEER. It is possible that the requirements of the engineer under this clause amount to an instruction and entitle the contractor to compensation under cl. 13 for unforeseen costs of consequential delay or disruption, apart from the right under this clause to "*the cost of the work carried out*" itself in some cases (p. 75).

The reference here to cl. 49 and also the terms of cl. 61 suggest that the intention is that this clause applies only in the maintenance period, but it is not so limited anywhere in the words used. *See also* p. 100, N. 7. Under the main provision for tests in cl. 36 the contractor may have to bear the cost of a test even if it shows that the work or materials are in accordance with the contract, if the test is clearly intended by or provided for, and in one case particularised, in the contract.

ORDERED VARIATIONS

51. (1) The Engineer shall order any variation[1,2] to any part of the Works that may in his opinion be necessary for the completion of the Works and shall have power to order any variation that for any other reason shall in his opinion be desirable[3] for the satisfactory completion and functioning of the Works.[4,5,6] Such variations may include additions omissions[7] substitutions alterations changes in quality form character kind position dimension level or line[8,9] and changes in the specified sequence method or timing of construction (if any).[10]

1. GENERAL. Most of the employment given the legal profession by engineering work is to do with disputes about variations. From the contractor's point of view the main concern is to get payment for extras, to which he is entitled only if the extras are outside the work he was bound to do for the original contract price (p. 27, N. 12) and not merely concessions

to him (p. 179, N. 2), and authorised properly. The contractor is in an extremely difficult position if he makes an unauthorised variation (N. 2), and variations may be unauthorised either because they are outside the engineer's powers (N. 8) or because written verifications or claims are missing (p. 177, N. 1, and *see* cl. 52 (2) and (4)).

The employer's main concern will be to avoid exorbitant prices for extras, but the contractor may be entitled to more than the original contract rates if variations are ordered by the employer and not the engineer (N. 3), or are outside the scope of this clause (N. 8), and in some cases under the system of valuing variations in cl. 52.

There may also be problems if the employer wishes to have varied or extra work done by another contractor (N. 6).

2. RIGHT TO VARY. Unless there is a clause of this kind in the contract, the contractor cannot be ordered to do more or different work than he originally agreed to do, nor can the employer omit any of the original work and reduce the contract price. Conversely, if the contractor alters the works without authority under the contract he is not entitled to payment for the altered work. He will also have broken the contract—the contract work has not been done and it is no defence in law that he has done equivalent or better work. It follows that the contractor will be liable for at least nominal damages and the employer may have a right of forfeiture under cl. 63, and the contractor will not be entitled to an extension of time for completion because of the extra work. The contractor will also be liable for any damage to the works or third party claims resulting from the unauthorised variation.

The Unfair Contract Terms Act 1977 has some potential, but probably no actual, relevance to the right to vary (p. 433).

3. "THE ENGINEER SHALL ORDER ANY VARIATION ... IN HIS OPINION ... NECESSARY ... DESIRABLE". The employer has no power under the Contract forms to order variations personally; if he does the contractor is not bound to carry out the order, and may ask whatever price he thinks fit—*see* p. 175 for the position where the price is not fixed in advance.

The contractor is entitled to make and to recover payment for a variation ordered by the engineer, only so far as the engineer has authority from the employer to give the order. Although the engineer prepares the plans, once the contract is made he has, merely from his appointment as engineer, no authority whatever to vary the works. This clause gives the engineer authority in relation to the contractor, and the contractor is entitled to rely on it and to recover payment for all variations ordered by the engineer within the scope of the clause, even if they were, in fact, not authorised or even forbidden by the employer.

Under the special wording of this clause this seems to be so even if the contractor knew of the limits on the engineer's authority. The words at the head of this note indicate that it is the engineer's decision whether a variation is "*necessary (or) desirable*" which the contractor binds himself and is entitled to obey. If that is so, the engineer may become disqualified by

pp

(pp) See *Davies & Co.* (*Shopfitters*) *Ltd.* v. *William Old* (1969) 67 L.G.R. 395, at p. 399: "Under Clause 11 (of the R.I.B.A. form) the architect may require a variation whether or not the contractor or the employer likes it." In *Benjamin Foster Co.* v. *Commonwealth*, 61 N.E. (2d) 147, the court assumed that the engineer was bound to act independently in exercising a power to "modify the plan of operation or of construction if, in his judgment, such modification is necessary or desirable on account of the quality, safety or speed of the work".

following his employer's orders to vary or not vary the works against his own judgment (p. 409). This provision seems to be intended to deal particularly with the case where the employer objects unreasonably to a variation which is necessary for the safety of the works, or which is a more economical method to meet unexpected problems (*see*, e.g. cl. 12(2)(d)) or to comply with bye-laws, etc. (cl. 26(2)(b)). The contractor may safely carry out such a variation order within the engineer's powers under this clause even though he knows that the employer has not authorised or has forbidden the engineer to make it, and if the engineer bows to the employer's orders his decision may be reversed in arbitration. But the employer, too, is entitled to arbitration, so that even if the engineer is prepared to take an independent line it may be preferable to try to reach a compromise direct with the employer.

For variations due to a breach of contract by the contractor *see* p. 179, N. 2.

On the other hand, if the engineer orders variations which are outside the scope of this clause (N. 8) without special authority from the employer, and the employer does not later ratify what he has done, the variations are not properly authorised and the results set out in N. 2 follow for the contractor. The contractor may be entitled to recover the loss he suffers from the engineer—p. 399.

Finally, this clause is for the contractor's protection only and does not affect the liability of the engineer to the employer if he goes beyond his actual authority—*see* p. 29.

4. VARIATIONS TO TEMPORARY WORKS. By the definition in cl. 1 (1) (l) "*Works*" appears (p. 29, N. 13) to include all temporary works, designed by the engineer or contractor. This clause says that the engineer "*shall order any variation*" of such works necessary for the "*completion of the Works*". It is therefore necessary to consider whether or not the engineer is bound to give a variation order in any of a variety of circumstances in which he may become involved with the contractor's temporary works:

(*a*) If the engineer wishes to alter the design of temporary works actually designed by him or to alter some design requirement included in the specification, such as a factor of safety, the contractor is entitled to a variation order with a valuation under cl. 52.

(*b*) Where temporary works are unsatisfactory in some matter of design by the contractor within the ambit left to him by the contract or if unsatisfactory construction of temporary works comes to the engineer's attention on site, the engineer may exercise his rights of disapproval under cl. 13 (2), or (at the risk of a claim under that clause) his powers under cl. 13 (1) or under cl. 14 for which *see* p. 83, N. 21. He acts to enforce the contractor's paramount duty under cl. 8 (2) to provide stable, safe and adequate temporary works.

(*c*) It is suggested that in none of the cases in class (*b*) above is the contractor entitled to claim that the engineer's action *per se* amounts to a variation order or that the engineer has a duty to give a variation order. A variation must vary the works from something laid down in the contract, and in these cases the engineer is merely requiring the temporary works to be in accordance with the contract.

(*d*) However, the contractor may claim that his temporary works were in fact in accordance with any specific terms of the contract and adequate, safe and stable as required by cl. 8. If that is so and the engineer has given a specific order enhancing the requirements of the contract the contractor may confirm the order as a variation. If the engineer restrains himself from giving a positive order but merely expresses disapproval under cl. 13 (2) of what has been done, it is not clear that the contractor may claim that the disapproval implies an order that may be confirmed as variation or recover compensation merely because the disapproval was unreasonable (p. 417).

The engineer also has powers over temporary works under cls. 39 (2) and 62.

For the results where the engineer does give an order or instruction to help the contractor out of difficulty with temporary works *see* p. 179, N. 2.

5. "FOR THE COMPLETION ... FOR THE SATISFACTORY COMPLETION AND FUNCTIONING OF THE WORKS". These are the only purposes for which the engineer has the right under this clause to vary the works. He is not entitled, for example, to substitute one piece of work for another or order an omission merely because the employer finds that he is exceeding his budget, or has changed his mind. Provided the engineer has special authority from the employer to make such an omission outside this clause (N. 3), the contractor may obey under protest and recover loss of the profit he would have earned on the work omitted, as damages for breach of contract (p. 428). The contractor may conceivably be entitled to ignore the order to omit on the grounds that it is invalid and insist on building the original work, provided he already has the drawings, etc., to enable him to do so. It is doubtful if these results are or should be intended.   *qq*

Alteration of the works to achieve equivalent results by cheaper engineering means does appear to be within these words.

6. VARIATIONS TO BE CARRIED OUT BY ANOTHER CONTRACTOR. The engineer may omit work only if it is not to be done at all, not to have it done by another contractor; any other rule would permit the employer to employ a contractor only for the parts of the works on which the contractor had tendered low rates, by omitting the parts on which the contractor had placed his profit and giving them to another contractor. On the other hand,   *rr*

(*qq*) See *White & Carter (Councils) Ltd.* v. *McGregor* [1961] 3 All E.R. 1178, H.L., but this decision has been criticised, and in the course of his judgment Lord Reid did say: "It may well be that if it can be shown that a person has no legitimate interest, financial or otherwise, in performing the contract rather than claiming damages, he ought not to be allowed to saddle the other party with an additional burden with no benefit to himself ..." Megarry J. refused to apply the decision to a building contract in *London Borough Council of Hounslow* v. *Twickenham Garden Developments* [1970] 3 All E.R. 326, and the decision was not applied where the contract required co-operation between the parties and the innocent party had no legitimate interest in enforcing the contract in *Attica CA Corp.* v. *Ferrostaal Posiedon GmbH* [1976] 1 Lloyd's Rep. 250, C.A.

(*rr*) In both *Gallagher* v. *Hirsch* (1899) N.Y. 45 Appl. Div. 467, and *Carr* v. *J. A. Beriman Pty. Ltd.* (1954) 89 C.L.R. 372 Aus'., omission of work to give it to another contractor was held to be a breach of contract. In the former case the contractor recovered the profit element in his rate for the work omitted, and in the latter the omission was held with other factors to be so serious a breach of contract as to entitle the contractor to refuse to go on with the work (below p.!425). See also *Simplex Floor Finishing Appliance Co.* v. *Duranceau* (1941) 4 D.L.R. 260 Can., where a sub-contractor recovered damages for loss of profit from a main contractor who employed another sub-contractor to do flooring which had been varied. The same principle was applied in *Commr. for Main Roads* v. *Reed & Stuart Pty. Ltd.* (1975) 48 A.L.J.R. 461. The basis of these decisions is that the power to omit is limited to omission of work from the project; that a change in the contract itself by omitting from it work that has been retained in the project is not permitted. *See also* p. 240, N. 7.

the employer is not bound to give extra work to the main contractor (and *see* cl. 31), subject to the danger that if he employs another contractor direct he may be liable for any delay or expense caused the main contractor (p. 364).

There is no power under these conditions to give extra work to the main contractor, so as to make him responsible for it, and to order him to sub-contract the work to a nominated sub-contractor. However, if there is already a provisional sum for contingencies in the bill, a nomination may be made under the sum (cl. 58 (1) and (7)).

ss

Whether a variation falls within the first or second sentence of this note must depend on the facts of the particular case—whether the work is genuinely extra to the original work or merely a variation of omitted work.

7. LATE OMISSIONS. What is the contractor's position if an omission is ordered at a late stage after he has bought and delivered materials to the site? In relation to the act of delivery it is clear that the engineer must allow for the fact that the rate for the omitted work covers delivery of materials, and that work having been done at the proper time it has not, in fact, been omitted from the contract. The engineer will on that basis deduct only part of the rate, allowing payment of a proportion for delivery to the site, administrative work in ordering the materials, etc. The same principle must apply whenever part of the work within an item has been carried out before the item is omitted.

tt

Where materials have been bought or bought and fabricated by the contractor before omission of the relevant supply or supply and construct item, if the materials have actually been delivered on site it is arguable that the contractor has supplied in accordance with the item and that therefore the supply element also should not be omitted by the engineer in his valuation. The materials will have vested in the employer under cl. 53 and may be sold by him. If the materials have not been delivered to site, the position is a little doubtful. It is difficult to read the terms of cl. 52 so as to authorise the engineer to include an allowance for the contractor's loss in valuing the work remaining. However, the courts may imply a term that the contractor will be paid for such loss (p. 42(*b*)).

8. EXTENT OF VARIATION PERMITTED. Because a contractor may refuse to do or charge exorbitant prices for variations not authorised by the contract (below) the practice has grown of using very wide variation clauses. Obviously this can be unfair to the contractor, who may find himself having to do work completely different from the work which he agreed to take on.

(*ss*) It has been suggested that under the J.C.T. contract the architect is entitled to issue a variation instruction omitting from the contract bills work priced by the contractor and substituting a prime cost sum. (Sir D. Walker-Smith and H. A. Close "The Standard Forms of Building Contract", at p. 120.) However, such a "variation" is not within the words "variation of the form quality or quantity of the Works" in this clause, and the power to omit work is generally thought to entitle the engineer to omit work, so as to deprive the contractor of the profit in his rates, only if the work is not to be done at all (see previous note). In *J. M. Reilly Ltd.* v. *Belfast Corp.* (1966), an unreported decision of the Court of Appeal of Northern Ireland, MacDermott L.C.J. stated that a letter from the architect entitled "Variation Order" which purported to omit a provisional sum and add a nomination of a sub-contractor was "misconceived and inept". Curran L.J. gave judgment to like effect.

(*tt*) In *White* v. *Dungannon etc. Board* (1966), High Court in Northern Ireland, unreported, Mr. Justice Lowry referred with approval to the equivalent of this passage in the first edition of this book.

For this reason it has been held in a number of cases that a variation clause, although worded very widely, must be read in the light of the circumstances when the parties made the contract. On that basis it has been held that such a clause will not authorise complete transformation of, or extra work not related to, the original project.

However, where the engineer has power to vary rates (*see cl.* 52 (2)) the potential unfairness to the contractor is lessened and the courts may hold that the right to vary goes very far. In a recent case, where the variation clause was equivalent to cl. 51 of the 4th edition of these Conditions but without the limitation in that clause to additional work "necessary for the completion of the Works", it was assumed by one judge that the employers could have ordered the contractors "to erect a series of buildings on the site, pull down, and put them up again, with or without alteration, as often and as long as they chose". *uu*

As a result it is wise to define the position in the contract. That appears to be done to some extent by this sub-clause, which may be divided into two components:

(*a*) The engineer "*shall order*", i.e. is bound to order, any variation "*to any part of the Works*" that is actually "*necessary for the completion of the Works*". Clearly "*Works*" in this context must mean the project originally planned, and a variation changing the works as a whole is excluded.

(*b*) The engineer in addition has power to order "*any variation that for any other reason shall in his opinion be desirable for the satisfactory completion and functioning of the Works*". We are told that "*such variations may include ... changes in quality form character kind position*"—but of what, the whole works or part only, is not vouchsafed specifically.

It is suggested that a change in the "*characteristic kind*" of the whole works can never be "*desirable for the satisfactory completion and functioning of the Works*", because "*Works*" in this phrase again must mean at most the broad project originally envisaged, and such a change in the works involves abandonment of the original project and substitution of a new project.

It would also be strange if this part of the clause were to be construed to give the engineer power to make the other changes mentioned, in "*quality form ... position dimension level or line*" of the whole as well as part of the works, where that is merely desirable for their satisfactory completion or functioning, although by the opening of this clause he has power to make such changes that are actually necessary only if they are confined to part of the works.

The results of the exercise in semantics made necessary by this clause are:

(i) Almost certainly the engineer has no power to alter the "*character kind*" of substantially the whole works. Obviously he cannot order a physical change to every ingredient in the works, but this limitation also prevents a physical change to part only if it has the effect of altering the "*character kind*" of the whole.

(ii) The engineer has full power to add to, or omit from or alter any part

(*uu*) *Sir Lindsay Parkinson & Co. Ltd.* v. *Commissioners of Works* [1950] 1 All E.R. 208, C.A. The variation clause in question gave the employers or their architect power at their absolute discretion "to modify the extent, character, sections quantities or dimensions of any works shown or described in the contract or the levels or positions of any of the works or to order any portion or portions of the works to be omitted ... or to order additional work". For the facts of this case see text p. 43.

of the works or change the quality, form, character, kind, position, dimensions, levels or lines of any part, so far as may be necessary for completion or desirable for satisfactory completion and functioning of the original project. He does not appear to have power to make any such change in, for example, the position of, substantially the whole works, even if that does not alter their "*character kind*".

Large omissions are unlikely to be "*necessary (or) desirable for the satisfactory completion and functioning of the Works*", as required by this clause.

If the above conclusions are correct, the following cases in which changes have been held to fall outside particular variation clauses are relevant, although none of the clauses is identical to this clause and the peculiar wording of this clause must always be kept in mind:

Contract to do all carpenter's, joiner's, glazing and tin work for two houses, after the work was executed the employer added attics and ordered the contractor to do the necessary additional carpenter's work in windows and doors and added large stables suitable for an inn;

contract to do plastering on the inside of a house, contractors ordered to build an entablature outside;

alterations in part of the route of a conduit from level ground through deep ravines and hills resulting in at least 53 times the estimated quantity of cut stone and masonry (the contract gave the employer the right to "make any alterations that may hereafter be determined upon as necessary or desirable");

division of storeys in a building into apartments which was not contemplated by the original contract;

over 1,000 feet extra added to the lower end of a sewer through soil of a different character and much more difficult to excavate, and change in location of the sewer from centre of a street to the side seriously interfered with working of *vv*   ditching machines.

Contracts for supply of stone for ten buildings, employer liable for loss of profits for reducing to five buildings;

employer liable for reducing tile drain from 16 to $7\frac{1}{2}$ miles where the contract gave power "to exclude any item to increase or diminish the quantities to any extent";

necessary omission of a half a mile out of a contract for $3\frac{3}{4}$ miles of a canal and elimination of other work totalling 41 % of the contract work has been held to be within a right to make deductions from the contract work, but omitting $2\frac{1}{2}$ % of the work has been held to be a breach of a contract by which the employer had the right "to alter in any way it may deem necessary for the public interest, the *ww*   drawings".

Any possibility that extra or changed work which may be held to go outside the scope of this clause will have to be ordered should be avoided, since the contractor is entitled to refuse to do such work and obviously in a position to hold out for his price because of the expense of bringing another contractor on the site. If and only if an omission is outside the power to vary, the contractor is entitled to damages, which normally will be the amount of profit he would have made on the omitted work. It may be

(*vv*) *Watson* v. *O'Beirne* (1850) 7 Up. Can. Q.B. 345; *Reid* v. *Battle* (1829) M. & M. 413; *Salt Lake City* v. *Smith*, 104 Fed. 457; *Lawrence* v. *Kern* (1910) 14 W.L.R. 337 Can.; *Boyd* v. *South Winnipeg* (1917) 2 W.W.R. 489 Can.
(*ww*) *McMaster* v. *State of New York*, 108 N.Y. 542; *Drainage District No. 1 of Lincoln County* v. *Rude*, 21 Fed.2d 257; *Kinser Construction Co.* v. *State of New York*, 204 N.Y. 381; *Whitfield Construction Co.* v. *City of New York*, 244 N.Y. 251.

necessary to warn the employer that his right to change the work after the contract is made is not unlimited.

The greatest danger is that variations outside this clause may be ordered by the engineer unwittingly. If that happens and the work is done by the contractor without fixing a price in advance, then (since the work falls outside the contract) normally he will be entitled to reasonable prices without any reference to the contract rates or prices, provided, of course, he can prove that the engineer had authority to order the work (N. 3). And such work may not be merely additional to the contract works, but may involve complete transformation of the original contract plan, so that no original contract work can fairly be traced in the work carried out to be priced at the contract rates. The parties will then be taken to have *xx* abandoned their original contract and to have impliedly made a new contract for the new works. In that case, unless a price is specially fixed in advance, the whole of the new works actually carried out must be paid for by measure and value at reasonable prices without any regard to the original contract rates and prices, and whatever the form (even pure lump sum) of the original contract. A complete transformation of the works sufficient to produce this result will be very rare.

The contractor may not lead the employer into a trap — if he carries out work which he realises does not fall within the right of variation in the original contract without claiming for payment outside the contract when the work is ordered, and accepts interim certificates under the original contract including payment for the new work, he may be held to have impliedly agreed that the work will be done on the terms of the original contract and at the original contract rates. *yy*

In view of all this, if the engineer considers that the nature of the project may be changing he must explain what is involved to the employer, and preferably negotiate a supplemental agreement with the contractor, fixing a price or rates for the new works in advance.

A clear-cut restriction on variations to a percentage of the original work would avoid these problems, but is not satisfactory for civil engineering.

9. VARIATIONS IN THE MAINTENANCE PERIOD. It is clear from the wording of cl. 49 that the engineer has no power to order variations in the maintenance period. Therefore he has no authority without the contractor's agreement to change to a different method of doing the works in the light of defects which have developed in the maintenance period, unless that is absolutely necessary to make good the defects (*see also* p. 164, N. 7).

10. "CHANGES IN SPECIFIED SEQUENCE METHOD OR TIMING OF CON-STRUCTION (IF ANY)". It is difficult to say exactly what is covered by these words:

(*xx*) *Thorn* v. *London Corporation* (1876) 1 App. Cas. 120 at pp. 127, 128.
(*yy*) Refer to the important decision in *Way* v. *Latilia* [1937] 3 All E.R. 759 H.L. In *Peter Kiewit Sons' Company of Canada Ltd.* v. *Eakins* [1960] 22 D.L.R. (2d) 465 Can. it was held that a contractor who does extra work falling outside the contract and knowing that it falls outside the contract must be taken to have agreed that the contract rates will apply to the work. This case held also that the fact that the contractor did the work under protest did not affect the position, but it is suggested that the decision would not be followed that far. The dissenting judgment appears to pay more regard to the reality of the contractor's dilemma. The decision is considered in *Morrison-Knudsen Co. Inc.* v. *British Columbia Hydro and Power Authority* (No. 2) [1978] 85 D.L.R. (3d) 186 Can. *See also Gilbert & Partners* v. *Knight* [1968] 2 All E.R. 248, C.A.

(a) An order to finish a section or sections of the works earlier or later than the separate time for completion of the section specified in the tender (see cl. 43) seems to be well within the words, but produces a peculiar side effect. The time for completion of a section may be extended for such a variation under the specific words of cl. 44, but there is no power to shorten the time for completion where the variation requires a section to be finished early. For example, if the engineer transposes the completion dates of two sections, he will give an extension of time for completion of the section changed to a later completion date, and the employer will be entitled to liquidated damages for late completion of that section, but not to liquidated damages in respect of the section moved to an earlier date (but he will have a right to any actual damages due to the delay that he can prove — p. 428).

(b) It is suggested that "*timing of construction*" clearly is not appropriate to cover an order to complete the whole works before the contract completion date, because of the ordinary meaning of the words, the fact that this provision again appears to relate only to a change affecting part of the works, and the effect of any such order on liquidated damages.

This power to vary is also limited by the overriding requirement that the variation is necessary or desirable for the satisfactory completion and functioning of the works, and therefore in any case does not cover a change of timing, etc., for the convenience of the employer because he wants the works finished early. Such acceleration is dealt with in ch. 12.

(c) Methods, sequence or timing of construction of the permanent or temporary works also may be included in a special condition or the specifications, and this right of variation will then apply carrying with it an adjustment in payment for the contractor.

(d) If the engineer gives approval to a manner, mode or speed of construction of the works under cl. 13 (2) or as set out in a contractor's programme, a change of mind by the engineer does not appear to amount to a variation under this clause. It is suggested that the words "*specified ... (if any)*" indicate that only some method, etc., particularly specified to the contractor in some contract provision additional to the standard contract documents brings this provision into effect, and that the contractor's only remedy for a change of approval of a method or timing specified by the contractor is under cl. 13 or 14 where applicable—as summarised in p. 83. This view is supported in relation to programmes by cl. 14 (7), which says that approval of a programme does not relieve the contractor of any of his duties under the contract. Most important, could it be that where the engineer orders a change in the contractor's programme because the change is actually "*necessary for the completion of the Works*" the contractor has a claim? Obviously that is the very case in which he must have no claim. Refer also to cl. 46, N. 1, p. 146.

(e) Where variations in the physical work affect the contractor's timing or intended sequence of operations, then irrespective of the words at the head of this note the contractor may require the effect to be included in the valuation of the varied work. See p. 77, N. 11.

(f) If there is a change in "*the specified ... timing of construction*" because of the engineer's delay with drawings or instructions, for example affecting the time of completion of a section specified for early completion in the tender, the relationship is not clear between the right of the contractor to claim for a variation order under this provision and his rights under cl. 7. It is possible that the contractor may argue that the engineer in such a case has a duty to give a variation order under this clause ("*The Engineer shall order any variation*"), that if he does not do so the arbitrator may make good the omission, and as a result the contractor may claim extra payment under cl. 52 including profit, instead of merely cost under cl. 7.

It is even possible to extend this argument to any delay in completing the whole works due to some cause for which the employer or engineer is responsible. But it is suggested that such an extension is incorrect for the reasons stated in para. (*b*) above.

This possible right to claim payment under cl. 52 also applies to a change of a method or sequence specified in the contract ordered by the engineer to make up delay for which he or the employer is responsible.

For valuation of a variation in sequence, method or timing *see* p. 187, N. 10(a).

Apart from the reference here to "*changes in the specified . . . method . . . of construction*", the opening reference in this sub-clause to a variation of the "*Works*" includes the contractor's temporary works, as discussed in N. 4.

Ordered Variations to be in Writing

51. (2) No such variation shall be made by the Contractor without an order by the Engineer. All such orders shall be given in writing[1] provided that if for any reason the Engineer shall find it necessary to give any such order orally in the first instance the Contractor shall comply with such oral order. Such oral order shall be confirmed in writing by the Engineer as soon as is possible in the circumstances.[2] If the Contractor shall confirm in writing to the Engineer any oral order by the Engineer and such confirmation shall not be contradicted in writing by the Engineer forthwith[3] it shall be deemed to be an order in writing by the Engineer.[4] No variation ordered or deemed to be ordered in writing in accordance with sub-clauses (1) and (2) of this Clause shall in any way vitiate or invalidate the Contract but the value (if any) of all such variations shall be taken into account in ascertaining the amount of the Contract Price.[5]

Changes in Quantities

(3) No order in writing shall be required for increase or decrease in the quantity of any work where such increase or decrease is not the result of an order given under this Clause but is the result of the quantities exceeding or being less than those stated in the Bill of Quantities.[6]

1. ORDERS, ETC., FOR VARIATIONS. To be validated by this clause variations must be authorised in advance by a written order or by a verbal order confirmed later in writing. The order need not be given as a variation, but there generally must be some order to do the work by the engineer—*see* particularly cl. 2, N. 4, on orders by the representative. Verbal orders may cause friction as to whether they were given as definite orders and about their scope, and (in theory) are only for emergencies.

Drawings or sketches may provide a written order if they are an absolute and definite direction to do the work, and may provide a written confirmation.

zz

(zz) *Munro* v. *Westville Town* [1903] 36 N.S.R. 313 and *Myers* v. *Sarl* [1860] 122 R.R. 710, particularly at p. 712. In the latter case it was held that unsigned sketches and drawings were not a sufficient variation order, but the contract specifically said that orders were to be "*under the hand*" of the architect.

The arbitrator has no power to award extra payment for work as a variation despite this sub-clause where the contractor does not ask for even a verbal order from the engineer before doing extra work. There is no "*decision*" of the engineer involved (cl. 66, N. 13, p. 302).

· Of course, this sub-clause says only that recovery by the contractor is barred for "*such variation*" made without an order of the engineer, and is tautologous since the "*such*" refers to a variation ordered by the engineer under sub-cl. (1). It follows that if the contractor does not have to rely on cl. 51 but can prove that the change was authorised in fact by the employer he may recover without being affected by the limitations in cl. 51 (e.g. p. 172, N. 8).

If the employer exercises a choice of keeping rather than returning to the contractor work which was not ordered he will then be taken to have made a new contract to pay a reasonable price for it. No such contract can be implied merely from keeping work which has become fixed to the site (case, p. 266), so that this principle rarely applies in relation to civil engineering works.

2. CONFIRMATION BY ENGINEER "AS SOON AS IS POSSIBLE IN THE CIRCUMSTANCES" appears to equate approximately with "*as soon as practicable*", discussed on p. 163, N. 3.

3. CONTRADICTION BY ENGINEER OF CONTRACTOR'S CONFIRMATION MUST BE "FORTHWITH". This is new, and may require very quick action if the engineer knows or the contractor tells him (as he should if necessary with the confirmation) that the work has been or is about to be started immediately or other decisive action taken in connection with a variation. The contractor for his own protection should of course confirm a variation order before starting the varied work, etc., but apparently is not bound to do so.

4. CONTRACTOR'S RIGHTS WHERE NO WRITTEN CONFIRMATION OF ORAL ORDERS. An arbitrator may award payment even if the engineer and contractor both fail to confirm, in theory by reversing the engineer's decision not to confirm.

5. LIMITS ON RIGHT TO VARY. *See* p. 172, N. 8.

6. CHANGE IN QUANTITIES. By the new cl. 56 the contractor may be entitled to a variation of rates for changes in quantities not resulting from a variation, and the new rates are assessed under that clause and not under cl. 52—p. 212, N. 8.

VALUATION OF ORDERED VARIATIONS

52.   (1) The value of all variations ordered by the Engineer in accordance with Clause 51 shall be ascertained by the Engineer[1,2] after consultation with the Contractor[3] in accordance with the following principles.[4] Where work is of similar character[5] and executed under similar conditions[6] to work priced in the Bill of Quantities it shall be valued at such rates and prices contained therein as may be applicable. Where work is not of a similar character or is not executed under similar conditions the rates and prices in the Bill of Quantities shall be used

as the basis for valuation so far as may be reasonable[7] failing which a fair valuation shall be made.[8,9,10,10a] Failing agreement between the Engineer and the Contractor as to any rate or price to be applied in the valuation of any variation[11] the Engineer shall determine the rate or price in accordance with the foregoing principles and he shall notify the Contractor accordingly.

ENGINEER TO FIX RATES

(2) Provided that if the nature or amount of any variation relative to the nature or amount of the whole of the contract work or to any part thereof shall be such that in the opinion of the Engineer or the Contractor any rate or price contained in the Contract for any item of work is by reason of such variation rendered unreasonable or inapplicable[12] either the Engineer shall give to the Contractor or the Contractor shall give to the Engineer notice before the varied work is commenced or as soon thereafter as is reasonable in all the circumstances[13] that such rate or price should be varied and the Engineer shall fix such rate or price as in the circumstances he shall think reasonable and proper.

1. "THE VALUE OF ALL VARIATIONS ... SHALL BE ASCERTAINED BY THE ENGINEER". No time is stated and the contractor may have to do work without knowing what he will be paid for it. But the engineer should give notice in time if he intends to vary a contract rate under cl. 52 (2) (N. 13) and he must order dayworks in advance (N. 15). If the engineer delays in valuing a variation and including the valuation in the next certificate after the notice provisions have been complied with and after the parties have failed in consultation to agree on a valuation (N. 11), the contractor may refer the resulting dispute back to the engineer for a decision under cl. 66 and arbitration (p. 305, N. 19).

2. DESIGN CHANGES CONTRIBUTED BY OR AS CONCESSIONS TO THE CONTRACTOR. It is not at all unusual for the contractor to suggest a change of materials or of some other contract design even though strictly speaking that is the engineer's business, and for the change to be allowed or even ordered by the engineer. The contractor may do so because a change will save the contractor or employer or both time or money or will improve the works. It may even happen that the engineer presses the contractor to submit a design for part of the works that on a proper interpretation of the contract the engineer should design himself.

The following complications may arise:

(a) The contractor may claim extra payment for making the change.
(b) It may be found eventually that the changed design does not function satisfactorily, resulting in extra cost of altering it or reverting to the original design.
(c) The changed design may cause collapse of or other loss or damage to the works.
(d) The changed design may cause injury to persons or damage to other property.
(e) The employer may disown the engineer's agreement to the change at a late stage when the contractor has already incurred expense in reliance on the agreement.

(*f*) The employer may claim compensation from the engineer for disimprovement in the works, upon the grounds of professional negligence in accepting the contractor's proposal or that the engineer had no authority to agree to it. Alternatively the employer may seek to recover from the engineer payments he has to make to the contractor or third parties under any of the above headings.

In considering these complications, it is helpful to divide such design changes into two categories. The first is where the engineer decides that the suggested change will benefit the employer alone or as well as the contractor, by improving the works or by saving the employer money (either because the contractor offers a reduction in his rates for the change or the change will allow consequential savings or will minimise a cl. 12 claim) or because the change will reduce the time for completion of the works. The change may even be found to be positively "*necessary for the completion of the Works*" within cl. 51 due to some design defect (see p. 170, N. 4 on temporary works) in which case the engineer is bound to order the variation. In other cases in this category it seems (p. 171, N. 5) that the engineer may properly conclude that the change is "*desirable for the satisfactory completion . . . of the Works*" within cl. 51. The engineer then has the right *vis-à-vis* the contractor to order the change as a variation (his position in relation to his client is discussed below).

The other category of change emanating from the contractor is a change solely for his own benefit. For example, where the change will make it easier for the contractor to construct his temporary works, but no reduction in cost is being offered to the employer, or where the contractor finds himself in difficulties in constructing the works from which he can more easily extricate himself if a change is allowed.

It is suggested that the engineer can never be under a duty under cl. 51 to give a variation order in a case within this second category. His duty *vis-à-vis* the contractor to give a variation order only arises where the variation is "*necessary or desirable*" with cl. 51 even though the contractor is performing his contract to the letter. Therefore the engineer is perfectly entitled (with his client's authority) to tell the contractor that he will merely permit the change and will do even that only if the contractor agrees terms. Those terms will then bind the contractor if he accepts them expressly or by acting on the conditional concession and will bind the employer, as a collateral contract side by side with the main contract (p. 59).

The differing responsibilities of the contractor for each of these two categories of change may consequently be summarised as follows:

(i) Where an order is or should have been given under the first category, there is a normal variation which the engineer or arbitrator must value. The engineer does not appear to have any power effectively to attach conditions to the order, such as "No extra payment".

In the second category, where the engineer says that the contractor is merely allowed to make the change, he should add specifically that the contractor shall not be entitled to any extra payment, although it seems clear on principle and authority that in any case the contractor is not entitled to extra for such a change not made by order of the engineer, but merely allowed as a concession:

(*a'*) There is a special class of case where the contract itself permits the engineer to relax specification requirements—for example, the Department of Transport Specification for Road and Bridge Works cls. 509 (4) and 602 (6).

Contractors applied for permission to increase the width of girders because they could not make them as specified, at least not without a great deal of expense.

Held: there was nothing to imply that the engineer intended when giving his oral consent to agree to extra payment for the increase. b'

Even if it is clear that the contractor is not entitled to extra payment for making the change itself, he may later claim for the consequences of the change, e.g. under cl. 12 where the position of a trench is changed and unforeseen soil conditions are encountered. The engineer may include as a condition of granting a concession that the contractor will not have any claim under cls. 12, 13 or otherwise for any circumstances that would not have arisen if the concession had not been given, but it may not always be fair to do so and in any case it may be uncertain that the physical conditions or other difficulties would not have been met if the change had not been made.

The engineer may in fact give a straightforward variation order in a case where the change is solely for the contractor's benefit, either because he does not appreciate the dangers of doing so or because the contractor will not act on a conditional concession and the works are held up. Although there is some authority that such an order entitles the contractor to claim as for a normal variation and cls. 51 and 52 do not place such a variation in any special category, there are three ways in which the employer may be protected. c'

The first possibility is that the engineer may be entitled to value the variation at nil or as a sum in favour of the employer, on the grounds that it saved the contractor greater expense in dealing in some other way with the difficulties. That possibility is doubtful because of the words of cl. 52.

Probably the solution is that the employer must pay the contractor a normal valuation of the varied work, but then is entitled to recover back from the contractor the amount paid as damages under the general law for the breach of contract by the contractor that resulted in the variation. The contractor will in most cases be in breach of contract either in causing the difficulty in the first place, e.g. by not adequately stabilising or bracing the works, or in refusing to remedy the difficulty by some possible, even if uneconomic, method that would not require a variation order.

It may be advisable for the engineer to give the contractor in writing the choice of a concessional change as above or of proceeding with the more expensive solution at his own cost, and to await a positive refusal by the contractor to proceed with the works before stepping in with the variation expressly made subject to the employer's right to damages for breach of contract. Because the contractual position is so uncertain the engineer will be wise to tell the employer fully about the difficulties so that the employer may make known his views for consideration by the engineer, who may take legal advice himself.

The final possibility is that the employer may be entitled later to disown

(b') *Tharsis Sulphur & Copper Co.* v. *McElroy & Sons* (1878) 3 App. Cas. 1040.

(c') In *Simplex Concrete Piles Ltd.* v. *St. Pancras Borough Council* (1958) (unreported), *see* Hudson "Building & Engineering Contracts", 10th ed. by I. N. Duncan Wallace, p. 526, contractors working under a design and construct contract found it impracticable to carry out the work as contracted. The architect wrote "we are prepared to accept your proposal that the piles ... should be of the bored type in accordance with quotation submitted" (by sub-contractors). Held that this letter was an architect's instruction under the R.I.B.A. form, and the contractors were entitled to be paid for the varied work in accordance with that quotation.

the variation order on the grounds that it was given as a result of economic
duress in the form of a threat by the contractor to break his contract by
holding up the works until he received the order.

c"

(ii) The contractor is not contractually liable for damage or loss to the
works due to design by the contractor within this note. The excepted risk
within cl. 20 applies to all design unless provided by the contractor
"pursuant to his obligations under the Contract" (p. 103, N. 12). *See also* the
inclusion in the definitions in cl. 1 (1) (f) and (g) of a specification or drawing
merely approved by the engineer.

It is reasonable that movement by the contractor over the traditional
demarcation line in order to help with a design difficulty that is not of his
own making does not place undue responsibility on him. However, where
the change is for the benefit of the contractor the agreed conditions for the
concession may specify that the contractor will be strictly liable for the
design under cl. 20. The engineer should then verify that the contractor's All
Risks insurance covers the design. Otherwise the employer may be advised
to consider paying for special insurance in joint names.

(iii) Unless agreement is reached that the contractor shall indemnify the
employer for losses and claims arising out of or in consequence of
construction or maintenance of the permitted change to the works in terms
of cl. 22 (1) without the benefit of the exceptions in paras. (a) and (b) and
sub-cl. (2) of that clause, the liability for third party claims as between
contractor and employer may be obscure. If a change is authorised
properly, even as a concession, construction of the works with the change
appears to rank as *"construction . . . in accordance with the Contract"* so that
the employer will be liable for *"damage which is the unavoidable result"* of
such construction and for *"interference . . . with . . . easement"*, etc. within cl.
22 (1) (b) (ii) and (iv). Particularly if the engineer takes part in settling the
details of the change, as often happens, there may also be a case for divided
liability under cl. 22 (2). What is most essential is to make sure that all those
who may be liable are covered by insurance.

(iv) It appears that the contractor may be liable to the employer outside
of the contract where his design is later found to have been negligent, for
any resulting extra cost incurred by the employer to complete the works.
Liability of the contractor to the employer in negligence as well as under the
contract is a developing area of the law that is discussed from p. 393. For
delay caused by his negligent design the contractor normally will not be
entitled to an extension of time for completion, and therefore may incur
liquidated damages.

(v) The powers of the arbitrator in respect of a design change initiated by
the contractor are not very clear. If the engineer attempts unilaterally to
attach conditions to a variation order, under cl. 66 the arbitrator may
"review or revise" the engineer's decision to do so. The arbitrator may also
revise an engineer's decision not to give a variation order but only a
concession, and in consequence may value the variation under cl. 52. The
arbitrator has no power to award the contractor compensation where the

(*c"*) *North Ocean Shipping Co. Ltd.* v. *Hyundi Construction Co. Ltd.* [1978] 3 All E.R. 1170
Shipbuilders threatened without justification to terminate their contract unless the owners
paid them an increased price following a dollar devaluation — the owners eventually agreed.
Held that but for special circumstances the agreement would have been void for lack of
consideration (text above, p. 3) or alternatively voidable by reason of the economic duress
applied to the owners. This decision must have wide potential in the construction industry
where an employer who needs his works is vulnerable to pressure to make concessions.

engineer refuses even a concession, although it might have been reasonable to grant it, unless the contractor was entitled to an actual variation order. By definition there cannot be a right to a concession. *See also* p. 302, N. 13.

At the behest of the employer, the arbitrator may even decide that the engineer should not have given a variation order and that work done by the contractor on foot of the order was covered by the original contract and rates, and disallow the engineer's valuation. However, the arbitrator does not appear to have any power to change a binding collateral agreement for consideration (p. 3) made by the contractor and the engineer (with his client's authority) to regulate a change.

The last but not least person concerned with a change of this kind is the employer. Whilst the contractor may rely on cl. 51 for the authority of the engineer to give a straightforward variation within that clause (p. 169, N. 3), there is no such authority in the Conditions for a concession or conditional variation. If the contractor does not wish to be restricted to a remedy against the engineer, which he will rarely want to exercise and which anyway will not apply in all cases (p. 399), he must ensure that the engineer has actual authority from his client. In practice that may be very difficult to do, but in major cases the contractor will have to ask the engineer to confirm the concession with the employer or do so by writing direct himself.

Turning to the relationship of the employer with the engineer, the prime consideration is that unless the engineer has a service agreement which gives him special power he has no authority *vis-à-vis* his client even to order a variation, still less to give a concession for the benefit of the contractor. Thus the step to be taken by the engineer to give himself reasonable freedom of action is basically the same for concessions as for actual variations; he should ensure that any discretion permitted to him in his service agreement for variations extends similarly to concessional changes (p. 401 on the A.C.E. service agreement). The engineer must obtain special authority from his client also to delegate performance of part of his duty to design the whole works, if he does not wish automatically to be liable for any defects in the contractor's design (p. 391).

Even if the engineer's permission for a change is fully authorised, the engineer is not freed from his general duty to his client to exercise reasonable care and skill (p. 386). If the change should not have been approved by a competent and careful engineer and does later cause the employer loss (whether in third party claims, payments to the employer or delays or detriment to the works) the engineer may have to face a claim by his client, particularly if the contractor is insolvent or there is some defect in insurance cover.

In practice concessions are often made informally on site. It is rarely a practical proposition for the engineer to take elaborate contractual precautions, and in the interests of good working relations with the contractor it is not always appropriate that he should try to do so. The engineer has to keep in mind also that he is ultimately responsible to the client, and paid, for designing the whole works. Therefore he may have to be prepared to vet the contractor's suggestions thoroughly (allowing of course for the danger of overlooking in a few moments on site design complications that were considered over years when the project was being planned), and then to allow the responsibility for the changed design to rest   *d'*

(d') *See* the *City of Prince Albert* case, text below p. 393.

in accordance with the Conditions and ultimately on his own shoulders virtually as if it were his own design. On that basis save for major changes, or those with unclear design implications (if such changes should ever be made), the only precaution that will be taken is to say clearly when a concession is being given without extra payment. Even then difficulties may particularly arise in the case of a mixed change, partly for the benefit of the contractor and partly for the benefit of the employer (either genuinely so or because the contractor will not proceed diligently with the works unless the change is ordered). Whether the engineer will have to give a full unqualified variation order or can agree terms with the contractor will depend on the bargaining strength of the parties—principally on which of them can hold out longer, the contractor with his overheads running or the employer despite the delay to the works.

The danger of any catalogue of contractual complications is always that it may inhibit action. The above reminder of the possible dangers is not intended to cause engineers to be less amenable to sensible suggestions by contractors for avoiding unnecessary difficulties; the beneficial reaction would be that the engineer's staff is warned to ensure that the contractor's suggestions are carefully considered at the right staff level and that the contractual implications are also considered, however informally. Even if the engineer decides to ignore the complications, that will at least be a calculated risk, preferably explained to and approved beforehand by his client in major cases.

Finally, if an alternative design submitted by the contractor with his tender is adopted, the principles and precautions referred to in this note are relevant to the clarification of the consequences that should be included in the contract documents.

3. "AFTER CONSULTATION WITH THE CONTRACTOR". *See* N. 11.

4. THIS NEW SCHEME FOR VALUING VARIATIONS is a considerable improvement on the old. The former enigmatic reference to a rate being "*applicable*" or "*inapplicable*" has been replaced here (but unfortunately retained in sub-cl. (2) and added to cl. 56). Now it is stated that (*a*) a bill rate will govern only if the real character of and conditions affecting the work are similar to the original work priced in the bill (see the next two notes); (*b*) where the rates do not govern completely they are nevertheless the basis of the valuation so far as reasonable (N. 7), rectifying another possible imbalance in the previous edition; and (*c*) where these two methods do not apply a fair valuation is made (N. 8).

Uniformity is achieved with the J.C.T. Standard Form of building contract, from which the words in this sub-clause are taken.

The special provision for varying rates in cl. 52 (2) is retained (N. 12).

Engineers very often claim that rate fixing is an esoteric procedure beyond the comprehension of mere lawyers. In fact it is normally a give-and-take operation between engineer and contractor. Whilst lawyers may find the imprecision of the procedure difficult to accept, rigid legal rules *e'* would certainly do more harm than good.

(*e'*) The paper "Rate Fixing in Civil Engineering Contracts" by C. K. Haswell, Proc. Instn. Civ. Engrs. (vol. 24, p. 223) and particularly the discussion (vol. 27, p. 192) are most informative on the variations in practice in the application of cl. 52 of the 4th edition I.C.E. Conditions and the multitude of factors affecting the contractor's distribution of costs and profits between the rates which make rigid rules inappropriate.

For changes outside the contract *see* p. 169, N. 3, and p. 172, N. 8.

A contractor who has quoted a low rate may gain, and a contractor who has quoted a high rate may lose by an order for work on a daywork basis.

For price and labour cost fluctuations on valuing variations *see* p. 318, N. 3.

5. "WORK ... OF SIMILAR CHARACTER ... TO WORK PRICED IN THE BILL OF QUANTITIES ... VALUED AT (BILL) RATES AND PRICES". The work priced in an item of the bill of quantities is the work which is both within the verbal description of the item and necessary to perform the particular original contract work. For example, a price opposite a rate for "*excavate in any material*" is not a price for excavating any material in any place, but is an average price covering only the types of material existing in the site areas to be excavated in accordance with the original drawings and specification. It would be impossible for a contractor to price save on this basis, and the grounds on which the contractor is tied to his bill rates is that he has an opportunity before tender to investigate the areas to be excavated. Unless he is a prophet he could not investigate before tender an area in which excavation is carried out only as a result of a later variation order.

The result is that if excavation is moved, the rate must be adjusted for any differences in character between the original and new areas, or in the conditions (access, for example) in which the excavation is carried out. Indeed there may be much argument as to whether excavation or other work in sub-soil in a new area is "*of similar character*" to work in the original contract area, or as to whether the difference in the two areas can be established sufficiently to enable new rates to be based to any extent on contract rates. It is suggested that under this new wording the question is to be decided in the ordinary way on the balance of probabilities from all available evidence, and that it is not a valid argument that the conditions that would have been encountered in the original location cannot be known with absolute certainty without opening up the whole area.

6. "WORK ... EXECUTED UNDER SIMILAR CONDITIONS". Not, e.g., different access or timing—*see* p. 364 on disruption.

7. "THE RATES AND PRICES IN THE BILL ... SHALL BE USED AS THE BASIS FOR VALUATION SO FAR AS MAY BE REASONABLE". For valuing work not of "*similar character and executed under similar conditions*" to work priced in the bill, the basis (dictionary: "main ingredient, foundation, beginning") of valuation is to be bill rates with adjustment for differences between the varied work and the work priced, but only "*so far as may be reasonable*".

No guidance is given on the adjustment of rates or on the circumstances that will render unreasonable the use of bill rates as a basis of valuation, but some conclusions may be ventured:

(*a*) It is not unreasonable to apply rates as a basis for pricing varied work merely because the rates are mistaken (p. 14) or uneconomic, certainly in relation to the normal type of variation which is endemic in civil engineering works. What is reasonable is to be decided purely by reference to the nature of the original and varied work, not extraneous considerations.

(*b*) The nub of the matter is the relationship of rates to the contractor's costs. Even if particular rates give the contractor a return for an extra less than his costs, despite efficient working, then if the work is of similar character and executed under similar conditions to the original work the rates must be applied without alteration subject only to cl. 52 (2). But if the character of the work has changed, for example due to a change of materials, is it reasonable where the bill rate for the material is less than cost, to price the new material also at less than cost on the "*basis*" of the rate, i.e. by substituting only the difference in market value of the two materials?

The basic consideration is that the contractor has agreed to do all work within the contract—original and varied—on the basis of his bill rates. Administration of this clause by engineers and arbitrators should not make it possible for a contractor to price work low and then by payment for normal variations escape out of that price level at which he obtained the work in competition. Nevertheless there is the subsidiary factor that a tender will almost always include some particularly good rates and a percentage of rates that are below cost. If a high proportion of either good or bad rates happens to apply to major variations the price for the varied work will be artificially low or high. A contractor may even price the whole works low because particular plant is available, or because he is prepared to do a particular volume or type of work at a loss to pay his overheads or promote his image, and then by variations the employer may obtain a greatly increased quantity or changed type of construction at the low rates.

It is suggested that where a variation is very large or much different in real character from the work included in a rate, the consideration that it is the rates and prices (in the plural) that are to provide a basis for valuation and the reference to reasonableness in this sentence may require the engineer to depart from the price level of a particular rate and consider the level of all or a group of other rates and prices in the bill. Further, the limitation that rates are to provide a basis for valuation only so far as is reasonable may in exceptional cases require the engineer to move towards a fair valuation giving the contractor a reasonable profit on the work done. It is impossible to be more precise on this matter which is for the judgment of the engineer, but it is suggested that it is only in exceptional cases that the basis of valuation from the contract rates should be abandoned, particularly as the power to order variations can no longer be exercised for the convenience of the employer but only for the satisfactory completion and functioning of the original project for which the contractor tendered. The engineer (or arbitrator) should very carefully investigate, and be satisfied that he is seized of the full facts, before departing from a basis of valuation in particular contract rates.

(*c*) Where the work carried out is completely different in character or executed under conditions completely different from those included for in any bill rate or price, so that there is no rate or price which can provide even the basis of valuation, a fair valuation is payable (next note).

8. "FAIR VALUATION" will normally mean cost plus a reasonable percentage for profit (but not contingencies if the work is being valued after it has been carried out on actual not estimated cost) with a deduction for any proven inefficiency by the contractor, but if there is proof of a general market rate for comparable work it may be taken into consideration or applied completely.

9. ERRORS AND DEDUCTIONS IN THE BILL OF QUANTITIES. Refer to pp. 12–17 for errors in pricing and deductions, and cl. 55 for errors in description and omission of items.

10. PRELIMINARIES. Disputes on the valuation of preliminary or general items are common, due to misunderstanding on one or both sides of the principles involved:

(*a*) The mere fact that the contractor is entitled to an extension of time does not confer any right to an increase in preliminaries, unless the extension is due to a variation or delay for which the employer is responsible (p. 142).

(*b*) There is a tendency to apply a rigid formula in increasing preliminary items for variations, etc., by extending the preliminaries as a whole *pro rata* either to the extra time taken by varied work or the cost of the work. The proper procedure is to decide separately for each item whether it is related to the time on site, volume of work, both or neither—and to value accordingly. For example, the cost of providing site supervision normally is related to time on site, unless the volume of work is so increased that supervisory staff must be augmented. Each preliminary item should be carefully defined by the wording of the bill, to avoid allowing the contractor undue flexibility in calculating increases claimed for variations.

(*c*) If the bill provides **an item** for a preliminary which is priced by the contractor, then only that price is to be dealt with where a *pro rata* increase becomes due under cls. 52 or 56 in respect of the preliminary involved in the item. The contractor takes the risk if he unbalances his bid by partly including the price of the item in other rates or prices.

(*d*) If a contractor fails to price a preliminary item, whether by marking "included" or a dash or blank, then by the general practice (usually reinforced by a statement in the bill) the item is deemed to be included in the contractor's other rates and prices. The price for the item is to be treated as divided *pro rata* over all the other rates for work which involves that particular preliminary, so that the adjustment of the preliminary is taken care of by the adjustment of these rates when such work is increased by a variation order.

However, if by a variation order the item unpriced is increased by itself and not as a consequence of an increase in other work, the contractor is entitled to extra payment. For example, if the contractor prices an item for a site hut as "included", the engineer may not order a second site hut without any payment. There is no rate in the bill for the provision of a hut other than as a necessary ingredient of supervision of other work, and therefore a valuation must be made under cl. 52.

(*e*) If a contractor is entitled to compensation for delay by the client which extends the period of the contract, in respect of on-costs he is not confined to claiming for preliminary items priced separately in the bill, but may claim for on-costs included in other rates. Indeed to a large extent his claim is independent of the rates and prices in the bill (*see* ch. 12 on disruption claims generally).

(*f*) For a variety of reasons it may be agreed that a sum stated against a preliminary item is to be a fixed lump sum, not to be altered up or down for any changes in the works. In such a case it is important for both parties to think carefully about whether they are satisfied to have no change even if there is an unexpected alteration in quantities or variation of the works however large (but if a variation is ordered to the item itself, the contractor or employer may be entitled to a re-valuation under cl. 52—para. (*d*) above).

(*g*) The task of evaluating preliminaries is simplified if method-related charges apply, which must be marked "fixed" or "time-related" or as a sum, but the dangers of ambiguous definition remain—p. 218.

10(a). VALUATION OF A VARIATION IN THE "SPECIFIED SEQUENCE METHOD OR TIMING OF CONSTRUCTION". It is not at all easy to apply precisely to this type of variation the method of valuation of variations in cl. 52. The most satisfactory interpretation is that if a sequence, method or timing is specified for work in any item in the bill, then if there is a change in any of these elements the work is no longer the work priced in the bill (*see* on this point p. 185, N. 5) and may be re-valued under the scheme set out in cl. 52 (1). That is, the rates and prices in the bill provide the basis of valuation so far as reasonable, adjusted by reference to the change in timing, etc., and beyond that a fair valuation is to be made allowing for the effect of the change.

11. "FAILING AGREEMENT BETWEEN THE ENGINEER AND THE CONTRACTOR AS TO ANY RATE OR PRICE". By this sub-clause the value of variations is to be ascertained by the engineer only "*after consultation with the Contractor*" *f'* and "*Failing agreement between the Engineer and the Contractor*". Although the engineer's valuation may be invalid if he does not consult with the contractor at all, the only practical remedy of a contractor if the engineer fails to consult or consults perfunctorily with him is arbitration on the amount of the valuation. However, a prudent engineer will remember that failure to consult properly may be used as an ingredient in establishing misconduct (p. 411), or in discrediting his evidence in arbitration.

12. VARIATION OF BILL RATES. Sub-cl. (1) of this clause starts out by saying that "*The value of all variations ... shall be ascertained ... in accordance with the following principles*", but then goes on to refer to re-valuation of "*work*" without limitation. It might therefore be argued that under that sub-clause the engineer may re-value all work affected by the variation, not merely the work in the variation itself—for example where additional work restricts the access to other original contract work. However, the reference to work which is or is not "*of similar character and executed under similar conditions to work priced in the Bill*" seems to imply that the work being valued is work that was not itself priced in the bill. Any wider interpretation of sub-cl. (1) would make this sub-cl. (2) almost totally unnecessary.

Nevertheless, there is little doubt that the valuation of the varied work itself under cl. 52 (1) should reflect any effect of the variation on preliminary items priced in the bill (N. 10) and even, it is suggested, any effect of the variation on other contract work. It is not reasonable to base a valuation of additional work on bill rates without allowing for the fact, e.g., that the variation inhibits access to other parts of the work, and even more clearly any such effect of the variation should be allowed for in fixing a fair valuation. This sub-clause therefore will mainly apply to valuation of omissions, allowing as it does specifically a change in rate for "*any item of work*". A reduction in quantity due to an omission may make excavation plant uneconomic and cause the contractor to do by hand other excavation

(*f'*) The decision in *F. R. Evans (Leeds)* v. *Webster* (1962) 112 L.J. 703 that the words "in default of agreement" mean only that the parties have not agreed, and not necessarily that they have tried to reach agreement and failed, does not appear to apply, as the duty of the engineer to consult with the contractor is stated specifically.

work not omitted, for which the contractor may be entitled to re-rating under this sub-clause. The wording is wide enough to cover also a case where the stage at which the omission is ordered disrupts the contractor's other work (*see* ch. 12 for disruption claims generally).

One other situation in which the sub-clause may apply is where additional work produces over-recovery of overheads for the contractor. A percentage of the contractor's bill rates may be for overheads that are fixed and will not be increased *pro rata* to the additional work, so that if the total bill rate for that work is paid under cl. 52 (1) the contractor will make an unjust profit. The engineer may adjust the rate for both the additional and original contract work accordingly, but should give notice in time under this sub-clause (N. 13).

The contractor has no remedy under this sub-clause for loss of profit on work omitted, even if intentionally or by mistake he included a disproportionate part of his expected profit in the rate for that work (pp. 17 and 187).

There is a change in this sub-clause in allowing a variation in the rate or price "*for any item of work*", as opposed to "*items of the Works*" in the 4th edition. For the relevance of this change to method-related charges in the bill refer to p. 218.

It is difficult to understand why this wording has not been changed from the previous edition to match the new wording of sub-cl. (1).

13. NOTICE "THAT ... RATE OR PRICE SHOULD BE VARIED". This special notice for a varied rate is to be given by the engineer in effect if he wishes to reduce a rate and by the contractor or engineer for an increased rate. In both cases the notice must be given before the varied work is commenced or as soon after "*as is reasonable in all the circumstances*", relaxing the previous "*as is practicable*". The draftsman has overlooked that there may be no commencement of the varied work if the variation consists of an omission, specifically included in the definition of variation in cl. 51 (1) and a most important case for variation of a rate under this sub-clause. Presumably the difficulty in applying the notice provision will not be interpreted so as to deprive the sub-clause of effect in relation to omissions, and possibly the date on which the omitted work would have been started according to the contractor's programme can be regarded as the commencement of the omission.

Written notice is not specified.

Unfortunately the words used, "*shall give ... notice ... and the Engineer shall fix such rate*", are ambiguous as to whether service of notice is a condition precedent to the engineer's right and duty to fix new rates. Does "*and*" mean "*and then*"? The courts may be expected to hold that in the absence of an unambiguous requirement, notice is not a condition. However, it is wise for the engineer or contractor to give proper notice, because should notice be held to be a condition, then if the engineer did not give notice in time neither he nor the arbitrator may reduce a rate under this

(g') It has been held on the 4th edition of these Conditions that a notice simply specifying that a claim was being made and identifying in general terms the varied work to which it related satisfied a similar requirement of notice (*Tersons* v. *Stevenage Development Corporation* (1963) reported at 5 B.L.R. 58, C.A. In that decision the Court of Appeal also refused to hold that there was no evidence to support (*see* text below p. 302, footnote (*x*)) an arbitrator's decision that notices given over four and almost six months respectively after an order for additional work were given "as soon ... as is practicable" in the particular circumstances of the case.

sub-clause (p. 302), and if neither the engineer nor contractor gave such notice the arbitrator may not increase a rate.

In this sub-clause there is no reference to any consultation by the engineer or attempt to agree rates with the contractor.

DAYWORK

52. (3) The Engineer may if in his opinion it is necessary or desirable order[14] in writing that any additional or substituted work shall be executed on a daywork basis.[15] The Contractor shall then be paid for such work under the conditions set out in the Daywork Schedule included in the Bill of Quantities and at the rates and prices affixed thereto by him in his Tender[16] and failing the provision of a Daywork Schedule he shall be paid at the rates and prices and under the conditions contained in the "Schedules of Dayworks carried out incidental to Contract Work" issued by The Federation of Civil Engineering Contractors current at the date of the execution of the Daywork.[17]

The Contractor shall furnish to the Engineer such receipts or other vouchers as may be necessary to prove the amounts paid and before ordering materials shall submit to the Engineer quotations for the same for his approval.

In respect of all work executed on a daywork basis the Contractor shall during the continuance of such work deliver each day to the Engineer's Representative an exact list in duplicate of the names occupation and time of all workmen employed on such work and a statement also in duplicate showing the description and quantity of all materials and plant used thereon or therefor (other than plant which is included in the percentage addition in accordance with the Schedule under which payment for daywork is made). One copy of each list and statement will if correct or when agreed be signed by the Engineer's Representative and returned to the Contractor. At the end of each month the Contractor shall deliver to the Engineer's Representative a priced statement of the labour material and plant (except as aforesaid) used and the Contractor shall not be entitled to any payment unless such lists and statements have been fully and punctually rendered. Provided always that if the Engineer shall consider that for any reason the sending of such list or statement by the Contractor in accordance with the foregoing provision was impracticable he shall nevertheless be entitled to authorise payment for such work either as daywork (on being satisfied as to the time employed and plant and materials used on such work) or at such value therefor as he shall consider fair and reasonable.[18]

14. "ENGINEER ... IF IN HIS OPINION ... NECESSARY OR DESIRABLE ... (ORDER) DAYWORK". It seems that the engineer has complete discretion, subject to arbitration, to order daywork for variations whether or not there are contract rates which may apply—and to go back again to rates or a lump sum where details of labour, etc., are not available (the last line of this sub-cl. (3)). As always, the discretion should be used for good reasons, in this case related to the fair valuation of the work done. For example, dayworks may be ordered where a valuation at rates is not practicable but not to deprive the contractor of the benefit of high rates or the burden of low rates on which the valuation of the variation would otherwise be based, and an arbitrator may review any dayworks order accordingly.

15. "THAT ... WORK SHALL BE EXECUTED ON A DAYWORK BASIS", i.e. daywork must be ordered by the engineer in advance.

16. "DAYWORK SCHEDULE ... IN THE BILL OF QUANTITIES AND AT THE RATES AND PRICES AFFIXED ... IN HIS (THE CONTRACTOR'S) TENDER". For the

danger for the contractor that such rates and prices may not be subject to adjustment under the wages and prices adjustment formula, refer to p. 317.

17. "SCHEDULES OF DAYWORKS ... ISSUED BY THE FEDERATION ... CURRENT AT THE DATE OF THE EXECUTION OF THE DAYWORK". The percentage addition on labour costs for dayworks has been increased frequently for increases in statutory charges. As a result the previous incorporation of the Federation dayworks schedule current at the date of submission of tender operated unfairly, especially in long contracts. Unless a special daywork schedule is provided in the bill (last note), this provision will apply to dayworks even in a fixed price contract where increases in labour, etc., costs are not otherwise payable.

18. RECOVERY OF PAYMENT WITHOUT SUBMISSION OF QUOTATIONS, VOUCHERS, ETC. *See also* p. 302, N. 13.

NOTICE OF CLAIMS

52. (4)[1] (a) If the Contractor intends to claim a higher rate or price than one notified to him by the Engineer pursuant to sub-clauses (1) and (2) of this Clause or Clause 56 (2) the Contractor shall within 28 days after such notification give notice in writing of his intention to the Engineer.[2]

(b) If the Contractor intends to claim any additional payment pursuant to any Clause of these Conditions other than sub-clauses (1) and (2)[3] of this Clause he shall give notice in writing of his intention to the Engineer as soon as reasonably possible after the happening of the events giving rise to the claim. Upon the happening of such events the Contractor shall keep such contemporary records as may reasonably be necessary to support any claim he may subsequently wish to make.[4]

(c) Without necessarily admitting the Employer's liability the Engineer may upon receipt of a notice under this Clause instruct the Contractor to keep such contemporary records or further contemporary records as the case may be as are reasonable and may be material to the claim of which notice has been given and the Contractor shall keep such records.[4] The Contractor shall permit the Engineer to inspect all records kept pursuant to this Clause and shall supply him with copies thereof as and when the Engineer shall so instruct.

(d) After the giving of a notice to the Engineer under this Clause the Contractor shall as soon as is reasonable in all the circumstances[5] send to the Engineer a first interim account giving full and detailed particulars of the amount claimed to that date and of the grounds upon which the claim is based.[6] Thereafter at such intervals as the Engineer may reasonably require the Contractor shall send to the Engineer further up to date accounts giving the accumulated total of the claim and any further grounds upon which it is based.

(e) If the Contractor fails to comply with any of the provisions of this Clause in respect of any claim which he shall seek to make then the Contractor shall be entitled to payment in respect thereof only to the extent that the Engineer has not been prevented from or substantially prejudiced by such failure in investigating the said claim.[7,8]

(f) The Contractor shall be entitled to have included in any interim payment certified by the Engineer pursuant to Clause 60 such amount in respect of any claim as the Engineer may consider due to the Contractor provided that the Contractor shall have supplied sufficient particulars to enable the Engineer to determine the amount due.[9] If such particulars are insufficient to substantiate the whole of the claim the Contractor shall be entitled to payment in respect of such part of the claim as the particulars may substantiate to the satisfaction of the Engineer.

1. NOTICES, ETC., OF CLAIMS. The requirements of this clause fall into three categories:

A. In the case of variations under cl. 51:

(i) The contractor must ensure that there is an order or confirmation in writing to satisfy cl. 51 (2).

(ii) Under this para. (a) the contractor must then give "*notice in writing of his intention . . . (to claim)*" if on foot of either cl. 52 (1) or (2) he requires any increase in a rate or price which has been fixed by the engineer for a variation.

It has been held that a requirement of notice of intention to claim is satisfied if the notice simply specifies that a claim is being made and identifies in general terms the nature of the varied work to which it relates.

This written notice must be given within 28 days (for calculation of the period *see* p. 133, N. 13) "*after . . . notification . . .*" by the Engineer of the rate or price. On general principle to start the time running there must be a clear notification. Cl. 52 (1) requires the engineer to notify his decision on a rate or price to the contractor, but unfortunately does not require written notification. Cl. 52 (2) does not mention notification. Clear notification in any breakdown of the make-up of an interim certificate supplied by the engineer would be sufficient.

Problems about this para. (a) are discussed in N. 2.

(iii) For variation of rates under cl. 52 (2) an additional notice is specified by that sub-clause, to be served by the contractor or engineer (p. 189, N. 13).

Note that the above requirements do not apply to variations outside the contract (pp. 169 and 172, N. 3 and 8)

B. In the case of a change of quantities within cl. 56 (2), under para. (b) of this clause notice is required from the contractor that he requires additional payment, the notice to be given "*as soon as reasonably possible after the happening of the events giving rise to the claim*". It appears that the happening of those events is complete so as to require notice as soon as reasonably possible thereafter, only when the changed, actual, quantities have been executed, according to the first five words of cl. 56 (2).

The engineer in turn is required by cl. 56 to notify the contractor if he increases or decreases a rate or price under that clause, and the contractor must then give a further notice as under A (ii) above for a variation, if he disagrees with the rate notified to him by the engineer.

C. For other money claims under the contract (collected in the key in ch. 11) only the written notice under para. (b) claiming additional payment and served "*as soon as reasonably possible . . . after the . . . events giving rise to the claim*" is required from the contractor. For the time for notice under

(h') *Tersons* v. *Stevenage Development Corporation* (1963) 5 B.L.R. 58, C.A.

cl. 12 *see* p. 70 N. 17, under cl. 13 *see* p. 73 N. 6, under cl. 59A (3) (b) *see* p. 242 N. 13, and under cl. 59B (4) (b) *see* p. 253 N. 14.

This clause does not apply at all to claims not "*pursuant to any Clause of these Conditions*" but outside this contract (N. 3).

In addition to notice of claim:

(i) Under this cl. 52 (4) (b) the contractor is bound automatically to keep and permit the engineer to inspect contemporary records to support any claim under cl. 56 (2) for a change of quantities or any other claim for payment under these conditions except a claim for variations. The contractor is bound to keep these records immediately "*Upon the happening of the* ... (*relevant*) *events*", even though that is before it is "*reasonably possible after the happening of the events*" to give notice of intention to claim in accordance with the other requirement of this paragraph. If the engineer wishes to have contemporary records kept in the case of variations he must ask the contractor for them under para. (c), and unfortunately on the words used cannot do so until he receives notice of claim from the contractor. The engineer also has power upon receipt of a notice of claim in either case to require the contractor to keep further contemporary records "*as are reasonable*".

(ii) "*as soon as is reasonable in all the circumstances*" after giving a notice of intention to claim under this clause, the contractor must send to the engineer a first interim account "*giving full and detailed particulars of the amount claimed to that date and of the grounds* ... (*of*) *claim*" (N. 6). The contractor must also send further accounts at such intervals as the engineer may reasonably require.

(iii) The contractor must give certain specified particulars and documentation with applications for payment under cl. 60—pp. 258–9.

On the extreme practical importance of these notice requirements, refer to pp. 442–3 on claims; on the slight relevance of the Unfair Contract Terms Act 1977 refer to p. 433.

2. NOTICE OF CLAIM FOR VARIATIONS. Claims under cl. 52 (1) and (2) for variations are excluded from para. (b) of this sub-clause, so that the contractor's only duty under this clause in respect of such claims for variations is to give notice in writing of intention to claim a higher rate or price than one notified to him by the engineer. The other requirements of this sub-clause arise only after that initial notice has been given.

If the engineer considers that an order of his does not amount to a variation he will of course not notify any "*rate or price ... pursuant to sub-clauses* (1) *and* (2)" of cl. 52 (particularly if the contractor has not alleged that an order by the engineer constitutes a variation) and apparently the contractor's notice and other duties under this sub-clause will not then arise at all. It is equally strange that para. (a) pre-supposes that the engineer fixes a rate or price for variations before he receives any accounts from the

---

(*i'*) The requirements that records are to be contemporary means that the recording may not be delayed to obtain the benefit of hindsight. In arbitration or court a witness is permitted to refresh his memory in the course of his evidence by documents made at the time of the events described or so shortly afterwards that the facts were fresh in the witness's memory, provided they were made by the witness personally or checked by him while the acts were fresh in his memory. In *Orr* v. *Simmonds* (1967) 51 Cr.App.Rep.316 notes made by customs officers at the first convenient opportunity after returning to their office from lengthy interviews were held to comply with that condition of contemporaneity, but a delay of 27 days was held too long in *Orr* v. *Graham* [1973] Crim.L.R.628.

contractor under para. (d), and contrasts with the statement in para. (f) that his duty to allow any claim in an interim certificate depends on receiving *"sufficient particulars"* from the contractor.

i"

· 3. NOTICE IF CONTRACTOR "INTENDS TO CLAIM . . . ADDITIONAL PAYMENT PURSUANT TO ANY CLAUSE OF THESE CONDITIONS OTHER THAN . . . (1) AND (2)". For a summary of relevant clauses *see* the key in ch. 11. Claims are not included if they are not *"pursuant to"* these Conditions but for breach of contract not referred to in the Conditions (examples are given on pp. 364 and 418) or outside the contract such as a claim for acceleration (p. 371). A claim for an indemnity under cl. 22 (2) is not included because it is not a claim for *"additional payment"*.

Apart from this notice clause there are some other formal requirements in the conditions, which are also collected in the key.

4. "CONTEMPORARY RECORDS . . . AS ARE REASONABLE"—COSTS. If the contractor refuses to keep records in accordance with this clause the engineer will rarely be able to compel him to do so—forfeiture usually will be impracticable and the engineer has no right to withhold certificates (p. 273). The engineer will have to choose between relying on an arbitrator excluding the contractor's claim under para. (e), which will not be certain to happen, or have the records kept (as far as possible) by his staff or an outside expert. The employer will have a claim to recover from the contractor the expenses of obtaining such records, as damages for the contractor's breach of contract.

Record-keeping on instructions from the engineer is unlikely to disrupt the contractor's arrangements or involve him in delay, so as to produce a claim for costs under cl. 13 (3) if it applies (p. 75). The contractor therefore in most cases will have to bear the expense of preparing the records and suppling copies, unless his claim goes to arbitration and the arbitrator awards him the costs on the grounds that the engineer's requirements were unreasonable (p. 418).

5. "AS SOON AS IS REASONABLE IN ALL THE CIRCUMSTANCES". *See* p. 163, N. 3, on the similar expression *"as soon . . . as practicable"*.

6. "FIRST INTERIM ACCOUNT GIVING FULL AND DETAILED PARTICULARS OF THE AMOUNT CLAIMED . . . AND OF THE GROUNDS UPON WHICH THE CLAIM IS BASED". Apart from failure to furnish this account at all, a gross understatement or misstatement of the claim eventually made, of the expenses which the contractor requires to be taken into account, or of the factual grounds of claim, could well prejudice the engineer in investigating the claim, and under the rest of this clause bar the final claim. It is difficult to see that a misstatement of the legal grounds of claim could have that effect, unless the basis of compensation on the grounds specified were to differ from the basis of compensation eventually claimed so that the engineer did not require the right records to be kept. That difficulty should not arise often; even where the contractor initially claims a change of rates under cl. 52 the engineer normally will require the contractor's costs for the varied work to be recorded, so that he will not be prejudiced, for example, by a

---

(*i"*) Indeed, the purpose of this whole para. (a) is mysterious—see the commentary on these Conditions by John Uff in Keating "Building Contracts", 4th ed., p. 510.

later claim by the contractor to ignore the rates and recover costs under cl. 12. Sadly this sub-clause therefore does not make it essential for contractors to have all claims vetted by a lawyer. .

Since the contractor is bound to state his grounds of claim with the first interim account, the right given in this paragraph to include "*further grounds*" in later accounts appears to refer to grounds arising or at least revealed later, and not to allow the contractor to change his mind at will without risking disqualification of the claim under para. (e).

7. "THE CONTRACTOR ... ENTITLED TO PAYMENT ... ONLY TO THE EXTENT THAT THE ENGINEER HAS NOT BEEN PREVENTED FROM OR SUBSTANTIALLY PREJUDICED BY SUCH FAILURE (TO COMPLY WITH ANY OF THE PROVISIONS OF THIS CLAUSE) IN INVESTIGATING THE ... CLAIM". This restriction applies to any failure to give an initial notice of claim under para. (a) or (b) of this clause, or to keep contemporary records required automatically under para. (b) or instructed by the engineer under sub-cl. (c), or to permit the engineer to inspect records or supply him with copies, or to send to the engineer a first interim or other required account. It does not apply to failure to give notice in time under cl. 52 (2) (p. 189), or to give the particulars required with a notice by cl. 12 (1) or an estimate under cl. 12 (2) (a), or give particulars of a claim to extension of time under cl. 44.

The required records are defined by reference to reasonableness without further guidance, but clearly reasonable records normally may include information about the labour, plant and material cost of extra work with at least the detail required under cl. 52 (3) for a dayworks claim.

On the importance of records, the possibility of making full use of contemporary records to avoid or shorten arbitration proceedings, and the vital importance of proper application of this clause by arbitrators, refer to ch. 17.

8. OTHER REMEDIES OF THE EMPLOYER FOR THE CONTRACTOR'S FAILURE TO GIVE NOTICE, PARTICULARS OF CLAIMS, ETC. If the contractor does not fulfil any requirement of this sub-clause he will be in breach of contract. Apart from the possible effects discussed in the previous note, the employer will be entitled to recover from the contractor any resulting damages he can prove; for an example *see* p. 319, N. 7, on the price variation formula.

9. WHOLE OR PART OF ANY CLAIM CONSIDERED DUE BY THE ENGINEER to be included in an interim certificate, provided sufficient particulars supplied.

Any attempt by the engineer to require the contractor to agree to accept some part payment in full and final settlement of his whole claim by the threat that if he does not he will be paid nothing, is in direct breach of the contractor's right under this paragraph to payment of any substantiated part of a claim. That is unless with the employer's authority the engineer is making an *ex-gratia* offer to dispose of a claim which in the exercise of his powers and duties under the contract he is satisfied is not contractually valid.

The engineer has no implied authority from the employer to make an offer to compromise some disrupted or 'nuisance' claim, as opposed to determining the amount due to the contractor in accordance with his powers under the contract. Typically a compromise offer will be identified by being described as *ex-gratia*, and it follows that the client is not bound by such an offer by the engineer even if accepted by the contractor, unless the engineer had special authority. The contractor may have a remedy against the engineer (p. 400).

See pp. 266–7 on payment of amounts that are established as due after the substantial completion certificate.

PLANT, ETC.—DEFINITIONS

53.   (1)[1] For the purpose of this Clause:
   (a) the expression "Plant" shall mean any Constructional Plant Temporary Works and materials for Temporary Works but shall exclude any vehicles engaged in transporting any labour plant or materials to or from the Site;[2]
   (b) the expression "agreement for hire" shall be deemed not to include an agreement for hire purchase.[3]

VESTING OF PLANT

(2) All Plant goods and materials[4] owned by the Contractor or by any company in which the Contractor has a controlling interest[5] shall when on the Site be deemed to be the property of the Employer.[6]

CONDITIONS OF HIRE OF PLANT

(3) With a view to securing in the event of a forfeiture under Clause 63 the continued availability for the purpose of executing the Works of any hired Plant the Contractor shall not bring on to the Site any hired Plant unless there is an agreement for the hire thereof which contains a provision that the owner thereof will on request in writing made by the Employer within 7 days after the date on which any forfeiture has become effective[7] and on the Employer undertaking to pay all hire charges in respect thereof from such date[8] hire such Plant to the Employer on the same terms in all respects as the same was hired to the Contractor[8a] save that the Employer shall be entitled to permit the use thereof by any other contractor employed by him for the purpose of completing the Works under the terms of the said Clause 63.[9,10]

COSTS FOR PURPOSES OF CLAUSE 63

(4) In the event of the Employer entering into any agreement for the hire of Plant pursuant to sub-clause (3) of this Clause all sums properly paid by the Employer under the provisions of any such agreement and all expenses incurred by him (including stamp duties) in entering into such agreement shall be deemed for the purpose of Clause 63 to be part of the cost of completing the Works.

NOTIFICATION OF PLANT OWNERSHIP

(5) The Contractor shall upon request made by the Engineer at any time in relation to any item of Plant forthwith notify to the Engineer in writing the name and address of the owner thereof and shall in the case of hired Plant certify that the agreement for the hire thereof contains a provision in accordance with the requirements of sub-clause (3) of this Clause.

IRREMOVABILITY OF PLANT, ETC.

(6) No Plant (except hired Plant)[11] goods or materials or any part thereof shall be removed from the Site without the written consent of the Engineer which

consent shall not be unreasonably withheld where the same are no longer immediately required for the purposes of the completion of the Works but the Employer will permit the Contractor the exclusive use of all such Plant goods and materials in and for the completion of the Works until the occurrence of any event which gives the Employer the right to exclude the Contractor from the Site and proceed with the completion of the Works.[12,13]

REVESTING AND REMOVAL OF PLANT

(7) Upon the removal of any such Plant goods or materials as have been deemed to have become the property of the Employer under sub-clause (2) of this Clause with the consent as aforesaid the property therein shall be deemed to revest in the Contractor and upon completion of the Works the property in the remainder of such Plant goods and materials as aforesaid shall subject to Clause 63 be deemed to revest in the Contractor.[14]

DISPOSAL OF PLANT

(8) If the Contractor shall fail to remove any Plant goods or materials as required pursuant to Clause 33 within such reasonable time after completion of the Works as may be allowed by the Engineer then the Employer may:
(a) sell any which are the property of the Contractor; and
(b) return any not the property of the Contractor to the owner thereof at the Contractor's expense;

and after deducting from any proceeds of sale the costs charges and expenses of and in connection with such sale and of and in connection with return as aforesaid shall pay the balance (if any) to the Contractor but to the extent that the proceeds of any sale are insufficient to meet all such costs charges and expenses the excess shall be a debt due from the Contractor to the Employer and shall be deductible or recoverable by the Employer from any monies due or that may become due to the Contractor under the contract or may be recovered by the Employer from the Contractor at law.[15]

LIABILITY FOR LOSS OR INJURY TO PLANT

(9) The Employer shall not at any time be liable for the loss of or injury to any of the Plant goods or materials which have been deemed to become the property of the Employer under sub-clause (2) of this Clause save as mentioned in Clauses 20 and 65.

INCORPORATION OF CLAUSE IN SUB-CONTRACTS

(10) The Contractor shall where entering into any sub-contract for the execution of any part of the Works incorporate in such sub-contract (by reference or otherwise) the provisions of this Clause in relation to Plant goods or materials brought on to the Site by the sub-contractor.[16]

NO APPROVAL BY VESTING

(11) The operation of this Clause shall not be deemed to imply any approval by the Engineer of the materials or other matters referred to herein nor shall it prevent the rejection of any such materials at any time by the Engineer.

1. GENERAL. This clause transfers to the employer ownership of the

contractor's (and sub-contractors' (N. 16)) plant, materials and temporary works while they are being used for the works, and deals specially with hired plant, so as to have them available as far as possible to complete the works if the contract is forfeited. Plant, etc., owned by the contractor is also a security which may be sold by the employer to raise any payments due to him on forfeiture, and this clause is drafted so as to allow this even if the contractor becomes bankrupt—N. 6.

j'

Plant, etc., is to be approved by the engineer under cl. 13 (2) and under cl. 35 he may require returns of plant.

2. "CONSTRUCTIONAL PLANT TEMPORARY WORKS AND MATERIALS". For definitions *see* cl. 1 (1) (k) and (o) Contractor's tools are included.

k'

It seems that it is the employer, not the contractor, who may let space on hoardings, which become the employer's property under this clause.

3. HIRE PURCHASE PLANT. *See* N. 10.

4. "GOODS AND MATERIALS". The inclusion of "*goods*" is new, and covers all tangible moveable property (except money).

l'

5. "COMPANY IN WHICH THE CONTRACTOR HAS A CONTROLLING INTEREST". Several pages of the Statute Book are taken up with efforts to define control of a company satisfactorily, for tax purposes, so it is probably wise that it is not defined here. 51 % of the voting shares of a company is a controlling interest, and a contractor may also control a company through the right to appoint directors or by a debenture. If the question of control reaches the courts they will probably deal with it realistically, and will certainly take into account shares or directorships held by a nominee of the contractor.

There is another problem about this provision. In law a company in which the contractor has a controlling interest is still an independent legal person distinct from the contractor and, therefore, he cannot bind the company under this clause unless he has authority from the company to vest plant which it owns in the employer. The engineer should therefore clarify the position by asking in his preliminary enquiries for information as to any plant to be hired from a company in which the contractor or a sub-contractor has a controlling interest. He should then before accepting a tender or agreeing to a sub-contract insist on written confirmation from the company that the contractor or sub-contractor has its authority to agree to the plant vesting in the employer as security for the contractor's liability, etc.

It is also possible for plant to be owned by and hired from an individual who is, for example, a shareholder or director of a contracting company or some subsidiary, to avoid the plant vesting in the employer under this clause. The engineer may in his preliminary enquiries ask for information about plant that will reveal any such expedient, and the employer may

(*j'*) In *Dublin Port & Docks Board* v. *Britannia Dredging Co. Ltd.* [1968] Ir.R. 136 an interlocutory injunction was granted to prevent removal of dredging equipment from a site in breach of this clause, where the employers believed (on good grounds) that the contractors intended to abandon the works. There was some discussion of the position of plant owned by a subsidiary of the contractor company, but no decision on appeal.

(*k'*) *Partington Advertising Co.* v. *Willing & Co.* (1896) 12 T.L.R. 176.

(*l'*) *See*, e.g., Sale of Goods Act, 1893, Sec. 62.

refuse to accept the tender unless the plant is first transferred to the contractor.

6. PLANT, ETC., AS SECURITY. So that he may sell them to recover his losses in case of forfeiture, this clause transfers the ownership of all contractor-owned materials and plant, etc., to the employer immediately they are brought on the site and not merely if and when the contractor is made bankrupt, because any agreement is void that "on a man becoming bankrupt that which was his property up to the date of the bankruptcy shall go over to someone else and be taken from his creditors". There is one *m'* decision which suggests that even this clause may not be effective on bankruptcy, because plant, etc., is only to "*be deemed to*" become the *n'* property of the employer. That decision probably is wrong and unlikely to be followed.

Apart from a special clause of this kind, the ownership of the contractor's materials passes to the employer when they are built into the works or included in interim certificates.

Some engineers order plant or materials which are transferred to the employer under this clause to be marked with the employer's name. This is to meet another bankruptcy rule, that any property which a bankrupt at the time of his bankruptcy has with the true owner's consent in his "possession, order or disposition under such circumstances that he is the reputed owner thereof", i.e. that a bystander not knowing the actual facts would necessarily assume him to be the owner, may be taken by the bankruptcy trustee and used to pay the bankrupt's creditors, though, in fact, the property belongs to someone else. This rule is intended to prevent credit being obtained on the faith of the apparent ownership of goods that do not actually belong to the debtor and which, but for this rule, his creditors could not touch.

Marking plant with the employer's name is certainly not necessary where the contractor is a limited company, since there is no "reputed ownership" provision in the legislation which regulates company liquidation. Although the law is not settled, it seems that materials belonging to the employer or to a sub-contractor are not in any case in the reputed ownership of the contractor merely because they are on the site, because a bystander must be taken to know of the customary use of a clause of this kind and of the possibility of sub-contracting. But all materials in the contractor's yard are in his reputed ownership. *o'*

Various other restrictions on the employer's security from plant and materials are mentioned in the notes to this clause. It may be helpful to review the steps that should be taken by the engineer to ensure that the employer has as much security as possible:

(*a*)   In his preliminary enquiries the engineer will ask for information and action to ensure that plant that is in reality being provided out

---

(*m'*) *Re Harrison ex. p. Jay* (1880) 14, Ch. D. 19, at p. 25 (C.A.).

(*n'*) *Bennett and White (Calgary) Ltd.* v. *Municipal District of Sugar City (No.* 5) [1951] A.C. 786, *see* discussion Hudson "Building & Engineering Contracts", 10th ed. by I. N. Duncan Wallace, pp. 668–669. Although the Bills of Sale Acts, 1878 and 1882, are very stringent in invalidating many transactions in which the owner of goods purports to transfer ownership without possession of them, there is authority that the Acts do not apply to this type of clause, *see* "Halsbury's Laws of England", 4th ed., vol. 4, paras. 624 and 625.

(*o'*) *Re Fox, ex. p. Oundle and Thrapston R.D.C.* v. *The Trustee* [1948] 1 All E.R. 849.

of the resources of the contractor or his associates is actually vested in the employer under this clause (N. 5).

(b) In the case of major sub-contractors the engineer may require similar information about the ownership of plant from the sub-contractors, and may verify that the contractor has complied with sub-cl. (10) of this clause (N. 16).

(c) In the case of hired plant the engineer should act under sub-cl. (5) before the plant is brought on site by the contractor or any sub-contractor.

(d) The employer's security by this clause may be very seriously eroded as a result of suppliers' retention of title clauses, by which the ownership of materials does not pass to the contractor (and therefore may not pass to the employer under this clause) so long as the contractor is in debt to the supplier. The engineer will be on the alert to deal in time with such clauses (p. 262).

(e) The engineer will use his power under sub-cl. (6) to prevent removal from site of plant, goods or materials so as to lessen the employer's security, particularly if there is any likelihood of forfeiture under cl. 63.

(f) If action has to be taken to expel the contractor, it may be necessary for the engineer to arrange for plant and materials on site to be taken into secure custody on behalf of the employer, and he will advise the employer to make any necessary requests to the owners of hired plant under sub-cl. (3).

(g) The engineer will fully administer cl. 54.

It is important for the engineer to try to prevent any breach by the contractor of this clause or cl. 54; otherwise whatever remedies he may have in damages the employer will lose the effective security for claims against the contractor (additional to any bond and retention) that it is the purpose of those clauses to provide.

7. "WITHIN 7 DAYS AFTER THE DATE ON WHICH . . . FORFEITURE HAS BECOME EFFECTIVE", i.e. seven full days after the date on which notice by the employer under cl. 63 (1) expires—see cl. 63, N. 9. The engineer must be careful not to let this short time-limit go by.

8. "HIRE CHARGES . . . FROM SUCH DATE". The employer is not bound to pay any arrears due by the contractor.

8(a). PROVISION THAT "OWNER . . . WILL . . . HIRE SUCH PLANT TO THE EMPLOYER ON THE SAME TERMS . . . AS THE SAME WAS HIRED TO THE CONTRACTOR". Presumably the purpose of this sub-clause is to give the employer protection in the case of some special item of plant on hire by the contractor that would not easily be replaced if it were removed from site on forfeiture. Since the owner of the plant is not a party to the construction contract and therefore may not be bound by this sub-clause (p. 221), the engineer would be wise to obtain (at the tender stage if possible, since that is the only time he can insist on it) an agreement by the owner of the plant direct with the employer to abide by this provision.

In any case this right to hire plant on forfeiture on similar terms to the contractor may not help the employer to finish the works if the contractor held the plant on short term hire. Special arrangements from the outset may be necessary to protect the employer.

9. EMPLOYER ENTITLED TO USE HIRED PLANT "FOR ... COMPLETING THE WORKS UNDER ... CLAUSE 63". Not if the employer takes over the works under the general law, or takes over part of the works, e.g. under cl. 39 (2). Compare N. 12 and p. 205, N. 6. The effectiveness of this provision is greatly reduced by the contractor's freedom to remove hired plant from the site—N. 11.

10. PLANT ON HIRE PURCHASE. By sub-cl. 3 "*hired Plant*" may not be brought on site by the contractor unless "*there is an agreement for the hire thereof*". By para. (1) (b) the expression "*agreement for hire*" is defined as excluding a hire purchase agreement. The effect, obtained in an extremely oblique and doubtful way, appears to be that the contractor may not bring hire purchase plant on to the site at all because that definition and the general law indicate that hire purchase plant is to be classed as "*hired Plant*" and there will be no "*agreement for hire*" within the definition in para. (1) (b).

The alternative interpretation is certainly open—that hire purchase plant is permitted on site and not subject to this sub-clause at all.   *p'*

11. "NO PLANT (EXCEPT HIRED PLANT) ... SHALL BE REMOVED FROM THE SITE". This restriction is not limited to plant owned by the contractor, so that he is not entitled to take plant owned by third parties off site of his own volition, but of course neither the employer nor the contractor can prevent the real owner claiming to take away his plant.

The exception of hired plant from the engineer's control means that the site may be denuded of plant by a contractor outside the control of the engineer, where the contractor has more profitable work elsewhere or has decided to default, provided only that he takes the precaution of hiring the plant (and hire from an associated company may even be sufficient—N. 5).

12. "WILL PERMIT THE CONTRACTOR THE EXCLUSIVE USE OF ... PLANT ... UNTIL", ETC. This means that plant, temporary works and materials cannot be used for work put in another contractor's hands without forfeiture of the whole contract, e.g. under cl. 39 (2). However, if the contractor will not consent to their use, under those clauses he eventually bears the extra cost to the employer of having the work done without them. Unlike sub-cl. (3), the wording of this clause gives the employer the right to use plant, etc., if he ends the contract under the general law.

13. EXECUTION AGAINST PLANT, ETC. Because of the contractor's right to use them, the materials, plant, etc., which have vested in the employer are not liable to be taken in execution under a court judgment against the

---

(*p'*) Although a hire purchase agreement creates "in reality a contract of hiring, not in name or pretence only" (*Helby* v. *Matthew* [1895] A.C. 471, 476), it is not a simple hiring—"*the contract (of hire purchase) was not merely a bailment for reward but ... conferred on the bailee an interest in the property*". *Whiteley Ltd* v. *Hilt* [1918] 2 K.B. 808. In the 4th edition of these Conditions not only was an agreement for hire defined to exclude an agreement for hire purchase but hired plant was defined as plant held by the contractor on an agreement for hire. There was also a specific sub-cl. (6) attempting to give the employer certain rights on forfeiture in respect of plant on hire purchase.

employer, unless the contractor has lost these rights on forfeiture of the contract. Nor, of course, since they no longer belong to him, can they be taken in execution of a judgment against the contractor.

14. "UPON COMPLETION OF THE WORKS . . . REVEST IN THE CONTRACTOR". This clause is effective even if the employer becomes bankrupt or goes into liquidation in the meantime.

There is no provision for re-vesting plant in the contractor if the works are not completed—*see* cl. 63, N. 11.

Presumably "*completion*" means certified substantial completion.

15. DEDUCTION. *See* p. 269.

16. INCORPORATION OF THIS CLAUSE IN SUB-CONTRACTS. For the importance of clear incorporation, so that the sub-contractor's plant, etc. will vest in the contractor and then pass from him to the employer, refer to footnote (*a*) on p. 222 below.

The whole of this clause is to be incorporated in the sub-contract, including this sub-cl. (10), so that if the sub-contract is worded properly sub-sub-contractors will be bound similarly.

VESTING OF GOODS AND MATERIALS NOT ON SITE

54. (1) The Contractor may with a view to securing payment under Clause 60 (1) (c) in respect of goods and materials listed in the Appendix to the Form of Tender before the same are delivered to the Site[1] transfer the property in the same to the Employer before delivery to the Site provided:

(a) that such goods and materials have been manufactured or prepared and are substantially ready for incorporation in the Works; and

(b) that the said goods and materials are the property of the Contractor or the contract for the supply of the same expressly provides that the property therein shall pass unconditionally to the Contractor upon the Contractor taking the action referred to in sub-clause (2) of this Clause.

ACTION BY CONTRACTOR

(2) The intention of the Contractor to transfer the property in any goods or materials to the Employer in accordance with this clause shall be evidenced by the Contractor taking or causing the supplier of the said goods or materials to take the following action:[2]

(a) provide to the Engineer documentary evidence that the property in the said goods or materials has vested in the Contractor;

(b) suitably mark or otherwise plainly identify the said goods and materials so as to show that their destination is the Site that they are the property of the Employer and (where they are not stored at the premises of the Contractor) to whose order they are held;

(c) set aside and store the said goods and materials so marked or identified to the satisfaction of the Engineer; and

(*q'*) In *Hart* v. *Porthgain Harbour Company Ltd.* [1903] 1 Ch. 690 a clause in the contract vested material in the employer when brought on the ground. Held: That the contractor who did not complete the works could not recover the material, although the employer did not complete the works himself or by another contractor.

(d) send to the Engineer a schedule listing and giving the value of every item of the goods and materials so set aside and stored and inviting him to inspect the same.

VESTING IN EMPLOYER

(3) Upon the Engineer approving in writing the said goods and materials for the purposes of this Clause the same shall vest in and become the absolute property of the Employer and thereafter shall be in the possession of the Contractor for the sole purpose of delivering them to the Employer and incorporating them in the Works and shall not be within the ownership control or disposition of the Contractor.[3]

Provided always that:

(a) approval by the Engineer for the purposes of this Clause or any payment certified by him in respect of goods and materials pursuant to Clause 60 shall be without prejudice to the exercise of any power of the Engineer contained in this Contract to reject any goods or materials which are not in accordance with the provisions of the Contract and upon any such rejection the property in the rejected goods or materials shall immediately revest in the Contractor;[4]

(b) the Contractor shall be responsible for any loss or damage to such goods and materials and for the cost of storing handling and transporting the same and shall effect such additional insurance as may be necessary to cover the risk of such loss or damage from any cause.[5]

LIEN ON GOODS OR MATERIALS

(4) Neither the Contractor nor a sub-contractor nor any other person shall have a lien on any goods or materials which have vested in the Employer under sub-clause (3) of this Clause for any sum due to the Contractor sub-contractor or other person and the Contractor shall take all such steps as may reasonably be necessary to ensure that the title of the Employer and the exclusion of any such lien are brought to the notice of sub-contractors and other persons dealing with any such goods or materials.[6]

DELIVERY TO THE EMPLOYER OF VESTED GOODS OR MATERIALS

(5) Upon cessation of the employment of the Contractor under this contract before the completion of the Works whether as a result of the operation of Clause 63 or otherwise[7] the Contractor shall deliver to the Employer any goods or materials the property in which has vested in the Employer by virtue of sub-clause (3) of this Clause and if he shall fail to do so the Employer may enter any premises of the Contractor or of any sub-contractor and remove such goods and materials and recover the cost of so doing from the Contractor.

INCORPORATION IN SUB-CONTRACTS

(6) The Contractor shall incorporate provisions equivalent to those provided in this Clause in every sub-contract in which provision is to be made for payment in respect of goods or materials before the same have been delivered to the Site.[8]

1. **PAYMENT FOR GOODS AND MATERIALS BEFORE DELIVERY TO THE SITE.**
This new clause (coupled with an addition to cl. 60) gives the engineer

power to certify payment for goods and materials before delivery on the site, provided the items are listed in the appendix to the form of tender and the procedure in this clause is followed to protect the employer. With the employer's authority the engineer may either list items in the appendix on issuing the documents to tenderers or possibly allow tenderers to add their own requirements. Only substantial and easily identifiable items should be included.

The engineer has a discretion whether to include any amount for such items in interim certificates, even though the items have become the property of the employer (p. 262, N. 9).

It may be beneficial to the employer as well as the contractor to operate this clause, in relation to such items as prefabricated steelwork where the supplier will add an appreciable percentage for his interest charges if he is not to be paid until delivery to the site. It may also be very useful to the employer to have ownership of materials before delivery, so that they will be available to any alternative contractor if the original contractor defaults (N. 6), particularly in these days of long delivery times. It is essential that the procedure in this clause is converted from paper into practice if the employer is to obtain the ownership for which he is paying, and if delay in obtaining possession of the goods on default by the contractor is to be minimised, particularly where the contractor is in liquidation.

2. PROCEDURE. Action by the contractor:

(a) The contractor himself, or through the supplier, gives documentary evidence to the engineer that the property (i.e. ownership) in the items is vested in the contractor. Many suppliers include in their quotations or acceptance forms special terms stating that the ownership in goods is not to pass until payment has been received for the particular goods or even until the contractor has paid in full his general account to the supplier. Such terms and their wider implications are discussed in p. 262, N. 9. The engineer will have to ensure that no such term applies in the particular case and that no lien affects the items (N. 6), and may have to take legal advice on the question of whether the ownership of items has passed fully to the contractor under a contract of supply.

(b) The contractor suitably marks or otherwise plainly identifies the goods to show their destination and that they are the property of the employer, and (where they are not stored at the premises of the contractor but, e.g., at a supplier's premises) to whose order they are held.

(c) The contractor sets aside and stores the marked items to the satisfaction of the engineer.

(d) The contractor sends the engineer a schedule listing and giving the value of every item and inviting him to inspect them.

(e) The contractor remains responsible for any loss or damage to the goods and materials and must if necessary extend his insurance under cl. 21, which under that clause need only cover materials delivered to the site. See also N. 5.

The engineer:

(a) Checks that the ownership of the items is in the contractor and free of all liens, and that the contractor has taken the other specified steps (above).

(b) Inspects the items.

(c) Checks the contractor's insurance of the items. See N. 5 on insurance by the employer.

(*d*) Approves the items in writing, and thereafter may include their value up to the percentage in the tender in interim certificates under cl. 60.

(*e*) May take steps to ensure that this clause is incorporated into sub-contracts and that where necessary the procedure is followed for goods supplied by sub-contractors (N. 8).

(*f*) Advises the employer of his rights under sub-cl. (5) if they arise, including the right to enter premises of the contractor or any sub-contractor to remove goods.

3. "SHALL NOT BE WITHIN THE OWNERSHIP CONTROL OR DISPOSITION OF THE CONTRACTOR". *See* p. 199, N. 6. Whether the goods are within the disposition of a bankrupt contractor as far as creditors are concerned is a question of law, and the creditors are not bound by the terms of this contract to which they are not parties.

It is suggested that the principles on which the Bills of Sale Acts do not invalidate cl. 53 are applicable to this clause.

4. EFFECT OF APPROVAL. *See* p. 127.

5. CONTRACTOR TO INSURE AGAINST "LOSS OR DAMAGE FROM ANY CAUSE". Responsibility for loss or damage due to the negligence of the employer or his servants or agents may nevertheless remain with the employer—p. 96, N. 1. The excepted risks defined in cl. 20 (3) are not specifically excluded, although largely uninsurable.

6. NO LIEN IN FAVOUR OF THE CONTRACTOR OR ANY SUB-CONTRACTOR OR OTHER PERSON. A lien in this context is a right to retain goods, in some cases with a right of sale, until the person in possession is paid either for work done on the items by way of repair, improvement, etc., or for the price of the items where he is an unpaid seller in possession. The latter is a statutory lien under the Sale of Goods Act, 1893. The seller in possession may exercise the right of lien when the goods not paid for have been sold on credit but the credit terms have expired, or the goods have been sold without any stipulation as to credit, or even if the credit terms have not expired if the buyer becomes insolvent.

A lien may be given up by agreement (*see* e.g. Sec. 43 (1) (c) of the Sale of Goods Act, 1893). Where the goods are in the hands of a third party the engineer should require the contractor to produce a letter from that party giving up any lien (or, although not mentioned here, right of stoppage in transit under Sec. 44 of the Sale of Goods Act, 1893) over the goods.

It may be mentioned in this context that we have no equivalent to the mechanic's lien system in force in some other countries, by which a contractor or sub-contractor may register a lien on the building for contract payments. If an employer or main contractor becomes insolvent, the contractor or sub-contractor has no right to preferential payment out of the value of the building for materials and work embodied in it. The only right in the absence of special agreement (pp. 255–6 and 257) is to prove as a general creditor for a dividend in the liquidation.

7. "UPON CESSATION OF THE EMPLOYMENT OF THE CONTRACTOR UNDER THIS CONTRACT . . . WHETHER AS A RESULT OF THE OPERATION OF CLAUSE 63 OR

(*r'*) Text above, p. 199, footnote (*n'*).

OTHERWISE". The "*or otherwise*" is obviously intended to include action under the general law (p. 425, and contrast cl. 53 (3)) and, it is suggested, is effective to do so although under the general law the contract itself is ended, there is not merely "*cessation of the employment of the Contractor under this contract*" as described here. The words used do not cover removal of part of the works out of the contractor's hands, e.g. under cl. 39 (2), but although he is not entitled to enter the contractor's premises as specified in this sub-clause the employer is entitled to take proceedings against the contractor for recovery of the items, which have become his property. In addition under cl. 39 (2) the contractor will ultimately bear any cost of duplicating the items due to his obstruction.

8. INCORPORATION OF THIS CLAUSE IN SUB-CONTRACTS. Refer to p. 202, N. 16.

QUANTITIES

55. '(1) The quantities set out in the Bill of Quantities are the estimated quantities of the work but they are not to be taken as the actual and correct quantities of the Works to be executed by the Contractor in fulfilment of his obligations under the Contract.[1]

CORRECTION OF ERRORS

(2) Any error in description in the Bill of Quantities or omission therefrom shall not vitiate the Contract nor release the Contractor from the execution of the whole or any part of the Works according to the Drawings and Specification or from any of his obligations or liabilities under the Contract. Any such error or omission shall be corrected[2] by the Engineer and the value of the work actually carried out shall be ascertained in accordance with Clause 52.[3] Provided that there shall be no rectification of any errors omissions or wrong estimates in the descriptions rates and prices inserted by the Contractor in the Bill of Quantities.[4,5]

1. CHANGES IN QUANTITIES. The effect of this clause is radically altered by the new cl. 56 (2), allowing a change in rates for a change in quantities — p. 209. Nevertheless, by this clause the employer appears to warrant that the quantities of the work have been "*estimated*". It follows that the contractor may have an alternative remedy in damages for breach of warranty (p. 58) if he can prove that some quantity in the bill was not genuinely estimated but chosen arbitrarily (either with no information to support it or contrary to the known information). There does not seem to be any advantage in that alternative except that the contractor is entitled to recover all his losses (p. 427) whereas the measure of compensation under cl. 56 is obscure.

It follows that an item with an arbitrary quantity should not be inserted merely to obtain a rate: a provisional sum may be used instead.

2. EXTRA PAYMENT FOR "ANY ERROR IN DESCRIPTION IN THE BILL OF QUANTITIES OR OMISSION THEREFROM". A cornerstone of these Conditions is that the works will be re-measured and valued on completion by reference to that curious creation, the bill of quantities. Yet a bill with only one item, for performing the whole of the contract, would infringe no provision of

these Conditions. The terms of cls. 55–57 actually place few contractual restraints on the draftsman of the bill; he is free to do what he likes, and therefore what is best for the project, provided he makes clear what he is doing. It is practical and not legal reasons that dictate that in the bill the works are divided into many items on some agreed system. *s'*

Main purposes of the bill are to enable the contractor to evaluate and allow for cost differentials between the different items of the works so that he can prepare his tender efficiently and accurately, and to supply the employer with rates and prices quoted by the contractor in competition at the time of tender that can be applied as directly and specifically as possible to changes in the works. It is important therefore that cls. 55–57 should be administered by engineers, arbitrators and courts not in a legalistic way but primarily so as to realise and not to frustrate their practical aims.

This sub-clause is a logical consequence of the fullblooded measure and value nature of this 5th edition based on a bill of quantities. If the contractor's payment is to be determined by applying rates and prices quoted by him against specific items in a bill, work improperly described in or omitted altogether from the bill cannot be deemed to have been included for by the contractor in the spaces between items, so to speak, however obviously necessary the work may be for completion of the project. Thus attempts by the 4th edition to retain part of the lump sum principle have been abandoned by this sub-clause and by changes of wording in cl. 11 (2) (p. 64, N. 10).

The starting point in applying this sub-clause must be to determine what contract work is covered accurately by the items in the bill, from which can be determined whether work is misdescribed or omitted. Despite the microscopic examination to which bills are sometimes subjected in a search for claims there is no special version of the English language that applies in writing or reading bills of quantities. The basic question of what work is covered by an item must be decided by reference to the ordinary meaning of the words used in the item, with the help of the method of measurement (p. 213) and standard rules of interpretation (p. 244).

Despite the reference in this clause to "*description in the Bill*", bill items do not necessarily describe the work in the sense of defining the quality and dimensions required; that is the task of the specification and drawings—to quote section 5.11 of the C.E.S.M.M. (p. 213) "Descriptions (in the bill) shall identify the work covered by the respective items, but the exact nature and extent of the work is to be ascertained from the Drawings, Specification and Conditions of Contract, as the case may be, read in conjunction with the Work Classification (in the method)". Part II.3 of the D.O.T. method is to like effect. In other words the description of work in an item needs to extend only so far as is necessary to perform the purpose of the item, that is to identify the work covered and to be priced by the contractor.

Conversely, this sub-clause says that an error in description or omission from the bill does not "*release the Contractor from the execution of the whole or any part of the Works according to the Drawings and Specification*", thus making clear that there may be an error in or omission from the bill and resulting claim under this sub-clause even for work which is described in the specification or is shown on the drawings (*see* also cl. 11 (2)). Despite cl. 5 of these Conditions, and recognising the realities of

(*s'*) For a full discussion of the uses and abuses of the traditional measurement system, read Barnes "Measurement in Contract Control".

estimating that make it unreasonable to require the contractor to find errors by the engineer in the bill, the contractor is accordingly entitled to price against an item only such work as is identified by the item description.

At the same time the distinction between the bill and the other contract documents is not absolute, because the work may be identified in a bill item by a cross-reference to another contract document—"Any detail of description required to be given in accordance with the Work Classification may be omitted from an item description provided that an equivalent reference to the Drawings or Specification is given in its place" (C.E.S.M.M. sec. 5.12). If a bill item incorporates a specification or drawing by referring to it, all work required to be done in the incorporated part of the document will then be covered by the item.

Each bill item identifies the work (in the wide meaning defined in sec. 1.5 of the C.E.S.M.M. that "includes work to be carried out, goods, materials and services to be supplied...") to be completed for the rate or price. Incidental operations necessary to complete that work obviously are included in the item, and do not give rise to a claim to extra under this clause. For example, an item for formwork covers all the materials and operations necessary to produce finished formwork—it is unnecessary to refer separately, for example, to the supply and driving of nails in timber forms for without them there will be no formwork. Similarly an item for trench excavation covers all operations necessary to produce trenches suitable for the purposes for which they are intended, including any support for the sides and keeping them free of water. The principle that such indispensable and contingent operations are included in the rate for finished work will be found confirmed in the methods of measurement in many of the cases that are likely to arise in practice (p. 216 (c)).

The experience even under the 4th edition of these Conditions, with no cl. 55 (2), was that only the slimmest pretexts were required for ingenious claims for alleged omissions from bills. To avoid argument the draftsman should err on the side of over-clarification and ensure that all the finished work and materials intended to be covered by the item are either mentioned specifically or included by an all-embracing formula, with any doubt about the coverage that might otherwise exist or be capable of manufacture removed via a standard method of measurement.

A specific case may clarify these general principles. Take the case of pre-cast concrete beams which are to be cast in a shape that will provide a hook as an integral part of the beam for use by the eventual occupants of the structure. An item stated to be for the beams in accordance with a specified drawing that shows the hook or even for beams without more, will cover the requirement of the hook that is part of the beam. On the other hand if the beam is to be cast and then a separate hook is to be fixed on independently, the contractor will have a claim under this sub-clause if the only relevant item in the bill is for beams without more. Even if the item refers to a drawing that shows the hooks attached to the beams, a reference to the drawing may not be sufficient to incorporate the part of the drawing that

---

(*r'*) In *Patman and Fotheringham Ltd.* v. *Pilditch* (1904) Hudson "Building Contracts" 4th ed., vol. ii, 368, the judge in holding that quantities formed part of a contract said that "I am not by any means sure that there might not be cases of accidental omissions from the quantities ... I should have to deal specifically with the cases of things that everybody must understand are to be done, but which happen to be omitted in the quantities. I think the case (*Williams* v. *Fitzmaurice*, set out in the text on p. 27) would cover that". Introduction of this sub-clause into these Conditions appears virtually to eliminate the relevance of that dictum.

does not refer to the beams but to the added hooks, but a reference to "all work shown on Drawing No. __" would be sufficient. An item for "Beams ... with hooks attached" with or without the addition of "in accordance with Drawing No. __ and Specification clause __" will remove any room for dispute. It is unnecessary to describe in such an item the incidental operations necessary to attach the hooks to the beams, which will appear in the specification or on the drawings.

There is nothing in this sub-clause to suggest that although work is misdescribed in or omitted from the bill the contractor is deprived of his right to extra payment because the facts that produced the misdescription or omission were not or could not have been known by the draftsman of the bill. For example, where there is an item in a bill to "socket piles in rock" and it is found only when the work is being carried out that the material in which the piles are to be socketed is not in fact rock as defined in the contract, then it appears that the contractor is entitled to a valuation of the work actually carried out under this sub-clause. The danger of such a claim may have to be explained to an employer reluctant to pay for adequate site investigations.

The large area for argument opened up by cl. 55 (2) is apparent.

The discussion in this note is carried further in relation to methods of measurement by N. 1 on p. 213.

3. "VALUE OF THE WORK ACTUALLY CARRIED OUT ... ASCERTAINED IN ACCORDANCE WITH CLAUSE 52". *"the work actually carried out"*, which is to be valued under cl. 52, appears to include work other than the item misdescribed or omitted, so that rates for other contract work affected may be varied under cl. 52 (2).

4. NOTICES. It does not seem that the notice requirements of cl. 52 (2) fit this clause. Notice is required under cl. 52 (4), under para. (b), since the claim is made pursuant to this clause and not under cl. 52 although the valuation is made under cl. 52. If the contractor claims an extension of time he should give notice in accordance with cl. 44.

5. "NO RECTIFICATION OF ANY ERRORS ... OR WRONG ESTIMATES IN THE DESCRIPTIONS RATES AND PRICES INSERTED BY THE CONTRACTOR IN THE BILL". The reference to an error in descriptions inserted by the contractor is for the case where the contractor inserts an extra item in the bill, usually a method-related charge (p. 218).

The prohibition of rectification clearly is limited to rectification under this clause, and does not prevent rectification under the general law—pp. 12 and 41.

MEASUREMENT AND VALUATION

56. (1) The Engineer shall except as otherwise stated ascertain and determine by admeasurement the value in accordance with the Contract of the work done in accordance with the Contract.[1]

INCREASE OR DECREASE OF RATE

(2) Should the actual quantities executed in respect of any item be greater or less than those stated in the Bill of Quantities[2] and if in the opinion of the

Engineer such increase or decrease of itself[3] shall so warrant the Engineer shall after consultation with the Contractor[4] determine an appropriate increase or decrease of any rates or prices rendered unreasonable or inapplicable in consequence thereof[5] and shall notify the Contractor accordingly.[6,7,8]

Attending for Measurement

(3) The Engineer shall when he requires any part or parts of the work to be measured give reasonable notice to the Contractor who shall attend or send a qualified agent to assist the Engineer or the Engineer's Representative in making such measurement[9] and shall furnish all particulars required by either of them. Should the Contractor not attend or neglect or omit to send such agent then the measurement made by the Engineer or approved by him shall be taken to be the correct measurement of the work.[10]

1. MEASUREMENT BY THE ENGINEER. Although the engineer has the duty to measure, the task of preparing monthly statements and a final detailed account for submission to the engineer is placed on the contractor by cl. 60. *See also* cl. 38.

2. VARIATION IN RATE FOR ALTERED QUANTITIES. The contractor is given specifically a right to an increase of rate in appropriate cases where a difference between the actual quantities and those shown in the bill adversely affects his economics in carrying out the works, even though the change is not the result of a variation order by the engineer. Examples are a decrease in quantity which makes use of particular plant uneconomic and reduces the contractor, e.g., to hand excavation, or an increase in unsuitable material which disrupts motorway works.

It appears that the contractor is entitled to price on the quantity in the bill, so that it is not necessary for the contractor to prove that the difference was unforeseeable, and no minimum percentage difference is required (refer to N. 5 as to where it is only because of some particular and peculiar method of working by the contractor that the change is significant). In respect of quantities, this clause therefore has the effect that the employer is guaranteeing the conclusions drawn by the engineer from site investigation—e.g. as to the quantities of suitable and unsuitable filling material on the site stated in the bill. For the alternative of requiring the contractor to price varying quantities, *see* p. 438.

The engineer has a corresponding power to reduce a rate, for example where increased quantities would otherwise produce over-recovery of overheads. If the amount of a particular overhead is fixed irrespective of the quantity of the work—e.g. provision of site offices—in the absence of a reduction the percentage for the overhead included in the rate multiplied by the increase in quantity would produce an unjustified increase in payment for the overhead. The engineer will adjust the rate accordingly under this power.

Where several types of work, disparate in difficulty, cost, etc., are bulked together in one item in the bill, the rate may be adjusted under this sub-clause so far as an increase or decrease in the total quantity affects the proportions of the two types of work covered by the item, but not if the proportions change for any other reason (unless there is a cl. 12 claim or variation).

Exceptionally, the contractor may have an alternative remedy for a wrong estimate in the bill of quantities—p. 206, N. 1.

3. "OF ITSELF". No change of rate is warranted, for example, where an increase in quantities imposes hardship on a contractor not in itself but for the extraneous reason that the contractor originally priced the item too low due to a clerical error or underestimation, so that the increase in quantities multiplies his loss, or where the contractor has a large profit in the rate for an item reduced in quantity. Still less is the contractor entitled to relief where he has lost on a gamble, e.g. by placing a low rate on an item which he expected to decrease, but which has actually increased.

4. "AFTER CONSULTATION WITH THE CONTRACTOR". See p. 188, N. 11.

5. "DETERMINE AN APPROPRIATE INCREASE OR DECREASE OF ANY RATES OR PRICES RENDERED UNREASONABLE OR INAPPLICABLE". The authors of this edition appear to have exhausted their impressive, if confusing, repertoire of definitions of extra payments, and in this case refrain from giving any guidance at all.

Should an increase equal the contractor's extra costs of working due to extra quantities (and if so why is this not stated), or should it take into account that the original bill rate is below or above the cost of the work or materials, if that is the case? For example, if a reduction in quantities involves a change from plant to hand excavation, should the rate be altered to cover the contractor's actual costs of hand excavation, or if the normal rate for hand excavation is treble machine excavation, should the contractor's bill rate simply be multiplied by three? Is the position different if the contractor has a low rate for plant because he has the particular machine readily available? May the engineer take into account any unreasonableness in the contractor's arrangements that affect the cost to the contractor of the change of quantities? With diffidence the answers suggested to these questions are that the increase or decrease should have reasonable regard to the level of the original rates unless the contractor can prove special circumstances (see for an analogy p. 185), and that the engineer may take any unreasonableness into account.

On this last question of the contractor's particular arrangements or methods affecting the cost to him of a change of quantities, the requirement in this clause that the change in quantities "of itself" warrants the change in rate is relevant. The contractor has a basic freedom to decide on his own methods and arrangements, but it is suggested that nevertheless in deciding on an "appropriate" adjustment of rate the engineer is entitled to exclude any cost incurred by the contractor due to unreasonable inflexibility in his methods or arrangements having regard to the fact that an experienced contractor must anticipate some degree of variation from the billed rates. To safeguard against such inflexibility is one of many reasons why the engineer should obtain as much information as possible about and consider carefully the contractor's proposed arrangements, preferably before acceptance of tender. Merely to mark a quantity "provisional" is not a protection against a claim under this clause, but it may possibly be read as requiring the contractor to allow particular flexibility in his methods to deal with varied quantities. A better system of itemisation in the bill is mentioned on p. 438.

Note that the engineer may increase or decrease '*any*' rates or prices rendered unreasonable or inapplicable, not merely the rate for the item that has changed in quantity.

For considerations relevant to the adjustment of preliminaries for changes in quantities refer to p. 187, and on method-related charges p. 219.

6. NOTICE OF CLAIM appears to be required by cl. 52 (4) only as soon as reasonably possible after the right to claim is complete when the actual quantities have been "*executed*", in accordance with the first line of this sub-clause.

7. EXTENSION OF TIME is specifically provided for in cl. 44, with a requirement of notice.

8. THE DIFFERENCE BETWEEN A CHANGE OF QUANTITIES UNDER THIS CLAUSE AND A VARIATION UNDER CLAUSE 51. This difference may be important—no order or confirmation is required under this clause as there is under cl. 51, the notice provisions are slightly different (p. 192, N. 1) and the descriptions of the extra payment to which the contractor is entitled vary (N. 5).

Although the reference to a change of quantities has been deleted from the definition of a variation in cl. 51, obviously a variation order may result in "*the actual quantities executed in respect of any item . . . (being) greater or less than those stated in the Bill*". It is suggested that it cannot be intended that the contractor should have a choice of claiming under this clause or under cl. 52. Despite cl. 51 (3) the distinction is between a change in quantities due to a variation in the works ordered by the engineer and a difference between the actual quantities and those stated in the bill due solely to an incorrect estimate in the bill of the quantities necessary for the original works. The example may be taken of a cut of 20,000 cu. yards, in which the bill estimates a quantity of 10,000 cu. yards unsuitable material. If by a variation order the cut is increased in size by one-quarter, and it is found that there is 17,000 cu. yards of unsuitable, of which 13,000 cu. yards is in the area of the original cut and the balance in the added area, then the balance falls to be valued under cl. 52 and the increase in the original area to be dealt with under this clause.

Complications can be envisaged in such a mixed case. If the total change in quantities alters the contractor's method of working in a way that either the change in quantities by itself or the variation order by itself would not have done, in theory it is necessary to decide which of the changes was the last straw which altered the contractor's methods, so as to decide whether cl. 52 or this clause applies to the change in method. This might particularly be so if no cl. 52 (2) notice had been given. In practice these subtleties are not likely to be important, but in any exceptional case where they are, full records will have to be kept of all relevant factors.

9. MEASUREMENT—"QUALIFIED AGENT". Suggested that an agent is not "*qualified*" by ability to hold a tape measure or drawing; that he must understand the principles of the bill of quantities and method of measurement which determine what is to be measured.

Section 5.18 of the C.E.S.M.M. and Part II.2 of the D.O.T. method (below) confirm the usual practice that quantities are measured net from the drawings, but *see* cl. 38.

Although this clause places the duty to measure on the engineer, by cl. 60 the contractor must compile and submit detailed monthly and final statements.

10. "SHALL BE TAKEN TO BE THE CORRECT MEASUREMENT". It is possible that the measurement may be reopened by an arbitrator if the contractor can put his finger on a mistake—p. 302, N. 13. In any case only the "*measurement*" is binding not the values placed on the measured quantities by the engineer.

If the engineer wishes to rely on measurement made by the representative, he should make sure that there is a written record that the measurement has been "*approved by him*", as specifically required by this sub-clause.

METHOD OF MEASUREMENT

57. Except where any statement or general or detailed description of the work in the Bill[1] of Quantities expressly shows to the contrary Bills of Quantities shall be deemed to have been prepared and measurements shall be made according to the procedure set forth in the "Standard Method of Measurement of Civil Engineering Quantities" issued by the Institution of Civil Engineers and reprinted in 1973 or such later or amended edition thereof as may be stated in the Appendix to the Form of Tender to have been adopted in its preparation notwithstanding any general or local custom.[2]

1. METHOD OF MEASUREMENT. The significance of the bill of quantities is discussed generally in N. 2 to cl. 55. Because the rate or price against each item in the bill in effect is a lump sum price (p. 28)|for|whatever|activity is properly covered by the item, it is essential that the items in the bill are systematically worded and divided in order that the contractor when he is tendering knows what is to be priced under each item, and the engineer when he is measuring and valuing the finished works similarly knows what is covered by each rate and price. So that the bill for each contract does not have to set out at length the system used, this clause provides for incorporation of one of the standard published systems of measurement that are accepted and understood in the industry.

There are three methods of measurement in common use. "The Standard Method of Measurement of Civil Engineering Quantities" reprinted in 1973 and for the time being mentioned in this clause ("the old method"); the "Civil Engineering Standard Method of Measurement" published by the I.C.E. in 1976 ("C.E.S.M.M.") which according to its preface supersedes the old method, but in fact has not yet done so completely; the Department of Transport "Method of Measurement for Road and Bridge Works" 2nd ed. published in 1977 ("D.O.T. method"). The appendix to the form of tender includes a space for referring to the C.E.S.M.M. if it is intended to apply instead of the old method; if the D.O.T. method is to apply that space should be completed accordingly and the D.O.T. has issued a special condition to adjust this cl. 57.

Whichever method is chosen, it has a lesser status than is traditionally conferred on the method of measurement in building contracts. The answer to the perennial question of whether the method of measurement chosen is

(*t''*) In the January 1979 revision of these Conditions the C.E.S.M.M. is substituted for the old method in this clause.

or is not a contract document is that the method is an effective part of the contract only to the defined and limited extent set out in this clause. This clause creates a presumption in favour of the chosen method—what is written in the bill is to be interpreted so as not to conflict with the method unless the draftsman shows clearly that he is departing from it (as he is perfectly entitled to do). The contractor is entitled to the benefit of any ambiguity on that score, but of a genuine ambiguity only. Thus:

(a) All three methods contain detailed terms that aim to prevent different types of work with different cost implications being included in one item in the bill, so that the bill performs its practical purposes (p. 207). For example:

> Old method cl. 39—"Separate items are to be provided for excavation differing in character, purpose or method of execution ... the various classes of excavation are to be sub-divided, as necessary, so that opportunity may be given for fixing different prices ... for ... Excavation in soft material, and excavation in hard material or rock".
>
> C.E.S.M.M. section 3.5—"The work shall be divided into items in the Bill ... so that the component of work which is included in each item does not exhibit more than one feature from each division of any one class, of the Work Classification". The second division of the Work Classification for earthworks Class E, for example, includes rock, topsoil, artificial hard material and other material each as a separate component. Note 6 to the class says "Material to be excavated shall be deemed to be natural material other than rock or topsoil, unless otherwise stated in item descriptions".
>
> D.O.T. method section 6.11—"Separate items shall be provided for excavation ... (in) Topsoil ... Suitable material except rock ... Unsuitable material ... Rock".

It is difficult to see any case where the draftsman of the bill will do any service to the employer by departing from these rules. Nevertheless as they are so typical of the way in which the various methods attempt to regulate the bill, the contractual effects of the methods will be illustrated by examples of such departure. Take a bill where the description in the only item for excavation is simply "Excavation of foundations ...". As under the note in the C.E.S.M.M. material to be excavated under the item is deemed

(u') In the course of his judgment in *A. E. Farr* v. *Ministry of Transport* (1965) now reported at 5 B.L.R. 94 Lord Pearson said: "I think it is strictly correct to say that clause 57 does not impose on the building owner an obligation to draft his bill of quantities in conformity with the standard method of measurement, but it would be natural and advisable for him to do so, as otherwise problems would arise in respect of the construction of the bill of quantities, and in respect of the application of the rates contained therein to the measurements taken in accordance with the procedure set forth in the standard method of measurement" (p. 116). Lord Guest (dissenting) expressed doubt as to whether the standard method could "properly be considered a contract document" (p. 114). However, the general question of the effect of failure to comply with the method did not arise for decision in that case, and the words of cls. 55 and 57 of this edition now appear to be quite clear to produce the results deduced in the text.

(v') Section 3.7 of the C.E.S.M.M. says that those notes in the work classification "which point out that the application of the C.E.S.M.M. either does or does not require separate items to be given for particular components of work ... do not extend or limit the separate itemization required by the C.E.S.M.M. They are given solely to draw attention to particular differences between the itemization required by the C.E.S.M.M. and that required by other methods of measurement". It is clear from the method as a whole that generally "the notes in the Work Classification are rules just as much as other parts of the document. The notes should not be thought of simply as helpful supplementary comments" (p. 28, and *see* pp. 23 and 100 of "Measurement in Contract Control" by Barnes, the principal author of the method.

to be natural material other than rock, if rock is encountered in foundations there is no rate in the bill describing it and under which it may be measured, so that there appears to be an omission from the bill which the contractor is entitled to have corrected under cl. 55 (2). On the other hand if either of the other two methods applies to the contract, since they contain no presumption in favour of any particular material if the material to be excavated is not described, it is suggested that the only reasonable interpretation of such an item is that the method is not being followed and excavation in any material is included. Of course if the only item is specifically for excavation in *natural material other than rock* then without any help from the method of measurement cl. 55 (2) entitles the contractor to a new rate if rock is found.

The relevant note that has been quoted from the C.E.S.M.M. itself says at the presumption in favour of natural material other than rock may be excluded by a statement in the item description, but of course cl. 57 in any case allows exclusion of the method. For example, under an item for excavation "in any material including rock", or even "in any material", the contractor must place a composite rate to cover any excavation whether in soft material or rock, and cannot claim under cl. 55 or this cl. 57 however unexpected the proportion of rock and soft material may be. (For additional quantities beyond those billed *see* cl. 56.)

The result is that there are no inflexible rules: all depends on the words of the bill.

(*b*) For the wording of the bill to deprive the contractor of a claim by reference to the method of measurement it is not necessary that a statement or description in the bill states specifically that the method has been excluded, it is enough if it shows that clearly.

The reference to exclusion by a *"statement"* in the bill (added in this edition of the Conditions) permits a method to be excluded by a broad statement, in the preamble which is normally part of the bill or elsewhere in the bill, that the method does not apply at all or in particular respects (a practice beloved of engineers in the past despite the doubtful efficacy of such a statement under the previous edition of these Conditions). However this change is of limited practical effect, because the contractor now by cl. 55 (2) is given a remedy for any error in description in or omission from the bill, whether or not there is a breach of an applicable method of measurement. Therefore, if the engineer excludes the method by a general statement but nevertheless fails to include a necessary item of work accurately or at all in the item coverage, the contractor will have a remedy (p. 207).

A statement that the bill "is prepared generally" in accordance with the

(w') In *Bryant & Son Ltd.* v. *Birmingham Hospital Saturday Fund* [1938] 1 All E.R. 503 a contractor was awarded extra payment for rock, where the architect knew there was some rock on the site but did not mention it in the plans or quantities, and the contract was in the R.I.B.A. form with clauses equivalent to this clause and requiring strict compliance with the building method of measurement that specifies a separate item for rock. As to the relevance of the knowledge of the engineer under these Conditions—text p. 216 below.

(x') In *Shaumugan* v. *Comm. for Reg. of Indian & Pakistani Residents* (1962) A.C. 515 it was held that to be an "express provision" with regard to something it is not necessary that that thing should be specifically mentioned. In *Metropolitan District Ry.* v. *Sharpe* (1881) 50 L.J.Q.B. 14, where one statute incorporated another save where "expressly varied", it was held that it was not necessary to constitute a variation that there should be express words saying that a particular provision was not to apply. "The word 'expressly' often means no more than plainly, clearly or the like"—*Chorlton* v. *Lings* (1868) L.R.4C.P. 374, per Byles J., at pp. 393, 394.

method is too vague to have any effect of excluding the method under this clause.

This clause only refers to exclusion of the method by the bill—on the dangers of putting provisions about item coverage elsewhere refer to p. 207.

(c) "item descriptions for Permanent Works shall generally identify the component of the Works and not the tasks to be carried out by the Contractor" C.E.S.M.M. section 3.3. Where there is any doubt as to whether incidental operations are to be included in an item the methods generally make special provision—e.g. by note 9 to Class E of the C.E.S.M.M. "Separate items are not required for disposal of excavated material, upholding the sides of excavations or keeping excavations free of water". To similar effect are paras. 4 and 46 of the old method and pp. 44 and 45 of the D.O.T. method. The general principle is that incidental operations necessary to complete the work that is described in an item are covered by it—p. 208.

(d) It seems that the rights of the contractor under the method apply whether or not the draftsman of the bill knew or should have known of the distinguishing feature which determines how the work is to be itemized. For example, section 5.20 of the C.E.S.M.M. says that "Item descriptions shall distinguish work which is affected by bodies of water . . .". If that paragraph is not excluded by a general statement in the bill and if the item description does not say that work is affected by a body of water or refer to works "whether or not affected by water", it seems that the contractor is entitled to presume that the work is not so affected by water and price accordingly. It appears to follow that if it is so affected then under cl. 55 (2) he may claim for a misdescription in the bill whether or not the draftsman of the bill knew or could with reasonable site investigation have known the true position. Section 5.20 says that the item description "*shall*" distinguish work affected by a body of water, so as to place an absolute duty on the draftsman to find out accurately whether or not the work is so affected, because he cannot do as he is told in that paragraph unless he does find out. There is a corresponding absence in cl. 55 (2) of any limitation that to entitle the contractor to a remedy the draftsman must or should have known of the error or omission.

The result of this interpretation is that this clause creates a potential for claims by the contractor arising out of inaccurate or insufficient site investigations that may not be apparent to the employer when he is considering the contract documents before tender, unless explained to him. The necessary explanation of the dangers will supply the engineer with further grounds for persuading the client to pay for proper site investigations (p. 433). If in fact the site investigations are unreliable or non-existent the engineer may have to take the risk of making unsubstantiated assumptions in identifying work in the bill, or alternatively to write wide items into the bill so as to try to exclude the method of measurement although that defeats the purpose of the system.

Conversely, what if the contractor knows at the time of tender, for example from site information supplied by the employer, that the interpretation placed on a bill item by the method of measurement is not intended by the draftsman of the bill? In the example already given where the C.E.S.M.M. interprets an item for excavation for foundations as covering excavation only in natural material other than rock, suppose that

(y') Discussed by Barnes, above, p. 56.

the site investigation supplied to the contractor shows rock in the foundation area. Because of the words of cl. 55 (2) and this clause (allowing exclusion of the method only by the wording of the bill) it seems again that the contractor's remedy is not excluded by the facts known at the time of tender.

(e) Both the old method and the C.E.S.M.M. declare some general principles. It does not seem that the relevant general cls. 8 and 9 of the old method confer any rights on the contractor in practice, apart from the fact that they are not all expressed as commands or worded precisely, because the bill normally will show clearly where they have not been followed.

Similarly if the work included in an item is properly identified the wording of the bill will show clearly that work, e.g. in all locations or in several locations that give rise to different considerations of cost are being included in one item contrary to the general section 2.5 of the C.E.S.M.M. In any case that paragraph also is not expressed as a command—it merely says what "*should*" and not as elsewhere what "*shall*" be done. *See* also section 5.8 as to what "*may*" be done. Again this legal result does not derogate from the practical reasons for wording the bill so as clearly to expose cost differentials.

(f) There are certain commandments in the methods for breach of which there is no defined sanction. For example, an item for excavation of materials for disposal on the site may fail to state the locations of the disposal areas, contrary to note 5 to Class E of the C.E.S.M.M. The choice open to the estimator appears to be either to make enquiries pre-tender and have the replies included as part of the contract or to make some allowance for transport to locations on the site as directed by the engineer. It does not seem that the contractor may presume that the material will be disposed of in the places on the site most convenient to him, although he may be entitled to assume that disposal will be in reasonable areas taking into account the haul distances, interference with construction of the works and the requirements of the employer. If that is so the contractor will have a claim for the extra costs if disposal in unreasonable locations is subsequently ordered by the engineer.

It has not been possible in this note to do more than explore some of the general principles that may in practice have to be applied to countless different bill wordings and to the many subtle ingredients in the methods of measurement. Nevertheless two important practical conclusions can be drawn. The contractor is not entitled to found a claim on a retrospective re-writing of a clearly written bill on which he tendered in order to make it conform to the chosen method. Conversely, it is the bill that performs its practical purpose by identifying what the contractor has to price in clear

z'

(z') "It is quite apparent that the draftsman of the Standard Method knew quite well how to express himself when an additional item was to be inserted for a particular matter", per Diplock L. J. in the Court of Appeal in the *Farr* case above, distinguishing such cases in the old method from cl. 40 which says only that "it may be necessary" to provide a separate item for working space, etc. for excavation—(the Court of Appeal decision is unreported, but see (1965) Estates Digest 256).

In that case the bill said that "any additional excavation which may be required for working space, etc., will be paid for under separate items". The only specific items for working space were in the portion of the bills relating to subsidiary parts of the works. Held by a majority of the House of Lords (over-ruling the decision of the Court of Appeal) that the quoted words amounted to a promise to pay the contractor extra for all working space required, whether or not described in a special item in the bills. Note the contrast between the peremptory language in those bills and the words of this cl. 57.

and unambiguous language with as much detail as may be necessary (whether in accordance with or additional to what is required by the applicable method of measurement) that will also minimise the claims that so often disfigure measurement and valuation of civil engineering works (p. 435).

aa'

2. METHOD-RELATED CHARGES. The discussion so far on methods of measurement has concentrated on the traditional work items in the bill, worded by the draftsman of the bill on behalf of the employer and priced by the contractor. An additional feature of the C.E.S.M.M. is the introduction of method-related charges (section 7.2), written into the bill by the tenderer "to cover items of work relating to the intended methods of executing the Works, the cost of which are not to be considered as proportional to the quantities of the other items and for which he has not allowed in the rates and prices for the other items".

The use of these charges recognises the unreality of requiring the contractor to spread over billed quantities of permanent work costs that are not proportionate to the amount of that work, but that nevertheless ordinarily will be adjusted up or down for the actual quantity found on final remeasurement.

The preface to the C.E.S.M.M. says that it is intended to deal with method-related charges in the next revision of the Conditions, but in the meantime they are being used with this 5th edition as it stands. It is therefore necessary to consider the implications of doing so:

(*a*) It is the contractor who chooses the words of any method-related item that he inserts in the bill. Nevertheless the wording may be taken into account in reconciling contract documents under cl. 5 of these Conditions. The wording may be defective in any of several senses. The contractor may use words ambiguously, in which case the item is likely to be read against the contractor (p. 45 (v)) or it may have a clear meaning but not the meaning the contractor intended, in which case normally he will be bound by the words actually used (p. 5). Alternatively there may be a clerical error in writing the description or the amount of the item in the bill, in which case the contractor has no remedy under cl. 55 (2) (p. 209, N. 5), but may exceptionally have a claim to rectification under the general law (p. 41).

(*b*) A most difficult case is where there is the defect in an item that it wrongly assumes that a particular method of construction, etc. is feasible. For example, an item may cover a fee payable to a landowner for extraction of material, but in fact the landowner may not be prepared to grant a right to extract or the material may not meet the contract specification. In that case the contractor will have to change his method to perform the contract but will be paid for the replacement method only at the amount of the original charge, and indeed he is always free to change from a stated method. But what if the engineer when he considers the tender does or should know that the assumption in the item is wrong?

Normally in law it is no concern of the engineer that the contractor has misled himself; he does not have any duty to warn the contractor. Nevertheless the engineer must be certain that no misinformation has been given to the contractor on behalf of the employer, by furnishing site investigation data or otherwise, that has caused the mistake, because if it

(*aa'*) Section 5.10 of the C.E.S.M.M. draws attention to the need for further itemization and additional description beyond the minimum requirement set out in the Work Classification.

has the contractor may have remedies for misrepresentation or negligence (p. 58). In addition the contractor may use the wording of a charge to support a case under cl. 12 that he did not and could-not reasonably have foreseen actual site conditions or obstructions or foreseen requirements of the engineer under cls. 13 or 14 of the Conditions. The engineer may be in a quandary when reporting on tenders if the wording of the item suggests that such a claim is on the cards, as to whether he should clarify the position with the contractor. Preservation of competitive tendering and the danger of allowing contractors to use "mistakes" in method-related charges to obtain a chance to adjust the tender, may restrict the engineer's freedom of action even if he thinks that a genuine mistake has been made.

(c) Interim payment is made by reference to cl. 60 (1) (d) in accordance with the proportion of the work covered by the charge carried out by the contractor in the month. Thus the engineer must consider carefully the wording used by a contractor in a charge, and "front end loading", such as a large charge payable in full on mobilisation of plant, may not be satisfactory to the employer's budget or from the aspect of security where there is no performance bond. In the case of a change of method interim payments are to be agreed between the engineer and the contractor, or in default of agreement treated as an addition against the adjustment item and paid in proportion to the other work (p. 15).

(d) Variations may affect the time of operations subject to a time-related charge, in which case there does not seem to be any difficulty in applying cl. 52, ordinarily by a *pro rata* adjustment of the rate to the actual time spent or saved due to the variation. In the case of a fixed charge normally of course no adjustment will be necessary for a variation, except that a variation may be so extensive as to involve the contractor, e.g. in a second fixed charge for installation of a second crane. Again, there does not appear to be any particular difficulty in applying cl. 52 to that case. Similar considerations apply to determining an "*appropriate increase or decrease*" under cl. 56 (2) for a change in quantities, with the difficulty caused by the vagueness of that phrase no greater than with traditional measured work items.

Though there is no inherent difficulty in valuing variations and changes of quantities, serious problems may be caused by the wording of the method-related charge below.

(e) Where the contractor is entitled to payment of his cost or to damages for breach of contract measured by his actual loss, he is not bound by any under-pricing or entitled to *pro rata* extension of any over-pricing in his method-related charges (just as other bill rates are not binding in assessing compensation—chs. 11 and 12). That does reduce the usefulness of such charges.

The contractor may try to aid escape from a low level of charge by arguing that his fixed or time-related costs were divided between a method-related charge and measured items. Where the charge is contractually applicable it covers all work within the words actually used in the charge, properly interpreted, whatever the contractor's intention or actual method of pricing. But even in that case there may be room for argument if the engineer has accepted an imprecisely worded charge. The case being considered here is where contractually the contractor's right to extra payment is not governed by the charge, so that the contractor has considerable room for manoeuvre. Perhaps in practice an engineer or arbitrator is likely to hold him to the level of his charge in assessing compensation. Conversely, there may be some tendency to consider that the engineer should not be allowed in practice to question the level of a charge even when assessing the contractor's actual cost of delay, etc. Such a view is hardly justified, since the engineer is unlikely to have had the information about the contractor's individual methods of construction necessary to enable him to question the level of his charges at the time of tender. The temptation to a contractor to unbalance method-related charges to give himself room to manoeuvre later would be increased by maintaining those charges unrealistically.

CHAPTER 6

Sub-Contracting:
Conditions Clauses 58 and 59

Some of the most complex problems in construction law are produced by
nominated sub-contracting. For that reason this chapter opens with a
general explanation of the principles of sub-contracting, leading to an
account of the system of nominated sub-contracting and problems created
by it, the attempted solutions in these Conditions, and a résumé of the
practicalities of nominated sub-contracting. Detailed notes on the relevant
clauses of these Conditions then follow.

THE BASIS OF DOMESTIC SUB-CONTRACTING. Sub-contracting originally
was for the convenience of the main contractor. The basis of such domestic
sub-contracting is sub-letting the physical construction of the works only,
not assignment of liability. The main contractor remains fully liable to the
employer for the works and may not excuse himself by proving that bad
work was done or delay caused by a sub-contractor (see cl. 4).

LIABILITY OF THE MAIN CONTRACTOR TO SUB-CONTRACTORS AND VICE
VERSA. The contractor is liable to a sub-contractor for breach of the sub-
contract, for example if he prevents him earning the sub-contract price by
causing the main contract to be forfeited, or disrupts his working. A sub-
contractor is liable to the main contractor if he involves him in liability to
the employer or other loss by a breach of his sub-contract. Refer to p. 370 on
the serious problems of programme co-ordination and disruption claims
between main and sub-contractors.

MAIN CONTRACTOR'S CONTROL OF SUB-CONTRACTORS. The sub-
contractor is an independent agent and not a servant of the main
contractor. Therefore unless there is special agreement the main contractor
has only the right to tell the sub-contractor what final result his work is to
produce; he has no right to tell the sub-contractor how to do the work or to
order him to submit to the detailed organisation of the job.

Further, a fundamental rule is that a contract is in the nature of a bond or
rope between the parties who have created the contract by their agreement,
so that generally it can confer rights and duties only on the parties at each
end of the rope. There is a contract between the employer and the main
contractor and a separate contract between the main contractor and sub-
contractor. It follows that the rights and duties of a sub-contractor are not
governed by the terms of the main contract unless they are incorporated
into the sub-contract:

> Some of the terms of the main contract were included in a sub-contract but not
> a particular term by which the employer's engineer had power to order the
> contractor to remove a sub-contractor.

221

The sub-contract also set out that the sub-contractor agreed to carry out the work in accordance with the terms of the main contract.

Held: This engineer's power in the main contract was not incorporated into the sub-contract. The main contractor therefore broke the sub-contract if he obeyed an order to dismiss the sub-contractor: if he did not he broke the main contract.

On the other hand it is not sufficient simply to specify in a sub-contract that the sub-contractor is bound by all the terms of the main contract—for example, the contractor will have no retention against a sub-contractor who starts work after the limit of retention money in the main contract has been reached, and the application of cl. 66 causes difficulty. The Federation of Civil Engineering Contractors publishes a form of sub-contract for use with these Conditions.

For liquidated damages see p. 428.

It follows from the above that the main contractor should ensure that there is a proper sub-contract executed at the proper time incorporating the terms of the main contract, and dealing with such matters as co-ordination of prográmme, attendances, retention, etc. Much unnecessary trouble is caused by slipshod sub-contract procedure (pp. 1–3).

THE ENGINEER AND SUB-CONTRACTORS. Although he should not interfere in the details of the contract between main contractor and domestic sub-contractor, before consenting to a sub-contract the engineer should satisfy himself that the sub-contracting will not interfere with co-ordination of the works and about the capabilities and finances of the proposed sub-contractor.

It is arguable that in respect of major sub-contracts the engineer has an interest even in going so far as ensuring that a proper sub-contract is made, so that in relation to the sub-contracted work he will be able to exercise effectively through the main contractor his powers of control under the main contract. If a sub-contractor is entitled to refuse to obey the engineer's orders, then the employer is protected in theory by the right to forfeit the main contract. But exercising legal remedies obviously is not as satisfactory

---

(a) *Chandler Bros. Ltd.* v. *Boswell* [1936] 3 All E.R. 179, and for a similar decision see *Mills* v. *McWilliams* (1914) 33 N.Z.L.R. 718, and see *Gilbert-Ash (Northern) Ltd.* v. *Modern Engineering (Bristol) Ltd.* [1973] 3 All E.R. 195. In the last case, main contract conditions were incorporated in a sub-contract in respect of provisions applicable to the works, and not in respect of payment, and the sub-contractor was deemed to have notice of the terms of the main contract. It was said (by Lord Diplock at p. 218) that the terms of the main contract could be considered if, but only if, there was an ambiguity in the sub-contract, to resolve the ambiguity in favour of a meaning which would involve the contractor's compliance with the main contract.

In *Brightside Kilpatrick* v. *Mitchell Construction* (1973) *Ltd.* [1975] 2 Lloyd's Rep. 493, C.A., the sub-contract said that "The Conditions applicable to the Sub-Contract . . . shall be those embodied in R.I.B.A. (1963 Ed.)." That was held to mean that the sub-contractual relationship between the parties was to be such as to be consistent with all those terms in the main contract which specifically dealt with matters relating to sub-contractors, so that there should be no conflict between the main contract and the sub-contract. In *Triangle Ltd.* v. *John Burrowes & Co. Ltd.* (1958) (1) S.A. 818 (SR) it was held that a main contract term for vesting plant, similar to cl. 53 above, was not incorporated into a sub-contract by a term by which the sub-contractor was bound to adhere to the conditions of the main contract. It was pointed out that even if the sub-contract was construed otherwise the only party who would have had standing to enforce the agreement would have been the contractor, and not the employer. For incorporation of cl. 53 in sub-contracts under these Conditions, refer to p. 202, N. 16.

(b) The form has not yet been revised for use with this 5th edition.

to the employer as having the works done properly in the first place, and the practical result may be that the employer and sub-contractor (*see* above) will be competing to extract damages from the main contractor.

THE EMPLOYER AND SUB-CONTRACTORS. As the sub-contract is made between the contractor and the sub-contractor only, the employer generally has no contractual bond with and therefore no contractual rights against or duties to a sub-contractor.

This means that a sub-contractor cannot sue the employer direct for payment or extra expenses or damages. Generally the employer pays the main contractor and the sub-contractor must recover his share of payment or damages from the main contractor, and again may lose if the contractor is insolvent. *See* p. 255 for the employer's option to make direct payment in some cases.

Conversely the employer has no contractual right to recover direct from the guilty sub-contractor compensation for any loss or damage caused to him by the sub-contractor's delay or bad work, etc. That is the kernel of the problems of nominated sub-contracting—below.

In exceptional cases it may be implied that an employer has entered into a direct contract with a sub-contractor. The fact that the sub-contractor is nominated by the employer and the sub-contract negotiated by his engineer is not sufficient. But if the employer, or the engineer acting clearly for the employer and with the employer's authority, negotiates with or gives orders direct to the sub-contractor, a direct contract may be created. If that happens the whole object of the sub-contracting system from the employer's point of view goes; the rules set out above do not apply and the employer is bound to see that the sub-contractor is paid:

> The architect in the presence of the employer asked a sub-contractor to carry out work by a process which was more expensive than the process specified and told the sub-contractor that he would be paid extra.
>
> Held: A contract was created between the employer and the sub-contractor under which the sub-contractor could recover the extra payment direct from the employer.

EMPLOYER'S DILEMMA ABOUT SPECIALIST SERVICES. Specialist work, mechanical or electrical installations or structural steelwork for example, may be a very large part of a total project. An employer may well wish to choose the contractor to do such work to ensure that the price is obtained in proper competition and particularly that the contractor has the capabilities to do good work. In some cases where there are long delivery times, the employer may have to ensure that orders are placed even before the main contractor is appointed. If the employer goes so far as to make a direct contract for this specialist work additional to the main contract, as mentioned above he loses all the advantage of the traditional main contractor/sub-contractor system. Co-ordination of the two or more contracts may be a problem, and the employer may find himself with claims by one contractor for extension of time and extra payment for disruption to his work by another contractor on the site, or for extra payment for work caused by the faulty work or materials of another (*see* p. 125, and for insurance p. 363).

It was in the hope of avoiding this problem and having the best of both

(c) *Wallis* v. *Robinson* (1862) 130 R.R. 841.

worlds that the system grew up by which the employer obtains tenders for specialist work, but then instructs the main contractor to enter into a sub-contract with the successful tenderer, who is called a nominated sub-contractor.

Unfortunately the cure has proved to be almost as painful as the disease. It is rarely satisfactory to use legal principles developed for one purpose for a quite different purpose, and the industry is now belatedly attempting to deal with dangers of nominated sub-contracting revealed by Court decisions.

DANGERS TO THE EMPLOYER OF NOMINATED SUB-CONTRACTING. The dangers to the employer arise mainly out of the absence of any contractual bond between the employer and the sub-contractor, with the result as explained above that the employer cannot successfully claim against the sub-contractor in contract for any misdemeanour he may commit—delay, defective work, bad design, etc. In all these cases the employer normally must rely on the chain of liability—employer recovers from main contractor under the main contract, main contractor recovers from sub-contractor under the sub-contract. The trouble arises where there is a link missing in the chain.

The classic example is in the J.C.T. Standard Form of building contract. The main contractor is given a right to an extension of time for delay caused by a nominated sub-contractor. The result is that if there is such delay the employer is not entitled to recover liquidated damages from the main contractor, who instead is entitled to an extension of time. The main contractor can only recover losses he himself suffers and therefore cannot recover from the sub-contractor liquidated damages for the delay suffered by the employer, since the main contractor does not have to pay those damages to the employer. The employer cannot recover damages direct from the sub-contractor, because he has no contract with him. The result is that the guilty sub-contractor escapes scot-free.

The situation under the 5th edition will be reviewed in the following sections under the headings of objections by the main contractor to nomination, his liability for work and materials, delay, design by the sub-contractor, and the vanishing sub-contractor.

MAIN CONTRACTOR'S RIGHT TO OBJECT TO A NOMINATION. The justice of the system of nominated sub-contracting depends on the main contractor being in a position effectively to pass on to the guilty sub-contractor any liability he may incur due to the activities of the nominated sub-contractor; on the contractual chain of responsibility being complete and the nominated sub-contractor solvent. By cl. 59A (1) of these conditions a main contractor may refuse to accept a nomination if he has reasonable objection to the nominated sub-contractor (defined to include a supplier of goods), or the sub-contractor declines to enter into a sub-contract undertaking towards the contractor "*such obligations and liabilities as will enable the Contractor to discharge his own obligations and liabilities towards the Employer*", indemnifying the main contractor against any failure to perform such obligations, etc., or any negligence by the sub-contractor or misuse of the contractor's plant or temporary works, and containing a forfeiture clause equivalent to cl. 63.

If the contractor exercises this right to refuse to accept a nomination, the choices open to the employer are not appealing (cl. 59A (2)). He may nominate an alternative sub-contractor, but will have to pay the main contractor for any extra charge by that sub-contractor and the main contractor will be entitled to an extension of time and damages for standing time and other loss suffered as a result of delay due to renomination. Alternatively the employer may vary the works by omitting the relevant work, etc., either indefinitely or so as to have it carried out by another direct contractor concurrently, but in the case of a P.C. item will nevertheless have to pay the original main contractor his charges and profit, and may of course find himself involved in claims by the main contractor for disruption by any new direct contractor, and vice versa (p. 371).

The third alternative open to the employer is to arrange for the main contractor to take over. In the case of a provisional sum the employer's position under this alternative is not too unsatisfactory because he has power to order the main contractor to do the work, etc., in the sum and payment is assessed under cl. 52. In the case of a P.C. item the contractor has an advantage; he may refuse to do the work or consent only if the employer agrees to pay him an exorbitant price.

The final alternative open to the employer (and he may exercise his choice differently for different parts of the relevant work) applies only where the objection is due to the refusal of the sub-contractor to enter into a proper sub-contract, and consists of the engineer directing the main contractor to enter into a sub-contract on terms specified by the engineer. Where this choice is exercised (for which the engineer is specifically required to have the employer's consent), by cl. 59A (3) the main contractor is not bound to discharge his duties under the main contract to the extent that "*the sub-contract terms so specified by the Engineer are inconsistent with the discharge of the same*". The contractor also becomes entitled to recover any loss or damage arising out of the refusal of the nominated sub-contractor to accept a full sub-contract. This alternative will arise where a sub-contractor insists on using his own or some standard sub-contract form which attempts to limit his liability—for example the Institution of Mechanical Engineers forms—and if chosen may leave the employer with serious limitations on the right to recover losses (p. 242).

Despite this full right of objection the contractor's ultimate liability to pay for the misdeeds of a nominated sub-contractor is further limited, as discussed in the following sections.

MAIN CONTRACTOR'S LIABILITY FOR WORK AND MATERIALS OF A NOMINATED SUB-CONTRACTOR. It is reasonably clear under the general law that the main contractor is liable for defective work or materials by a nominated sub-contractor, unless the employer is responsible for a break in the chain of liability:

> Employer-contractors obtained an estimate from sub-contractors to supply and fix a type of tile known as "Somerset 13" for houses on an estate. The choice of this brand of tile had been made by the employers, and such tiles were made by only one manufacturer.
> A particular batch of tiles contained a defect which could not be detected. House purchasers sued the employers; who sued the sub-contractors. Because the ordinary period for limitation of actions (p. 430) had expired as between them, the sub-contractors could not in turn sue the suppliers of the tiles in

contract. Therefore the Court had to determine liability as between the employers and the sub-contractors.

Held by the House of Lords that it was not to be implied that the sub-contractors had given any warranty that "Somerset 13" tiles would be suitable for the particular job, because the employers had relied on their own judgment and not that of the sub-contractors in choosing the brand of tile. Nevertheless the ordinary warranty implied in a contract for work and materials, that the materials would be of good quality, was not displaced. The employers were entitled to recover from the sub-contractors.

Nominated suppliers delivered concrete columns containing defects which were then undetectable. After the columns had been passed by the architect and the consulting engineers acting for the employer and had been incorporated into the building, the defects became apparent. The P.C. sum referred merely to erecting the columns as supplied by the nominated suppliers. The contract was in the standard building form—to execute and complete the work shown on drawings and described by or referred to in Bills of Quantities—the nominated sub-contractor's quotation was accepted by the architect and the main contractor had never seen the specification for the columns.

The 'Court held that the main contractor was not liable for the defects. A crucial factor in the decision was that the main contractor had no right under the particular form of main contract to object to the supplier, despite the fact that the terms of the suppliers' quotation negotiated by the architect incorporated special conditions exempting the supplier in certain circumstances from liability to the main contractor.

Under these Conditions, as explained above the main contractor has a right to object to a sub-contractor if the chain of responsibility is not preserved. If the nomination is such that no occasion for objection arises or the main contractor waives his right to object by entering into a sub-contract with the sub-contractor despite the existence of grounds for objection, it is specifically stated that the main contractor is liable for work and materials by the nominated sub-contractor—"*Except as otherwise provided in this Clause and in Clause 59B the Contractor shall be as responsible for the work executed or goods materials or services supplied by a Nominated Sub-contractor employed by him as if he had himself executed such work or supplied such goods materials or services or had sub-let the same in accordance with Clause 4*" (cl. 59A (4)).

An intermediate situation may arise where the main contractor objects to a nomination and the engineer acts under cl. 59A (2) (c) so as to reduce the main contractor's liability to equate with the reduced liability for work or materials of a nominated sub-contractor—p. 242.

However, in any case the main contractor's liability for a sub-contractor holds good only up to a certain point. If the main contractor becomes liable to pay compensation to the employer for a breach of the main contract caused by a breach of the sub-contract by the sub-contractor, even though the main contractor did not object to the nomination, the employer cannot enforce any arbitration award or court judgment for the compensation unless and until the contractor recovers the amount from the sub-contractor (cl. 59A (6)). That restriction is subject only to the proviso that the contractor must take all necessary steps and proceedings to recover as required by the employer. In addition the main contractor's liability may end if and when a nominated sub-contractor vanishes—below.

(d) *Young & Marten Ltd.* v. *McManus Childs Ltd.* [1968] 2 All E.R. 1169, H.L.
(e) *Gloucestershire C.C.* v. *Richardson* [1968] 2 All E.R. 1181, H.L.

DELAY. If the nominated sub-contractor's work is delayed by a cause which is a ground for extension of time within cl. 44, such as exceptional adverse weather conditions, then of course the main contractor is entitled to an extension as if he were doing the work involved himself. Where the delay is due to breach of contract or default by the nominated sub-contractor, then it is clear from cl. 44 and cl. 59A (4) just quoted (although that sub-clause could be more clearly drafted) that the main contractor is not entitled to any extension of time and the chain of liability is preserved, by which the employer claims against the main contractor for the delay and the main contractor against the nominated sub-contractor. Again the liability of both main contractor and sub-contractor may be reduced in accordance with cl. 59A (2)(c), and the main contractor's liability may be affected by the disappearance of the nominated sub-contractor, or by the terms of cl. 59A (5).

The employer is not liable to the main contractor for the latter's standing time and other losses due to delay by a nominated sub-contractor, but the employer is liable for his own delay in nominating (p. 364) or due to re-nomination of (p. 246) a sub-contractor.

DESIGN. There has slowly dawned on the industry the significance of the fact that specialist sub-contractors do much more than supply materials and execute work in accordance with a design and specification supplied by the engineer. More often the engineer or employer chooses a specialised system because of an assurance by the sub-contractor that the system will work and is suitable for the particular project, an assurance given either in general publicity about the system or in particular discussions, and in addition the detailed shop-drawings are produced by the sub-contractor. The result is that employers have been relying on sub-contractors for matters which may not be part of the main contract at all, for under the 4th edition I.C.E. Conditions the main contractor in no way undertakes design of the permanent works, and cl. 59 (1) authorises nomination of sub-contractors for "*the execution of . . . work or the supply of . . . goods*", with no reference to design or preparation of drawings. As a result the chain of liability may not even commence: it is obviously difficult in such a case to imply into the main contract that the main contractor is accepting design responsibility. Once again therefore the guilty sub-contractor may escape scot-free, unless the employer can recover from him on some special grounds:

The main contract bill of quantities for a factory and office block included a P.C. sum for the "supply, delivery and erection complete of the superstructure of the factory . . .". The form of tender indicated that the superstructure was to be supplied and erected by nominated sub-contractors but none of the tender documents showed that a special building system designed and marketed by the sub-contractors (with whom the employers had business relations) was to be used. Before the main contract had been signed the employers' engineers sent to the main contractors drawings submitted by the sub-contractors, but did not ask them to approve the drawings. The main contractors entered into a standard form of sub-contract with the sub-contractors.

After the end of the defects liability period under the main contract, leaks occurred in roof lights designed by the sub-contractors, details of which were on the drawings supplied by them that had been sent to the main contractors and that had been approved by the engineers. An arbitrator found that the roof lights as designed by and shown on the specification and drawings supplied by the sub-contractors were not suitable for use in a roof of the type designed by them.

Held by the Irish Supreme Court that the main contractors were little more than an ordering agent for a roof that had already been vetted by the employers' engineers, which the main contractors had no option but to accept. The employer did not rely at all upon the main contractors' skill and judgment in regard to the superstructure. Therefore the parties could not be presumed to have intended, nor would it have been reasonable to require, the main contractors to undertake responsibility for the design of the superstructure. The main contractors were not liable to the employers for the patent error in design.

f

An employer asked a manufacturer whether his paint was suitable for use below water level. Relying on the manufacturer's statement that it was, the employer specified that the main contractor should use this paint for a contract to build a pier. The paint was used, but was not satisfactory.

Held: There was a contract between the employer and the manufacturer (quite separate from the contract between the main contractor and sub-contractor, which did not specify that the paint was to be used for a pier) by which in consideration of the employer specifying the use of this paint the manufacturer guaranteed that it was suitable for the job. The manufacturer was liable to the employer for breach of this contract.

g

This is a most unsatisfactory situation, because it may be extremely difficult for the employer to prove that he relied on some definite assurance from the sub-contractor sufficient to bring himself within the principle of the last case. The employer may also be involved in the expense and hazard of multiplicity of proceedings, since any direct claim against the nominated sub-contractor is outside the arbitration clause in the main contract, and must be brought in the courts.

It is possible that developments in the general law may solve these problems. For example, it has been suggested that if any assurances are given to the engineer or employer by a potential nominated sub-contractor in negotiations for nomination, since he knows that his tender will actually be accepted by the main contractor he is to be taken to be agreeing that his assurances will become a part of his sub-contract with the main contractor, even though not referred to in it. The chain of responsibility is completed by a further implication that since the main contractor is getting the benefit of these assurances, he is to be taken to agree to be bound to the employer in the terms of the assurances, although again they are not mentioned in the main contract.

It is even possible that, irrespective of any special assurance by a sub-contractor to the employer creating a contract between them, the employer may recover some losses direct from the sub-contractor under the general law of negligence, if he can prove that the sub-contractor failed to take reasonable care in performing the sub-contract, including the design of the works. That possibility is part of a larger issue that is discussed on pp. 395-6.

Interesting as these possibilities are, an employer driven to rely on them will find himself in a legal sea which can only be charted by those expensive cartographers, judges of the House of Lords, and with the fees of the

---

(*f*) *Norta Wallpapers (Ireland) Ltd.* v. *John Sisk (Dublin) Ltd.* (unreported judgment delivered the 9th July 1977). The decision was on the Irish equivalent of the J.C.T. Standard Form of building contract but the judgments were based on general principles applied to the extreme facts of the case.

(*g*) *Shanklin Pier Ltd.* v. *Detel Products Ltd.* [1951] 2 All E.R. 471. This situation might now be held to be covered by liability for a negligent misstatement under *Hedley Byrne & Co. Ltd.* v. *Heller & Partners Ltd.* [1963] 2 All E.R. 575, see text p. 394, quite apart from any question of contract.

navigating lawyers not reduced for the fact that they will not know where they are going. It is therefore vitally important for the engineer carefully to consider the choice now given by the 5th edition of the Conditions.

Under these Conditions, if the services to be provided under a provisional sum or prime cost item include any matter of design or specification, such requirement must be expressly stated in the main contract and included in any nominated sub-contract. The main contractor's liability in respect of design services by a nominated sub-contractor is only that which has been expressly stated in this way (cls. 58 (3) and 8 (2)).

Thus the engineer has the choice between stating the design requirement in the main contract so that the chain of responsibility through the main contractor to the sub-contractor is complete, and the main contractor is liable to the employer, or if he considers that tenderers for the main contract will not take on liability for a specialist's design, the engineer must require the specialist to enter into a collateral warranty or agreement with the employer. If neither is done, the sub-contractor may escape scot-free for a design failure. The engineer will then be in a hazardous position in relation to his client, on several counts—pp. 376, N. 11 and 391.

Where the design services to be performed by the nominated sub-contractor involve preparation of drawings to enable the main contractor to construct bases, apertures, etc., for the sub-contractor or to enable the engineer to prepare drawings necessary for the main contract, it should be made clear in the main and sub-contract specification that the timely provision of such drawings is a matter for the main contractor and sub-contractor. This will avoid any argument by the main contractor that any delay by the sub-contractor in supplying drawings resulting in delayed approval or issue by the engineer entitles him to an extension of time and compensation. In any case, it does seem clear that where cl. 58 (3) is complied with, the contractor is responsible for any such delay under cl. 59A (4).

THE VANISHING NOMINATED SUB-CONTRACTOR. The above is not the end of the perils. The final problem, of what may be called the vanishing nominated sub-contractor, is the most difficult of all for the employer:

A sub-contractor nominated under a prime cost sum went into liquidation and the liquidator refused to complete the sub-contract. In the absence of appointment of a second nominated sub-contractor by the employer the main contractors completed the sub-contract work under protest.

Held: That they were entitled to extra payment for doing so.

The decision was on the particular wording of the 1963 edition of the standard building form, but appeared to apply to the 4th edition I.C.E. Conditions.

The major objection to this *Bickerton* doctrine is that the employer has no redress against anyone for the losses he has suffered because of the

(h) That is, a contract separate to and side by side with the main contract and sub-contract, by which the sub-contractor gives assurances about his design direct to the employer, and on which therefore the employer can sue the sub-contractor direct if the design fails. The R.I.B.A. publishes a form, which would need alteration for these Conditions.
(i) *North West Metropolitan Regional Hospital Board* v. *T. A. Bickerton & Son Ltd.* (1970) 1 All E.R. 1039, H.L.
(j) Refer to 2nd edition of this book, pp. 141–2.

sub-contractor's default, and the guilty sub-contractor escapes scot-free once again as far as those losses are concerned. If the main contractor recovers the full cost of the sub-contract work from the employer he has no claim against the sub-contractor for that cost (in contrast to his own standing time, etc., costs) since he has not suffered the loss. The employer may not recover the extra payments he makes to the main contractor direct from the sub-contractor, since he has no contract with him.

The *Bickerton* decision has been severely criticised. Despite these criticisms and the peculiar results, it is difficult to fault the logic of the proposition that where the original contract provides for work to be done by a nominated sub-contractor, then if the nominated sub-contractor ceases to exist as such the employer must provide a substitute at his own cost or pay the main contractor for taking over the uncompleted work. The nominated sub-contractor ceases to exist as such if he ceases to be a sub-contractor because the main contractor has validly determined the sub-contract, whether because of the liquidation or serious default of the sub-contractor.

However, whatever the rights and wrongs of the decision, it has been embraced in the 5th edition of these Conditions, with some safeguards for the employer.

By cl. 59B if the sub-contractor goes into liquidation or his misbehaviour reaches the stage which entitles the main contractor to forfeit the sub-contract either under the forfeiture clause (which the contractor is entitled to have included in the sub-contract) or under the general law if there is no forfeiture clause, then the main contractor becomes entitled to so act and sever his relationship with the sub-contractor. He may then require the engineer either to nominate an alternative sub-contractor, order a variation of the works or arrange for the main contractor to finish the sub-contract work, with the disadvantages stated on p. 225 above, for the employer. An elaborate code of notices is provided, below.

Although in this way the *Bickerton* decision is accepted insofar as the employer must remedy the practical situation where a nominated sub-contract is forfeited, there is the major improvement for the employer that the chain of liability is preserved. The contractor is liable to pay the employer all the employer's extra costs arising out of replacing the vanishing sub-contractor, etc., and therefore has a right to recover those costs from the guilty party, the ex-nominated sub-contractor. Nevertheless, for the protection of the main contractor an extra link is added into the chain. Insofar as the main contractor does not actually succeed in enforcing his rights by recovering money from the ex-sub-contractor (despite taking all necessary steps and proceedings required by the employer) he is entitled to relief from liability to pay or to receive back any compensation already paid to the employer for the employer's expenses, etc., arising out of the forfeiture. Thus the chain of liability is now from the employer to the main contractor, the main contractor to the sub-contractor and, if the sub-contractor cannot be made to pay, from the main contractor back to the employer.

In this way and as a result of the similar limitation on the main contractor's liability for a nominated sub-contractor who is still on the job, the result is achieved that the risk of insolvency of a nominated sub-contractor is borne by the employer who chose him and not the main contractor.

SUMMARY OF PRACTICALITIES:

(a) The engineer in "Instructions to Tenderers" may require details of intended domestic sub-contracting. He should look to the co-ordination of the works and the finances and capabilities of the sub-contractor before consenting to any sub-contracting, and in major cases eventually check that a proper sub-contract has been made.

(b) There is the authority of the drafting Committee of the Conditions that nomination of sub-contractors should be avoided if at all possible, because of the contractual pitfalls. The alternatives are discussed below.

(c) As to the choice between P.C. item or provisional sum, where nomination has to be used, see p. 235, N. 1.

(d) The aim of the engineer in seeking tenders from potential nominated sub-contractors should be to put himself into a position to make a "clean" nomination—that is, to send out tender documents containing all necessary terms, so that he will be entitled to instruct the main contractor to accept a tender on these documents as they stand. Therefore the documents sent out for tender should specify the form of sub-contract and deal with co-ordination with the main contractor, attendances and so on. It may be wise to specify a maximum prompt payment discount (p. 243, N. 18) and a special retention (p. 222).

If the documents sent out are complete, there will be no occasion for tenderers to add special terms, and the engineer will look out for any printed or other special conditions in tenders, and take care to have them withdrawn before acceptance.

(e) The engineer must obtain his client's approval to delegation to a sub-contractor of any design or detailed drawing, and obtain competent advice on supervising and certifying for such work if it is outside the sphere of his own expertise (p. 391). He must either place any design duty on the main contractor under cl. 58 (3) or obtain a collateral warranty from the sub-contractor.

(f) The main contract must include any special terms imposed on nominated sub-contractors, so that the chain of liability is complete. For example, it may not be effective to require a sub-contractor to prepare and submit for approval detailed drawings, samples, models, etc., for mechanical plant, unless that duty is also placed on the main contractor. The required result can be achieved by including the terms in a sub-contract specification also bound in as a section of the main contract specification. Special care should also be taken to see that the main contractor is bound to provide at his own cost all the attendances which the sub-contractor has been told he will obtain.

(g) A nominated sub-contractor should be chosen with extremely careful investigation of his finances, resources, expertise and dependability. These qualities are particularly important because of the main contractor's right to object to a nominee on any reasonable grounds. They are also important because of the very serious consequences to the employer of any major default by the sub-contractor. If the sub-contractor is a subsidiary of a large group the engineer must take into account only the finances of the subsidiary, since the group will not be liable if the subsidiary defaults or goes into liquidation unless it has been required to guarantee the sub-

(k) Written summary provided for and discussion at the I.C.E. etc. Official Conference on the 5th edition, on June 25, 1974.

contract. It may be wise to specify that the sub-contractor will give a bond to the main contractor, since in most cases it is the employer who loses if the main contractor cannot recover the resulting losses from a defaulting sub-contractor (cls. 59A (6) and 59B (4)).

(*h*) The engineer at all costs should avoid nominating the sub-contractor and then at a late stage finding that the main contractor has grounds for objection, since that may involve the employer in serious additional cost and delay. It may be possible to include with the main contract tender documents a list of the names of nominated sub-contractors chosen or from which they will be chosen, and specify that unless the main contractor notifies his objection to a name on the list before or with his tender he will be deemed to have waived his right of objection.

It should also be possible to include the sub-contract terms for nominated sub-contractors in the tender documents for the main contract, and specify that they shall be deemed to satisfy the requirements of cl. 59A (1) of the main contract conditions. The main contractor will not then be free to object to a nomination on the grounds of some trivial failure by the sub-contract to give him the protection to which he is entitled under that clause.

(*i*) The engineer should merely pass on the sub-contract tender to the main contractor with instructions to accept. He should not himself first accept the tender, because if he does so the employer may be liable to the sub-contractor for breach of a separate contract to nominate, if the engineer eventually cannot make an effective nomination because of some valid objection by the main contractor.

Where there is reason for the engineer to accept the sub-contract tender, for example where the employer wishes to bind the sub-contractor before the main contract has been let, a special term should be included in the tender documents. The term will say that the sub-contractor will be bound to the employer to accept nomination but that the employer's corresponding liability to nominate will end if the main contractor validly refuses to make a sub-contract. In some cases it may be necessary for the employer to reserve a right to end the liability to nominate if for any reason he cannot obtain a main contractor on satisfactory terms.

(*j*) If it has not been possible or it is known that it will not be possible to obtain sub-contract tenders which accept the substantial equivalent of the I.C.E. main contract liability, the practice has grown up prior to the 5th edition of specifying in the main contract that the main contractor nevertheless is to be fully liable for the sub-contractor without equivalent limitation of liability, but giving him an opportunity to price such liability in the bill. This expedient is simple, but unfortunately it is also wrong—not only because the main contractor is required to price the unpriceable, but because the wording used is rarely sufficient to produce the full intended result.

If such a provision is not included and the sub-contractor's liability is restricted in any way, then under the 5th edition the main contractor's liability is cut down to the equivalent of the liability accepted by the sub-contractor, and the employer may have no remedy against anyone for loss outside that area (p. 442).

(*k*) If the worst comes to the worst and a nominated sub-contractor misbehaves, it is prima facie in the main contractor's interests to forfeit the sub-contract if and as soon as he becomes entitled to do so. Then he ceases to be liable for that sub-contractor, and is entitled to renomination, etc. Until then, although protected against ultimately having to bear himself the employer's losses, he may have the trouble of pursuing the sub-contractor and be out of pocket for a time, and *vis-à-vis* the employer he will bear his own standing time, etc., costs due to any delay by the nominated sub-contractor. For his own protection the contractor should serve the notice provided for, seeking the employer's consent to forfeit.

The employer has no right to compel the main contractor to forfeit a sub-contract (if notice is not served on him by the main contractor), as he may want to do, e.g. where the sub-contractor is constantly doing sub-standard work. In such a case the employer's only remedy is to use his powers under the main contract against the main contractor for the defects, for example under cls. 39 (2) and 63.

Where the main contractor does serve notice asking for consent to forfeit, the employer should refuse consent if he considers that the main contractor is not entitled to forfeit; if he is right the main contractor will have to bear the employer's losses if he forfeits. The employer loses out if he consents where forfeiture is not justified, and may even be liable to the sub-contractor if he directs forfeiture without taking reasonable steps to satisfy himself that there are grounds for doing so. The contractor also should consider carefully before attempting to forfeit in any doubtful case, because if the forfeiture is held to have been unjustified he will be liable out of his own pocket for the sub-contractor's damages, and if he did not receive the employer's consent he will also have to bear the employer's losses.

When faced with a justified notice seeking consent to forfeit, it may be wise for the employer to negotiate some arrangement with the main contractor, and possibly sub-contractor, to avoid the expense and delays of forfeiture. The employer and engineer should be careful in such negotiations not to commit themselves more than they intend.

CONCLUSION. If the ideal procedure outlined above is carried out and a responsible sub-contractor accepting full liability is nominated, the employer is reasonably well protected under this 5th edition. If the sub-contractor nevertheless defaults, then provided he is then either solvent or bonded, the employer will have a full remedy, although he may have to wait some time for completion of the works and recovery of his losses. However, powerful sub-contractors may insist on trying to limit their liability, for example by tendering only on the Institution of Mechanical Engineers, etc. model forms. In that case the employer may suffer from those limitations whether he nominates or employs direct several independent contractors, and in the latter case there will be the danger of disruption claims from the presence of two or more direct contractors on site (p. 371). Recent statutory protection against unreasonable limitations on liability is not certain to protect the employer (p. 431). Employers may be tempted to return where possible to letting the whole contract to one main contractor, leaving him to use domestic sub-contractors and grapple with any restrictions on their liability they try to impose. That is certainly the system with fewest contractual pitfalls.

The engineer will perform his duty to his client (and protect himself) only if he takes care to understand precisely what is involved in nomination, so as to be able to weigh and explain to the client the advantages and disadvantages, and leaves it to the client to take the final policy decision whether or not to use nominations. Main contractors and nominated sub-contractors also should study carefully their complicated rights and duties before committing themselves to contracts.

The points made in general terms in this note are examined in detail in the commentary on the relevant I.C.E. clauses that follows.

PROVISIONAL SUM

58. (1) "Provisional Sum" means[1] a sum included in the Contract and so designated for the execution of work or the supply of goods materials or services[2] or for contingencies which sum may be used in whole or in part or not at all at the direction and discretion of the Engineer.

PRIME COST ITEM

(2) "Prime Cost (P.C.) Item" means[1] an item in the Contract which contains (either wholly or in part) a sum referred to as Prime Cost (P.C.) which will be used for the execution of work or for the supply of goods materials or services[2] for the Works.

DESIGN REQUIREMENTS TO BE EXPRESSLY STATED

(3) If in connection with any Provisional Sum or Prime Cost Item the services to be provided include any matter of design or specification[3] of any part of the Permanent Works or of any equipment or plant to be incorporated therein[4] such requirement shall be expressly stated in the Contract and shall be included in any Nominated Sub-contract. The obligation of the Contractor in respect thereof shall be only that which has been expressly stated in accordance with this sub-clause.[5]

USE OF PRIME COST ITEMS

(4) In respect of every Prime Cost Item the Engineer shall have power to order the Contractor to employ a sub-contractor nominated by the Engineer for the execution of any work or the supply of any goods materials or services included therein. The Engineer shall also have power with the consent of the Contractor to order[6] the Contractor to execute any such work or to supply any such goods materials or services in which event the Contractor shall be paid in accordance with the terms of a quotation submitted by him and accepted by the Engineer or in the absence thereof the value shall be determined in accordance with Clause 52.[7]

NOMINATED SUB-CONTRACTORS—DEFINITION

(5) All specialists merchants tradesmen and others nominated in the Contract for a Prime Cost Item or ordered by the Engineer[8] to be employed by the Contractor in accordance with sub-clause (4) or sub-clause (7) of this Clause for the execution of any work or the supply of any goods materials or services[2] are referred to in this Contract as "Nominated Sub-contractors".

Production of Vouchers, etc.

(6) The Contractor shall when required by the Engineer produce all quotations invoices vouchers sub-contract documents[9] accounts and receipts in connection with expenditure in respect of work carried out by all Nominated Sub-contractors.[10]

Use of Provisional Sums

(7) In respect of every Provisional Sum the Engineer shall have power to order either or both[11] of the following:

(a) work to be executed or goods materials or services to be supplied by the Contractor[12] the value of such work executed or goods materials or services supplied being determined in accordance with Clause 52[7] and included in the Contract Price;

(b) work to be executed or goods materials or services to be supplied by a Nominated Sub-contractor in accordance with Clause 59A.

1. DISTINCTIONS BETWEEN "PROVISIONAL SUM" AND "PRIME COST (P.C.) ITEM". Under this 5th edition the differences between these two are:

(a) Both are stated to be for "*the execution of work or (for) the supply of goods materials or services*" in identical words, but a provisional sum may also be "*for contingencies*".

For convenience in these notes "*work*" will be used to include also "*supply of goods materials or services*" unless otherwise stated.

(b) A provisional sum "*may be used in whole or in part*"—the engineer has a discretion. A prime cost item "*will be used*". Consistent with this distinction, the work in a P.C. item can be omitted only by a variation order, with attendant rights under cl. 52, and in the case set out in cl. 59A (2) (b) the contractor is entitled to his charges and profits despite the omission.

(c) The main contractor is entitled to refuse absolutely or refuse unless his price is accepted to carry out work under a P.C. item otherwise than by a nominated sub-contractor, but under a provisional sum may be ordered to do the work himself (N. 6 and 12).

(d) Any quotation from the main contractor accepted by the engineer is to provide the valuation of work done by the main contractor under a prime cost item, and if none the work is to be valued under cl. 52 (cl. 58 (4)). In the case of a provisional sum, work done by the main contractor is specified to be priced in all cases under cl. 52 (cl. 58 (7) (a)).

(e) Cl. 58 (5) allows for nomination in the main contract itself under a P.C. item only.

(f) For additions for labours *see* N. 19, p. 244.

For extension of time in respect of provisional sums and P.C. items refer to p. 142.

2. "OR SERVICES". *See* N. 5 and 10.

3. "ANY MATTER OF DESIGN OR SPECIFICATION". For definition of design *see* p. 102.

4. DESIGN "OF ANY PART OF THE PERMANENT WORKS OR OF ANY EQUIPMENT OR PLANT TO BE INCORPORATED THEREIN". The case of temporary works designed by the engineer is not mentioned, as it is in cl. 8 (2).

5. "SUCH REQUIREMENT SHALL BE EXPRESSLY STATED IN THE CONTRACT . . . INCLUDED IN ANY NOMINATED SUB-CONTRACT. THE OBLIGATION OF THE CONTRACTOR IN RESPECT (OF DESIGN OR SPECIFICATION) . . . SHALL BE ONLY THAT WHICH HAS BEEN EXPRESSLY STATED IN ACCORDANCE WITH THIS SUB-CLAUSE". It does not seem that a particular item has to be labelled a matter of design or specification if it is clear from the description that design is involved, as in a specification by results (p. 215, footnote (*x'*) as to "*expressly*").

The statement of design requirement may be in a specification for the sub-contract work included as a separate section of the main contract specification, perhaps for safety labelled "Design of", etc.

Presumably one benefit to the main contractor of this provision is that he will know the liability for design he is taking on, and be able to verify that the sub-contractor's design is satisfactory (in the case of highly specialised work this is likely to be so only to a limited extent). Most important he will be able to check that the terms of any nomination impose on the nominated sub-contractor a clear and full duty to provide the services.

6. "THE ENGINEER SHALL . . . HAVE POWER WITH THE CONSENT OF THE CONTRACTOR TO ORDER" THE CONTRACTOR HIMSELF TO DO P.C. WORK. A contradiction in terms. The contractor is given an unrestricted right to refuse consent, and may do so e.g. unless greater payment than would be payable under cl. 52 is agreed to by the engineer for his performance of the P.C. item.

It is reasonable in many cases that the contractor is entitled to refuse to consent to take on himself work included in a P.C. item where the work is specialised and outside the main contractor's usual sphere of operations. However, there is no requirement that the contractor's consent should not be unreasonably withheld. The engineer therefore should use a provisional sum wherever there is a possibility that he may want to insist on the work being done by the main contractor, which is preferable to nomination (p. 234).

7. "PAID IN ACCORDANCE WITH . . . QUOTATION . . . ACCEPTED . . . OR IN THE ABSENCE THEREOF THE VALUE SHALL BE DETERMINED IN ACCORDANCE WITH CLAUSE 52". The need for such a valuation is unlikely to arise, since the main contractor is entitled to refuse to do work in a P.C. item unless the price he requires for the work is first accepted (previous note).

Notice, etc., by the contractor under cl. 52 (4) (b) appears to be required. Insofar as cl. 52 (2) is relevant it is not at all clear whether the notice under that sub-clause also applies, but it is obviously safer to give it.

8. "NOMINATED IN THE CONTRACT FOR A PRIME COST ITEM OR ORDERED BY THE ENGINEER TO BE EMPLOYED" replaces and improves on "*nominated selected or approved by the Employer or Engineer*" in the previous edition. The employer may no longer personally nominate except in a P.C. sum in the original contract documents, but it is suggested may tell the engineer whom to choose.

l

(*l*) In the judgment in *Davies & Co. (Shopfitters) Ltd.* v. *William Old Ltd.* (1969) 67 L.G.R. 395 the suggestion is made that the architect is not the agent of the employer or contractor in nominating a sub-contractor under the R.I.B.A. form (at p. 400). It is difficult to see any reason on the wording of these Conditions why the engineer should owe any duty to the contractor in choosing a nominee, particularly in view of the contractor's right to object under cl. 59A (1). *See also* p. 241, N. 8.

9. PRODUCTION OF "SUB-CONTRACT DOCUMENTS". A new power is given to the engineer to require production of sub-contract documents in respect of nominated sub-contractors. The terms of these documents should have been specified in the tender documents sent out by him in inviting tenders for nominated sub-contracts, but it may be important to check that the sub-contract form has actually been executed by both parties without alteration. Unfortunately the wording of this provision is flawed—next note.

10. PRODUCTION OF QUOTATIONS ... SUB-CONTRACT DOCUMENTS, ETC., "IN RESPECT OF WORK CARRIED OUT BY ALL NOMINATED SUB-CONTRACTORS". On the literal meaning of this unhappy wording the engineer is entitled to these documents only in respect of work which has already been carried out, not or work yet to be carried out. There is also no duty to produce documents in relation to "*services*" as opposed to work.

11. "EITHER OR BOTH", i.e. an item of work may be ordered to be performed partly by a nominated sub-contractor and partly by the main contractor as well as exclusively by either.

12. ORDER FOR WORK BY MAIN CONTRACTOR UNDER PROVISIONAL SUM. The contractor has no power to refuse to carry out work or supply goods, materials or services under a provisional sum, as opposed to a P.C. item. However, subject to cl. 4 he may sub-let to a domestic sub-contractor.

NOMINATED SUB-CONTRACTORS—OBJECTION TO NOMINATION

59A. (1) Subject to sub-clause (2) (c) of this Clause the Contractor shall not be under any obligation to enter into any sub-contract[1] with any Nominated Sub-contractor against whom the Contractor may raise reasonable objection[2] or who shall decline to enter into a sub-contract with the Contractor containing provisions:[2a]

(a) that in respect of the work goods materials or services the subject of the sub-contract the Nominated Sub-contractor will undertake towards the Contractor such obligations and liabilities as will enable the Contractor to discharge his own obligations and liabilities towards the Employer[3] under the terms of the Contract;

(b) that the Nominated Sub-contractor will save harmless and indemnify the Contractor against all claims demands and proceedings damages costs charges and expenses whatsoever arising out of or in connection with any failure by the Nominated Sub-contractor to perform such obligations or fulfil such liabilities;

(c) that the Nominated Sub-contractor will save harmless and indemnify the Contractor from and against any negligence by the Nominated Sub-contractor his agents workmen and servants and against any misuse by him or them of any Constructional Plant or Temporary Works provided by the Contractor for the purposes of the Contract and for all claims as aforesaid;

(d) equivalent to those contained in Clause 63.[4]

ENGINEER'S ACTION UPON OBJECTION

(2) If pursuant to sub-clause (1) of this Clause the Contractor shall not be obliged to enter into a sub-contract with a Nominated Sub-contractor and shall decline to do so[5] the Engineer shall do one or more of the following:[6]

(a) nominate an alternative sub-contractor in which case sub-clause (1) of this Clause shall apply;
(b) by order under Clause 51 vary the Works or the work goods materials or services the subject of the Provisional Sum or Prime Cost Item including if necessary the omission of any such work goods materials or services so that they may be provided by workmen contractors or suppliers as the case may be employed by the Employer either concurrently with the Works (in which case Clause 31 shall apply) or at some other date. Provided that in respect of the omission of any Prime Cost Item there shall be included in the Contract Price a sum in respect of the Contractor's charges and profit being a percentage of the estimated value of such work goods material or services omitted at the rate provided in the Bill of Quantities or inserted in the Appendix to the Form of Tender as the case may be;[7]
(c) subject to the Employer's consent[8] where the Contractor declines to enter into a contract with the Nominated Sub-contractor only on the grounds of unwillingness of the Nominated Sub-contractor to contract on the basis of the provisions contained in paragraphs (a) (b) (c) or (d) of sub-clause (1) of this Clause direct the Contractor to enter into a contract with the Nominated Sub-contractor on such other terms as the Engineer shall specify[9] in which case sub-clause (3) of this Clause shall apply;
(d) in accordance with Clause 58 arrange for the Contractor to execute such work or to supply such goods materials or services.[10]

DIRECTION BY ENGINEER

(3) If the Engineer shall direct the Contractor pursuant to sub-clause (2) of this Clause to enter into a sub-contract which does not contain all the provisions referred to in sub-clause (1) of this Clause:
(a) the Contractor shall not be bound to discharge his obligations and liabilities under the Contract to the extent that the sub-contract terms so specified by the Engineer are inconsistent with the discharge of the same;[11]
(b) in the event of the Contractor incurring loss or expense or suffering damage arising out of the refusal of the Nominated Sub-contractor to accept such provisions[12] the Contractor shall subject to Clause 52 (4) be paid in accordance with Clause 60[13] the amount of such loss expense or damage as the Contractor could not reasonably avoid.[14]

CONTRACTOR RESPONSIBLE FOR NOMINATED SUB-CONTRACTS

(4) Except as otherwise provided in this Clause and in Clause 59B the Contractor shall be as responsible for the work executed or goods materials or services supplied by a Nominated Sub-contractor employed by him as if he had himself executed such work or supplied such goods materials or services or had sub-let the same in accordance with Clause 4.[15]

PAYMENTS

(5) For all work executed or goods materials or services supplied by Nominated Sub-contractors there shall be included in the Contract Price:
(a) the actual price paid or due to be paid by the Contractor in accordance with the terms of the sub-contract[16] (unless and to the extent that any

such payment is the result of a default of the Contractor)[17] net of all trade and other discounts rebates and allowances other than any discount obtainable by the Contractor for prompt payment;[18]

(b) the sum (if any) provided in the Bill of Quantities for labours in connection therewith or if ordered pursuant to Clause 58 (7) (b) as may be determined by the Engineer;[19]

(c) in respect of all other charges and profit a sum being a percentage of the actual price paid or due to be paid calculated (where provision has been made in the Bill of Quantities for a rate to be set against the relevant item of prime cost) at the rate inserted by the Contractor against that item or (where no such provision has been made) at the rate inserted by the Contractor in the Appendix to the Form of Tender as the percentage for adjustment of sums set against Prime Cost Items.

BREACH OF SUB-CONTRACT

(6) In the event that the Nominated Sub-contractor shall be in breach of the sub-contract which breach causes the Contractor to be in breach of contract the Employer shall not enforce any award of any arbitrator or judgment which he may obtain against the Contractor in respect of such breach of contract except to the extent that the Contractor may have been able to recover the amount thereof from the Sub-contractor. Provided always that if the Contractor shall not comply with Clause 59B (6) the Employer may enforce any such award or judgment in full.[20] [23]

1. "THE CONTRACTOR SHALL NOT BE UNDER ANY OBLIGATION TO ENTER INTO ANY SUB-CONTRACT". It is clear that if the engineer makes a nomination which is not in accordance with this contract and the contractor enters into a sub-contract with the nominated sub-contractor nevertheless, the contractor will have waived (p. 157, N. 11) his rights under this clause (*see also* N. 5 below).

2. "WITH ANY NOMINATED SUB-CONTRACTOR AGAINST WHOM THE CONTRACTOR MAY RAISE REASONABLE OBJECTION". Reasonable objection will relate typically to the sub-contractor's ability to do the work, the necessary skills, plant and other resources, or his finances. Commercial facts of life may make it difficult for a main contractor to object to a sub-contractor, particularly as the roles of sub-contractor and main contractor are often interchanged.

The contractor takes a serious risk in persisting with an objection unless it is clearly reasonable—if he is wrong he will be liable to the employer for the delay to the works and any extra charges of a substitute sub-contractor.   *m*

One particular question is whether a main contractor who is bound to furnish a bond may insist on the nominated sub-contractor in turn furnishing a bond for the sub-contract works. The answer is that under this clause if the main contractor has grounds to question the financial stability of the sub-contractor he may object to him, and of course may agree to withdraw the objection in return for a bond. The mere fact that the employer requires the main contractor to supply a bond does not automatically make it reasonable for the main contractor to require a bond from the sub-contractor irrespective of the sub-contractor's financial

(*m*) By positive implication from the negative terms of cl. 59A (1), the contractor is "*under . . . obligation to enter into . . . (a) sub-contract with . . . (the) Nominated Sub-Contractor . . .*" if all the conditions for nomination are fulfilled.

position, since the employer's requirement is related to the finances of the main contractor and the extent of the main contract works. The remainder of this clause merely requires a sub-contractor to enter into a sub-contract containing particular terms; it does not require the sub-contractor to have the performance of those terms guaranteed by a bond.

2. (a) PROVISIONS REQUIRED IN NOMINATED SUB-CONTRACT. If the sub-contract contains terms contrary to those required provisions that are void because they offend against the Unfair Contract Terms Act 1977 (for example, possibly a restriction on liability for liquidated damages where the sub-contract form emanates from the sub-contractor—p. 434) the position is obscure. The sub-contract will not physically contain the terms required by this sub-clause, but may nevertheless effectively give the contractor the required protection. Probably the contractor is entitled to object since his rights under the Act are not clear cut until a court applies the test of reasonableness.

3. SUB-CONTRACT PROVISIONS "AS WILL ENABLE THE CONTRACTOR TO DISCHARGE HIS OWN OBLIGATIONS AND LIABILITIES TOWARDS THE EMPLOYER". An improvement on the previous edition of these Conditions. For example, this change recognises that the completion date for the sub-contract usually will differ from the date for the main contract, but must be such as "*will enable the Contractor to discharge his own*" duty to complete on time.

4. "EQUIVALENT TO . . . CLAUSE 63" is taken up in cl. 59B.

5. "AND (IF THE CONTRACTOR) SHALL DECLINE TO" ENTER INTO A SUB-CONTRACT CONTAINING PROVISIONS. *See* N. 1.

6. "THE ENGINEER SHALL DO ONE OR MORE OF THE FOLLOWING". The engineer may, e.g., nominate an alternative sub-contractor for part of the work involved, arrange for the main contractor to execute another part, and omit the balance.

The engineer should ensure that he is in a position to take such action without involving the employer in liability to the original sub-contractor (p. 232).

Unreasonable delay by the engineer in acting under this sub-clause will in most cases give the contractor a right to compensation under cl. 7 (3) as delay with an instruction (p. 49, N. 11). It appears that even if there is no such unreasonable delay the contractor is entitled to compensation if the works are at all delayed because of a valid objection by the contractor under sub-cl. (1). The delay arises from the engineer's failure to make a proper choice of and terms with the original nominated sub-contractor as he has an implied duty to do.

Of course such delay is very likely to occur if the engineer has to change sub-contract horses at a late stage because of objection, and therefore it may be wise for the engineer to take the precautions against unreasonable objection suggested on p. 232.

7. EXECUTION OF PROVISIONAL SUM OR PRIME COST ITEM WORK BY THE EMPLOYER. Under the general law the contractor is entitled to loss of profit on work omitted from his contract by a variation order only if the work is

carried out by the employer or another contractor and not left out of the works altogether (p. 171, N. 6). In this case of omission of a P.C. item, whether or not the work is done by another "*concurrently with the Works or at some other date*" (query if it is never to be done) the contractor is entitled to the percentage stated in the bill or the appendix to the form of tender for charges and profit other than for labours covered by a separate sum (cl. 59 A (5)). The form of tender makes clear that this is not a special percentage, but the full percentage which applies where the work is done by a nominated sub-contractor.

This entitlement is doubly peculiar. In the first place attendances will not be provided. For attendances is substituted at most the much less onerous duty under cl. 31 (1) to afford all reasonable facilities for the contractor employed direct by the employer if the omitted work goes ahead during this contract, and with rights to extra payment under cl. 31 (2). In the second place the contractor's charges and profits in respect of a nominated sub-contractor are calculated with an element included for the risk involved in taking at least partial responsibility for the sub-contractor's work, which risk the contractor does not bear when a direct contractor is substituted.

An engineer who brings another direct contractor on to the site during the course of the works may be placing his client in a vulnerable position (p. 125, liability for faulty materials and disruption, and p. 362 on insurance).

"*The estimated value*" on which the percentage for profit and charges is to be calculated should be available in the quotation of the sub-contractor with whom the main contractor has declined to contract, or in the case of a dispute will be settled by the engineer or arbitrator under cl. 66. Presumably the estimated value is used because the payment to the contractor is calculated at the time when the P.C. item is omitted, from which it follows that the contractor has no claim to an additional percentage because of an increase in the final value of the work that was originally included in the item.

8. "SUBJECT TO THE EMPLOYER'S CONSENT". These words mean that in deciding on this very far-reaching alternative the engineer is not bound or entitled to act independently of his client, but must have his consent. The contractor is bound to satisfy himself that the consent has been given. It is suggested that in giving a direction to the contractor under this paragraph the engineer should attach a letter of consent from the employer.

9. SUB-CONTRACT "ON SUCH OTHER TERMS AS THE ENGINEER SHALL SPECIFY". The engineer must specify the terms clearly and in detail, preferably by a full specimen sub-contract form. At this stage the engineer will often find himself with terms on his hands that he must specify, that is, conditions of tender on which the sub-contract was invited and, if the engineer was not alert, special printed conditions incorporated by the sub-contractor when quoting and accepted inadvertently by the engineer.

10. "ARRANGE FOR THE CONTRACTOR TO EXECUTE SUCH WORK", ETC., i.e.

(n) Does this specific right to "*order under Clause* 51" an omission of work and to have it carried out by another contractor imply that contrary to court decisions on other forms (text p. 171, N. 6) the general power to vary under cl. 51 includes an order to omit work which is to be done for the employer by another contractor? It is suggested that it does not; that this case, with the special rights given to the contractor to payment of charges and profits, is mentioned to extend the ordinary scope of cl. 51.

order the contractor in the case of a provisional sum (cl. 58 (7) (a)), or try to persuade the main contractor to agree to do so in the case of a P.C. item (sub-cl. (4)).

11. "THE CONTRACTOR ... NOT ... BOUND ... TO THE EXTENT THAT THE SUB-CONTRACT TERMS SO SPECIFIED BY THE ENGINEER ARE INCONSISTENT WITH THE DISCHARGE OF" THE MAIN CONTRACT OBLIGATIONS AND LIABILITIES.

The effects of this provision may be tested by a case most likely to arise in practice, where plant sub-contractors will tender only on an Institution of Mechanical Engineers, etc., model form. If the engineer directs the contractor to enter into a sub-contract with the nominated sub-contractor on the terms of, say, Model Form A (for use in connection with home contracts with erection), many problems of interpretation are created by the approximately twenty differences between that form and the I.C.E. Conditions. In addition, by cl. 26 of the I.Mech.E. Conditions the amount payable for liquidated damages is limited to a maximum percentage of the contract value of such portion or portions of the works as cannot be put to the use intended. The effect of the words at the head of this note appears to be that (if the limitation is valid—p. 433) the main contractor is liable only for an equivalent sum of damages for delay caused by a nominated sub-contractor, and when the maximum sum is reached will cease to be liable altogether for such damages however long the nominated sub-contractor's delay continues.

There is no provision by which the employer automatically obtains *vis-à-vis* the main contractor the benefit of any special duties taken on by the sub-contractor under the sub-contract form, for example the provisions of the I.Mech.E. Conditions about tests on completion. In order to have a complete chain of responsibility so that such additional duties can be enforced through to the sub-contractors, they should be specified in detail or otherwise incorporated into the main contract specification (p. 231).

12. RECOVERY BY CONTRACTOR OF "LOSS OR EXPENSE OR ... DAMAGE ARISING OUT OF THE REFUSAL OF THE NOMINATED SUB-CONTRACTOR TO ACCEPT ... PROVISIONS" IN CLAUSE 59A (1). For example, if by the sub-contract a nominated sub-contractor only accepts liability for limited liquidated damages for delay which do not even cover the main contractor's own costs of standing time, etc., and are binding (p. 434), the main contractor is entitled to recover such excess costs from the employer.

13. "SUBJECT TO CLAUSE 52 (4) ... IN ACCORDANCE WITH CLAUSE 60", dealing with notice of money claims and inclusion of payment in interim and final certificates, subject to retention. Note that according to the words of this paragraph it is not until the contractor has actually incurred loss or expense or suffered damage that he has a right to payment and that therefore "*the events giving rise to the claim*" have happened within cl. 52 (4) (b) so as to start running the period within which the contractor is to give notice.

14. "COULD NOT REASONABLY AVOID" contrasts with "*unavoidably*" in cl. 14 (6), *see* p. 82, N. 18.

15. "EXCEPT AS ... PROVIDED IN THIS CLAUSE AND IN CLAUSE 59B THE CONTRACTOR ... (IS) RESPONSIBLE FOR THE WORK EXECUTED OR GOODS

MATERIALS OR SERVICES SUPPLIED BY A NOMINATED SUB-CONTRACTOR ... AS IF HE HAD HIMSELF EXECUTED SUCH WORK", ETC. This important declaration of principle, and the exceptions to it, are discussed generally on pp. 226–9. It is clearly implied that the main contractor is not entitled to an extension of time for delay caused by a nominated sub-contractor, as suggested in the second edition of this book. However, the main contractor's liability for delay may be severely restricted by cl. 59A (3) and (6)—N. 11 and 20—or if he forfeits the sub-contract under cl. 59B.

16. "THE ACTUAL PRICE PAID OR DUE TO BE PAID BY THE CONTRACTOR IN ACCORDANCE WITH THE TERMS OF THE SUB-CONTRACT". For the position where the sub-contractor does not finish his work, see p. 252, N. 11.

This price is to be included in interim certificates, listed separately (cl. 60 (1)).

The sub-contractor in his tender may insist on special payment terms. If the main contractor is directed by the engineer to enter into the sub-contract with him on those terms, the contractor will be protected by cl. 59A (3) (a) or (b). For example, if the sub-contractor requires a reduced retention, the main contract retention will be reduced accordingly under para. (a). If the sub-contractor requires payment of retention before completion of the main contract works, it appears that the main contractor will be bound to make early payment in accordance with the sub-contract but will be entitled to compensation by interest under para. (b).

17. "UNLESS AND TO THE EXTENT THAT ANY SUCH PAYMENT (OF THE SUB-CONTRACT PRICE) IS THE RESULT OF A DEFAULT OF THE CONTRACTOR". It seems clear that "default" means default in relation to the sub-contractor and not the employer. The "price" may be increased by such default, e.g. where it leads to a variation of the sub-contract works.

18. "NET OF ALL TRADE AND OTHER DISCOUNTS REBATES AND ALLOWANCES OTHER THAN ANY DISCOUNT OBTAINABLE BY THE CONTRACTOR FOR PROMPT PAYMENT". This phrase removes from the contractor his normal duty to give the employer credit for all discounts received from nominated sub-contractors, in the case of any prompt payment discount he may succeed in obtaining from a nominated sub-contractor. The discount position is disimproved for the contractor to the extent that he is no longer specifically entitled to object to a nomination merely because the sub-contractor will not allow him a discount. Of course the right to a discount in the 4th edition of these Conditions was almost valueless if they were applied strictly. At the same time the contractor's position is considerably improved by allowing him to pocket any discount for prompt payment he can obtain, without the previous limit of $2\frac{1}{2}\%$.

It is suggested that the mere fact that a discount is stated in the sub-contract to be for "prompt payment" is not enough to entitle the contractor to keep it. It must be an essential ingredient that the discount is stated to cease to be payable after a period of time. What period is the maximum after which the discount will cease to be for "prompt" payment is difficult to say; possibly 14 days from receipt of payment from the employer with a maximum of 30 days from the end of the month in which the work, etc., is done whether such payment is received or not, might be reasonable having regard to the usage of the industry. If the main contractor is allowed a discount by the sub-contractor despite having paid late, it is arguable that the employer may then claim the discount on the grounds that it was not in fact for prompt payment.

It is for the main contractor to obtain a discount for himself. The engineer is not required to provide for any discount in inviting tenders from nominated sub-contractors or allow the main contractor an opportunity to negotiate the discount before accepting a sub-contract tender on behalf of the employer (for other reasons it may be unwise for the engineer to accept the tender at all, p. 232). There is no reason to suggest that refusal to give a discount is ground for "*reasonable objection*" within cl. 59A (1) (what size of and period for discount would the contractor be entitled to? and note the word "*obtainable*" here which clearly leaves it to the contractor to obtain what he can).

It is hardly necessary to dwell on the startling vista opened up by this new freedom of main contractor and sub-contractor to negotiate any size of prompt payment discount. At the time of reporting on main contract tenders or negotiating with tenderers the engineer will have no way of knowing what the hidden profit is by way of discounts from nominated sub-contractors, which often constitutes a very large part of the main contractor's profit. Competitive tendering is affected; one contractor may be in a position to extract an extra discount because of the size of his business or some other special relationship with a sub-contractor. Whenever a sub-contractor is in a strong position to get a nomination because of the specialist nature of his work or equipment, he can add on to his price any extra discount agreed with a particular contractor or tenderer for the main contract, so that the employer will not always get the benefit of a discount in a reduced overall price even if the discount is given for a laudable reason such as the main contractor's reputation for prompt payment.

In pricing a tender the contractor may have to consider the possibility that he will lose his discount by an order to do provisional sum work himself (the words of cl. 52 are not appropriate to include an allowance for lost discount in the valuation of the work) or if the work is omitted (in which case he will also lose his charges and profit). In pricing a P.C. item he may allow for the fact that he is in a more advantageous position—although he will lose his discount he is in a position to bargain for a good price if he is requested to do the work himself, and if the employer either originally or in response to the contractor's price omits the item from the contract the contractor may still obtain his charges and profit under cl. 59A (2) (b) (N. 7).

19. THE PAYMENTS TO THE MAIN CONTRACTOR FOR ATTENDANCES AND PROFIT ON SUB-CONTRACTORS ARE:

(*a*) For labours any sum (without adjustment) provided in the bill of quantities in the case of P.C. items. For definition of "*labours*" *see* C.E.S.M.M. section 5.15. In the case of provisional sum work executed by the sub-contractor under cl. 58 (7) (b), such sum for labours "*as may be determined by the Engineer*" is payable. No guidance on the basis of calculation is given to the engineer, but presumably it should be cost plus a reasonable percentage profit.

(*b*) In respect of all other charges and profit a percentage of the price calculated at the rate (if any) inserted in the bill against the item or if none the percentage in the appendix to the form of tender for adjustment of sums set against prime cost items. The latter percentage apparently applies if the sub-contractor is nominated under a provisional sum—*see* cl. 58 (7) and the opening two lines of this sub-cl. (5).

20. LIMITATIONS ON THE EMPLOYER'S REMEDIES, AGAINST THE MAIN CONTRACTOR FOR LOSS ARISING OUT OF DEFAULT OF A SUB-CONTRACTOR. These serious limitations are:

(a) Where the sub-contractor is not actually in breach of contract because the sub-contract effectively limits his liabilities and the contractor has operated the appropriate procedure, the employer has no remedy at all against anyone (N. 11).

(b) Where the sub-contractor is in breach of the sub-contract, the employer has no effective remedy unless and until the main contractor succeeds in extracting payment from the sub-contractor. The contractor must take all necessary steps and proceedings to recover, as required by the employer (N. 23). Even if the sub-contractor is solvent the employer may have to wait some time for his money.

(c) The main contractor may end his responsibility for a particular sub-contractor by forfeiting the sub-contract (cl. 59B).

(d) On correction of certificates see cl. 60 (7).

The practical results of these limitations are discussed in the general note on pp. 231-4.

21. "THE EMPLOYER SHALL NOT ENFORCE ANY AWARD . . . OR JUDGMENT . . . AGAINST THE CONTRACTOR (FOR BREACH OF THE MAIN CONTRACT DUE TO BREACH OF THE SUB-CONTRACT) EXCEPT TO THE EXTENT THAT THE CONTRACTOR MAY HAVE BEEN ABLE TO RECOVER THE AMOUNT . . . FROM THE SUB-CONTRACTOR". Because a nominated sub-contractor will almost certainly have express or implied notice of the terms of the main contract under which he is nominated and of the contractor's liability to the employer, the compensation payable by the contractor to the employer should not be too remote (pp. 427-8) to be recoverable in law by the contractor from the sub-contractor as envisaged by this sub-clause. Nevertheless many complications spring from this limitation on the employer's rights:

(a) The employer's rights under cls. 39 (2) and 49 (4) are not specifically restricted here or in cl. 60 (7) (b), and see cl. 59A (4). Where the sub-contractor's breach consists of defective work it appears therefore that the employer may have the defects remedied by another contractor, and deduct the cost from the main contractor even if the main contractor does not succeed in recovering a corresponding amount from the sub-contractor. The employer has a similar right directly to deduct liquidated damages, under cl. 47 (4). Since deductions may validly be made by the employer under those clauses without first obtaining and enforcing a prior arbitration award or court judgment the words at the head of this note do not prevent the deduction being made by the employer even though the contractor has not been able to recover, nor had any opportunity to recover, the amount from the sub-contractor, thus limiting seriously the protection to the contractor under this sub-clause. The main contractor will however pass on to the sub-contractor   o

(o) The contractor may try to overcome eventually this limitation on his protection by claiming back the deduction from the employer and carrying the claim as far as arbitration. If the arbitrator's award is that the deduction has not been made validly under the main contract, then of course there is no problem. If the award is that there is no repayment due from the employer to the contractor, it might be argued that in continuing to keep the deducted money the employer is then enforcing the award of the arbitrator within this sub-clause. That is an extremely doubtful argument, because the employer does not have to take any action on foot of the award; what he has already enforced is these Conditions and the arbitrator's award is merely that the contractor is not entitled to undo such enforcement.

an engineer's order to remedy defective sub-contract work, and if the defects are serious and the order is not obeyed may act to forfeit the sub-contract under cl. 59B with the resulting effects on the employer's rights. In the chaos that may be produced by these various clauses applying to nominated sub-contractors' work, the prize is likely to go to the party who first obtains and acts quickly on legal advice.

(*b*) Breach of the main contract may be caused partly by a breach of the sub-contract and partly due to the contractor's own works, e.g. where sub-contract works fail because of a combination of a defect in the works and of attendance work by the main contractor. An arbitrator may be asked in his award on the claim by the employer against the main contractor to apportion the percentage of the employer's losses due to the sub-contractor's breach, to which this provision will then apply. It is not clear if or on what basis a court will do so but the contractor may obtain an apportionment by joining the sub-contractor in the proceedings.

(*c*) The contractor may claim against a sub-contractor for breach involving the contractor in liability to the employer and for the contractor's own consequential losses, in standing time, etc. An arbitrator must be asked to apportion any amount awarded, and a court may give a breakdown of the amount in giving the reasons for the judgment.

(*d*) If the contractor succeeds in actually extracting from the sub-contractor only a proportion of the total damages awarded in a case such as (*c*), the conditions do not say how the amount recovered is to be apportioned; presumably it should be *pro rata* to the proportion of the total amount that he recovers from the sub-contractor (*see* cl. 59B (6) dealing expressly with costs).

(*e*) If the sub-contractor has some valid set-off against the main contractor, it is reasonably clear that *vis-a-vis* the employer the main contractor will be deemed to have recovered from the sub-contractor to the extent of the set-off.

22. "EMPLOYER SHALL NOT ENFORCE", i.e. by one of the various methods of execution, such as the sheriff, a garnishee order attaching a debt due to the main contractor from a creditor of his, receivership or liquidation, etc. *See also* N. 21 para. (*a*).

23. "IF THE CONTRACTOR SHALL NOT COMPLY WITH CLAUSE 59B (6)", i.e. fails to "*take all necessary steps and proceedings as may be required by the Employer to enforce the provisions of the sub-contract and/or all other rights and/or remedies available to him so as to recover the Employer's loss from the Sub-contractor*". It is reasonably clear from the run of these words that they all refer only to employer's requirements designed to ensure that the contractor recovers the employer's losses from the sub-contractor; they do not give the employer any right to direct the contractor as to the manner of enforcing the sub-contract in respect of the performance of the sub-contract work.

Although it is not stated specifically here that the contractor loses his protection against the employer "to the extent that any act or default of the Contractor may have caused or contributed to any of the Employer's loss" (as it is in cl. 59B (4) (c) (ii)), it must be implied in the main contract that the contractor will take all reasonable steps by way of follow-up, reminders and other pressures and reasonable supervision to ensure that the sub-contractor carries out his work promptly and properly.

It must also be implied that the contractor is liable to the employer where his failure to recover from the sub-contractor is due to his default in voluntarily making a less favourable sub-contract than he is entitled to under these clauses, for example restricting the sub-contractor's liability for damages for delay.

If the main contractor recovers only by putting the sub-contractor into bankruptcy or liquidation, the employer is likely to have to wait a long time before recovering even part of his losses.

FORFEITURE OF SUB-CONTRACT

59B. (1) Subject to Clause 59A (2) (c) the Contractor shall in every sub-contract with a Nominated Sub-contractor incorporate provisions equivalent to those provided in Clause 63[1] and such provisions are hereinafter referred to as "the Forfeiture Clause".

TERMINATION OF SUB-CONTRACT

(2)[2] If any event arises which in the opinion of the Contractor would entitle the Contractor to exercise his right under the Forfeiture Clause (or in the event that there shall be no Forfeiture Clause in the sub-contract his right to treat the sub-contract as repudiated by the Nominated Sub-contractor)[3] he shall at once notify the Engineer in writing[4,5] and if he desires to exercise such right by such notice seek the Employer's consent to his so doing. The Engineer shall by notice in writing to the Contractor inform him whether or not the Employer does so consent and if the Engineer does not give notice withholding consent within 7 days of receipt of the Contractor's notice the Employer shall be deemed to have consented to the exercise of the said right. If notice is given by the Contractor to the Engineer under this sub-clause and has not been withdrawn[6] then notwithstanding that the Contractor has not sought the Employer's consent as aforesaid the Engineer may with the Employer's consent direct the Contractor to give notice to the Nominated Sub-contractor expelling the Nominated Sub-contractor from the sub-contract Works pursuant to the Forfeiture Clause or rescinding the sub-contract as the case may be.[7] Any such notice given to the Nominated Sub-contractor is hereinafter referred to as a notice enforcing forfeiture of the sub-contract.

ENGINEER'S ACTION UPON TERMINATION

(3) If the Contractor shall give a notice enforcing forfeiture of the sub-contract whether under and in accordance with the Forfeiture Clause in the sub-contract or in purported exercise of his right to treat the sub-contract as repudiated the Engineer shall do any one or more of the things described in paragraphs (a) (b) and (d) of Clause 59A (2).[7a]

DELAY AND EXTRA COST

(4) If a notice enforcing forfeiture of the sub-contract shall have been given with the consent of the Employer or by the direction of the Engineer[8] or if it shall have been given without the Employer's consent in circumstances which entitled the Contractor to give such a notice:[9]
   (a) there shall be included in the Contract Price:[9]
      (i) the value determined in accordance with Clause 52 of any work the

Contractor may have executed or goods or materials he may have provided subsequent to the forfeiture[10] taking effect and pursuant to the Engineer's direction;

    (ii) such amount calculated in accordance with paragraph (a) of Clause 59A (5) as may be due in respect of any work goods materials or services provided by an alternative Nominated Sub-contractor together with reasonable sums for labours and for all other charges and profit as may be determined by the Engineer;

    (iii) any such amount as may be due in respect of the forfeited sub-contract in accordance with Clause 59A (5);[11]

(b) the Engineer shall take any delay to the completion of the Works consequent upon the forfeiture into account in determining any extension of time to which the Contractor is entitled under Clause 44[12] and the Contractor shall subject to Clause 52 (4) be paid in accordance with Clause 60[13] the amount of any additional cost which he may have necessarily and properly incurred as a result of such delay;[14]

(c)[15] the Employer shall subject to Clause 60 (7) be entitled to recover from the Contractor upon the certificate of the Engineer issued in accordance with Clause 60 (3):[16]

    (i) the amount by which the total sum to be included in the Contract Price pursuant to paragraphs (a) and (b) of this sub-clause exceeds the sum which would but for the forfeiture have been included in the Contract Price in respect of work materials goods and services done supplied or performed under the forfeited sub-contract;

    (ii) all such other loss expense and damage as the Employer may have suffered in consequence of the breach of the sub-contract;[17]

all of which are hereinafter collectively called "the Employer's loss".

Provided always that if the Contractor shall show that despite his having complied with sub-clause (6) of this Clause he has been unable to recover the whole or any part of the Employer's loss from the Sub-contractor the Employer shall allow or (if he has already recovered the same from the Contractor) shall repay to the Contractor so much of the Employer's loss as was irrecoverable from the Sub-contractor except and to the extent that the same was irrecoverable by reason of some breach of the sub-contract or other default towards the Sub-contractor by the Contractor[18] or except to the extent that any act or default of the Contractor may have caused or contributed to any of the Employer's loss.[19] Any such repayment by the Employer shall carry interest at the rate stipulated in Clause 60 (6) from the date of the recovery by the Employer from the Contractor of the sum repaid.

TERMINATION WITHOUT CONSENT

(5) If notice enforcing forfeiture of the sub-contract shall have been given without the consent of the Employer and in circumstances which did not entitle the Contractor to give such a notice:

(a) there shall be included in the Contract Price in respect of the whole of the work covered by the Nominated Sub-contract only the amount that would have been payable to the Nominated Sub-contractor on due completion of the sub-contract had it not been terminated;

(b) the Contractor shall not be entitled to any extension of time because of such termination nor to any additional expense incurred as a result of the work having been carried out and completed otherwise than by the said Sub-contractor;

(c) the Employer shall be entitled to recover from the Contractor any additional expense he may incur beyond that which he would have incurred had the sub-contract not been terminated.[20]

RECOVERY OF EMPLOYER'S LOSS

(6) The Contractor shall take all necessary steps and proceedings as may be required by the Employer to enforce the provisions of the sub-contract and/or all other rights and/or remedies available to him so as to recover the Employer's loss from the Sub-contractor. Except in the case where notice enforcing forfeiture of the sub-contract shall have been given without the consent of the Employer and in circumstances which did not entitle the Contractor to give such a notice the Employer shall pay to the Contractor so much of the reasonable costs and expenses of such steps and proceedings as are irrecoverable from the Sub-contractor provided that if the Contractor shall seek to recover by the same steps and proceedings any loss damage or expense additional to the Employer's loss the said irrecoverable costs and expenses shall be borne by the Contractor and the Employer in such proportions as may be fair in all the circumstances.[21]

1. "THE CONTRACTOR SHALL IN EVERY SUB-CONTRACT . . . INCORPORATE PROVISIONS EQUIVALENT TO THOSE . . . IN (FORFEITURE) CLAUSE 63". A clause similar to but slightly different from cl. 63 is included in the blue sub-contract form published by the Federation of Civil Engineering Contractors for use with the I.C.E. Conditions.

2. THE PROCEDURE FOR FORFEITING A NOMINATED SUB-CONTRACT. The procedure is:

(*a*) The contractor forms the opinion that an event has occurred which entitles him to exercise his right under the forfeiture clause in the sub-contract or (if there is no forfeiture clause) his right under the ordinary law to treat the sub-contract as repudiated by the nominated sub-contractor (p. 425) (in these notes for convenience both rights are referred to as forfeiture). This will usually happen as a result of serious delay or defective work by or insolvency of the sub-contractor. Note that the procedure can be put in motion only by the contractor, never by the employer or engineer.

(*b*) On forming this opinion the contractor is bound to notify the engineer in writing at once, and if he wishes to exercise the forfeiture rights must in his notice ask the employer for consent to do so.

(*c*) The action then passes to the engineer, who should advise the employer on making one of the following responses to the notice:

(i) If the employer is prepared to leave it to the contractor to make the decision whether to forfeit or not and the contractor has asked for consent to forfeiture in his notice, the employer need do nothing. In that case his consent is deemed to have been given after 7 days. Alternatively the employer may direct the engineer to give the contractor written notice that the employer consents to the contractor's request. The notice comes from the engineer, but says that the employer consents. For the danger of consent *see* N. 8.

(ii) If the employer wishes to insist on the sub-contract being forfeited, at any time until the contractor withdraws notice the engineer may give notice of consent under (i) and with the notice direct the contractor to enforce the forfeiture rights (whether or not the contractor has asked in his notice for consent). For possible dangers of a direction *see* N. 7.

(iii) If the employer does not consent to forfeiture, the engineer must tell the contractor so in writing within 7 days if the notice includes a forfeiture request; if it does not the employer need do nothing.

(*d*) If the contractor forfeits the sub-contract, whether at the employer's direction (when presumably he has no choice, N. 7) or with or even without the employer's consent, the engineer must do one or more of the things described in paras. (a), (b) and (d) of cl. 59A (2) (nominate an alternative sub-contractor, vary or omit the sub-contract work, arrange for the main contractor to execute the sub-contract work). As to payment and liabilities, there are three possible situations:

(i) If the sub-contract is validly forfeited with the employer's consent or direction, then the contractor is liable for the employer's losses only so far as he succeeds in recovering them from the guilty sub-contractor. The contractor of course has no liability to the guilty sub-contractor.

(ii) If the sub-contract is validly forfeited *vis-à-vis* the sub-contractor, then even if the main contractor did not have the employer's consent to forfeiture he is protected as in the previous case against himself bearing the employer's losses.

(iii) If the forfeiture is in breach of the sub-contract, then the employer bears his own losses if he consented to the forfeiture, and the main contractor bears those losses if he did not have the employer's consent.

(iv) If the forfeiture by the main contractor is in breach of the sub-contract, then whether or not the main contractor had the consent or direction of the employer to attempting the forfeiture, the main contractor bears the damages for breach of sub-contract payable to the sub-contractor.

Each of the points mentioned in this note is taken up in the following notes, and the practical considerations for the employer in operating this procedure are discussed on p. 233.

3. "IN THE EVENT THAT THERE SHALL BE NO FORFEITURE CLAUSE IN THE SUB-CONTRACT . . . (THE CONTRACTOR'S) RIGHT TO TREAT THE SUB-CONTRACT AS REPUDIATED BY THE NOMINATED SUB-CONTRACTOR". It is odd that the contractor is not given the choice of treating the contract as repudiated under the general law even if there is a forfeiture clause (which he is entitled to have included in the sub-contract—N. 1), since there may be some advantages in choosing that alternative (p. 276, N. 1).

4. CONTRACTOR TO "NOTIFY THE ENGINEER IN WRITING" THAT FORFEITURE RIGHTS HAVE ARISEN. The consequences for the contractor may be serious if he serves this notice and follows through with attempted forfeiture when the default of the sub-contractor is not sufficient to justify forfeiture (N. 8 and 9). Since it may be a difficult question of law to determine whether or not forfeiture is justified, the contractor should take legal advice unless the case is absolutely clear-cut.

5. FAILURE OF THE CONTRACTOR TO NOTIFY THE ENGINEER IN WRITING THAT FORFEITURE RIGHT HAS ARISEN. No penalty is placed on the contractor for failing to give this notice. In most cases it will be for the contractor's benefit to give notice where the works are suffering by delay, etc., by the sub-contractor, in view of his general responsibility for a nominated sub-contractor (p. 242, N. 15). However, a case might well arise where it suits the main contractor to join with the sub-contractor in alleging that delay is outside the sub-contractor's control so as to get an extension of time for that delay which will give him more time to finish the main contract works. Or where the sub-contractor's liability and as a result the main contractor's liability for liquidated damages are subject to a limit (p. 242, N. 11) it may suit

the main contractor to allow the sub-contractor to delay the works so that he has more time to finish off his own work whilst taking advantage of the limit of liability. Again, there may be reasons such as business association which make the main contractor reluctant to serve notice. Apart from refusal of an extension in some of these cases, the employer's only remedy to advance the work is to threaten or carry out forfeiture of the main contract under cl. 63, with all the practical difficulties involved, or in the case of defects to act under cls. 39 (2) or 49 (4).

6. "IF NOTICE ... BY THE CONTRACTOR ... HAS NOT BEEN WITHDRAWN". Clearly it must be implied that the contractor is entitled to withdraw notice only if the default of the sub-contractor giving rise to the right of forfeiture has ended. Unfortunately it is not clear that if the notice is in fact withdrawn prematurely the employer may treat it as still in force, or what is his position.

7. "ENGINEER MAY WITH THE EMPLOYER'S CONSENT DIRECT THE CONTRACTOR TO GIVE NOTICE ... EXPELLING THE NOMINATED SUB-CONTRACTOR". Presumably the contractor is bound to obey the direction to forfeit the sub-contract, but that is not spelled out and the employer is given no effective remedy if the contractor refuses to do so.

There is also no indication that the contractor must carry out the direction within a specific time, or even "*forthwith*" as elsewhere, but it must be implied that he will act within a reasonable time.

What if the sub-contractor ends his default after the employer's direction? Possibly it is implied that if the contractor unreasonably gives the forfeiture notice despite a change of circumstances, he bears the employer's losses—but the position is most obscure. (The drafting of these clauses must bear the blame for the many unhelpful doubts about their meaning in these notes.)

A warning is necessary that there is a species of civil wrong by which the employer could be directly liable to a sub-contractor for damages (including damages for loss of reputation) for causing him loss by directing the main contractor to serve a forfeiture notice when forfeiture is not justified in law. The employer is liable only if he intended to bring about a breach of the sub-contract or was recklessly indifferent whether or not the attempted forfeiture would be a breach of the sub-contract. The protection to the employer is to avoid giving a direction unless he has reliable information establishing a major default by the sub-contractor.

_p

7(a). "THE ENGINEER SHALL DO ANY ONE OR MORE OF THE THINGS DESCRIBED IN" CLAUSE 59A (2) (a) (b) OR (d). If the forfeiture is for delay by the sub-contractor it may be very difficult for the engineer to find a replacement sub-contractor who will agree to complete within such time as will enable the main contractor to complete the main contract works on time, and if he does not under cl. 59A (1) (a) the main contractor may object to the nomination.

For delay consequent on the forfeiture the contractor is entitled to an extension of time and cost under sub-cl. (4) (b).

(*p*) For more information on this civil wrong of inducing another to break a contract refer to "Salmond on Torts", 16th ed. by R. F. V. Heuston, p. 373.

8. "IF A NOTICE ENFORCING FORFEITURE OF THE SUB-CONTRACT SHALL HAVE BEEN GIVEN WITH THE CONSENT OF THE EMPLOYER OR . . . DIRECTION OF THE ENGINEER". The advantage to the contractor of serving notice under sub-cl. (2) and obtaining this consent or direction is that he becomes entitled to the rights set out here even if his original opinion was wrong that events had arisen giving him a right *vis-à-vis* the sub-contractor to forfeit the sub-contract. Provided he genuinely reaches the opinion that he has such a right, serves notice and obtains a consent or direction, then the terms of this sub-clause apply so as to relieve the contractor against having to pay the employer's losses, even if it transpires that the forfeiture was in breach of the sub-contract. In such a case the employer will bear his own losses since the main contractor can never be entitled to recover from the sub-contractor losses resulting from a forfeiture which was a breach of the sub-contract. The employer should consider carefully before consenting to forfeiture in a doubtful case. Since the main contractor may have an interest in putting the blame for defects or delays on the sub-contractor, investigation of his allegations may be necessary. If the contractor positively misrepresents the position negligently or fraudulently the employer may have a remedy against him independent of this clause p. 60.

See N. 20 for the contractor's liability for the employer's losses from a wrongful forfeiture to which the employer did not consent.

Cl. 59A (5) (a) says that the main contractor is repaid by the employer for work, etc., done by a nominated sub-contractor the price paid or due to be paid by the contractor "(*unless and to the extent that any such payment is the result of a default of the Contractor*)" (p. 243, N. 17). It follows from that provision and the end of this sub-clause (N. 18) that if the main contractor exercises the forfeiture rights in breach of the sub-contract, he and not the employer will bear the resulting damages payable to the sub-contractor, whether or not he had the employer's consent or a direction from the employer to exercise the right. This is a reasonable result since it is the contractor who initiates the procedure by serving the notice stating that the forfeiture rights have arisen.

9. "IF A NOTICE ENFORCING FORFEITURE . . . SHALL HAVE BEEN GIVEN WITHOUT THE EMPLOYER'S CONSENT IN CIRCUMSTANCES WHICH ENTITLED THE CONTRACTOR TO GIVE SUCH A NOTICE". In this case the contractor is still protected against having to bear the employer's losses. The risk a contractor takes in attempting to forfeit the sub-contract without the employer's consent is that if it is eventually decided that the attempted forfeiture was in breach of the sub-contract, he will be liable to the employer under sub-cl. (5) of this clause, as well as having to pay damages to the sub-contractor (last note).

10. CONTRACTOR RECEIVES "THE VALUE . . . OF ANY WORK THE CONTRACTOR MAY HAVE EXECUTED OR GOODS OR MATERIALS . . . PROVIDED SUBSEQUENT TO THE FORFEITURE". Noticeably missing is any reference to "*services*", although by sub-cl. (3) of this clause the main contractor may be directed to provide services on forfeiture of a sub-contract.

11. CONTRACTOR RECOVERS IN THE CONTRACT PRICE "SUCH AMOUNT AS MAY BE DUE IN RESPECT OF THE FORFEITED SUB-CONTRACT IN ACCORDANCE

WITH CLAUSE 59A (5)". The sub-contractor, and therefore the main contractor, will not be entitled to recover any retention money or balance earned for the sub-contract work unpaid by the employer to the main contractor at the time of forfeiture, if the sub-contractor has not substantially completed the works—p. 266. Therefore no further sum will be due from the employer to the main contractor, and the balance may be useful to offset the employer's losses.

12. EXTENSION OF TIME. The contractor is entitled to an extension only for delay to completion consequent upon the forfeiture; he is responsible for delay by a nominated sub-contractor so long as he remains a sub-contractor (p. 242, N. 11, and *see* N. 7(a) above).

13. "CONTRACTOR SHALL SUBJECT TO CLAUSE 52 (4) BE PAID IN ACCORDANCE WITH CLAUSE 60". These clauses deal respectively with notice of money claims and inclusion of payment in interim and final certificates, subject to retention.

14. "THE AMOUNT OF ANY ADDITIONAL COST WHICH . . . (THE CONTRACTOR) MAY HAVE NECESSARILY AND PROPERLY INCURRED AS A RESULT OF SUCH DELAY". *See* p. 31 for a discussion of "*cost*". Note that according to the words of this paragraph it is not until the contractor has actually incurred loss or expense or suffered damage that he has a right to payment and that therefore "*the events giving rise to the claim*" have happened within cl. 52 (4) (b) so as to start running the period within which the contractor is to give notice.

15. RECOVERY BY EMPLOYER OF LOSSES DUE TO FORFEITURE OF NOMINATED SUB-CONTRACT. By the rest of this sub-clause the employer is entitled to recover from the main contractor the extra he has to pay the main contractor or second sub-contractor due to the forfeiture, plus any other "*loss expense . . . damage*" he may have suffered in consequence of the breach of the sub-contract (discussed N. 17).

If the breach is defective work, the cost of remedying defects will be recovered as part of the extra for making them good paid to the main contractor or substitute sub-contractor.

Where the breach involves delay, then the situation is regulated by cl. 59A (5) and (6) insofar as the delay occurred before the forfeiture. Insofar as the delay is "*consequent upon the forfeiture*" by cl. 59B (4) (b) the main contractor is entitled to his additional costs but in turn is liable under this provision to repay those costs to the employer with any other costs suffered by the employer. It appears that in the latter case the employer must prove actual loss due to delay, but possibly may recover such loss even if it is more than the liquidated damages specified in the main contract, which are not applicable under this provision.

This right of the employer to recover his losses from the main contractor (like his right to recover from the main contractor losses due to breach by the sub-contractor prior to forfeiture) is subject to the serious limitation that the employer has to pay back to the main contractor the compensation received from him or (more likely, N. 16) loses his right to recover compensation not already received, if the contractor takes '*all necessary steps and proceedings as may be required by the Employer*" to enforce the sub-contract and recover the amount of the employer's loss from the sub-contractor and fails to do so. On that limitation refer to N. 21 and 23, pp. 245–6, and N. 18 below. Repayment carries interest by sub-cl. (4) (c).

16. "EMPLOYER ... SUBJECT TO CLAUSE 60 (7) ... ENTITLED TO RECOVER FROM THE CONTRACTOR UPON THE CERTIFICATE ... ISSUED ... (UNDER) CLAUSE 60 (3)", i.e. the employer's expenses, etc., due to the forfeiture are payable by the contractor with the final payment certificate—that is, not until after the end of the maintenance period for the whole works. As a result the contractor has a substantial period of grace, but (in contrast to cl. 59A (6)) may then have to pay first and stand out of his money until he has taken all necessary steps and proceedings and recovered from the sub-contractor, or failed to recover so that he is entitled to repayment from the employer under this clause.

It is not at all clear why "*subject to Clause* 60 (7)" is included since that sub-clause (so far as it could be relevant at all) merely duplicates the proviso at the end of this sub-clause.

17. "SUCH OTHER LOSS EXPENSE AND DAMAGE AS THE EMPLOYER MAY HAVE SUFFERED IN CONSEQUENCE OF THE BREACH OF THE SUB-CONTRACT". "*the breach of the sub-contract*" is not defined, and there may be many breaches of the sub-contract in the history of the works. The breach giving rise to the forfeiture is intended, and the employer recovers from the contractor in the ordinary way for any other breach of the main contract caused by a breach of the sub-contract, subject to cl. 59A (6). The difficulty remains that if the forfeiture is, e.g., under cl. 17 (1) (d) of the F.C.E.C. blue form of sub-contract by reason of the liquidation of the sub-contractor itself, there is no breach of the sub-contract involved and the strange result is that on this wording the employer has no right to recover his expenses. In such a case the employer can only refuse to consent to forfeiture for the liquidation itself and try to persuade the contractor to wait to forfeit for the delay or default with the works which is likely to occur as a result of the liquidation.

18. "IRRECOVERABLE BY REASON OF SOME BREACH OF THE SUB-CONTRACT OR OTHER DEFAULT TOWARDS THE SUB-CONTRACTOR BY THE CONTRACTOR". If the contractor serves a forfeiture notice when he is not entitled to do so under the sub-contract, he may fail to recover from the sub-contractor the expenses claimed from him by the employer because the sub-contractor will have a right to counter-claim for damages due to him for this breach of the sub-contract. In that case under the words at the head of this note and cl. 59A (5) (a) (N. 8) the main contractor loses the right to recover from the employer to that extent, even if the forfeiture was by direction or with consent of the employer.

19. "TO THE EXTENT THAT ANY ACT OR DEFAULT OF THE CONTRACTOR MAY HAVE CAUSED OR CONTRIBUTED TO ANY OF THE EMPLOYER'S LOSS". Refer to p. 247, N. 23.

20. IF A FORFEITURE NOTICE IS GIVEN WITHOUT EMPLOYER'S CONSENT AND IN BREACH OF SUB-CONTRACT "EMPLOYER SHALL BE ENTITLED TO RECOVER FROM THE CONTRACTOR ANY ADDITIONAL EXPENSE ... BEYOND THAT WHICH HE WOULD HAVE INCURRED HAD THE SUB-CONTRACT NOT BEEN TERMINATED",

e.g. provable costs of delay due to the forfeiture (the liquidated damages in the main contract do not apply), legal expenses, extra payment to get the sub-contract work completed, etc.

If the sub-contractor was in breach of the sub-contract, although not sufficiently so to justify forfeiture, the employer's right to recover from the main contractor damages for that breach, as opposed to his losses from the wrongful forfeiture, is still subject to cl. 59A (6).

21. STEPS BY CONTRACTOR TO RECOVER EMPLOYER'S LOSS. Refer to p. 246, N. 23.

PAYMENT TO NOMINATED SUB-CONTRACTORS

59C.[1] Before issuing any certificate under Clause 60[2] the Engineer shall be entitled to demand from the Contractor reasonable proof that all sums (less retentions provided for in the sub-contract) included in previous certificates in respect of the work executed or goods or materials or services supplied by Nominated Sub-contractors have been paid to the Nominated Sub-contractors or discharged by the Contractor in default whereof[3] unless the Contractor shall:

    (a) give details to the Engineer in writing of any reasonable cause he may have for withholding or refusing to make such payment;[4] and

    (b) produce to the Engineer reasonable proof that he has so informed such Nominated Sub-contractor in writing;

the Employer shall be entitled to pay to such Nominated Sub-contractor direct[5] upon the certification of the Engineer all payments (less retentions provided for in the sub-contract)[6] which the Contractor has failed to make to such Nominated Sub-contractor and to deduct[7] by way of set-off the amount so paid by the Employer from any sums due or which become due from the Employer to the Contractor. Provided always that where the Engineer has certified and the Employer has paid direct as aforesaid the Engineer shall in issuing any further certificate in favour of the Contractor deduct[7] from the amount thereof the amount so paid direct as aforesaid but shall not withhold or delay the issue of the certificate itself when due to be issued under the terms of the Contract.[8]

1. DIRECT PAYMENT TO NOMINATED SUB-CONTRACTORS. A clause in the main contract giving the employer the right to pay them direct is an important security to nominated sub-contractors. If there is no direct payment clause the employer must pay any money due for a sub-contractor's work to the liquidator of the main contractor, and the sub-contractor's only right is to prove for a dividend in the liquidation as an ordinary creditor.

This clause, which is very limited (N. 3), must be followed strictly before direct payment may be made, otherwise the employer will have no right to deduct the amount paid from payments to the main contractor. Nevertheless the engineer may have a moral duty to protect sub-contractors nominated by him, or it may be necessary to do so to induce them to finish their sub-contract work after forfeiture of the main contract. Unfortunately a recent decision has cast some doubt on the validity of this clause to entitle the employer to make direct payment after the contractor has gone into

(q) *British Eagle International Airlines Ltd.* v. *Compagnie Nationale Air France* [1975] 2 All E.R. 391. The decision was about a clearing house system between airlines, and earlier decisions (particularly *re Tout and Finch* [1954] 1 All E.R. 127) specifically upholding the right to make direct payment under a clause such as this notwithstanding bankruptcy or

q

liquidation (but not to deduct after liquidation the amount of a direct payment already made beforehand). It is suggested that in view of the special considerations applying to this clause the doubt would be resolved in favour of upholding the clause. If agreement cannot be reached with the main contractor or receiver or liquidator, the engineer may advise the employer that before making direct payment he should require a form of indemnity from the sub-contractor promising to repay the money if the direct payment is found to be wrongful, if necessary backed by a bond at the sub-contractor's expense.

2. EXTENSION OF THE EMPLOYER'S RIGHT TO MAKE DIRECT PAYMENT. Because the limitation in the 4th edition of these Conditions that direct payment may be made only before issuing "*any certificate which includes any amount in respect of . . . any Nominated Sub-contractor*" is omitted, the employer may now pay direct the last payment certified for a nominated sub-contractor. In addition the payments included in certificates, in respect of which the right of direct payment applies, have been increased by cl. 60 (2). Direct payment may also be facilitated by the requirement in cl. 60 of separate listing in progress statements and certificates of payments due to nominated sub-contractors.

Unfortunately, because there is no further "*certificate under Clause* 60" after forfeiture (cl. 63 (4)), direct payment may not be made unless before the forfeiture a demand for proof of payment had already been made prior to issue of a cl. 60 certificate, so as to comply with the opening of this clause. *See also* N. 1.

3. PRIOR DEFAULT BY THE CONTRACTOR. The necessity for prior default by the contractor lessens the protection to sub-contractors. Every payment must first be made to the contractor, or his trustee in bankruptcy or liquidator, so that in paying direct the employer must rely on his right to recoup himself from money becoming payable to the contractor in later certificates. If there is any immediate danger that he may have to take all or part of the works out of the contractor's hands (cls. 63, 39 (2) and 49 (4)), or once that is done, since the plant, etc., retention and payments due to the contractor may not be sufficient to recoup the employer's expenses and damages in completing the works, the employer may not be inclined to add to those expenses by payments direct to sub-contractors for work for which the main contractor has already been paid. *See also* N. 7.

4. "THE CONTRACTOR SHALL . . . GIVE DETAILS . . . OF ANY REASONABLE CAUSE . . . FOR WITHHOLDING OR REFUSING . . . PAYMENT". This alteration partly meets the difficulty under the previous edition that if the contractor informed the engineer that he had reasonable cause for withholding or refusing payment, the engineer apparently had no right to verify that this was so in fact. Under this new wording the employer may make direct payment if either the contractor gives no details or the details he gives do

---

liquidation of the main contractor were not mentioned. The decision was that it was against public policy to distribute the debtor's assets other than equally amongst the unsecured creditors in accordance with the Companies Act 1948. The fact that this clause is for the benefit of the employer as much as of the sub-contractor who receives the payment and the importance for the system of nominated sub-contracting of this long standing system of direct payment, with its careful limitations, suggest that public policy is on the side of upholding the clause.

not amount to reasonable cause—i.e. are not "*details . . . of any reasonable cause*". A reasonable cause might be a counter-claim for delay caused by the sub-contractor (p. 221) or special credit terms agreed. If the engineer has evidence that the details given are inaccurate so that they are not details of a factual reasonable cause but only of an imaginary cause for withholding payment, then it appears that the employer also may validly make direct payment, but obviously he should be wary of doing so except in a clear case (N. 1).

5. "THE EMPLOYER SHALL BE ENTITLED TO PAY . . . DIRECT". The employer has a personal discretion; he is not bound to pay direct on the engineer's certificate. Even if it were provided here that the employer shall pay direct, a sub-contractor would not be entitled to enforce direct payment, since he is not a party to the main contract (p. 221).

6. DIRECT PAYMENT LESS RETENTIONS "PROVIDED FOR IN THE SUB-CONTRACT". These new words recognise that it is the terms of the sub-contract and not of the main contract which govern the deduction of retention from a sub-contractor. The sub-contractor's share of the main contract retention cannot be the subject of direct payment if not paid over to him by the main contractor on release, because it is released under these Conditions with but not in certificates.

7. DEDUCTION AND DIRECT PAYMENT AS AGAINST SURETY. The only way in which the employer is entitled to recover direct payments to sub-contractors from the main contractor is by deduction against money due or to become due to the main contractor. The employer has no right to sue the main contractor for sums paid direct.

The employer may make direct payment by deduction, even though it leaves him with less money to finish the works and as a consequence increases the amount recoverable by him from a bondsman. But, as above, the employer cannot pay out to sub-contractors more than he holds and recover the balance from the guarantor.

8. SUB-CONTRACTOR'S OTHER REMEDIES. If the contractor does not pay over money due to the sub-contractor which he has received, the sub-contractor may, of course, sue for payment. The sub-contractor may also be entitled to stop work (p. 426), but to do so has dangers: if the threat to stop work does not persuade the main contractor to pay up, actual stoppage may entitle the employer to forfeit the contract. That may speed on the main contractor's liquidation, in which the sub-contractor may lose the payments which the main contractor has already received for him.

Under the sub-contract form of the Federation of Association of Specialists and Sub-Contractors the sub-contractor also has certain trust rights over money received for him by the main contractor. These rights can be particularly useful in the case of a receivership or liquidation of the main contractor. They are not included in the standard sub-contract form published by the F.C.E.C. for use with these Conditions.

CHAPTER 7

Conditions Clauses 60–65

MONTHLY STATEMENTS

60. (1) The Contractor shall submit to the Engineer after the end of each month a statement (in such form if any as may be prescribed in the Specification)[1] showing:

    (a) the estimated contract value of the Permanent Works executed up to the end of that month;

    (b) a list of any goods or materials delivered to the Site for but not yet incorporated in the Permanent Works and their value;

    (c) a list of any goods or materials listed in the Appendix to the Form of Tender which have not yet been delivered to the Site but of which the property has vested in the Employer pursuant to Clause 54 and their value;

    (d) the estimated amounts to which the Contractor considers himself entitled in connection with all other matters for which provision is made under the Contract[2] including any Temporary Works or Constructional Plant for which separate amounts are included in the Bill of Quantities;[3]

unless in the opinion of the Contractor such values and amounts together will not justify the issue of an interim certificate.

    Amounts payable in respect of Nominated Sub-contractors are to be listed separately.[4]

MONTHLY PAYMENTS

    (2) Within 28 days of the date of delivery to the Engineer or Engineer's Representative in accordance with sub-clause (1) of this Clause of the Contractor's monthly statement the Engineer shall certify[5] and the Employer shall pay to the Contractor[6] (after deducting any previous payments on account):

    (a) the amount which in the opinion of the Engineer[7] on the basis of the monthly statement[8] is due to the Contractor on account of sub-clause (1)(a) and (d) of this Clause less a retention as provided in sub-clause (4) of this Clause;

    (b) such amounts (if any) as the Engineer may consider proper (but in no case exceeding the percentage of the value stated in the Appendix to the Form of Tender) in respect of (b) and (c) of sub-clause (1) of this Clause[9] which amounts shall not be subject to a retention under sub-clause (4) of this Clause.[10]

The amounts certified in respect of Nominated Sub-contracts shall be shown separately in the certificate.[11] The Engineer shall not be bound to issue an interim certificate for a sum less than that named in the Appendix to the Form of Tender.[12]

FINAL ACCOUNT

    (3) Not later than 3 months after the date of the Maintenance Certificate the Contractor shall submit to the Engineer a statement of final account[13] and

supporting documentation showing in detail the value[14] in accordance with the Contract of the work done in accordance with the Contract together with all further sums which the Contractor considers to be due to him under the Contract up to the date of the Maintenance Certificate.[15] Within 3 months after receipt of this final account and of all information reasonably required for its verification[16] the Engineer shall issue a final certificate stating the amount which in his opinion is finally due under the Contract up to the date of the Maintenance Certificate and after giving credit to the Employer for all amounts previously paid by the Employer and for all sums to which the Employer is entitled under the Contract[17] up to the date of the Maintenance Certificate[15] the balance if any due from the Employer to the Contractor or from the Contractor to the Employer as the case may be. Such balance shall subject to Clause 47[18] be paid to or by the Contractor as the case may require within 28 days of the date of the certificate.[19]

RETENTION

(4) The retention to be made pursuant to sub-clause (2) (a) of this Clause shall be a sum equal to 5 per cent of the amount due to the Contractor until a reserve shall have accumulated in the hand of the Employer up to the following limits:

- (a) where the Tender Total does not exceed £50,000 5 per cent of the Tender Total but not exceeding £1,500; or
- (b) where the Tender Total exceeds £50,000 3 per cent of the Tender Total;[20]

except that the limit shall be reduced by the amount of any payment that shall have been made pursuant to sub-clause (5) of this Clause.

PAYMENT OF RETENTION MONEY

(5) (a) If the Engineer shall issue a Certificate of Completion in respect of any Section or part of the Works pursuant to Clause 48 (2) or (3)[21] there shall become due on the date of issue of such certificate and shall be paid to the Contractor within 14 days[22] thereof a sum equal to $1\frac{1}{2}$ per cent of the amount due to the Contractor at that date in respect of such Section or part as certified for payment pursuant to sub-clause (2) of this Clause.[23]

(b) One half of the retention money less any sums paid pursuant to sub-clause (5) (a) of this Clause shall be paid to the Contractor within 14 days after the date on which the Engineer shall have issued a Certificate of Completion for the whole of the Works pursuant to Clause 48 (1).[22]

(c) The other half of the retention money shall be paid to the Contractor within 14 days after the expiration of the Period of Maintenance[24] notwithstanding that at such time there may be outstanding claims by the Contractor against the Employer. Provided always that if at such time there shall remain to be executed by the Contractor any outstanding work referred to under Clause 48 or any works ordered during such period pursuant to Clauses 49 and 50 the Employer shall be entitled to withhold payment until the completion of such works[25] of so much of the second half of retention money as shall in the opinion of the Engineer represent the cost of the works so remaining to be executed.[26,27]

Provided further that in the event of different maintenance periods having become applicable to different Sections or parts of the Works pursuant to Clause 48 the expression "expiration of the Period of Maintenance" shall for the purposes of this sub-clause be deemed to mean the expiration of the latest of such periods.[24]

1. CONTRACTOR'S STATEMENTS AFTER THE END OF EACH MONTH "IN THE FORM ... PRESCRIBED IN THE SPECIFICATION". Month means calender month, not

a   every 31 days after commencement of the works, which may be important for calculation of cost fluctuations under any price fluctuation formula—p. 316.

For the minimum requirements of a statement and the importance of prescribing a form in the specification *see* N. 5.

This sub-clause says that the contractor "*shall submit to the Engineer*" the monthly statement, but sub-cl. (2) refers to delivery of the statement to the Engineer "*or Engineer's Representative in accordance with sub-clause* (1) *of this Clause*". The Contractor is entitled to the benefit of the ambiguity so that the time for certification will run from delivery to a resident engineer.

N. 27 deals with the problem of interim certificates and the maintenance period.

2. PAYMENT FOR "ALL OTHER MATTERS FOR WHICH PROVISION IS MADE UNDER THE CONTRACT" is now to be included in interim and the final payment certificates, and subject to retention.

Damages for breach of contract (*see* e.g. pp. 364 and 418) are not paid "*under the Contract*" and are therefore not included in certificates or subject to retention. In law the damages are payable immediately they are suffered, but the procedure in cl. 66 applies to any dispute.

The contractor is entitled to have included in a certificate any part of a claim substantiated, even if the rest of the claim is unsubstantiated—cl. 52 (4) (f).

For a possible disadvantage to the employer of delay in certifying a claim, under the price variation formula, *see* p. 319, N. 7.

3. CERTIFICATES INCLUDING AMOUNTS DUE FOR "ANY TEMPORARY WORKS OR CONSTRUCTIONAL PLANT FOR WHICH SEPARATE AMOUNTS ARE INCLUDED IN THE BILL OF QUANTITIES". For definitions *see* cl. 1 (1) (k) and (o). The amount to which the contractor is entitled in interim certificates "*in connection with*" temporary works or constructional plant will depend entirely on the precise words of the bill item. For example, if the item is for mobilisation of plant then the full amount will be due when the plant is placed on site. Items of this kind therefore should be very carefully worded (and method-related charges scrutinised—p. 219) so that they make clear when interim payment is due, to prevent, e.g., plant being brought on site prematurely to obtain payment.

4. "AMOUNTS PAYABLE IN RESPECT OF NOMINATED SUB-CONTRACTORS ... LISTED SEPARATELY". This listing may facilitate direct payment of a nominated sub-contractor under cl. 59C.

5. "WITHIN 28 DAYS OF THE DATE OF DELIVERY ... OF THE CONTRACTOR'S MONTHLY STATEMENT THE ENGINEER SHALL CERTIFY AND THE EMPLOYER SHALL PAY THE AMOUNT". If the engineer does not certify within this new time limit the contractor may become entitled to interest (p. 267, N. 28).

(*a*) Interpretation Act 1978, section 5 and Sch. 1. "A calender month ends upon the day in the next ensuing month having the same number as that on which the computation began, but if the next ensuing month has no day which has the same number as that on which the computation began, then the calender month ends on the last day of the next ensuing month": Norton on Deeds, 2nd ed. p. 174.

In exceptional cases the contractor may be entitled to end the contract for breach of this commandment to the engineer: suggested examples are where the engineer repeatedly and appreciably over-runs the period for certification due to administrative inefficiency or shortage of staff, or as a matter of policy or influence by the employer certifies substantially less than the full sums which he believes to be due (for the principle that applies *see* p. 418).

Note that this new period for certifying and paying is stated as a maximum, and there is no reason why the engineer should not certify well within the time where possible.

As to what constitutes a "*Contractor's monthly statement*" so as to start the time limit running, it is submitted that to "show" the contract value as specified in the opening of this clause the statement must calculate the estimated contract value of permanent work by reference to detailed quantities and rates. Reference in sub-cl. (1) (d) to the amounts (in the plural) of the contractor's claims suggests that each claim also must be stated separately, and by cl. 52 (4) (f) the engineer is only bound to certify claims for which "*sufficient particulars*" have been given. A form of statement should be prescribed in the specification, as allowed for here.

The "*estimated*" value and amounts referred to are specifically in the case of claims and by implication in respect of the value of the works, the contractor's estimates—so that the fact that the contractor's estimate is wrong will not invalidate a statement unless the errors are so gross as to prevent it deserving the description of a statement within this clause.

If the contractor's statement falls substantially short of these requirements, then the engineer is not bound to issue his certificate until the deficiencies in it are made good, but should draw the contractor's attention to them.

There is a key on pp. 354–5 to the various time limits under this clause.

6. "AND THE EMPLOYER SHALL PAY". For interest if he does not *see* sub-cl. (6). For deductions by the employer *see* N. 33.

There is still in this edition no clear-cut right given to the contractor to end the contract for the employer's failure to pay, as there is included in the F.I.D.I.C. International Form. *See* p. 425 for the general law.

There is no provision for repayment by the contractor to the employer where an interim certificate produces a balance due to the employer because too much has been certified and paid under a previous certificate. As it is established that a prior certificate is subject to adjustment (sub-cl. (7) and on principle) it is suggested that the duty of the contractor to repay on a negative interim certificate must be implied and the employer need not wait for recovery until the final certificate. Nevertheless there is danger for the engineer in failing to make a precise calculation in reliance on the right to adjust a valuation in a later certificate (p. 398).

7. "THE AMOUNT WHICH IN THE OPINION OF THE ENGINEER". The contractor or employer may dispute the engineer's opinion under cl. 66 and in arbitration, but the employer must pay up unless and until he obtains a decision altering the certificate, subject to counterclaim (N. 33) or correction of a certificate (N. 34). In many cases the contractor (but not the employer) may go to arbitration before completion of the works, *see* pp. 304–7.

8. "ON THE BASIS OF THE MONTHLY STATEMENT". It appears from these words that generally the engineer is not bound to go outside the matters dealt with in a statement, in assessing value for an interim certificate. It is suggested nevertheless that if he realises that an item which is due is omitted from a monthly statement, he should include the amount in his certificate and the contractor will be entitled to interest under sub-cl. (6) if he does not. The valuation is to be based on the statement, not absolutely restricted to matters in it. Alternatively if the statement is seriously defective the engineer may give the contractor an opportunity to withdraw the statement and replace it with a corrected version, in which case the 28 days for the certificate and payment will run from delivery of the replacement. The contractor should be careful to include all claims in his statement—N. 2.

9. "SUCH AMOUNTS (IF ANY) AS THE ENGINEER MAY CONSIDER PROPER ... (NOT) EXCEEDING THE PERCENTAGE ... STATED IN THE APPENDIX ... IN RESPECT OF" GOODS OR MATERIALS DELIVERED TO SITE. If he thinks proper, the engineer may certify nothing or less than the stated percentage of the full value for such goods. Why and when he should do so is not indicated, but premature delivery of materials to the site would be very relevant. For possible reduction of the percentage to prevent the contractor recovering too much under the price fluctuations formula see p. 318.

Much the most important case in which the engineer may refuse to certify for goods or materials on site is where their ownership is affected by a retention of title clause.

a'   Because the courts have held the reservation to be effective, it has become common for manufacturers and suppliers to include in their conditions of sale a clause saying that they retain ownership of the goods notwithstanding delivery, until the goods have been paid for or sometimes until all debts due by the buyer to the seller have been paid. As a result, unless the engineer is careful the employer may pay for goods in a certificate but nevertheless have to buy them a second time after forfeiture of the contractor's employment if the supplier claims them back under a clause of this kind. The engineer has a duty to verify that either no such clause applies or no debt within the clause is due by the contractor: often that will be done most conveniently and safely by requiring the contractor to obtain written confirmation to the engineer direct from the seller.

"Site" as defined by cl. 1 (1) (n) may (p. 30, N. 13) include places where the contractor's temporary works alone are being executed, but the

(a') Aluminium Industrie Vaassen B.V. v. Remalpa Aluminium Ltd. [1976] 2 All E.R. 552, C.A.

By section 25 (2) of the Sale of Goods Act 1893 "where a person having bought or agreed to buy goods obtains, with the consent of the seller, possession of the goods or the documents of title to the goods, the delivery or transfer by the person ... of the goods or documents of title, under any disposition thereof, to any person receiving the same in good faith and without notice ... of any right of the original seller in respect of the goods ...", passes ownership of the goods notwithstanding any retention of title clause in the agreement with the seller. However, the employer or engineer on his behalf may well have notice of a retention clause. In addition the goods are usually delivered not to the employer but to the contractor himself who is in possession of the site, so that the section may not operate at all for the benefit of the employer (the "transfer" which is stated as an alternative to delivery to the person relying on the section may refer only to transfer of a document of title and there will be no such transfer to the employer).

Fortunately ownership passes to the employer as soon as the goods are actually built into the works, notwithstanding any reservation of title—Reynolds v. Ashby [1904] App. Cas. 406.

engineer presumably will rarely "*consider proper*" under this paragraph that the value of goods or materials delivered to such places should be included in interim certificates.

Refer to p. 200 on the importance of following the procedure under cl. 54 in respect of goods and materials off site.

10. NO RETENTION FROM PAYMENT FOR GOODS OR MATERIALS NOT YET INCORPORATED IN THE WORKS. Since the goods and materials will become subject to retention when incorporated in the works, a retention at this stage would be inappropriate.

11. "AMOUNTS CERTIFIED IN RESPECT OF NOMINATED SUB-CONTRACTS ... SHOWN SEPARATELY IN THE CERTIFICATE". This separation may facilitate direct payment to the sub-contractors under cl. 59C. The amount should be stated gross, before deduction of retention—p. 257, N. 6.

12. MINIMUM AMOUNT OF INTERIM CERTIFICATE. *See* N. 27, p. 266. By saying that the engineer is not "*bound to issue*" an interim certificate for less than the minimum, this sentence implies that he may nevertheless do so if he wishes—which may be convenient and just, for example, to deal with a small balance at the time of substantial completion (*also see* p. 319).

13. "NOT LATER THAN 3 MONTHS AFTER THE DATE OF THE MAINTENANCE CERTIFICATE THE CONTRACTOR SHALL SUBMIT ... FINAL ACCOUNT". Because the payments to be included in interim certificates have been greatly extended, in theory there should be very little extra money due to the contractor on the final account. If contractors deliver proper and full monthly statements and insist on their right to full certification on time; if arbitrators use their power to make it clear to contractors that notices of and details of claims under cl. 52 (4) must be given in time so that claims can be dealt with as the works proceed; if all engineers perform their duties by dealing with claims as they arise and not as a matter almost of policy rejecting them in the first instance (which also may cost the employer money under the price variation formula, p. 319, N. 7, and even the engineer money in an action by the contractor, p. 398)—then there may be improvement in the time taken for contractors to obtain payment (which should be reflected in lower prices for employers).

"*months*" means calender months (N. 1).

There is no sanction for delay in submitting the final account, except delay in payment and possibly loss under cl. 52 (4) of claims made in the account for the first time. An addition is sometimes made to this clause empowering the engineer to issue a final certificate without waiting for the contractor's final statement where it is delayed, since the employer may have an interest in finalising the contract accounts, particularly before staff are dispersed.

The final account is to be delivered "*Not later*" than the specified time—it may be submitted earlier—but by implication from the rest of this clause, not before the maintenance certificate.

14. "A STATEMENT OF FINAL ACCOUNT AND SUPPORTING DOCUMENTATION SHOWING IN DETAIL THE VALUE". Failure to include sufficient or accurate documentation or detail may prevent the start of the time-limit for certification.

The information to which the engineer is entitled under this provision will depend partly on the way in which the contractor's account is formulated, particularly claims. For example, if a claim purports to be built up on a breakdown of the contractor's original tender rates, the engineer is entitled to full information about relevant rates, and may be entitled to demand to see the relevant parts of the original estimating papers as "*supporting documentation showing ... the value*". In the battle which sometimes develops for proper information the engineer's hand is strengthened by this clause. And if he considers that he has not received full and accurate information, he need not certify for the claim involved and the contractor's remedy is arbitration, in which all the contractor's original documents will have to be produced on an order for discovery (p. 298).

15. "UP TO THE DATE OF THE MAINTENANCE CERTIFICATE". The account between contractor and employer may alter after the maintenance certificate, for indemnities e.g. under cl. 22, and common law damages for defective work (p. 427). The contract remains in force for the purpose of regulating such obligations (*see* cl. 61).

16. FINAL CERTIFICATE "WITHIN 3 MONTHS . . . OF THIS FINAL ACCOUNT AND OF ALL INFORMATION REASONABLY REQUIRED FOR ITS VERIFICATION". For a key to the various time limits for certificates, payments, etc., *see* pp. 354 5.

The engineer is in a position to extend the time for considering the final account by reasonably asking for more information.

This final certificate now takes the place of the maintenance certificate as the last exercise of power by the engineer specifically provided for in the contract. For the position of the engineer after it *see* p. 274, N. 2.

17. "FINAL CERTIFICATE STATING . . . AFTER GIVING CREDIT . . . FOR ALL SUMS TO WHICH THE EMPLOYER IS ENTITLED UNDER THE CONTRACT . . . THE BALANCE . . . DUE", e.g. deducting payments due to the employer under cl. 39 (2) or liquidated damages under cl. 47, but not damages under the general law for breach of contract (pp. 427 30). Save under cl. 59C the final certificate is the only one in which credit for such sums is to be allowed within the certificate itself. In the case of other certificates the engineer should notify the employer that any such deductions due may be made against the amount certified. Deductions against certificates are dealt with generally in N. 33.

The draftsman has forgotten to say that amounts due to nominated sub-contractors are to be listed separately in this certificate, as he does for interim certificates. Nevertheless the engineer should do so, particularly in view of cl. 60 (7).

The engineer's wide potential liability for a negligent certificate to the employer, contractor or even third parties is the subject of a discussion from p. 386.

18. "SUBJECT TO CLAUSE 47". Since both liquidated damages under cl. 47 (1) (4) and a refund under cl. 47(5) are sums "*due under the Contract*" or to which "*the Employer is entitled under the Contract*" and therefore already to be included in calculating the final certificate under this sub-clause, it is not clear why cl. 47 is also mentioned as a further deduction from the balance certified.

19. "SUCH BALANCE SHALL . . . BE PAID TO OR BY THE CONTRACTOR . . . WITHIN 28 DAYS OF THE DATE OF THE CERTIFICATE". Interest may be recoverable on late payment—N. 28 and 29. By cl. 60 (7) the engineer may correct or change a certificate, and a party who disputes a certificate has a right to arbitration via an engineer's decision under cl. 66. The contractor in most cases has a right under that clause to arbitration before completion, but not the employer. The employer may defend proceedings for recovery of a balance by a bona fide claim that the certificate is not in accordance with the contract or that he has a right of counterclaim—N. 33. For interest in favour of the employer on overpayment *see* N. 32.

20. RETENTION AND LIMIT OF RETENTION. The tendency in recent years has been to reduce the amount of retention, because the number of cases is small in which the retention has to be used by the employer, and the employer in the contract price pays the contractor's costs of financing the retention fund. The limits in this clause are quite low. Obviously £1,500 will not go far in the case of seriously defective work, or towards the extra cost of employing another contractor to finish works after forfeiture. The retention may be further reduced by partial release (*see* the next note).

21. PARTIAL RELEASE OF RETENTION ON CERTIFICATE OF COMPLETION OF SECTION OR PART. A serious fault in the previous edition is rectified by this provision for partial release of retention (but of the first half only, N. 24).

22. DELAY IN PAYMENT OF RETENTION. For interest *see* p. 267, N. 28, and for the contractor's right to end the contract in an exceptional case, p. 426 (unlikely to be very helpful at this late stage).

23. "$1\frac{1}{2}$ PER CENT OF THE AMOUNT DUE TO THE CONTRACTOR . . . IN RESPECT OF SUCH SECTION OR PART AS CERTIFIED FOR PAYMENT PURSUANT TO SUB-CLAUSE (2) OF THIS CLAUSE". The phrase "*the amount due . . . as certified for payment pursuant to sub-clause (2) of this Clause*" is contradictory, since by cl. 60 (2) the amount certified is "*the amount . . . due . . . less a retention*". Presumably what is intended is $1\frac{1}{2}\%$ of the amount due for the part of the works before deduction of retention, but that is not what is said.

As a result of increases in value of a section or part under any price fluctuation formula in the contract (assuming that retention is calculated on price fluctuations, p. 317) $1\frac{1}{2}\%$ of the amount certified for the section or part may be a disproportionate deduction from the overall retention fund, which is limited to 3% of the original tender total, but see now the January 1979 revision of these Conditions.

24. RELEASE OF SECOND HALF OF THE RETENTION MONEY does not depend on the issue of the maintenance certificate, but is delayed entirely until the end of the last maintenance period as a result of the definition in the last paragraph of this sub-clause. There is now partial release of the first half of the retention (N. 21).

25. "UNTIL THE COMPLETION OF SUCH WORKS". There is no further maintenance period or retention for this work.

26. "THE COST OF THE WORKS". Presumably the estimated cost of having

the work done by another contractor under cl. 49 (4) in case that should be necessary, not the contract value of such work (contrast the reference to "*value*" in cl. 49 (3) with this clause). The possibility of maintenance work remaining to be done by the contractor for which the employer is liable to pay him at the contract rates (cl. 49 (3)) has apparently been overlooked by the draftsman. On the literal wording the engineer may withhold the full cost in this case also, which is probably reasonable in order to put pressure on the contractor to finish minor work.

27. RETENTION WHERE THE CONTRACTOR DOES NOT COMPLETE THE WORKS. There is a general rule of law that if a contractor agrees to build a complete works, in the absence of special agreement he is entitled to payment only if he finishes substantially the whole works:

> A contractor abandoned a contract when he had three-quarters completed the contract buildings, and the employer completed the work.
> Held: The contractor could recover nothing for the work he had done. He was not entitled to any payment under the original contract because he had not completed the contract work. A new contract to pay for the work could not be implied merely because the employer had completed the buildings, since he was not obliged to go to the expense of removing the buildings or leave them on his land in a state in which they were a nuisance.

This rule, of course, generally is no longer important, because of the provision for interim payments as the work progresses, but a relic of the rule may remain under this clause. If the employer validly ends the contract under the general law because of the contractor's default (p. 425) before the contractor substantially completes the works, the contractor may not be entitled to recover any part of the retention money, since under this clause it only becomes payable after the engineer certifies substantial completion. This is an odd result, since if the employer forfeits under cl. 63 he must account for the retention money, and it has been held that any clause expressly allowing him to keep the retention money is void as a penalty (p. 150). Therefore occasionally it may be to the employer's advantage to end the contract under the general law rather than forfeiting under cl. 63, although usually there will be greater disadvantages—*see* p. 276, N. 1.

In any case, if the employer has to sue the contractor for further damages for failure to complete, he must give credit for any retention money which he holds. It is also settled that the contractor will be entitled to the retention money (apart from other compensation) when substantial completion is prevented by the employer, e.g. by failing to give the contractor possession of the site.

It is a possible corollary to the rule discussed in this note that after substantial completion the contractor is entitled to payment before the final certificate of any balance established as due, even if it is less than the minimum sum for an interim certificate (*see* in any case p. 263, N. 12). It is also arguable that any money earned after substantial completion, e.g.

(*b*) *Sumpter* v. *Hedges* [1898] 1 Q.B. 673 and see *Hoenig* v. *Isaacs* [1952] 2 All E.R. 176, C.A. These decisions were followed in *Bolton* v. *Mahadeva* [1972] 2 All E.R. 1322, C.A. where warmth in rooms was from 10% to 36% less than it should have been if a contract to install central heating for a lump sum had been performed properly, and the heating gave off fumes: Held that because the heating did not function properly there was no substantial completion and the contractor was not entitled to any part of the contract sum, although the cost of making good the defects was assessed by the trial judge at less than half that sum.

under cl. 49 (3), is similarly payable immediately—that although cl. 60 (1) and (2) do not say so specifically, interim certificates have no application to months after the contractor has established his basic right to payment for the works by achieving substantial completion. Indeed this clause assumes that there will be no payment certificate between substantial completion and the final certificate—it does not include any mechanism for deducting and repaying further retention after the first half has been released. But what if the certificate of substantial completion is given in the middle of a month?

Interest on Overdue Payments

60. (6) In the event of failure by the Engineer to certify or the Employer to make payment in accordance with sub-clauses (2), (3) and (5)[28] of this Clause the Employer shall pay to the Contractor interest[29] upon any payment overdue thereunder at a rate per annum equivalent to $\frac{3}{4}$ per cent plus the minimum rate at which the Bank of England will lend to a discount house having access to the Discount Office of the Bank[30] current on the date upon which such payment first becomes overdue. In the event of any variation in the said Bank Rate being announced whilst such payment remains overdue the interest payable to the Contractor for the period that such payment remains overdue shall be correspondingly varied from the date of each such variation.[31,32,33]

Correction and Withholding of Certificates

(7) The Engineer shall have power to omit from any certificate the value of any work done goods or materials supplied or services rendered with which he may for the time being be dissatisfied and for that purpose or for any other reason which to him may seem proper may by any certificate delete correct or modify any sum previously certified by him.[34,35]

Provided always that:

(a) the Engineer shall not in any interim certificate delete or reduce any sum previously certified in respect of work done goods or materials supplied or services rendered by a Nominated Sub-contractor if the Contractor shall have already paid or be bound to pay that sum to the Nominated Sub-contractor;

(b) if the Engineer in the final certificate shall delete or reduce any sum previously certified in respect of work done goods or materials supplied or services rendered by a Nominated Sub-contractor which sum shall have been already paid by the Contractor to the Nominated Sub-contractor the Employer shall reimburse to the Contractor the amount of any sum overpaid by the Contractor to the Sub-contractor in accordance with the certificates issued under sub-clause (2) of this Clause which the Contractor despite compliance with Clause 59B (6) shall be unable to recover from the Nominated Sub-contractor together with interest thereon at the rate stated in Clause 60 (6) from 28 days after the date of the final certificate issued under sub-clause (3) of this Clause until the date of such reimbursement.[36]

28. "IN THE EVENT OF FAILURE BY THE ENGINEER TO CERTIFY . . . IN ACCORDANCE WITH SUB-CLAUSES (2), (3) AND (5) . . . INTEREST". This specific right to interest for delay by the engineer in certifying is new and made practicable by new time limits (pp. 354–5). Interest is calculated on the

amount certified late by the engineer, or held by the engineer or arbitrator under cl. 66 to have been due for payment in or with a certificate.

There is an unfortunate drafting error. Sub-cls. (2) and (3) require the engineer to certify the amount in his "*opinion*" due to the contractor, so that it might be argued that there is a failure "*to certify . . . in accordance with sub-clauses (2), (3)*" so as to attract interest only when the engineer acts in bad faith by certifying less than is due in his own opinion, not merely when his opinion is later found to be wrong.

Since sub-cl. (5) of this clause does not specify when the certificate(s) of completion shall be given by the engineer (which is dealt with in cl. 48), under the words at the head of this note this specific right to interest does not apply to late issue of a certificate of completion so as to delay payment of retention money, but only to late payment of retention by the employer after certification.

It appears that interest under this sub-clause is itself to be included in interim certificates, as an amount due in connection with a matter "*for which provision is made under the Contract*" (cl. 60 (1) (d)), so that interest may become payable on interest. Apart from that case, on the words of this sub-clause and general principle only simple interest is payable   N. 30.

The statutory right to interest is dealt with in the next note.

29. STATUTORY RIGHT TO INTEREST ON OVERDUE CERTIFIED PAYMENTS. In addition to the right to interest discussed in the previous note, an arbitrator or court has by statute a general power to award interest. This power suffers from the disadvantages that it only arises in proceedings, so that a party in default may defeat it by paying without interest before judgment or award (but *see* p. 301, footnote (*r*)), and the rate of interest is at the discretion of the arbitrator (although there is normally no reason why an arbitrator should award less than the full commercial level).

Interest to the contractor on repayment of liquidated damages by the employer is dealt with in cl. 47 (5).

30. "RATE PER ANNUM EQUIVALENT TO $\frac{3}{4}$ PER CENT PLUS THE MINIMUM RATE AT WHICH THE BANK OF ENGLAND WILL LEND TO A DISCOUNT HOUSE", ETC. This minimum lending rate has taken the place of the old Bank Rate and is published weekly on Friday after close of business. The rate is itself usually about $\frac{1}{2}\%$ lower than the lowest lending rate of clearing banks to their customers, and is calculated as simple interest. This increase in the rate of interest should remove the temptation to which some employers have succumbed to hold up payment because the rate on the necessary borrowing would be higher than the rate previously payable to the contractor.

31. CONTRACTOR'S OTHER REMEDIES FOR NON-PAYMENT. In exceptional cases the contractor may be entitled to end the contract for failure by the engineer to certify or by the employer to pay in accordance with the contract—p. 425.

32. INTEREST IN FAVOUR OF EMPLOYER FOR OVERPAYMENT. There is no

(c) Law Reform (Miscellaneous Provisions) Act, 1934, Sec. 3 (1). There is useful information on the award of interest in the Law Commission Working Paper No. 86 of 1976.
(d) *The Medina Princess* [1962] 2 Lloyd's Rep. 17.

reference here to interest in favour of the employer if the amount of a
certificate is reduced under sub-cl. (7) or by the engineer or arbitrator under
cl. 66. Apart from the other disadvantages, the statutory right to interest
(N. 29) only applies in the period from the date when the cause of action for
the overpayment arises, which appears not to occur until the certificate is
corrected or the decision or award given.

33. DEDUCTIONS AND COUNTERCLAIM BY THE EMPLOYER AGAINST d
CERTIFICATES. In a previous edition of this book the law was stated to be
that the employer has the standard wide right to set off claims, for bad work,
delay or otherwise, against payment of certificates. For a time that account
of the law appeared to be wrong, following a spate of decisions by the Court
of Appeal creating what became known as the rule in *Dawnays* v. *Minter*, by e
which (on the grounds of the importance of cash flow to a contractor) the
right of set-off against certificates was severely limited. The supposed rule
has now been disowned by a majority in the House of Lords. Although the f
actual decision was on a special clause in a sub-contract, the case effectively
re-establishes the former law:

"Indeed, no scintilla of authority prior to the decision in the *Dawnays* case can
be found for the proposition that the amount certified by the architect in an
interim certificate as the value of work done, and consequently payable to the
contractor, is in a special position in that the employer cannot lawfully
counterclaim and set off against the liability amounts due to him from the
contractor." g

"My Lords, I accept the importance of 'cash flow' in the building industry. In
the vivid phrase of Lord Denning M.R.: 'it is the very lifeblood of the enterprise'.
But so it is of all commercial enterprises engaged in the business of selling goods
or undertaking work or labour.... It is also the lifeblood of the contractor
whose own cash flow has been reduced by the expense to which he has been put by
the sub-contractors' breaches of contract. It is not to be supposed that so
elementary an economic proposition as the need for cash flow in business
enterprises escaped the attention of judges throughout the 130 years ... (up to
the *Dawnays* decision)." h

Thus the substance of that decision is that claims to certified money,
whether by a main contractor or sub-contractor, are not in any special class
so far as the right of counterclaim is concerned, unless specially put there by
some term in the relevant contract. Where parties have claims and cross
claims against each other the general rule is that the courts will maintain the
status quo by giving no judgment until all the disputes can be heard fully and
resolved. Of course it is only the nominal *status quo* that is maintained;
given the time it takes in practice to reach a hearing, the reality is that a
contractor or sub-contractor, who does work on credit, may expire in the
meantime due to refusal by his employer in possession of the money to pay

(d') For convenience "counterclaim" is used alone in this book to embrace all crossclaims
whether or not giving a right to set-off. On the differences, not relevant to the issues discussed
here, see D. Keating "Building Contracts", 4th ed., p. 276.
(e) *Dawnays Ltd.* v. *F. G. Minter Ltd.* [1971] 2 All E.R. 1389 C.A., and seven subsequent Court
of Appeal decisions.
(f) In *Gilbert-Ash (Northern) Ltd.* v. *Modern Engineering (Bristol) Ltd.* [1973] 3 All E.R. 195,
H.L.
(g) *Gilbert-Ash*, per Viscount Dilhorne at p. 205.
(h) *Gilbert-Ash*, per Lord Diplock at pp. 215–16.

on the grounds of a doubtful or exaggerated counterclaim made as a way to extract a discount or help his cash flow:

> During charter of a motor vessel the market rate for the vessel fell, and the charterers tried various devices to escape from the charter. Eventually the owners sued them for four million dollars for hire as damages for wrongful repudiation of the hire contract. The charterers admitted liability but denied that the plaintiffs were entitled to the amount of damages claimed.
>
> Held: The whole claim for damages was in issue and therefore it could not be said that any definable or quantified part of the claim was not in fact in dispute. Therefore the plaintiffs were not entitled to immediate summary judgment for any sum, and the court proceedings would be stayed (text below p. 303 (b)), leaving the damages to be assessed in arbitration under the arbitration clause in the contract.
>
> Although in this case a counterclaim by the charterers had already been dismissed, a majority of the court made clear that the principle of the decision applies to the case where a claim is met by a counterclaim—that summary judgment is possible only for any part of the claim that is "indisputably due" despite the counterclaim—where "there is by admission, or can be by a decision of the court, a quantified sum as to which 'there is not in fact any dispute'". The majority affirmed that principle in discussing a previous court decision made between a sub-contractor and main contractor (the *Ellis* case below) with no suggestion that construction cases are in any special category.

A later rearguard attempt by admirers to resurrect the so-called *Dawnays* rule having failed, there are now only the following protections against abuse of the right to counterclaim:

(a) Quick summary judgment may be obtained in the courts for an amount which is "*indisputably due*" because a counterclaim is not bona fide and arguable:

> Main contractors retained a large sum of retention money against sub-contractors, out of an amount certified for the main contractors in an interim certificate under the main contract. The sub-contractors claimed and obtained summary judgment for the retention.
>
> The main contractors had sought leave to defend the whole claim on the grounds that there was a great number of errors, or possible errors, in the sub-contractors' figures.
>
> "He (Counsel for the contractors) ... is making bricks without straw. He had not got a surveyor who had seen the work done, measured it or the like. He did, with much ingenuity, under the terms of the clauses and on the affidavits, seek to

---

(i) *Associated Bulk Carriers Ltd.* v. *Koch Shipping Inc.* [1978] 2 All E.R. 254, 263, 265, 266 C.A. Lord Denning M.R. dissenting.

(j) The attempted resurrection was based on microscopic academic examination of a decision of the House of Lords in *Mottram Consultants Ltd.* v. *Bernard Sunley & Sons Ltd.* [1975] 2 Lloyd's Rep. 197 and 2 B.L.R. 31, given after the *Gilbert-Ash* decision, and was maintained without argument by Lord Denning in his dissenting judgment in the *Koch* case (above). The reality is that in the *Mottram* decision all five of the Law Lords either delivered or agreed with judgments that emphasised that the *Dawnays* principle was decreased.

Having failed to apply the *Dawnays* decision when it was alive in its home jurisdiction, the Irish High Court has applied a ghostly version of it after its demise, in *John Sisk & Son* v. *D. Lawter Products B.V.* (unreported, judgment delivered 15th Nov. 1976). The judgment was based largely on the fact that the wording of the standard Irish building contract provides for specific deductions from interim certificates and restricts the right of the parties to refer disputes to arbitration until practical completion of the works. With respect the draftsman of a commercial contract might be surprised to learn that if he mentions specific deductions in some cases he will be held thereby to exclude the general right of counterclaim. By contrast in the *Mottram* decision the contract said that "*only*" specified deductions could be made. *See also* the *Gilbert-Ash* decision at p. 207.

raise first this suggestion and then that suggestion that the sums were too high.
But, looking at it in broad outline . . . it seems to me as plain as can be that at least
the sum of £52,137 is owing to the sub-contractors."

"The ordinary practice is that there must be some real basis, not a shadowy
basis, for showing that there is an issue worthy of investigation by the courts. The
defendant's answer comes to no more than 'We dispute the claim'. That is not
enough".   k

This last decision must be read in the light of the interpretation later
placed on it by the Court of Appeal itself in the *Koch* case discussed above.
The essential ingredient was that as retention money the amount claimed
was a quantified sum, and was indisputably due. A claim for unliquidated
damages for delay where the amount of the damages is in the dispute, is not
within the principle of the decision.

(*b*) A claim for money due under one contract cannot ordinarily be
defended by a counterclaim for money due under a different and
unconnected contract between the same parties. Some public authorities do   *l*
try to alter this rule by a special condition, because they will frequently have
several current contracts running with the one contractor.

(*c*) It has also been stated that if a party withholds a certified payment by
alleging a counterclaim and tries to defer the day of reckoning by relying on
the postponement of arbitration until after completion of the works, a court
may refuse to enforce the arbitration clause and allow the other party to
have the counterclaim dealt with by a court before completion. That relief is of   *m*
limited relevance under these Conditions because of the contractor's wide
right to arbitration before completion under cl. 66, but many large main
contractors in their own forms of sub-contract do try to defer the sub-
contractor's right to arbitration until completion of the main contract
works. In any case the relief does not solve the problem that even if   *n*
arbitration may be started before completion it will take some time to finish.

(*d*) In a decision that perhaps might be regarded as part of the rearguard
effort to resurrect *Dawnays*—

> Contractor obtained summary judgment on an interim certificate, although
> the employers disputed the right to payment on the grounds that it included sums
> for variations and extras not instructed in writing by their architect in
> accordance with the contract.
> Lord Denning said that—"So long as a certificate is good on the face of it and
> it was within the authority given by the contract, then it is in accordance with the
> conditions. It must be honoured. I do not think it is open to the employers or the
> contractors to challenge an interim certificate by saying that it is too much, or too
> little, or includes this or omits that, or that the extras were not sanctioned in
> writing. Such matters must be left till after the practical completion of the work".
> Both of the other members of the court decided the case merely on the grounds
> of lack of evidence and refrained from deciding the question of law involved.   *o*

(*e*) Turning specifically to these Conditions, counterclaims by the
employer fall into two classes: those that are supported by the engineer
(whether initially or after the employer points out some error he has made in

(*k*) *Ellis Mechanical Services Ltd* v. *Wates Construction Ltd*. (1976) 2 B.L.R. 60, C.A.
(*l*) *Ellis* decision above, p. 63. Special rules apply where the debtor is a company in
liquidation.
(*m*) *Gilbert-Ash* at p. 223.
(*n*) *See also* p. 431 below on the Unfair Contract Terms Act 1977.
(*o*) *Killby & Gayford Ltd.* v. *Selincourt Ltd.*, decided by the Court of Appeal in 1973 and
reported in 3 B.L.R. 104.

a previous certificate) and those that are not. The extent to which deductions in the first class are allowed for in certificates is dealt with in N. 17 on p. 264, and in respect of defective work in N. 34, below. Except in the rare case where the engineer can be shown to be disqualified or mistaken in principle (ch. 14), the engineer's support in this way should at least provide an arguable defence to an application by the contractor for summary judgment for the amount deducted by or in favour of the employer, unless and until the contractor persuades the engineer to reverse his views by a decision under cl. 66 or obtains a reversal in arbitration.

The employer is entitled to have a counterclaim considered in an engineer's and if necessary arbitrator's decision, and the engineer should act speedily if the employer can clearly establish that he has previously been in error, for example. Even if there is not time to obtain the decision before proceedings if the employer satisfies the court that there is a genuine dispute which he has submitted or is in the process of submitting to the engineer under cl. 66, it seems that the court should not give summary judgment to the contractor. If and as soon as the contractor receives a favourable decision from the engineer he may again proceed for summary judgment.

If the employer cannot persuade the engineer to support him, it seems that he cannot effectively counterclaim so as to prevent the contractor obtaining summary judgment on a certificate. By cl. 66 any dispute must first be "*settled by the Engineer*", and it appears that the engineer's decision binds the employer (p. 295, N. 6 (a)) unless and until reversed in arbitration. Thus despite the *Gilbert-Ash* decision, where these Conditions apply the contractor should have some protection in the shape of the engineer against abuse by the employer of the right to counterclaim.

34. ENGINEER'S POWER TO 'OMIT FROM ANY CERTIFICATE THE VALUE OF . . . WORK . . . WITH WHICH HE MAY FOR THE TIME BEING BE DISSATISFIED . . . DELETE CORRECT OR MODIFY ANY SUM PREVIOUSLY CERTIFIED". The first part of this phrase has become redundant; since publication of this edition of the Conditions the courts have confirmed that a contractor is entitled to be paid only for work properly done. This conclusion was reached in respect of the R.I.B.A. conditions of contract, but clearly applies to these Conditions where the "*contract value*" of the work is certified; for the purpose of the full revaluation made for each certificate work then known not to be in accordance with the contract does not have any or full contract value.

Refer to N. 32 on the question of interest in favour of the employer on reduction of a previous certificate.

An unanswered question is what is to happen if the engineer exercises in the final payment certificate (as he may do, *see* sub-cl. (7) (b)) this power to delete, etc., a sum previously certified. May the contractor make good defective work, where that is the reason for the adjustment, and recover the amount omitted? It seems not; that as soon as all work to be done under cl. 49 is completed the contractor has no right to enter on the site to do remedial work.

As a correction may be made only by certificate, the final payment certificate itself may not be altered by the engineer under this clause. The employer may in effect obtain an alteration by applying for a decision of the engineer and if necessary arbitration under cl. 66.

_o'_

(o') In the *Gilbert-Ash* decision, above.

The engineer is given power to delete or correct a sum previously settled *"for any other reason which to him may seem proper"*. This must be read as limited to cases where the sum should not be certified because it is not properly due under cl. 60; the engineer cannot be intended to have power to delete a large sum for a small breach of contract or it appears any sum because, e.g., the contractor has not delivered a programme on time. *See* the next note also.

For recovery of any balance due to the employer after correction of a previous certificate, *see* p. 261, N. 6.

It seems that the engineer may change a sum previously certified only if it is or has become wrong, not to change a rate for a variation agreed with the contractor or determined by the engineer after consultation and notified to the contractor under cl. 52 (1) that still stands, or a decision by a delegate under cl. 2, or a decision of the engineer himself under cl. 66.

A correction may be in favour of the contractor.

35. NO RIGHT TO WITHHOLD CERTIFICATES. Contrary to the mistaken marginal note to this sub-clause, the engineer's right in the previous edition to withhold certificates has been removed from this edition. This is a serious loss of control over the contractor in circumstances where it is often the case that forfeiture under cl. 63 is impracticable.

36. "THE ENGINEER SHALL NOT . . . DELETE OR REDUCE ANY SUM PREVIOUSLY CERTIFIED IN RESPECT OF . . . A NOMINATED SUB-CONTRACTOR . . . .". The scheme of this restriction is that if the engineer over-certifies in favour of a nominated sub-contractor and the contractor has already paid or become bound to pay the sub-contractor the amount over-certified, the engineer must allow the overpayment to stand until the final certificate. The correction may be made in the final certificate, but the contractor then has an independent right to recover from the employer the amount of the reduction (with interest), provided he has paid the sub-contractor and taken *"all necessary steps and proceedings as may be required by the Employer"* as set out in cl. 59B (6) but failed to recover the amount from the sub-contractor.

There is no specific negation of this right of recovery where the engineer's over-certification is due to misinformation supplied by the contractor under cl. 60 (1). Admittedly the contractor usually will obtain his information from the nominated sub-contractor, but if the contractor is negligent in giving information to the engineer he may be bound under the general law to hand back to the employer money reimbursed to him under this paragraph (p. 396).

It is particularly difficult to find the justice in limiting the engineer's power to correct an over-certification where it is due to the fact that defective work by a sub-contractor was not discovered before a certificate. Fortunately cl. 39 does not appear to be affected by this paragraph. The main contractor may be ordered to make good any such defect and if he does not do so the employer may engage another contractor under cl. 39 (2) and recover the resulting cost from payments becoming due to the main contractor (but *see* p. 245 for further complications involved).

(p) See the discussion of a somewhat similar clause in the *Gilbert-Ash* case above.

MAINTENANCE CERTIFICATE

61. (1) Upon the expiration of the Period of Maintenance or where there is more than one such period upon the expiration of the latest period and when all outstanding work referred to under Clause 48 and all work of repair amendment reconstruction rectification and making good of defects imperfections shrinkages and other faults referred to under Clauses 49 and 50 shall have been completed the Engineer shall issue to the Employer (with a copy to the Contractor) a Maintenance Certificate stating the date on which the Contractor shall have completed his obligations to construct complete and maintain the Works to the Engineer's satisfaction.[1]

UNFULFILLED OBLIGATIONS

(2) The issue of the Maintenance Certificate shall not be taken as relieving either the Contractor or the Employer from any liability the one towards the other arising out of or in any way connected with the performance of their respective obligations under the Contract.[2]

1. MAINTENANCE CERTIFICATE. This clause is a blessed simplification of the former cls. 61 and 62.

The maintenance certificate is now issued when all work under cls. 48, 49 and 50 has been completed and simply says that on a date specified the contractor has "*completed his obligations to construct complete and maintain the Works to the Engineer's satisfaction*". The certificate will not be effective unless it actually uses these words or words to the same effect.

The certificate is issued to the employer with a copy to the contractor. The only effects of the certificate are as evidence that the contractor has done all maintenance work he is bound to do under cl. 49, and the certificate starts the time limit running for delivering the final account (p. 263, N. 13).

2. THE END OF THE MAINTENANCE PERIOD AND THE MAINTENANCE CERTIFICATE DO NOT END THE CONTRACTOR'S LIABILITY FOR DEFECTS—LATE CLAIMS BY CONTRACTOR—POWERS OF ENGINEER. The vexed question under the previous edition of these Conditions of whether the contractor remains liable for defective work or materials after the maintenance certificate is determined against the contractor. The contractor remains liable and for a long time (p. 430). The employer's remedy after the end of the maintenance period is damages for breach of contract (pp. 427–30); he has no right to have the work actually carried out by the contractor, but nor has the contractor any right to do the work. The burden is on the employer to prove that a defect is due to the contractor's breach of contract, which may be difficult after lapse of time.

Conversely the employer remains liable to the contractor for many years (p. 430) on claims arising out of the contract. The only special limitation is that the contractor may lose a claim for failure to comply with cl. 52 (4) or

(*q*) This would not be so in the absence of the word "*stating*". It has, for example, been held that a certificate that the works were completed to the supervisor's satisfaction was provided where the supervisor certified for a "Final Instalment" (*Lowther* v. *Swan & Co.* (1915) T.P.D. 494 S.Af.), or for the release of the second half of the retention money (*Machin* v. *Syme* (1892) 18 V.L.R. 472 Aus., *Stratford Borough* v. *J. H. Ashman Ltd.* (1960) N.Z.L.R. 503), but not where an architect wrote "Balance due as per conditions" in the margin of the contractor's account (*Goodman* v. *Layborn* (1881) Roscoe's "Digest of Building Cases" 4th ed., App. p. 162 C.A.).

any of the other requirements of the contract about orders, notice, etc., collected in the key on p. 323.

It is no longer implied, as it was in the old cl. 61, that the maintenance certificate concludes the powers of the engineer. The final payment certificate is issued later (cl. 60 (3)). In addition, after maintenance of the works apparently the engineer still may be called on to decide a dispute under cl. 66, and (if the original engineer is dead or refuses to act) the employer may be required to appoint a substitute under cl. 1 (1) (c).

URGENT REPAIRS

62. If by reason of any accident or failure or other event occurring[1] to in or in connection with the Works[2] or any part thereof either during the execution of the Works or during the Period of Maintenance any remedial or other work or repair shall in the opinion of the Engineer be urgently necessary[3] and the Contractor is unable or unwilling at once to do such work or repair the Employer may by his own or other workmen do such work or repair as the Engineer may consider necessary.[4] If the work or repair so done by the Employer is work which in the opinion of the Engineer the Contractor was liable to do at his own expense under the Contract all costs and charges properly incurred by the Employer in so doing shall on demand be paid by the Contractor to the Employer or may be deducted by the Employer from any monies due or which may become due to the Contractor.[5] Provided always that the Engineer shall as soon after the occurrence of any such emergency as may be reasonably practicable notify the Contractor thereof in writing.

1. "IF BY REASON OF ANY ACCIDENT ... OCCURRING"—should be altered by adding "*or threatened*".

2. "ACCIDENT OR FAILURE ... IN CONNECTION WITH THE WORKS" covers failure of temporary works (cl. 1 (1) (l)).

3. "BE URGENTLY NECESSARY". The 4th edition adds "for security" after these words. The omission obviously widens the scope of the clause.

4. EMERGENCY WORK BY THE CONTRACTOR. The contractor is given no right to do emergency work if it involves a variation without at least a verbal order from the engineer (cl. 51 (2)).
See cl. 45 on emergency work at night and on Sundays.

5. WORK BY ANOTHER CONTRACTOR—NOTICE TO CONTRACTOR—DEDUCTION. *See* pp. 126 and 269. The employer is given no specific right to claim from the contractor the extra cost of employing another contractor to do work that the original contractor should have done, e.g. at bill rates. Such extra cost may be recoverable under the general law where the contractor refuses to do emergency work promptly even as a variation, as damages for breach of contract.

FORFEITURE

63. (1) If the Contractor shall[1,2] become bankrupt or have a receiving order made against him or shall present his petition in bankruptcy or shall make an arrangement with or assignment in favour of his creditors or shall agree to carry out the Contract under a committee of inspection of his creditors or (being a corporation) shall go into liquidation (other than a voluntary liquidation for the purposes of amalgamation or reconstruction)[3] or if the Contractor shall assign the Contract without the consent in writing of the Employer first obtained or shall have an execution levied on his goods or if the Engineer shall certify in writing to the Employer that in his opinion[4] the Contractor:

(a) has abandoned the Contract; or

(b) without reasonable excuse has failed to commence the Works in accordance with Clause 41 or has suspended the progress of the Works for 14 days after receiving from the Engineer written notice[5] to proceed; or

(c) has failed to remove goods or materials from the Site or to pull down and replace work for 14 days after receiving from the Engineer written notice[5] that the said goods materials or work have been condemned and rejected by the Engineer; or

(d) despite previous warning by the Engineer in writing[5] is failing to proceed with the Works with due diligence[6] or is otherwise persistently or fundamentally in breach of his obligations under the Contract;[7] or

(e) has to the detriment of good workmanship or in defiance of the Engineer's instruction to the contrary sub-let any part of the Contract;

then the Employer may[8] after giving 7 days' notice in writing[9] to the Contractor enter upon the Site and the Works and expel the Contractor therefrom without thereby avoiding the Contract or releasing the Contractor from any of his obligations or liabilities under the Contract[10] or affecting the rights and powers conferred on the Employer or the Engineer by the Contract and may himself complete the Works or may employ any other contractor to complete the Works[11] and the Employer or such other contractor may use for such completion so much of the Constructional Plant Temporary Works goods and materials which have been deemed to become the property of the Employer under Clauses 53 and 54 as he or they may think proper and the Employer may at any time sell any of the said Constructional Plant Temporary Works and unused goods and materials and apply the proceeds of sale in or towards the satisfaction of any sums due or which may become due to him from the Contractor under the Contract.[12]

ASSIGNMENT TO EMPLOYER

(2) By the said notice or by further notice in writing within 14 days of the date thereof the Engineer may require the Contractor to assign to the Employer and if so required the Contractor shall forthwith assign to the Employer the benefit of any agreement for the supply of any goods or materials and/or for the execution of any work for the purposes of this Contract which the Contractor may have entered into.[13]

1. GENERAL. It may be very difficult to know whether a breach of the contract by the contractor is serious enough to entitle the employer to bring the contract to an end under the general law, so as to avoid further harm by the contractor, as opposed to allowing the contractor to continue with the works and merely claiming damages (*see* ch. 16). A forfeiture clause of this kind is designed mainly to allow the employer to take the work out of the contractor's hands in certain clearly defined cases, where under the general law he might not be held entitled to do so. Even if a forfeiture clause and the employer's ordinary rights overlap it may be wiser to act under the forfeiture clause—*see* p. 281, N. 3, and cl. 53, N. 9, but *see* p. 266, N. 27, and N. 9 and 11 below, and the postponement by sub-cl. (4) of the right to recover any loss until the end of the maintenance period.

It is clear that the right to end the contract under the general law is not superseded by the right of forfeiture—it would take a very specific provision to take away the ordinary rights. In attempting to use his right under the general law as an alternative to or with forfeiture under this clause, the employer should keep in mind that under the general law he notifies the contractor that he is treating the contract as ended, whereas in his notice under this clause he only tells the contractor to leave the site and does not purport to end the contract itself. Legal advice is advisable before acting.

In some cases the employer has the alternative of taking part of the work out of the contractor's hands without forfeiting the whole contract, *see* cls. 39 (2) and 49 (4).

Forfeiture is an extreme remedy and a clause of this kind is interpreted by the courts strictly against the employer. Any attempt to exclude the contractor from the site which is not in strict accordance with this clause will amount to a repudiation of the contract by the employer and entitle the contractor to throw up the contract and claim damages, unless, of course, the employer had at the same time a right to bring the contract to an end under the general law. For the possibility of the contractor preventing the employer wrongfully putting him off the site, *see* p. 306.

The contractor is given no similar rights beyond his rights under the general law (*see* p. 425) to refuse to go on with the contract where the employer misbehaves, except under cl. 40 (2) if the work is suspended. *See* particularly N. 6 below, and also cl. 69 of the F.I.D.I.C. International Form.

2. FORFEITURE IN THE MAINTENANCE PERIOD. This clause is not limited to "*during the execution of the works*" (cl. 12, N. 2), so that there is no doubt that it applies on liquidation and under headings (a), (c) and (d) of this clause during the maintenance period. There are however two pecularities about the relationship between this clause and the maintenance period. Sub-cl. (1) in several places says that the employer may "*complete the Works*" without adding any reference to maintenance, and sub-cl. (4) refers to sums that would have been due to the original contractor on "*due completion by him*". Nevertheless the proper final result is produced by sub-cl. (4) which gives the employer the right to deduct from payments to the original contractor "*the costs of completion and maintenance*". The second point is that the words in this sub-clause that the employer may "*enter upon the Site and the Works and expel the Contractor*" may not be fully applicable in the maintenance period where the employer is usually in at least shared possession of the works, but expulsion of the contractor may still be necessary where he is on the works carrying out maintenance operations. Particularly where the contractor is insolvent, the employer may prefer to forfeit the contractor's employment entirely under this clause even though only maintenance duties remain rather than possibly having to

(*q'*) In *Union Transport Finance Ltd.* v. *British Car Auctions Ltd.* [1978] 2 All E.R. 385, C.A. it was held that it would need very clear words to exclude a bailor's common law right to terminate a hire purchase letting for conduct by the hirer repugnant to the agreement, and that a clause in the agreement providing for termination only on notice did not do so.
(*r*) In *Wellington (Mayor, etc.)* v. *Roberts and McNaught* (1883), 2 N.Z.L.R.C.A. 56 a forfeiture clause entitled the employers in certain circumstances to take the work out of the hands of the contractor on notice and either carry it on under the direction of the city surveyor or re-let it to another contractor. An attempted forfeiture was held invalid because the notice did not say that the employer intended to take the latter course.

operate cl. 49 (4) several times with notice of the maintenance requirement to the contractor each time.

· 3. "BANKRUPTCY . . . LIQUIDATION", ETC. It is not certain that this clause is valid to prevent the trustee or liquidator taking over and completing the contract on the contractor's bankruptcy or liquidation. The trustee or liquidator certainly cannot take over a contract where the personal ability, etc., of the contractor is relevant to the employer (*see* p. 40). In other cases bankruptcy or liquidation will usually result in other breaches of the contract by delay, etc., so that it may be preferable to forfeit the contract for those rather than-the bankruptcy or liquidation itself.

If the trustee does not continue the contract the employer may, of course, prove for a dividend in the bankruptcy or liquidation as well as recovering his losses from plant, etc., which has vested in him under cl. 53.

There is no right under cl. 66 to arbitration before completion in this case, but whether or not liquidation, etc., justifying forfeiture has occurred will not often be in doubt.

4. "IF THE ENGINEER SHALL CERTIFY IN WRITING . . . THAT IN HIS OPINION". It is implied that the engineer must give his certificate within a reasonable time of the action of which he is complaining.

For the right to immediate arbitration on a certificate and the effect of reversal of the certificate by the arbitrator, *see* cl. 66, N. 21.

For the possible liability of the engineer for acting negligently under this clause *see* p. 398, N. 31.

5. "14 DAYS AFTER RECEIVING FROM THE ENGINEER WRITTEN NOTICE". This notice should as far as reasonably possible tell the contractor what he has to do to make good his default so as to give him an opportunity of avoiding forfeiture by doing it.

Notice sufficient for this paragraph is inherent in an order under cl. 39, but the right to give such a notice by itself is implicit in this paragraph and cl. 13 (2). Such a notice may have the advantage over an instruction or order that it cannot give the contractor any rights under cl. 13 (3).

6. "THE CONTRACTOR . . . WITHOUT REASONABLE EXCUSE . . . HAS SUSPENDED THE PROGRESS OF THE WORKS . . . IS FAILING TO PROCEED WITH THE WORKS WITH DUE DILIGENCE". The employer may not forfeit the contract for delay in progress which he has caused, e.g. by not supplying drawings in time. On the other hand it does not seem that failure of the employer to pay certificates on time is a reasonable excuse for suspension of work or entitles the contractor to be less than normally diligent, unless the failure entitles the contractor actually to end the contract and he does so (p. 426). Any other view would introduce uncertainty as to what amount of underpayment or delay in payment would justify total suspension, and as to what degree of slowing-up is justified for what degree of default by the employer. Cl. 60 gives the remedy of interest only for late payment, and if the contractor were intended to have other rights this could have been said specifically (e.g. cl. 69 of the F.I.D.I.C. International Form). Further, the effect of non-payment on the contractor will depend on his financial situation, and in adjudicating on a contract the courts normally will not take into account the particular finances of a party.

The contractor therefore must make a decision whether or not to carry on fully with his contract, notwithstanding the employer's default in paying, or to bring the contract itself to an end where the employer's default is sufficiently serious to entitle him to do so. Unfortunately that can be a difficult decision, but there is some indication that the courts will be realistic in protecting the contractor's interests (p. 426).

A contract may be forfeited for lack of due diligence under a clause of this kind, though there is no completion date fixed by the contract, since the contractor is still bound to complete in a reasonable time. For the position where there are omissions *see* cl. 44, N. 2.

7. "DESPITE PREVIOUS WARNINGS ... IN WRITING ... PERSISTENTLY OR FUNDAMENTALLY IN BREACH OF ... THE CONTRACT". There are a number of changes in this paragraph, including the omission of "*is not executing the Works in accordance with the Contract*" from the previous edition.

Is failure to provide a programme under cl. 14 a fundamental breach, for example? It is suggested that it is. In any case the engineer normally will not want to take the drastic action under this clause unless the breach becomes persistent. In many cases, which have been pointed out in the text, action under this paragraph is the only (often impracticable) sanction for failure by the contractor to give information, etc., essential for the proper administration of the contract.

In relation to the requirement of written warning of lack of due diligence, refer to cl. 46.

8. WAIVER. No time limit is fixed after the event giving rise to the forfeiture or the engineer's certificate within which the employer must exercise his rights. If the employer delays beyond a reasonable time he may be held to have waived the right to forfeit in that particular case. For the effect of the doctrine of waiver generally on forfeiture *see* cl. 47, N. 11.

9. "AFTER GIVING 7 DAYS' NOTICE IN WRITING". This notice is to allow the contractor time to get off the site, but if he makes good his default within the time it is possible that it would be held that the employer may not forfeit the contract—*see* N. 5—although technically the contractor's default is complete when the engineer gives his certificate. The notice tells the contractor to leave the site; it should not say that the employer is ending the contract—N. 1 and 10.

Seven days' notice should be given, excluding the day on which notice was given or would in the ordinary course of post reach the other party and the day on which it ends. For service of notice *see* cl. 68.

(s) There may be waiver particularly if the contractor is allowed to alter his position adversely, e.g. possibly by buying expensive plant for the works, in the belief that he will be allowed to complete the contract.

A right of forfeiture which has arisen may also be waived if the employer with knowledge of his rights makes advances of money to the contractor for the purposes of the contract or in any other way treats the contract as still subsisting. *Re Garrud ex. p. Newitt* (1881) 16 Ch.D. 522.

(s') In *re Lympne Investments Ltd.* [1972] 2 All E.R. 385 a petition presented at noon on 25th November following a demand served on 4th November was held too soon, where by statute the company petitioned against was required to have "for a period of 3 weeks neglected to pay the sum" claimed in the demand. It was said in the judgment that—"it must be possible to point to a period of three weeks during which the neglect has continued" (at p. 387).

The employer in urgent cases may be entitled to end the contract under the general law without any notice, but see the opening note to this clause.

10. "WITHOUT ... AVOIDING THE CONTRACT OR RELEASING THE CONTRACTOR FROM ... HIS ... LIABILITIES UNDER THE CONTRACT" *See* in particular N. 3, p. 281.

11. ABANDONMENT OF THE WORKS BY THE EMPLOYER. The terms of this whole clause are appropriate only where the employer has the works completed. It does not seem, therefore, that he may abandon the works completely after forfeiture, although the engineer retains the right to vary the work under cl. 51. If the employer may not wish to complete he will have to try to rescind the contract under the general law as well as acting under this clause. Where the rescission is valid under the general law the employer may abandon the works and sue for damages—*see* N. 1.

For the employer's duty to complete without unnecessary cost *see* p. 429.

12. "MAY USE ... PLANT ... DEEMED TO BECOME THE PROPERTY OF THE EMPLOYER UNDER CLAUSE 53". *See* cl. 53 (3) as to hired plant.

13. ASSIGNMENT OF SUB-CONTRACTS AND SUPPLY AGREEMENTS ON FORFEITURE. It is not at all certain that the employer is entitled to enforce this provision if the contractor's employment is forfeited for bankruptcy or liquidation. Particularly in these days of extended delivery times such contracts may have a high saleable value. That is another reason why it may be preferable for the employer to wait for delay to the works after liquidation, and forfeit for that delay rather than the liquidation itself— N. 3.

This right to an assignment of a sub-contract, etc., will not be effective unless the sub-contract permits assignment (p. 39, N. 2) or the sub-contractor consents. But if the sub-contractor unreasonably refuses consent he may effectively lose his right to damages against the main contractor for any failure to complete the sub-contract consequent on the forfeiture. For direct payment to sub-contractors for work done before the forfeiture *see* cl 59C.

The employer's right to take over goods and materials for which he has paid under cl. 54 may also be very useful on forfeiture.

For no apparent reason, the assignment of an agreement for services is not mentioned here (*see* cl. 58 (3)). It is suggested that an agreement may still be an "*agreement for the supply of any goods or materials and/or for the execution of any work*" even though there are some minor and incidental design details or other services included.

(*t*) This is an odd result, but there is no provision in the contract for revesting plant until completion, or for accounting by the employer to the original contractor unless there is completion, and there will be no "*costs of completion ... damages for delay in completion*" to be deducted from payments to the contractor under sub-cl. (3).

(*u*) *Brace* v. *Calder* [1895] 2 Q.B. 253—two out of four partners retired; held that although this dissolution of the partnership technically amounted to a wrongful dismissal of a manager he was entitled to only nominal damages, since the two remaining partners had offered to employ him on the same terms. In *Shindler* v. *Northern Raincoat Co. Ltd.* [1960] 2 All E.R. 289 the plaintiff recovered substantial damages because it was held that in all the circumstances his refusal of an offer of re-employment by the company which had wrongfully dismissed him was not unreasonable.

This sub-clause says that "*By the said notice . . . the Engineer may require the Contractor to assign . . .*", but the notice referred to is given by the employer.

VALUATION AT DATE OF FORFEITURE

63. (3) The Engineer shall as soon as may be practicable after any such entry and expulsion by the Employer fix and determine *ex parte*[1] or by or after reference to the parties or after such investigation or enquiries as he may think fit to make or institute and shall certify what amount (if any) had at the time of such entry and expulsion been reasonably earned by or would reasonably accrue to the Contractor in respect of work then actually done by him under the Contract and what was the value of any unused or partially used goods and materials any Constructional Plant and any Temporary Works which have been deemed to become the property of the Employer under Clauses 53 and 54.

PAYMENT AFTER FORFEITURE

(4) If the Employer shall enter and expel the Contractor under this Clause he shall not be liable to pay to the Contractor any money on account of the Contract[2] until the expiration of the Period of Maintenance and thereafter until the costs of completion and maintenance damages for delay in completion[3] (if any) and all other expenses incurred by the Employer have been ascertained and the amount thereof certified by the Engineer.[4] The Contractor shall then be entitled to receive only such sum or sums (if any) as the Engineer may certify would have been due to him upon due completion by him after deducting the said amount. But if such amount shall exceed the sum which would have been payable to the Contractor on due completion by him then the Contractor shall upon demand pay to the Employer the amount of such excess and it shall be deemed a debt due by the Contractor to the Employer and shall be recoverable accordingly.[5]

1. HEARING, ETC., BY THE ENGINEER. *See* p. 415.

2. "THE EMPLOYER . . . SHALL NOT BE LIABLE TO PAY TO THE CONTRACTOR ANY MONEY ON ACCOUNT OF THE CONTRACT". It seems that despite these words the employer is not entitled to hold back money actually overdue under cl. 60 before the forfeiture. The employer could hardly be allowed to gain from his own fault in delaying payment.

Under this clause payment of any balance of the contract money to the contractor is postponed not merely to completion but to the end of the maintenance period, which may be disastrous for a contractor in financial difficulty.

3. "DAMAGES FOR DELAY IN COMPLETION"—LIQUIDATED DAMAGES AFTER FORFEITURE. It is suggested that by this clause the employer may recover from the contractor not only any liquidated damages which had become due for delay before forfeiture, which is all he is entitled to if he brings the contract to an end under the general law, but may also recover liquidated damages to cover the full period from the completion date fixed by the

v

(*v*) *Geiger* v. *Western Maryland Ry.* (1874) Md. 43 U.S.A.

contract to actual completion, even though for part of the time the work is
out of the contractor's control. The contractor will be entitled only to an
extension of time for unnecessary delay in getting a contractor to take over
the work or caused by the substitute contractor.

4. EMPLOYER'S DUTY TO MITIGATE LOSS. *See* p. 429.

5. EMPLOYER'S RIGHTS AFTER FORFEITURE. Rights given by a contract to
the employer after forfeiture may be void if they infringe the bankruptcy
laws (cl. 53, N. 6) or if they amount to a penalty— p. 149.

In the unlikely event of the employer saving money by having another
contractor complete, the saving belongs to the original contractor.

PAYMENT IN EVENT OF FRUSTATION

64. In the event of the Contract being frustrated whether by war or by any other
supervening event which may occur independently of the will of the parties the
sum payable by the Employer to the Contractor in respect of the work executed
shall be the same as that which would have been payable under Clause 65 (5) if the
Contract had been determined by the Employer under Clause 65.[1]

1. FRUSTRATION. The English law of contract is strict in holding a party to
his bargain, although it turns out to be more difficult or expensive to carry
out than he anticipated or could have anticipated when he made it. But in
very extreme cases the parties may be released from further performance of
a contract because events outside their control have frustrated the venture
for which it was made, for example, where performance of the contract
becomes actually impossible or illegal:

> The plaintiff agreed to build machinery on the defendant's premises and to
> keep it in repair for two years. The premises were burnt down when the
> machinery was partly built.
> Held: The plaintiff was not liable to pay damages for not completing the
> machinery. It had become impossible to carry out the contract and both parties
> were released from further performance.

The doctrine may be applied even though performance of the contract is
still theoretically possible, where events have so altered the circumstances in
which the contract is to be carried out that to hold a party to it would be to
hold him to something essentially different from that which he agreed to
originally:

> A contractor agreed to build a reservoir within six years, but the contract
> included a clause (similar to cl. 44 above) giving the engineer wide powers to
> extend the time for completing. Eighteen months later, after the outbreak of the

(w) See p. 129, n (q), and N. 10 to this clause, above. It has been said that not to allow liquidated
damages for a reasonable time for completion of works after their abandonment by a builder
"would be giving a premium to contractors who have no professional ethics, by encouraging
them to abandon their contracts as soon as they realise they will not be able to complete . . .
within . . . time" in *Desrosiers* v. *Gauthier* (1977) 17 N.R. 301, 305 Can. U.S.A. courts are
divided in their conclusions on the point. Of course it is the strong wording of these
Conditions that governs, and in *re Yeadon Waterworks Co. & Wright* (1895) 72 L.T. 538, 832
similar words were held to preserve the right to liquidated damages after forfeiture.

(x) *Appleby* v. *Myers* (1867) L.R. 2 C.P. 651.

First World War, the Government prohibited further work and ordered the contractor's plant and machinery to be sold.

Held: That, although in theory the engineer could have given an extension of time under that contract and the work could have been finished after the war, the commercial venture intended had been frustrated and the contractor was released from the contract as from the date of the Government order. The engineer's power to extend the time for completing was intended to apply only to the usual type of temporary delay, and not to extraordinary and indefinite delay of this kind.

To end the contract the change of circumstances must be catastrophic, so as to have been quite outside the vision of the parties when they made the contract; it must be quite clear that the risk of the particular type of occurrence was not intended to be carried by one of the parties:

A contractor agreed to build a number of houses for a lump sum, to be completed in eight months. Due to shortage of labour caused by unexpected delay in demobilisation after the war the completion date was extended and the work took twenty-two months, of course at heavy extra expense to the contractor.

The contractor argued that the contract had been frustrated at an early stage because of this delay, and that the work done after the date on which it was frustrated should be taken to have been done under a new implied contract so as to entitle him to payment at reasonable rates.

Held: That the original contract had not been frustrated because the whole object of a lump sum contract is to place the risk of this class of unexpected delay or expense on the contractor.

The net result is that the doctrine of frustration will rarely apply so as to release a contractor from a construction contract. Unfortunately there is confusion abroad in the industry about this doctrine, and a reference to frustration is often thrown into claims documents where it has no possible relevance.

It is the essence of the doctrine that the frustrating event is outside the parties' control, so that a party cannot plead that the contract is frustrated by a change of circumstances which he caused, e.g. where the contractor deliberately delayed the works so that they were affected by pending legislation, and see the opening note to cl. 34.

Legal and physical impossibility is also referred to in cl. 13.

The service agreement (ch. 13) may in the same way be ended by the death of the engineer, or illness if likely to be so long as to frustrate the purpose of his employment.

Under the Law Reform (Frustrated Contracts) Act, 1943, the court or arbitrator has power to adjust the rights of the parties as to payment for work, etc., already done before frustration (not very satisfactorily in the case of a construction contract), except so far as the contract expressly regulates the position, as in this clause.

WAR—WORKS TO CONTINUE FOR 28 DAYS ON OUTBREAK OF WAR

65. (1)[1] If during the currency of the Contract there shall be an outbreak of

(y) *Metropolitan Water Board* v. *Dick Kerr & Co.* [1918] A.C. 119.

(z) *Davis Contractors* v. *Fareham U.D.C.* [1956] 2 All E.R. 145, H.L., also discussed on p. 20 of the text.

(aa) *Mertens* v. *Home Freeholds Co.* [1921] 2 K.B. 526.

war (whether war is declared or not) in which Great Britain shall be engaged on a scale involving general mobilisation[2] of the armed forces of the Crown the Contractor shall for a period of 28 days reckoned from midnight on the date that the order for general mobilisation is given continue so far as is physically possible to execute the Works in accordance with the Contract.

Effect of Completion Within 28 Days

(2) If at any time before the expiration of the said period of 28 days[3] the Works shall have been completed or completed so far as to be usable[4] all provisions of the Contract shall continue to have full force and effect save that

(a) the Contractor shall in lieu of fulfilling his obligations under Clauses 49 and 50 be entitled at his option to allow against the sum due to him under the provisions hereof the cost (calculated at the prices ruling at the beginning of the said period of 28 days) as certified by the Engineer at the expiration of the Period of Maintenance of repair rectification and making good any work for the repair rectification or making good of which the Contractor would have been liable under the said Clauses had they continued to be applicable;

(b) the Employer shall not be entitled at the expiration of the Period of Maintenance to withhold payment under Clause 60 (5) (c) hereof of the second half of the retention money or any part thereof except such sum as may be allowable by the Contractor under the provisions of the last preceding paragraph which sum may (without prejudice to any other mode of recovery thereof) be deducted by the Employer from such second half.

Right of Employer to Determine Contract

(3) If the Works shall not have been completed as aforesaid the Employer shall be entitled to determine the Contract (with the exception of this Clause and Clauses 66 and 68) by giving notice in writing to the Contractor at any time after the aforesaid period of 28 days has expired and upon such notice being given the Contract shall (except as above mentioned) forthwith determine but without prejudice to the claims of either party in respect of any antecedent breach thereof.

Removal of Plant on Determination

(4) If the Contract shall be determined under the provisions of the last preceding sub-clause the Contractor shall with all reasonable despatch remove from the Site all his Constructional Plant and shall give facilities to his sub-contractors to remove similarly all Constructional Plant belonging to them and in the event of any failures so to do the Employer shall have the like powers as are contained in Clause 53 (8) in regard to failure to remove Constructional Plant on completion of the Works but subject to the same condition as is contained in Clause 53 (9).

Payment on Determination

(5) If the Contract shall be determined as aforesaid the Contractor shall be paid by the Employer (insofar as such amounts or items shall not have been already covered by payment on account made to the Contractor) for all work

executed prior to the date of determination at the rates and prices provided in the Contract and in addition:

   (a) the amounts payable in respect of any preliminary items so far as the work or service comprised therein has been carried out or performed and a proper proportion as certified by the Engineer of any such items the work or service comprised in which has been partially carried out or performed;

   (b) the cost of materials or goods reasonably ordered for the Works which shall have been delivered to the Contractor or of which the Contractor is legally liable to accept delivery (such materials or goods becoming the property of the Employer upon such payment being made by him);

   (c) a sum to be certified by the Engineer being the amount of any expenditure reasonably incurred by the Contractor in the expectation of completing the whole of the Works in so far as such expenditure shall not have been covered by the payments in this sub-clause before mentioned;

   (d) any additional sum payable under sub-clause (6) (b) (c) and (d) of this Clause;

   (e) the reasonable cost of removal under sub-clause (4) of this Clause.

PROVISIONS TO APPLY AS FROM OUTBREAK OF WAR

   (6) Whether the Contract shall be determined under the provisions of sub-clause (3) of this Clause or not the following provisions shall apply or be deemed to have applied as from the date of the said outbreak of war notwithstanding anything expressed in or implied by the other terms of the Contract *viz:*

   (a) The Contractor shall be under no liability whatsoever whether by way of indemnity or otherwise for or in respect of damage to the Works or to property (other than property of the Contractor or property hired by him for the purposes of executing the Works) whether of the Employer or of third parties or for or in respect of injury or loss of life to persons[5] which is the consequence whether direct or indirect of war hostilities[6] (whether war has been declared or not) invasion act of the Queen's enemies civil war rebellion revolution insurrection military or usurped power and the Employer shall indemnify the Contractor against all such liabilities and against all claims demands proceedings damages costs charges and expenses whatsoever arising thereout or in connection therewith.[7]

   (b) If the Works shall sustain destruction or any damage by reason of any of the causes mentioned in the last preceding paragraph the Contractors shall nevertheless be entitled to payment for any part of the Works so destroyed or damaged and the Contractor shall be entitled to be paid by the Employer the cost of making good any such destruction or damage so far as may be required by the Engineer or as may be necessary for the completion of the Works on a cost basis plus such profit as the Engineer may certify to be reasonable.[8]

   (c) In the event that the Contract includes the Contract Price Fluctuations Clause the terms of the Clause shall continue to apply but if subsequent to the outbreak of war the index figures therein referred to shall cease to be published or in the event that the contract shall not include a Price Fluctuations Clause in that form the following paragraph shall have effect:

     If under decision of the Civil Engineering Construction Conciliation Board or of any other body recognised as an appropriate body for regulating the rates of wages in any trade or industry other than the Civil Engineering Construction Industry to which Contractors undertaking works of civil engineering construction give effect by agreement or in practice or by reason of any Statute or Statutory Instrument there shall during the currency of the Contract be any increase or decrease in the wages or the rates of wages or in the allowances or rates of allowances (including allowances in respect of holidays) payable to or in respect of labour of any kind prevailing at the date of outbreak of war as then fixed by the said Board or such other body as aforesaid or by Statute or Statutory Instrument or any increase in the amount payable by the Contractor by virtue or in respect of any Scheme of State Insurance or if there shall be any increase or decrease in the cost prevailing at the date of the said outbreak of war of any materials consumable stores fuel or power (and whether for permanent or temporary works) which increase or increases decrease or decreases shall result in an increase or decrease of cost to the Contractor in carrying out the Works the net increase or decrease of cost shall form an addition or deduction as the case may be to or from the Contract Price and be paid to or allowed by the Contractor accordingly.

(d) If the cost of the Works to the Contractor shall be increased or decreased by reason of the provisions of any Statute or Statutory Instrument or other Government or Local Government Order or Regulation becoming applicable to the Works after the date of the said outbreak of war or by reason of any trade or industrial agreement entered into after such date to which the Civil Engineering Construction Conciliation Board or any other body as aforesaid is party or gives effect or by reason of any amendment of whatsoever nature of the Working Rule Agreement of the said Board or of any other body as aforesaid or by reason of any other circumstance or thing attributable to or consequent on such outbreak of war such increase or decrease of cost as certified by the Engineer shall be reimbursed by the Employer to the Contractor or allowed by the Contractor as the case may be.

(e) Damage or injury caused by the explosion whenever occurring of any mine bomb shell grenade or other projectile missile or munition of war and whether occurring before or after the cessation of hostilities shall be deemed to be the consequence of any of the events mentioned in sub-clause (6) (a) of this Clause.

1. GENERAL. As it is unlikely that a general war will leave any engineering works for engineers or lawyers to argue about, if there are engineers or lawyers to argue, this clause is dealt with shortly.

2. "WAR . . . INVOLVING GENERAL MOBILISATION". For lesser wars *see* cl. 64.

3. "28 DAYS", ETC. The period ends on midnight of the last day, but *see* cl. 45.

4. "COMPLETED SO FAR AS TO BE USABLE". There is no provision for a deduction in the contract price where the works are usable but not completely finished. This would not be material where the contract is measure and value or quantities, and in other cases the engineer might give an order to omit any work which clearly could not be completed within the 28-day limit and make a deduction under cl. 52.

5. DAMAGE TO PROPERTY, ETC. *See* cls. 20–24.

6. "CONSEQUENCE ... OF WAR HOSTILITIES". *See* sub-cl. (e).

7. INDEMNITY. *See* p. 95.

8. MATERIALS ON THE SITE. The ambiguous reference in this paragraph of the 4th edition of these Conditions to materials on the site has been removed.

CHAPTER 8

Arbitration and Litigation:
Conditions Clause 66

Apart from a commentary on cl. 66 of the general conditions (below), these notes do not aim to give more than an overall picture of what may be expected of arbitration as opposed to ordinary court proceedings. On the conduct of the arbitrator *see* fully ch. 14, and on the importance in respect of claims of improved arbitration procedure, pp. 446–7.

The major attraction of arbitration is that an arbitrator is partly free to ignore strict legal rules and to decide as he thinks equitable (p. 302). Whether or not this is, in fact, an advantage depends very much on the choice of arbitrator. There is a difference between an arbitrator working out the legal position and then not following it because he feels that it is unjust, and an arbitrator giving both sides something because he has failed to analyse the case. A good arbitrator also knows the dangers of relying entirely on his own judgment — legal rules and precedents are there to help with complex disputes that cannot be solved simply by a broad idea of what is fair. It also encourages bad tendering and makes it difficult for the engineer to take a reasonably firm line where there is an arbitration clause, unless he can depend on the arbitrator applying the rules except for good reasons.

And, of course, errors of judgment do happen, but an arbitrator will usually avoid giving reasons for his award so that there is no appeal, as there is from the decision of a judge. That can be bitterly frustrating to the loser (*see* the first case on p. 304).

The parties should choose an experienced arbitrator, if possible, after checking with those who know his work (it is extraordinary how often there is no real investigation of this kind before the appointment is made). They should not, in any case, insist automatically on applying the arbitration clause. The primary use of arbitration should be for technical disputes, where there is the advantage that an expert may be appointed arbitrator; where there is an acrimonious dispute about non-technical facts an experienced judge (who is the expert at this) may be more able than an arbitrator to control the proceedings and to find and keep the parties to the relevant facts. Where a dispute is solely about the law the parties should always let it go before the ordinary courts from the outset; if they do not, it

---

(*a*) Further reading: D. M. Lawrence "Law and Practice of Arbitration and Awards", 9th ed., Parris "The Law and Practice of Arbitration", and "Casebook of Arbitration Law", and the practitioner's standard work "Russell on Arbitration", 18th ed. by Anthony Walton.

(*b*) "Not only do reasons concentrate the mind (of the arbitrator) but on the whole they tend to satisfy the parties more than silence": *Tramountana Armadora S.A.* v. *Atlantic Shipping Co. S.A.* [1978] 2 All E.R. 870, 872 (facts at p. 299 of text below).

(*c*) A list with the relevant details of available arbitrators is published by the I.C.E.

will probably reach the courts in the end and they will have the worst of both worlds (pp. 302-3).

Again, although the privacy of arbitration is a decided advantage, if a dispute involves charges against the character of a party or of the engineer, he should be given an opportunity to meet these charges in open court, and in that case also the courts may not enforce the agreement to arbitrate (p. 303).

Additionally it has been said in the past that arbitration is cheaper and quicker than court proceedings. Now it is becoming fashionable amongst lawyers to claim that it is not. Many say that arbitration is generally no improvement on ordinary litigation (a truly serious criticism). It is not so often mentioned that it is lawyers who have distorted arbitration to make it as like ordinary litigation as possible, and are now condemning arbitration for not being better than the model they have wrongly chosen for it. If one party is manufacturing a dispute in the hope that something to his advantage will turn up, he will see to it that no procedure is quick or cheap, but where there is a genuine difference arbitration has the great advantage that the parties may regulate it so that it is most effective for their particular dispute. Special procedure may be specified in the original contract or by agreement when the dispute occurs (or the arbitrator may guide the parties to agreement at the usual preliminary meeting). Such procedure for construction arbitration is discussed on pp. 297 and 446-7.

SETTLEMENT OF DISPUTES—ARBITRATION

66. (1) If any dispute or difference of any kind whatsoever shall arise between the Employer and the Contractor in connection with or arising out of the Contract or the carrying out of the Works[1] including any dispute as to any decision opinion instruction direction certificate or valuation of the Engineer[2,3,4] (whether during the progress of the Works or after their completion and whether before or after the determination abandonment or breach of the Contract) it shall be referred to and settled by the Engineer[5,6] who shall state his decision in writing and give notice of the same to the Employer and the Contractor. Unless the Contract shall have been already determined or abandoned the Contractor shall in every case continue to proceed with the Works with all due diligence and he shall give effect forthwith to every such decision of the Engineer unless and until the same shall be revised by an arbitrator as hereinafter provided. Such decisions shall be final and binding upon the Contractor and the Employer unless either of them shall require that the matter be referred to arbitration as hereinafter provided.[6a] If the Engineer shall fail to give such decision for a period of 3 calendar months after being requested to do so or if either the Employer or the Contractor be dissatisfied with any such decision of the Engineer then and in any such case either the Employer or the Contractor may within 3 calendar months after receiving notice of such decision or within 3 calendar months after the expiration of the said period of 3 months (as the case may be) require[7] that the matter shall be referred to the arbitration of a person to be agreed upon between the parties or (if the parties fail to appoint an arbitrator within one calendar month of either party serving on the other party a written notice to concur in the appointment of an arbitrator)[8,9] a person to be appointed on the application of either party by the President for the time being of the Institution of Civil Engineers. If an arbitrator declines the appointment or after appointment is removed by order of.a competent court or is incapable of acting or dies and the parties do not within one calendar month of the vacancy arising fill the vacancy then the President for the time being of the Institution of

Civil Engineers may on the application of either party appoint an arbitrator to fill the vacancy. Any such reference to arbitration shall be deemed to be a submission to arbitration within the meaning of the Arbitration Act 1950[10] or the Arbitration (Scotland) Act 1894[11] as the case may be or any statutory re-enactment or amendment thereof for the time being in force. Any such reference to arbitration may be conducted in accordance with the Institution of Civil Engineers' Arbitration Procedure (1973)[12] or any amendment or modification thereof being in force at the time of the appointment of the arbitrator and in cases where the President of the Institution of Civil Engineers is requested to appoint the arbitrator he may direct that the arbitration is conducted in accordance with the aforementioned Procedure or any amendment or modification thereof. Such arbitrator shall have full power to open up review and revise any decision opinion[13] instruction[14] direction certificate or valuation of the Engineer and neither party shall be limited in the proceedings before such arbitrator to the evidence or arguments put before[15] the Engineer for the purpose of obtaining his decision above referred to. The award of the arbitrator shall be final and binding on the parties.[16] Save as provided for in sub-clause (2) of this Clause no steps shall be taken in the reference to the arbitrator until after the completion or alleged completion[17] of the Works unless with the written consent of the Employer and the Contractor. Provided always:

(a) that the giving of a Certificate of Completion under Clause 48 shall not be a condition precedent to the taking of any step in such reference;

(b) that no decision given by the Engineer in accordance with the foregoing provisions shall disqualify him from being called as a witness and giving evidence before the arbitrator on any matter whatsoever relevant to the dispute or difference so referred to the arbitrator as aforesaid.

INTERIM ARBITRATION

(2) In the case of any dispute or difference as to any matter arising under Clause 12[18] or the withholding by the Engineer of any certificate[19] or the withholding of any portion of the retention money under Clause 60[20] to which the Contractor claims to be entitled or as to the exercise of the Engineer's power to give a certificate under Clause 63 (1)[21] the reference to the arbitrator may proceed notwithstanding that the Works shall not then be or be alleged to be complete.[22]

VICE-PRESIDENT TO ACT

(3) In the case where the President for the time being of the Institution of Civil Engineers is not able to exercise the functions conferred on him by this Clause the said functions may be exercised on his behalf by a Vice-President for the time being of the said Institution.[23]

1. "ANY DISPUTE OR DIFFERENCE OF ANY KIND WHATSOEVER ... IN CONNECTION WITH OR ARISING OUT OF THE CONTRACT OR THE CARRYING OUT OF THE WORKS", ETC. Some engineers suffer from the misconception that disputes other than those involving a claim under a specific clause in the contract do not fall within their right and duty to give a decision under this clause, for example some claims by the contractor for breach of contract. Many public authorities too label such claims "ex-contractual", whatever that may mean, and seek to deny the engineer his role under this clause in respect of them. On the contrary, the words at the head of this note are wide

enough to cover almost all possible disputes—for example, a claim that the contract has been frustrated (cl. 64) or broken or repudiated (p. 425) is included. But the arbitrator or engineer has no jurisdiction to decide any dispute as to whether the contract was void from the beginning, e.g. for mistake (p. 12), or to decide whether one of the parties had a right from the beginning to bring the contract to an end, e.g. for misrepresentation (p. 60), because generally the same flaw invalidates this clause as affects the contract as a whole. Although there are some cases to the contrary, it seems that a claim for rectification (p. 41 (a)) is included. *See also* N. 17.

It follows that issues to be settled by the engineer fall into two groups:

(i)   Those that are dealt with in the first instance by the engineer, such as the amounts to be included in certificates under cl. 60 including cost payable to the contractor under cl. 13 (3) and many other clauses (key in ch. 11), and *see* p. 264, N. 17 on deductions by the employer. There is then a further decision by the engineer under this clause if required by either party.

(ii)   Issues on which no initial jurisdiction is vested in the engineer by these Conditions, but on which nevertheless he may eventually have to rule under this clause if a dispute arises. If a contractor claims payment for variations outside the contract (pp. 169 and 172) or compensation for disruption in some cases (p. 362) there is no provision in these Conditions for the engineer to determine and certify in the first instance any amount due. However, if the employer refuses extra payment, whether directly or through the instrumentality of the engineer if he decides to authorise him to deal with the claim, then a dispute has arisen that must be referred to and decided by the engineer under this clause if it is to go further. Because this edition of the Conditions delegates to the engineer certification on so many claims by the contractor that fell outside certificates in the previous edition, there are fewer cases left in this group.

2. "INCLUDING ANY DISPUTE AS TO ANY DECISION OPINION ... (ETC.) OF THE ENGINEER". These words have been added following deletion of the reference to "*any dispute ... between the Engineer and the Contractor*" which was incorrectly included in the previous edition.

Where, but only where, there is no genuine dispute at all to be remitted to arbitration, but merely a debt "indisputably due" to be collected, then the procedure in this clause does not have to be followed but relatively speedy summary judgment may be obtained from the courts—*see* p. 270.

3. DECISIONS BY THE ENGINEER. The engineer has the fearfully heavy burden of deciding fairly and independently a wide range of disputes where a decision favourable to the contractor may involve the engineer himself in liability to the client—for example in respect of late drawings. For the

---

(d) *Printing Machinery Co. Ltd.* v. *Linotype & Machinery Ltd.* [1912] 1 Ch. 566, approved *Crane* v. *Hegeman-Harris Co. Inc.* [1939] 4 All E.R. 68. In the *Printing Machinery* case the arbitration clause was limited to disputes "touching the construction, meaning or effect" of the lease in question, or "the rights or liabilities of the ... parties ... under ... or otherwise howsoever in relation to" the lease. In *Kathmer Investments (Pty.) Ltd.* v. *Woolworths (Pty.) Ltd.* 1970 (2) S.A. 498 S.Af., held that a clause providing for arbitration on disputes "arising out of or concerning" an agreement was wide enough to cover a dispute about whether a term of that agreement should be rectified.

importance of meticulous performance of this duty, of the engineer not taking on more responsibility than necessary, and a discussion of the future of this special role, *see* pp. 397 and 445.

· 4. DISPUTES BETWEEN THE MAIN CONTRACTOR AND A SUB-CONTRACTOR. The simple incorporation of main contract conditions in the I.C.E. form by reference in a sub-contract does not by itself incorporate arbitration for disputes purely between the main contractor and a sub-contractor (in particular the opening of this clause is not appropriate to such disputes). However, where a sub-contractor agrees to accept such payment for extras or otherwise as is obtained by the main contractor under the main contract, the sub-contractor is bound by the results of any arbitration between the employer and main contractor. Arbitration on disputes concerning both the main and sub-contracts and arbitration on disputes purely between the contractor and sub-contractor are regulated by cl. 18 of the Federation of Civil Engineering Contractors' published form of sub-contract designed for use with these Conditions.

5. "ANY DISPUTE ... BETWEEN THE EMPLOYER AND THE CONTRACTOR ... SHALL BE REFERRED TO ... THE ENGINEER". The effect of these words is that there must be (i) a dispute, followed by (ii) a referral of that dispute by one of the parties to the engineer, followed by (iii) a decision of the engineer notified to both parties, before the time limit for claiming arbitration begins to run under the remainder of this clause:

> On March 8, 1961, contractors wrote enclosing 11 claims, some of which they had put forward almost a year before and which had been disputed by the engineer, and some of which were new. The letter read: "We have pleasure in enclosing herewith our semi-final A/c ... together with our claims under the contract ... we are hoping to receive your comments on the remainder of the claims (i.e. those not agreed) as soon as possible convenient (*sic*) to you."
>
> The engineer wrote to the contractors enclosing his "observations and comments on your (the contractors') claims" and at the end of his comments on each claim wrote "I cannot agree with or consider this claim". The engineer did not use the word "decision" in relation to any of the claims save one, and in that case he asked for further details.
>
> The contractors wrote thanking the engineer for that letter and asking for a meeting "before we officially give this notice (i.e. that contractor ... wishes the matter to be dealt with under (Clause 66))". They did not give notice of arbitration within three months of the letter.
>
> Held: (i) that there could not be a decision by the engineer on the claims which had not already been rejected, since there was no pre-existing dispute or difference and therefore no referral to him under this clause, and (ii) that in any case an engineer must make it quite clear that a statement is intended as a decision under the clause. The engineer's letter was not a decision on any of the claims, and therefore the contractors were not barred from arbitration.

The procedure under this clause as interpreted in this decision obviously serves a useful purpose, in ensuring that the contractor is not caught unawares by the time limit for arbitration, and in giving the engineer a chance to reconsider decisions. The contractor should make it quite clear when he is applying for an engineer's decision and not merely negotiating,

(e) *Monmouth C.C.* v. *Costelloe & Kemple Ltd.* (1964) 63 L.G.R. 131 Mocatta J., and (1965) 63 L.G.R. 429, C.A.

and the engineer should state specifically that he is making a decision under this clause and send a copy of the decision to both parties. Otherwise problems may still arise. For example, it appears that a dispute is created if a claim has been included by the contractor in a progress statement under cl. 60 and is not allowed in the next interim certificate. If the contractor subsequently asks for a decision from the engineer on the same matter, even orally perhaps when he is carried away in argument, it is possible that the contractor's rights will be lost if he does not give notice of arbitration within three months of the engineer issuing a decision for which he follows the procedure in this clause, even though he does not mention the clause, or six months from the request if the engineer does not give a decision at all. However, the courts may come to the rescue in a case of genuine confusion—N. 7.

The mere fact that the contractor changes the grounds on which he makes a claim or the employer the grounds on which he defends will not normally result in a new *"dispute or difference"*, so as to require a new referral back to the engineer followed by a new request for arbitration under this clause. In the case of a claim by the contractor for a sum of money, liability for which is denied by the employer, a change in the grounds of claim, for example from cl. 12 to a claim for damages for breach of contract, will not amount to a new dispute.

A claim by the contractor for an additional sum of money not merely as a recalculation of a claim already made but as a new claim, does amount to a new dispute. New claims of this kind are often added in when it becomes clear that arbitration is going to take place, and it does happen that the procedure in this clause is overlooked, and they are brought into the arbitration without prior referral to the engineer. Since it appears that such referral must take place even if the works are completed, the employer is entitled to object to the arbitrator dealing with a new claim without this procedure having been followed, unless the arbitrator has been given jurisdiction to hear the claim by a submission executed by the parties. It may be sensible for the employer to agree to include a new claim in arbitration without the rigmarole of referral back to the engineer, to avoid waste of time and possibly a second arbitration.

The contractor has the useful option of first referring a decision by other supervisors to the engineer under cl. 2 instead of under this clause.

For the position where the engineer is disqualified see p. 416.

6. LIABILITY OF THE ENGINEER FOR A DECISION UNDER THIS CLAUSE. The recent court decisions that in performing such duties as issuing interim certificates the engineer is no longer to be classed as a quasi-arbitrator so as to be exempt from liability to his client for negligence are discussed on p. 398, N. 31. It is not clear whether that precedent goes so far as to make the engineer liable to the employer even for a negligent decision under this clause.

The background to the decisions has been stated as follows:

"It is well settled that judges, barristers, solicitors, ... enjoy an absolute immunity from any form of civil action being brought against them in respect of anything they say or do in court during the course of a trial. This is not because the law regards any of these with special tenderness but because the law recognises that, on balance of convenience, public policy demands that they shall

all have such an immunity. It is of great importance that they should all perform their respective functions free from fear that disgruntled and possibly impecunious persons who have lost their cause or been convicted may subsequently harass them with litigation .... The law takes the risk of their being negligent and confers on them the privilege from enquiry in an action as to whether or not they have been so. The immunity which they enjoy is vital to the efficient and expedient administration of justice. Since arbitrators are in much the same position as judges ... the law has for generations recognised that public policy requires that they too shall be accorded the immunity to which I have referred. The question is—does this immunity extend beyond arbitrators properly so called, and if so, what are its limits?"

The judgments in the cases refer to four main reasons why an engineer or architect does not generally enjoy the immunity in issuing payment certificates under the construction contract: (1) he is not employed in such a case to decide an actual dispute that has arisen between the parties but to avoid a dispute; (2) he is not jointly engaged by the parties; (3) the parties do not submit evidence to him, but he makes his own investigations and comes to a decision; and (4) there is a full arbitration clause in the contract. Numbers (2) and (4) of these considerations against holding the engineer to be a quasi-arbitrator apply under this cl. 66. Number (1), possibly the most important, does not, and the position about (3) is doubtful (p. 42).

If this immunity is not to be regarded as created by the legal profession for the legal profession, it is difficult to see why it should not apply to an engineer in his special role of decision-maker under this clause. It is in the interests of efficient and speedy and fair decisions that the engineer should not be open to harassment by an action for negligence. But whether in such a mixed case a court will or will not hold the engineer liable is unpredictable; the general tendency of the courts seems to be towards wherever possible making a person liable for loss due to his negligence.

Fortunately an employer will rarely suffer loss from a negligent decision, because of his right to have it corrected in arbitration. This liability can apply only in rare cases, where the employer can prove actual negligence (not a mere error of judgment by the engineer) and loss because, for example, the contractor has gone into liquidation before the employer can obtain an arbitration award and get back money wrongly awarded by the engineer.

There is also the point that the engineer's decision under this clause is usually preceded by prior action of the engineer giving rise to the dispute that is referred back to him (N. 5). When a dispute is referred back to the engineer, the employer therefore may have an opportunity to point out to him any matters he overlooked previously. If the employer does not know of such matters because the engineer has not kept him informed about the works, then the employer's remedy may be for that failure by the engineer in his duty to keep him informed; it may be unnecessary to rely on the negligence of the engineer in again ignoring those matters in his final decision.

It is even possible that the engineer may be liable to the contractor for loss

(f) Sutcliffe v. Thackrah [1974] 1 All E.R. 859, H.L., per Lord Salmon at p. 881.
(g) See Lord Kilbrandon in Arenson v. Casson Beckman Rutley & Co. [1975] 3 All E.R. 901, 918, H.L.
(h) This tendency noted in the previous edition of this book has been carried forward since by the Arenson (pp. 398–9) and Anns (p. 395) decisions.

due to a negligent decision (p. 398). Again, the contractor will rarely suffer loss from such a decision, because of his right to arbitration.

6(a). "SUCH DECISIONS SHALL BE FINAL AND BINDING UPON THE CONTRACTOR AND THE EMPLOYER UNLESS EITHER OF THEM SHALL REQUIRE THAT THE MATTER BE REFERRED TO ARBITRATION". This change of wording from the 4th edition, and the statement in the preceding sentence that the contractor shall give effect to an engineer's decision unless and until it is revised by an arbitrator, with no similar provision about the employer, read literally imply that the engineer's decision is not binding on the employer, as well as not final, if either of the parties requires arbitration. It would be very strange to have an elaborate procedure of this kind producing a decision of no binding effect on the employer unless accepted by him, so that pending arbitration the employer could refuse to pay a sum awarded by an engineer's decision. Taking this clause as a whole, and particularly the statement in the first sentence that a dispute will be "*settled*" by the engineer's decision, the more rational interpretation that a decision is binding on the employer also unless and until it is actually upset in arbitration, is open.

In many cases a decision will merely confirm a past certificate or be embodied in a future certificate, itself enforceable, but this ambiguity may give difficulty particularly in the case of decisions after the final certificate or where the engineer's decision is that the employer is not entitled to a counterclaim against the amount of the certificate (p. 269, N. 33).

7. "MAY WITHIN THREE CALENDAR MONTHS AFTER ... NOTICE OF ... DECISION ... REQUIRE (ARBITRATION)", i.e. within three full months, excluding the day on which notice is received.

Formal notice under cl. 68 that arbitration is required is not specified. Oral notice by the contractor to the engineer as the employer's agent is almost certainly effective, but it is wise to give written notice to the employer. The employer must give notice to the contractor; notice by him to the engineer as his own agent is not effective.

The third sentence of this clause specifies that a party who does not require arbitration in time loses his right to contest a decision, in arbitration or by proceedings in the courts. Under the Arbitration Act, 1950, the court has power before or after the time limit has expired to extend the time for giving notice if "in the circumstances of the case undue hardship would

i

(*i*) The words "please advise your proposals in order to settle the matter, or name your arbitrators. Expecting your reply ..." were held to amount to an unequivocal requirement of arbitration, in *Nea Agrex S.A.* v. *Baltic Shipping Co. Ltd.* [1976] 2 All E.R. 842, but not the words "In view of the attitude taken by Charters ... Owners will be putting the matter to arbitration. We will be advising you concerning details of the Arbitrator appointed in due course" because they merely referred to an arbitration in the future and contained no present requirement of any kind, in *Surrendra Overseas Ltd.* v. *Government of Sri Lanka* [1977] 2 All E.R. 481.

Effective notice of arbitration may be important not only because of the time limit in this clause but also exceptionally to stop the Statute of Limitations running (p. 430). For the latter purpose the Limitation Act 1939 decrees that notice requiring appointment of an arbitrator (interpreted by the decisions in this footnote), must be delivered to the other party, or left at or sent by registered post or recorded delivery to his usual or last known place of abode in England.

j   otherwise be caused" (Sec. 27). An extension has been granted on the grounds that the plaintiffs would otherwise have suffered undue hardship in forfeiting forever a large claim because of an excusable oversight about the time limit for claiming arbitration, where the few days delay in claiming could not have prejudiced the other party. Nevertheless an extension will generally only be given for delay outside a party's control or contributed to by the other party; a court cannot be relied on to give an extension where the delay is due merely to an oversight or mistake, so that this is the most important time limit in these Conditions.

In order to secure the right to interest under statute (not where interest is specified in the contract) it may be important to give early notice of arbitration—p. 268, N. 29.

8. "IF THE PARTIES FAIL TO APPOINT AN ARBITRATOR WITHIN ONE CALENDAR MONTH OF EITHER PARTY SERVING THE OTHER PARTY A WRITTEN NOTICE TO CONCUR IN THE APPOINTMENT OF AN ARBITRATOR" replaces *"failing agreement"*. Apparently until the month has elapsed one party may not apply to the President for an appointment without the consent of the other. If disagreement on the choice of arbitrator is likely it may be wise to serve this notice immediately rather than negotiate first and then have to suffer one month's more delay (next note).

It does not seem that this notice must actually name a proposed
k   arbitrator.

9. SUGGESTED PRELIMINARY PROCEDURE. The following procedure is recommended to a party who wishes to reach the arbitration hearing as quickly as possible:

(*a*) As soon as the engineer's decision under cl. 66 is received, or the three months for the decision ends, serve notice on the other party to concur in the appointment of an arbitrator. In the notice give brief particulars of, say, three persons and ask the other party either to accept one of them as arbitrator or put forward three alternative names. Because the choice of arbitrator is so vitally important, it is worth making a reasonable effort to agree rather than leave the choice to nomination, but very often too much time is wasted on attempts to agree an arbitrator which are doomed to failure because of hostility and mistrust between the parties.

(*j*) *Liberian Shipping Corporation "Pegasus"* v. *A. King & Sons Ltd.* [1967] 1 All E.R. 934, C.A. In *Richmond Shipping Ltd.* v. *Agro Co. of Canada Ltd.* (1973) 2 Lloyd's Rep. 145 the Court of Appeal held that the existence or non-existence of "undue hardship" did not involve the application of any rule of law. In considering the question the court must take all the relevant circumstances of the case into account, the degree of blameworthiness of the claimants, the amount at stake, the length of the delay, whether the claimants had been misled, whether through some circumstances beyond their control it was impossible for them to proceed in time, and whether the other side had been prejudiced by the delay. In *International Tank & Pipe S.A.K.* v. *The Kuwait Aviation Fueling Co.* (1977) 5 B.L.R. 147, C.A., the 90-day period for claiming arbitration under the F.I.D.I.C. International Conditions for civil engineering works was extended where the contractors had written to the employer that "*we reserve our right to have the matters in dispute settled by arbitration . . .*" within the 90 days, but did not actually claim arbitration, where the employer took the point of the time limit after it had expired and, according to Lord Denning (p. 153) "The employers knew perfectly well that the contractors were reserving their rights in regard to arbitration. The employers suffered no prejudice whatsoever".

(*k*) *Re Eyre and Leicester Corporation* [1892] 1 Q.B. 136, on the similar wording of Sec. 5 of the Arbitration Act, 1889.

(b) Attempt to agree on the Arbitration Procedure of the Institution, as part of the agreement to the arbitrator (N. 12) or ask the President if he is making an appointment to direct that the procedure shall apply.

(c) Immediately an arbitrator has been appointed, ask him to call a preliminary meeting of the parties. All communications to or from the arbitrator should be by letter, with a copy to the other party (p. 412).

l

(d) Before or at the preliminary meeting seek to agree a sensible procedure taking maximum advantage of the available records and the expertise of the arbitrator who may himself "assist" the parties to be sensible (pp. 446–7).

(e) At the preliminary meeting the arbitrator should be asked to direct time limits for preliminary pleadings by the parties, formal or informal discovery of documents, the date for the hearing, etc. Far too often the time limits for the preliminary stages are agreed to by the parties, without any real intention of making the necessary effort to keep to them. If a party does not insist that his legal advisers give maximum sustained attention to the preparation of his documents and ensure that the maximum pressure is, put on the other side to keep to the time limits, the preliminary stages will last the usual ludicrous time.

m

A great deal depends on the force of personality of the arbitrator. If one party does not deliver his documents and it would be a disadvantage to the other party to proceed without them, all the arbitrator can do is make his dissaproval clear. But in an appropriate case he should be asked to exercise his power to go further and proceed to a hearing without the documents of a party and even in the absence of a party who refuses to co-operate:

> "If, therefore, one of the parties, after having been duly summoned, neglects to attend before the arbitrator, and the latter is of opinion, from the circumstances which are brought to his notice, that the party is absenting himself with a view to prevent justice and defeat the object of the reference, it is the arbitrator's duty to give due notice to the absent party that he intends, at a specified time and place, to proceed with the reference, whether the said party shall attend or not. If this notice is ineffectual to secure his attendance, and he does not allege some excuse satisfactory to the arbitrator, the matter not only may, but ought, to proceed *ex parte*."

n

It is suggested that undue delay amounts to prevention of justice.

o

(l) The I.C.E. Arbitration Procedure in sections 4–5 says that "The parties shall endeavour to agree, within one calender month of the appointment of the Arbitrator" on an order for directions, and that if they do not do so within that time the arbitrator will normally arrange a preliminary meeting. Nevertheless that does not appear to compel a party to wait for a month before calling a meeting where agreement is unlikely.

(m) Partly due to their tendency to overbook, like airlines and holiday hotels, lawyers are often driven to taking many small, partial steps in the hope of giving an illusion of satisfactory progress despite the long pauses in between.

(n) "Russell on Arbitration", 18th ed. by Anthony Walton, p. 223. See also *Crawford* v. *Prowting* [1972] 1 All E.R. 1199, where it was held that an arbitrator has no power to dismiss a claim for delay in the absence of disobedience by a party to a specific direction of his, but said that if a party does not obey a direction in the time stated then the arbitrator may go so far as to proceed to make an award ex parte after a warning stated to be peremptory, in particular on the basis of his powers under Sec. 12 of the Arbitration Act, 1950: "Unless a contrary intention is expressed therein, every arbitration agreement shall ... be deemed to contain a provision that the parties ... shall ... do all ... things which during the proceedings on the reference the Arbitrator ... may require'."

(o) "Justice delayed is justice denied"—see (1977) 40 M.L.R., p. 669 on the source of this often quoted and more often ignored maxim.

(*f*) Notice by a party to the other that he will seek full solicitor and client costs for any expenses due to unreasonable failure to co-operate in agreeing facts and documents or to keep to a reasonable procedure, may also be helpful. Solicitor and client costs are a fuller measure than the more usual party and party scale. *See* p. 299 on costs.

(*g*) If a party is trying to postpone unfairly the evil day of a final award against him, for example by a case stated on one claim, an arbitrator may be encouraged to make use of his power to give an interim award, determining the other claims. A recent case illustrates both the possibilities open to a forceful arbitrator to shorten proceedings, and also the dangers:

Having endured eight days hearing and considered voluminous documents, including nearly 400 pages of correspondence, the arbitrator invited Counsel for both parties to talk to him in private. He told them that he had heard a great deal of evidence and read a great deal of documents, and had come to a conclusion so far as one major dispute was concerned which he was unlikely to change, and with the parties' agreement he was prepared to announce this conclusion. Both Counsel ultimately decided to invite the arbitrator to do so, and agreed that neither would apply to the High Court on the ground that the procedure which was to be adopted by the arbitrator amounted to misconduct or was irregular. The arbitrator announced his conclusion and one party nevertheless applied to the High Court to have his interim award set aside for misconduct.

The learned judge stated that although the arbitrator had been criticised for taking this initiative, he had some sympathy with the course which he adopted. The interim award was upheld, but on the basis that it still remained for the arbitrator to decide whether or not the claim—which he had held justifiable on the facts—was wholly or partly barred for lack of proper notice under Clause 12 of the 4th edition I.C.E. General Conditions.

10. ARBITRATION ACT, 1950. The major terms of the Act applying to arbitration under this clause are, briefly:

An arbitration agreement is not ended by the death or bankruptcy of either party.

The arbitrator has the powers of a court to examine witnesses on oath and to order the production and inspection of documents.

An arbitrator may correct any accidental clerical mistake in the award.

The parties may be ordered by the arbitrator to make discovery of documents to each other, swearing they have produced all relevant and unprivileged documents which are or have been in their or their agent's possession, custody or power. Privilege is narrowly limited, mainly to documents passing between a party and his lawyer.

In a building dispute the arbitrator ordered disclosure to the employer of the personal files of the contractor's employees, without reading the files. The contractor objected by way of a case stated to the court.

Held: The sole issue was one of relevance, the test being whether the documents contained information to advance the case of the other party. Since arbitration proceedings are private, confidentiality, which might otherwise be a

(*p*) Arbitration Act 1950, Sec. 14. The claimant ought to elect his cause of action when seeking an interim award, and the court set aside an award by an arbitrator in a building contract dispute because he did not specify the cause of action or the head of the claim under which he made his interim award, in *Stanley Hugh Leech* v. *Haringey London Borough Council*, The Times, March 23rd, 1977, Sir Douglas Franks Q.C.

(*q*) *Hughes (Norman) & Co. Ltd.* v. *Ruthin B.C.* (1971) 222 E.G. 163.

factor to be taken into account, was of minor importance. Disclosure was ordered.

Private diaries, inter-office memos, the contractor's estimating papers—all have to be disclosed to the other party.

The arbitrator has a general discretion in relation to the award of costs. But the courts have in recent cases held that the arbitrator must follow the rules applied by the courts and award party and party costs to the successful party unless there is some good reason to order him to pay his own costs:

> An arbitrator ordered the successful party to pay two-thirds of the costs of the arbitration, on the grounds that the claim was small and could have been dealt with fully by arbitration, but that party had added to the costs by insisting on having the award stated in the form of a special case to the court.
> The award of costs was set aside.

> An award of costs was remitted by the court to the arbitrator to reconsider his whole order for costs. The arbitrator was held to have misdirected himself in awarding costs to the respondents simply because they were proportionately more successful in their counterclaim than the claimants were in their claim. The claimants having been successful overall were entitled to costs up to the date on which an offer was made unless the claim was so inflated as to deter the respondents from seeking a settlement or in some other way to increase the costs of the arbitration, and subject to the claimants being deprived of their own costs and also having to pay the respondents' costs if the sum recovered was so trifling as not to justify bringing the claimants to court. In addition, of the arbitrator's other grounds for his award one was wrong and the other was right. He was wrong to award that the claimants were to pay all the costs after the respondents had offered a lump sum without interest or costs in full and final settlement of the claim, during an adjournment after two days' hearing, on the grounds that the offer was "much larger" than the award, because in comparing the offer with the award he had ignored the interest payable and the question of costs. He was right to award the costs after the first two days of the hearing to the respondents on the grounds that the remaining two days were devoted entirely to a rectification issue which should have been put forward by the claimants before the arbitration began and the claimants' success on that issue had not increased the sum awarded to them.

A patent departure in an award from the general rule awarding costs to the successful party (whether by ordering him to pay the whole or part of the costs of the other party or arbitrator's fees or only to bear his own costs) without giving any sufficient reasons for doing so gives rise to a rebutable presumption that the arbitrator has erred, so as to justify intervention by the court. Although the arbitrator cannot be compelled to declare his reasons in his award, if he does so in most cases there will be the advantage that the parties may be saved the expense of trying to ascertain his reasons and possibly moving the court to set aside his award (although his reasons will then be subject to full scrutiny by the court).

If an award does depart from the ordinary rule but contains no full statement of reasons supporting the departure, the party objecting to the award may bring before the court such evidence as he can obtain as to the grounds or lack of grounds for the award. It is considered only sensible that

(r) *Mitchell Construction Kinnear Moodie Group* v. *East Anglia Regional Hospital.Board* (1971) T.R. 215.

(s) *Messers* v. *Heidner & Co.* (No. 2) (1961) 1 Lloyd's Rep. 107.

(t) *Tramountana Armadora S.A.* v. *Atlantic Shipping Co. S.A.* [1978] 2 All E.R. 870.

the parties to the arbitration should be entitled to place material before the
court which will enable it to decide whether or not it should intervene.

This control has been developed by the courts because of the tendency of
some arbitrators to refuse to award costs against the loser, perhaps when
they consider he had some moral right, or merely from indecisiveness. But it
is not easy to reconcile this extreme scrutiny of the arbitrator's award on
costs with the general principles applied otherwise to assist arbitration to
fulfill the intended function of speedy and final settlement of disputes (p.
304).

The courts, in any case, accept that there is good reason for ordering a
successful party to pay, e.g. the extra costs caused by his unreasonable
refusal to admit facts or documents, or introduction of unnecessary
evidence. By Sec. 18 of the Act the arbitrator may award solicitor and client
costs to one party (*see* p. 298 above).

A procedure has developed in practice, although not mentioned in the
Act, by which one party may make a written offer open for acceptance by
the other party. The intention is that the arbitrator will follow the practice
of a court, and award costs to the offerer from the date of the offer if it is
equal to or more than any amount he may award against him, because the
other party could have avoided the later expense of the arbitration by
accepting the offer:

> "Offers of settlement in arbitral proceedings can be of three kinds, namely
> 'without prejudice', 'sealed' and 'open'.
> A 'without prejudice' offer can never be referred to by either party at any stage
> of the proceedings, because it is in the public interest that there should be a
> procedure whereby the parties can discuss their differences freely and frankly and
> make offers of settlement without fear of being embarrassed by these exchanges
> if, unhappily, they do not lead to a settlement.
> A 'sealed offer' is the arbitral equivalent of making a payment into court in
> settlement of the litigation or of particular causes of action in that litigation.
> Neither the fact, nor the amount, of such a payment into court can be revealed to
> the judge trying the case until he has given judgment on all matters other than
> costs. As it is customary for an award to deal at one and the same time both with
> the parties' claims and with the question of costs, the existence of a sealed offer
> has to be brought to the attention of the arbitrator before he has reached a
> decision. However, it should remain sealed at that stage and it would be wholly
> improper for the arbitrator to look at it before he has reached a final decision on
> the matters in dispute other than as to costs, or to revise that decision in the light
> of the terms of the sealed offer when he sees them.
> I know that there are arbitrators and umpires who feel that this procedure is
> not as satisfactory as making a payment into court. They take the view that
> respondents will feel that their defence is weakened if the arbitrator knows that
> they have made a sealed offer, even if the figure is concealed. If this is so,
> respondents may be deterred from making a 'sealed offer'.
> There may be something in this point of view, but the solution to the problem
> is not, I think, difficult. If an arbitrator or umpire thinks it appropriate, he can
> always invite, and possibly require, the respondents to give him at the end of the
> hearing a sealed envelope which is to contain either a statement that no sealed

(*u*) The above principles were adopted in the *Tramountana* decision (previous note) from
Figueiredo Navegacas S.A. v. *Reederei Richard Schroeder K.G.* (1974) 1 Lloyd's Rep. 192. In
the former case, the arbitrator stated one reason for his award of costs in the award and
added to it later by affidavit.
In *Dineen* v. *Walpole* (1969) 1 Lloyd's Rep. 261, C.A. an award of costs against the
successful party was set aside although no reasons for the award had been given by the
arbitrator.

offer has been made or the sealed offer itself. If this procedure were adopted, the existence of a sealed offer would be hidden from the tribunal until the moment at which it had to consider that part of the award which related to costs, the delivery of a sealed envelope of itself being devoid of all significance.

An 'open offer', properly so called, is one to which either party can refer at any stage of the proceedings. In an appropriate case, it may influence the arbitrator both in his decision on the matters in dispute and on the order as to costs."   *v*

The possibility of making an offer should be carefully considered by the employer where the contractor is pursuing an exaggerated claim. The contractor may be blind to the defects in his claim or hope to obtain a large award by confusing the arbitrator, so there may even be little risk that he will accept an offer, yet it may save the employer costs if the contractor does obtain a small award.

A procedure is provided by the Act for dealing with an arbitrator who does not proceed with the arbitration and give an award with "all reasonable dispatch", or who claims payment of excessive fees before he will deliver his award.

Any sum directed to be paid by an award shall, unless the award directs otherwise, carry interest at $7\frac{1}{2}\%$. The arbitrator has a general power to   *w* award interest on claims—cl. 60, N. 29.

An award may by leave of the court be enforced in the same way as a court judgment or order.

And *see* N. 9 on procedure, ch. 14 on the conduct of an arbitrator, and N. 16 on a case stated to the courts.

11. ARBITRATION (SCOTLAND) ACT, 1894. This Act does not include the procedure by case stated (N. 16) but that procedure has been applied to Scotland by the Administration of Justice (Scotland) Act, 1972, Sec. 3, in a modified form which permits the right to a special case to be excluded in the arbitration agreement.

12. "INSTITUTION OF CIVIL ENGINEERS' ARBITRATION PROCEDURE (1973)". The importance of developing arbitration procedure tailor-made for construction disputes is discussed on p. 446 in the context of claims. This I.C.E. procedure has now been published. As specified here the parties may agree to it at the time of the dispute, or the President of the Institution may direct them to follow the procedure when appointing an arbitrator. Therefore if a party wishes to have this procedure apply he should not agree an arbitrator unless the other party will also agree to use the procedure, otherwise he will lose the chance of having the President direct that it is to apply.

(*v*) *Tramountana* case above, at pp. 875. It is also pointed out in the judgment that whereas by the Rules of the Supreme Court a payment into court may include only a contractual claim for interest and not interest under statute (text above, p. 268), no such restriction applies in arbitration and "I can see no reason in principle or practice why a 'sealed offer' should not be expressed to relate to interest under the 1934 Act as well as to principal. Indeed, I think it should be, because, if it is accepted, the arbitrator will have no power to make an award of interest by itself. This stems from the wording of the 1934 Act and its application ... to arbitral awards" (p. 877).

(*w*) Judgments Debts (Rates of Interest) Order (1971), No. 491 (L.12). The arbitrator may not validly specify that his award is to carry a higher rate of interest—*London & Overseas Freighters* v. *Timber Shipping Co.* [1971] 2 All E.R. 599, H.L., a decision which hardly promotes quick payment of awards. In view of the low rate of interest a party may be advised to start speedily the procedure for enforcing an award, unless early payment is assured.

The procedure is comprehensive, with specimen letters, forms and draft orders for directions by the arbitrator on the pleadings and procedures. There is an alternative draft order for arbitration on written evidence alone, but only where both parties agree. The more trenchant use of written records to facilitate arbitration is discussed on p. 447.

13. "SUCH ARBITRATOR SHALL HAVE FULL POWER TO OPEN UP . . . ANY DECISION OPINION INSTRUCTION DIRECTION CERTIFICATE OR VALUATION OF THE ENGINEER". In the past the engineer's decision was often made absolutely conclusive and not subject to arbitration on some points. Under this clause the engineer's decisions are not conclusive and therefore can also be reopened in litigation should a dispute reach the courts. For the effect of an engineer's decision pending arbitration *see* N. 6(a).

If the arbitrator holds that an engineer's decision refusing an instruction or variation order was wrong, it appears that he may reverse the decision, give the instruction or order retrospectively and award the contractor extra payment in respect of doing in fact what he should have been instructed to do, or value under cl. 52 any work done that should have·been ordered under cl. 51. The position of the contractor as to compensation where he has in fact before the arbitration completed the works in accordance with the original contract, because of the engineer's refusal in good faith of a variation order or instruction, is not clear (p. 417). Similarly the rights of the employer where the arbitrator reverses an instruction or variation which the contractor has already performed, are unclear.

For the arbitrator's powers to award damages for unreasonable decisions of the engineer *see* p. 417; as to errors in measurement *see* cl. 56, N. 9.

14. "INSTRUCTION" is new, and discussed in the last note.

15. "THE EVIDENCE OR ARGUMENTS PUT BEFORE THE ENGINEER". Whether or not the engineer has any duty to hear evidence and arguments is discussed on p. 415.

16. "THE AWARD OF THE ARBITRATOR SHALL BE FINAL AND BINDING ON THE PARTIES". The settlement of disputes cannot be given over completely to an arbitrator, who is always subject to some control by the courts,·under the Arbitration Act:

(*a*) Special case. The courts will not allow an arbitrator to create his own system of law. He may, and must if ordered by the courts on an application by either party, state any question of law (for example, the interpretation of the contract, or even of a letter) that arises in the course of the arbitration for decision by the courts. This is done either by adjourning the arbitration hearing until the point is decided by the court, or by completing the

(*x*) *Woodhouse* v. *Nigerian Produce Ltd.* [1972] 2 All E.R. 271. The position is complicated by the rule that the question of whether there is any evidence to support a finding of fact is itself a question of law. However, "That rule should be applied reasonably and with moderation" and normally only the arbitrator's conclusions of fact inferred or deduced from the primary findings of the basic facts (such as the events which occurred) may be the subject of a special case, the arbitrator's findings of the primary facts are binding—per Pearson, L.J., *Tersons Ltd.* v. *Stevenage Development Corp.* (1963) reported in 5 B.L.R. 58, 81, 82, C.A.

arbitration and giving the award in the form of a special case, i.e. alternative awards depending on the court's decision on the point of law.

(*b*) Before an award has been made the courts may refuse to stay court proceedings brought by one of the parties in defiance of the arbitration agreement, and so make the agreement ineffective. They may also remove or revoke the authority of an arbitrator and may appoint a substitute, or even after an award has been made may remit it to the arbitrator for reconsideration or set it aside. The courts use these powers guardedly—"parties should not be relieved from a tribunal they have chosen because they find they are likely to lose owing to the mistakes in the arbitrator's decision which they have agreed to be bound by"—and will generally only interfere:

(i) Where the principal question in dispute is one of law, particularly where it is about the interpretation of the contract; arbitration is not appropriate on questions of this kind, which will usually, in any case, come back to the courts by way of a special case. But the courts may let a dispute on law go to arbitration, particularly where the question of law is mixed with technical questions of fact.

(ii) Where the dispute involves charges of fraud or other charges against the character of a party.

(iii) Apart from the above two cases, a court retains a general discretion to refuse to stay court proceedings even though there is an applicable arbitration agreement. In an unusual case:

A plumbing sub-contractor sued a main contractor in the courts for damages for delay to his work and in making payment. The main contractor applied to stay the action and leave the dispute to be dealt with under the wide arbitration clause in the sub-contract. The sub-contractor was insolvent and had obtained legal aid for the court proceedings, but would have been unable to pursue the claim in arbitration because legal aid is not available for arbitration.

Held: That because there was reasonable grounds for believing the sub-contractor's allegation that his insolvency was itself due to the main contractor's breach of contract, or at least a triable issue about it, a stay of action would be refused so as to prevent a denial of justice.

(iv) A court may intervene after an award, where fresh evidence of weight is discovered which could not with reasonable diligence have been discovered before the award.

(v) Where there is misconduct by the arbitrator, for example by admitting evidence wrongly. Generally the arbitrator is bound by the ordinary law of evidence, but the courts may hold that an award is valid despite relaxation of technical rules, particularly if the parties did not object at the time. For other classes of misconduct *see* ch. 14.

(*y*) The arbitrator has power to alter the question of law agreed between the lawyers for the parties if he thinks necessary to do so in order to state a case properly—*Faghirzadeh* v. *Rudolf Wolff* (S.A.) (*Pty.*) [1977] 1 Lloyd's Rep. 630. The court in turn has jurisdiction to amend or reformulate the questions of law before it on a special case on the application of one or both of the parties, so that the real issues between them will be decided, provided the arbitrator has found the facts sufficiently for that purpose—*Ismail* v. *Polish Ocean Lines* [1976] 1 All E.R. 902.

(*z*) *Bristol Corporation* v. *Aird* [1913] A.C. 241 at p. 252.

(*aa*) *Radford* v. *Hair* [1971] 2 All E.R. 1089, action permitted despite an arbitration clause in a partnership agreement, because the dispute involved allegations of dishonesty affecting the professional reputation of one of the partners.

(*bb*) *Fakes* v. *Taylor Woodrow Construction Ltd.* [1973] 1 All E.R. 670, C.A.

(vi) Where there is an error on the face of the award—that is, where the award itself shows an error of fact or law or reasoning made by the arbitrator in reaching his decision. The courts will not interfere merely because the decision is wrong in the sense that a court would have reached a different decision on the facts of the case, only where the error on which it is based appears on the face of the award or some document incorporated in it:

An arbitrator made an award without reading the written submission of the dispute, which directed him to decide on the basis of a custom known as Riga Usance. It was proved that he did not know what that meant.
Held: The award was binding nevertheless, since it did not set out the facts found by the arbitrator or any reasons for his decision.

cc

Contractors working under the 4th edition I.C.E. forms met unexpected difficulties and gave notice under cl. 12, but they did not follow the rest of the procedure in that clause.
In an interim award the arbitrator accepted the contractor's claim for extra on the grounds, stated in his award, that cl. 52 (4) of the conditions "implies that the engineer has power to consider a claim for any additional expenses to which the contractor may consider himself entitled, provided such claim is delivered to the engineer at the earliest practicable opportunity".
Held: That was completely wrong; cl. 52 (4) gives the contractor no independent rights at all. There was therefore an error on the face of the award and it was set aside.

dd

Defendants contracted to sell stewed steak to the plaintiffs at a fixed price, but did not deliver the goods because they were offered a better price elsewhere. The plaintiffs claimed damages in arbitration, but the defendants denied liability on the grounds that the contract was illegal (see cl. 26, N. 5)) under certain statutory orders. The arbitrator awarded the plaintiffs substantial damages without giving reasons.
Held: The award must be set aside—the arbitrator was not entitled to act directly against the law by ignoring the obvious illegality of the contract simply because he thought that in fairness the plaintiffs should have been entitled to damages.

ee

17. ARBITRATOR'S JURISDICTION—COMPLETION AND ARBITRATION BEFORE COMPLETION. It appears that the arbitrator has jurisdiction under this clause to decide whether there is a right to arbitration before completion (N. 1). The words "or alleged completion" imply that the arbitrator also has power to decide whether or not the works have been completed. Unless both parties waive the right to test his jurisdiction in court, if there is any real doubt on either point the arbitrator should not open the arbitration on other issues until any objecting party has had the matter decided by a court, to avoid a hearing which will be a costly nullity if the objection is upheld.

"completion" appears to mean substantial completion—see sub-cl. (a) of this clause.

ff

18. ARBITRATION BEFORE COMPLETION ON A DISPUTE UNDER CLAUSE 12. Refer to p. 71, N. 22.

(cc) Bland v. Russian Bank for Foreign Trade (1906) 11 Com.Cas. 71.
(dd) Blackford & Son (Calne) Ltd. v. Christchurch Corp. (1962) 1 Lloyd's Rep. 349.
(ee) Taylor (David) & Sons v. Barnett Trading Co. [1953] 1 All E.R. 843, distinguished in Prodexport State Company for Foreign Trade v. E.D. & F. Mon Ltd. [1973] 1 All E.R. 355.
(ff) The point was treated as doubtful in the Farr case below, p. 95.

19. ARBITRATION BEFORE COMPLETION ON "THE WITHHOLDING BY THE ENGINEER OF ANY CERTIFICATE". The controversy about the meaning of these words is largely solved in this edition of the Conditions by deletion from cl. 60 of the specific power to withhold certificates and retention money. The result is that the contractor has the right to immediate arbitration on "any dispute or difference which relates to something in consequence of which a certificate has been refused, which on one view of the question ought to have been given". Where "in accordance with mistaken principles, because he has misdirected himself about the law (the Engineer) refuses a certificate altogether or refuses to certify more than £15,000 of a proper claim of £20,000" there is a "dispute or difference as to the withholding of the certificate".

One doubt which unfortunately is not removed by this edition is whether the contractor is entitled to arbitration before completion on a claim of undermeasurement in a certificate not involving a dispute of principle, as to the measurement of quantities or valuation of items. If he is so entitled, then an extremely wide right to arbitration before completion is given to the contractor, and incidentally the discrimination against the employer is virtually complete; the employer has no right to arbitrate before completion of the works on over-certification by the engineer or any other question whether of principle or amount, with the one exception of a dispute under cl. 12.

The "*withholding*" appears to commence with the next interim certificate after the payment becomes legally due and is claimed in the contractor's monthly statement, and in the case of variations after the engineer and contractor have failed to agree a valuation in consultation (p. 188, N. 11). The engineer may have very little time to make an initial decision, but he will have the three months for a decision under cl. 66 before the contractor may start arbitration.

The payments to be included in certificates have been greatly extended by this edition, but still do not include damages for breach of contract, in respect of which therefore there is no right to arbitration before completion.

20. ARBITRATION BEFORE COMPLETION ON "THE WITHHOLDING OF ANY PORTION OF THE RETENTION MONEY UNDER CLAUSE 60". Such a dispute may arise before completion because of the provision in cl. 60 (5) (a) for partial release of retention on completion of parts and sections of the works.

21. IMMEDIATE ARBITRATION "AS TO THE EXERCISE OF THE ENGINEER'S POWER TO GIVE A CERTIFICATE UNDER CLAUSE 63 (1)". In view of the wide powers given to the arbitrator "*to open up review and revise any decision ...of the Engineer*" it seems that in immediate arbitration under this provision the arbitrator may decide whether an order of the engineer which

---

(gg) *Farr (A.E.) Ltd.* v. *Ministry of Transport* [1960] 3 All E.R. 88.

(hh) In the *Farr* decision, above, it was said that such a dispute was not a dispute about the withholding of a certificate and therefore there was no right to arbitration before completion. The distinction is doubtful, but it is perhaps relevant that in *Killby & Gayford Ltd.* v. *Selincourt Ltd.* (1973) 229 E.G. 1343, C.A., a case on the R.I.B.A. form of contract, Lord Denning said that he "would deplore any too ready resource to arbitration in the case of these interim certificates, to go into questions of quantity or the like, when clearly the arbitration clause contemplated that all those matters should be dealt with as one whole, at the end of the contract or after the works were practically completed". That case is discussed also on p. 271.

has led to the forfeiture was right, so that the contractor is in a position to challenge any order of the engineer immediately by refusing to obey it and (unless cl. 39 (2), 49 (4) or 62 applies) forcing the engineer to forfeit the contract.

If the employer forfeits the contract on the engineer's certificate and the certificate is then reversed by the arbitrator, it appears that the employer is not liable to pay damages to the contractor for expelling him from the site, since he had a certificate authorising forfeiture when he acted and he is not liable for the independent decisions of the engineer except where the certificate is invalid (pp. 416–18). Nevertheless if forfeiture is reversed by the arbitrator, if the employer does not allow the contractor back on site the contractor will then be entitled to full damages and the employer will not be entitled to recover the extra cost of completing by another contractor.

It has recently been held that where the validity of a forfeiture notice depends on disputed matters of fact, the court will not give the employer a temporary injunction to prevent the contractor from remaining on the site, unless the court feels a "high degree of assurance" that the disputed matters will at the trial of the full action for the permanent injunction be resolved in favour of the employer. Insofar as that decision applies, the result is that provided the contractor remains on the site despite the forfeiture notice or other attempted termination of the contract by the employer (N. 22), he may be entitled to prevent the employer completing the works until it is decided in an action or arbitration whether or not the forfeiture is valid. Given the normal time taken for an action or arbitration to get to hearing, the result is to give a contractor who can put forward any excuse for delay or otherwise contest the validity of a forfeiture notice, issued or threatened, a strong weapon with which to prevent the employer taking decisive action against him and getting on with the works. That may be most unfair to the employer, and the decision has been criticised. There are certainly two important reservations about the effects of the decision.

In the first place, if the contractor does not accept the validity of a determination he must proceed with the works (although under cl. 63 (4) the employer will stop payments). He may not refuse to give the employer possession of the site and himself discontinue or slow down with the works; if he does so the employer will then be entitled validly to forfeit or end the contract. The choice open to the contractor is to refuse to accept the employer's action, in which case the contract is still in existence and he must proceed with the works, or to treat the employer's action as a wrongful repudiation of the contract and bring the contract to an end, in which case he may claim damages but must hand back the possession of the site to which he is entitled only so long as the contract continues.

The second limitation is that the decision was on the R.I.B.A. conditions of contract, under which the employer's right to forfeit the contract depends on the contractor in fact failing "to proceed regularly and diligently with the Works", etc. Under this clause the employer's right to forfeit is dependent

(ii) *London Borough Council of Hounslow* v. *Twickenham Garden Developments* [1970] 3 All E.R. 326. In an earlier case of *Foster & Dicksee* v. *Hastings Corpn.* (1903) 87 L.T. 736 an injunction was granted to prevent forfeiture pending arbitration.

(jj) 36 M.L.R. (1973) 199. The decision was not followed in *Mayfield Holdings* v. *Moana Reef* [1973] 1 N.Z.L.R. 309, or in *Graham H. Roberts Pty. Ltd.* v. *Maurbeth Investments Pty. Ltd.* (1974) 1 N.S.W.L.R. 93 Can., and see *American Cyanamid* v. *Ethicon Ltd.* [1975] 1 All E.R. 504, H.L., on the proof necessary to obtain an injunction.

on his obtaining a certificate from the engineer that certain facts have arisen, rather than on proof of the existence of such facts. It is strongly arguable that if the employer can produce a certificate from the engineer he has irrefutably established his right to forfeit the contract, unless and until that certificate is upset in arbitration, and it is not for the court in proceedings for an injunction to go behind the certificate. The basis of the decision is that the court should not assist the employer to break his contract where there is some evidence that the forfeiture may be a breach of contract, but clearly the employer is not in breach of contract in forfeiting under this clause on foot of an engineer's certificate (unless of course the certificate is not issued in accordance with the procedure under this clause, or otherwise is invalid when issued (p. 416)).

22. IMMEDIATE ARBITRATION ON TERMINATION OF THE CONTRACT IN OTHER CASES. There is no express right to immediate arbitration where the contract is brought to an end by either party under the general law (ch. 16) or by the contractor under cl. 40 (2). However, it will generally be in the interests of both parties to agree to immediate arbitration, unless there is no doubt about the position. Otherwise, for example, if the contractor is held to have acted wrongly, he will already have become liable for the costs of completing and will not have an opportunity of offering to complete the work once his liability is established. Even if the contractor is held to be in the wrong, such completion may be the most satisfactory solution for the employer as well as the contractor if the contractor is not able to pay damages. If the employer is held to have wrongfully attempted to end the contract under the general law, as opposed to acting under cl. 63 (see N. 21), he will be liable to pay damages to the contractor.

It is suggested that the contractor is entitled to arbitration despite non-completion if the employer abandons the works or delays unreasonably in having them completed, i.e. "*until ... completion*" means "pending" completion.

23. "IS NOT ABLE" is rather vague. This right for the Vice-President to appoint would apply where the President is too ill to be able to decide on an appointment. Where he is merely very busy it would not. If the President is abroad, particularly if he is away only for a short time and can make the appointment on his return, it may be unsafe to rely on this paragraph.

(*kk*) See on this point p. 345 of the *Hounslow* judgment.

(*ll*) Where a contract is brought to an end under the general law for the default of one party an arbitration clause normally survives and remains binding on the grounds that "it is quite distinct from the other clauses. The other clauses set out the obligations which the parties undertake towards each other ... but the arbitration clause does not impose on one of the parties an obligation in favour of the other. It embodies the agreement of both parties that, if any dispute arises with regard to the obligations which the one party has undertaken to the other, such dispute shall be settled by a tribunal of their own constitution." *Heyman* v. *Darwins Ltd.* [1942] A.C. 356, per Lord Macmillan at pp. 373, 374. Considered in *Blocman Pty. Ltd.* v. *Council of Gold Coast* [1972] 3 All E.R. 357, P.C. It is difficult to see that the statement in this clause that "*no steps shall be taken in the reference to the arbitrator until after the completion or alleged completion of the Works*" can be separated from the arbitration clause and treated as an "executive" or "substantial" obligation within the above decisions so as to cease to apply on termination of the contract.

CHAPTER 9

Conditions Clauses 67–72
and Price Fluctuations Clause

67. If the works are situated in Scotland the Contract shall in all respects be construed and operate as a Scottish Contract and shall be interpreted in accordance with Scots law.[1]

1. SCOTS LAW. *See* e.g. cl. 66, N. 11, above, referring to the Arbitration (Scotland) Act, 1894. Any contract for use in Scotland should be vetted by a local lawyer.

NOTICES — SERVICE ON CONTRACTOR

68. (1) Any notice to be given to the Contractor under the terms of the Contract shall be served[1] by sending the same by post to or leaving the same at the Contractor's principal place of business (or in the event of the Contractor being a Company to or at its registered office).

SERVICE OF NOTICES ON EMPLOYER

(2) Any notice to be given to the Employer under the terms of the Contract shall be served[1] by sending the same by post to or leaving the same at the Employer's last known address (or in the event of the Employer being a Company to or at its registered office).

1. "NOTICE . . . SHALL BE SERVED". This clause applies to notices which the contract expressly requires (e.g. under cls. 27 (4), 52 (2), 63, 65 and 66). It does not apply where the requirement of notice is only implied into the contract (cl. 39, N. 5), or to notices by the contractor to the engineer.

Notice given in accordance with the clause will take effect on the date on which it would in the ordinary course of post reach the other party.

69. (1)[1] The rates and prices contained in the Bill of Quantities take account of the levels and incidence at the date for return of tenders[2] (hereinafter called "the relevant date") of the taxes levies and contributions (including national insurance contributions but excluding income tax and any levy payable under

(a) Relevant decisions on the interpretation of this clause are *Browne* v. *Black* [1912] 1 K.B. 316, *Retail Dairy Co. Ltd.* v. *Clarke* [1912] 2 K.B. 388 and *Holywell Securities Ltd.* v. *Hughes* [1974] 1 All E.R. 161.

the Industrial Training Act 1964) which are by law payable by the Contractor in respect of his workpeople and the premiums and refunds (if any) which are by law payable to the Contractor in respect of his workpeople. Any such matter is hereinafter called "a labour-tax matter".

The rates and prices contained in the Bill of Quantities do not take account of any level or incidence of the aforesaid matters where at the relevant date such level or incidence does not then have effect but although then known is to take effect at some later date. The taking effect of any such level or incidence at the later date shall for the purposes of sub-clause (2) of this Clause be treated as the occurrence of an event.

(2) If after the relevant date there shall occur any of the events specified in sub-clause (3) of this Clause and as a consequence thereof the cost to the Contractor of performing his obligations under the Contract[3] shall be increased or decreased then subject to the provisions of sub-clause (4) of this Clause the net amount of such increase[4] or decrease shall constitute an addition to or deduction from the sums otherwise payable to the Contractor under the Contract as the case may require.

(3) The events referred to in the preceding sub-clause are as follows:

(a) any change in the level of any labour-tax matter;

(b) any change in the incidence of any labour-tax matter including the imposition of any new such matter or the abolition of any previously existing such matter.[5]

(4) In this Clause workpeople means persons employed by the Contractor or manual labour whether skilled or unskilled but for the purpose of ascertaining what if any additions or deductions are to be paid or allowed under this Clause account shall not be taken of any labour-tax matter in relation to any workpeople of the Contractor unless at the relevant time their normal place of employment is the Site.[6]

(5) Subject to the provisions of the Contract as to the placing of sub-contracts with Nominated Sub-contractors the Contractor may incorporate in any sub-contract made for the purpose of performing his obligations under the Contract provisions which are *mutatis mutandis* the same as the provisions of this Clause[7] and in such event additions or deductions to be made in accordance with any such sub-contract shall also be made under the Contract as if the increase or decrease of cost to the sub-contractor had been directly incurred by the Contractor.

(6) As soon as practicable after the occurrence of any of the events specified in sub-clause (3) of this Clause the Contractor shall give the Engineer notice thereof. The Contractor shall keep such contemporary records as are necessary[8] for the purpose of ascertaining the amount of any addition or deduction to be made in accordance with this Clause and shall permit the Engineer to inspect such records. The Contractor shall submit to the Engineer with his monthly statements full details of every addition or deduction to be made in accordance with this Clause. All certificates for payment issued after submission of such details shall take due account of the additions or deductions to which such details relate. Provided that the Engineer may if the Contractor fails to submit full details of any deduction nevertheless take account of such deduction when issuing any certificate for payment.[9,10]

1. FLUCTUATIONS IN TAX MATTERS—LIMITS. The words of this clause are sufficiently clear to doom to failure efforts by contractors to extend the clause beyond strictly tax matters, for example to cover increases in such matters as Employers Liability insurance premiums, which are not "*taxes levies and contributions*" and are payable for insurance cover and not "*in respect of workpeople*", although based on the contractor's payroll.

2. "THE DATE FOR RETURN OF TENDERS" irrespective of the actual date of

tender. In theory the contractor may have problems if he returns his tender before the latest return day, in a case where there is a last-minute change in legislation, but in most cases it will be known in advance when such changes are on the cards and whether they will take effect before or after the return date. The contractor is free to recall his tender and amend it for any changes, before the original or any extended date for return.

3. "THE COST TO THE CONTRACTOR OF PERFORMING HIS OBLIGATIONS UNDER THE CONTRACT" includes the cost of complying with the administrative duties under sub-cl. (6) of this clause and cl. 60. The contractor is entitled to claim for the extra cost of administration in complying with this clause in respect of any new tax or change in tax. These words would also appear to include costs of extra administrative duties which in the process of performing his contract the contractor has to perform for the tax authorities due to a tax change.

4. "THE NET AMOUNT OF SUCH INCREASE". No profit or overheads are permitted, but *see* the last note.

5. "CHANGE IN THE INCIDENCE OF ANY LABOUR-TAX MATTER INCLUDING THE IMPOSITION OF ANY NEW SUCH MATTER" does not include the formal ending and reimposition of some tax legislated for annually.

6. "WORKPEOPLE MEANS PERSONS EMPLOYED ... ON MANUAL LABOUR WHETHER SKILLED OR UNSKILLED ... (AND) AT THE RELEVANT TIME THEIR NORMAL PLACE OF EMPLOYMENT IS THE SITE". Foremen and other supervisors are excluded:

> "A person is not employed in 'manual labour' for the purpose of any of the Acts, if his occupation is primarily or substantially an activity of a different kind and the manual work that he does is merely ancillary or accessory to that activity. ... Examples of activities which are primarily non-manual, though involving some manual work, are (i) the work of a painter, sculptor or lithographic artist; (ii) managerial or supervisory work; (iii) selling in a shop; (iv) clerical work; (v) driving a vehicle or acting as conductor of a public service vehicle".

b

In this context, particularly with the reference to "*skilled*" labour, it is suggested that a plant operator is included.

For the definition of the "*Site*" *see* cl. 1 (1) (n).

7. "CONTRACTOR MAY INCORPORATE IN ANY SUB-CONTRACT ... PROVISIONS WHICH ARE MUTATIS MUTANDIS THE SAME AS THE PROVISIONS OF THIS CLAUSE". This sub-clause arises out of the fact that the contractor will suffer no loss or gain from a change in a labour-tax matter affecting a sub-contractor's work, unless the sub-contractor has a right to or is subject to reduction in price under his sub-contract for such change. Given the purpose of this sub-clause, the requirement of incorporation in the sub-contract of "*provisions ... the same as the provisions of this Clause*" is probably met by a simple statement that this clause is to apply to the sub-contract *mutatis mutandis*, without the necessity of setting out in the sub-contract the equivalent of this clause. Unfortunately the drafting is not as clear as cl. 53 (10). The type of

(*b*) *Stone* [*F. & J.*] *Lighting & Radio Ltd.* v. *Haygarth* [1966] 3 All E.R. 539 H.L. per Lord Pearson at p. 555, in a different context.

clauses standard in sub-contracts by which the sub-contractor is given notice or made subject to the terms of the main contract are not sufficient, because of their generality and because they do not give the sub-contractor the benefit of this clause whereas this sub-clause requires incorporation of the whole of the clause, both benefit and burden.

8. "As soon as practicable ... the Contractor shall give the Engineer notice ... keep such contemporary records as are necessary". *See* p. 163, N. 3. This clause does not say specifically that failure to give notice, etc., automatically invalidates the contractor's claim. However, the notice provisions in cl. 52 (4) (b) and (e) appear to apply also, and the engineer is likely to be prejudiced by any failure by the contractor to keep records of the men on the site, etc.

9. Increases incurred as a result of Contractor's own delay in completion. The courts have held, in a case not on this form of contract, that where liquidated damages are specified for delay in completion they are the employer's only remedy for that delay; that, in the absence of a special provision, the employer is bound to pay and cannot recover back from the contractor increases under a fluctuation clause even though the increases came into force after the date by which the contractor should have finished the works. It was made clear in that decision, on the other hand, that if there is no liquidated damages clause, the employer is entitled to claim back from the contractor any increases paid under a fluctuation clause resulting from the contractor's delay, as part of the ordinary damages for delay in completion (p. 428).

It is respectfully suggested that the first conclusion is fallacious. The amount of tax, price, etc., increases incurred is not related to the contractor's delay in completing the whole works, but to the volume of work behind schedule. For example, if the contractor finishes the whole works except for some small part vital to use by the employer, the employer will not be able to use the works and it is right that liquidated damages should run whilst completion of that part is late, but any increases in tax or costs will have very little effect because they will be incurred by the contractor only in relation to the small part of the works uncompleted. On the other hand, if the contractor does the works in an irregular way so that a very large volume of work is completed towards or after the end of the contract period, then the employer may have to meet a substantial extra burden under a fluctuation clause.

In short, the increase in fluctuation payments is related not to delay in completion as such, but to the extent of the failure by the contractor to "*proceed with the Works with due expedition*". These quoted words are taken from cl. 41, which places a duty on the contractor to proceed with due expedition which appears to be additional to the duty to complete on time in cl. 43, and see cl. 63 (1) (d). The employer should therefore be entitled to recover damages from the contractor for breach of that separate duty and, since the liquidated damages under cl. 47 apply only to failure to complete on time, to recover general damages including any increases payable to the contractor under the fluctuation clause as a result of the failure to proceed with due expedition.

(c) *Peak Construction (Liverpool) Ltd.* v. *McKinney Foundations* (1970) reported in 1 B.L.R. 114, C.A.

Admittedly there may be difficulties in calculating such a claim, but the calculation should be possible. Where the contractor completes on time, it may be argued that he has achieved due expedition even if he did an undue amount of the work in a late period, on the grounds that cl. 41 does not specifically require regular progress; on the other hand failure to complete on time is clear evidence of absence of due expedition.

It is also extremely difficult to cover possible losses of the employer under a clause such as this in liquidated damages, both because of the difficulty of foreseeing the level of increases and because the longer the contractor is late the higher the level of increase is likely to become, whereas the liquidated damages under cl. 47 are stated as a flat weekly sum however long the delay may be. There is nothing to prevent the employer altering that clause to provide for increasing damages, provided they are calculated by reference to a genuine estimate of likely increases covered by the fluctuation clause and the calculations made at the time are preserved (p. 149, N. 1), and there does not appear to be any legal objection to stating the liquidated damages as "£   ,   *plus a sum equivalent to any amount payable by the Employer to the Contractor under Clause* 69 *in respect of an increase of cost in such week/day that would not have been incurred by the Contractor if the Works had been completed by the due date for completion prescribed by Clause* 43".

10. FLUCTUATIONS ON VALUING VARIATIONS AND IN DISRUPTION CLAIMS. *See* respectively p. 318 and p. 370.

VALUE ADDED TAX CLAUSE 70

Disputes between the employer and contractor may go to the Value Added Tax Tribunal under this clause, and not to arbitration under cl. 66. As a taxation matter the clause is outside the scope of this book, but (too) many publications on V.A.T. are available.

METRICATION

71.   (1) If any materials described in the Contract or ordered by the Engineer are described by dimensions in the metric or imperial measure and having used his best endeavours the Contractor cannot[1] without undue delay or additional expense[2] or at all procure such materials in the measure specified in the Contract but can obtain such materials in the other measure to dimensions approximating to those described in the Contract or ordered by the Engineer then the Contractor shall forthwith give written notice to the Engineer of these facts stating the dimensions to which such materials are procurable in the other measure. Such notice shall where practicable be given in sufficient time to enable the Engineer to consider and if necessary give effect to any design change which may be required and to avoid delay in the performance of the Contractor's other obligations under the Contract. Any additional cost or expense incurred by the

---

(d) This argument was foreshadowed in the *Peak* decision above, at p. 120. In *London Borough Council of Hounslow* v. *Twickenham Garden Developments Ltd.* [1970] 3 All E.R. 326, 351, Megary J. held that the contractor under the R.I.B.A. Conditions has a separate duty to proceed with the works "regularly and diligently" as well as to complete on time and may be in breach of the former duty even though he completes on time. The argument appears to have been somewhat overlooked in the decision in *City of Westminster* v. *Jarvis Ltd.* [1970] 1 All E.R. 943, H.L.—particularly p. 951.

Contractor as a result of any delay arising out of the Contractor's default under this sub-clause[3] shall be borne by the Contractor.

(2) As soon as practicable[4] after the receipt of any such notice under the preceding sub-clause the Engineer shall if he is satisfied that the Contractor has used his best endeavours[5] to obtain materials to the dimensions described in the Contract or ordered by the Engineer and that they are not obtainable without undue delay or without putting the Contractor to additional expense[2] either:

(a) instruct the Contractor pursuant to Clause 13[6] to supply such materials (despite such delay or expense) in the dimensions described in the Contract or originally ordered by the Engineer; or

(b) give an order to the Contractor pursuant to Clause 51:[6]

(i) to supply such materials to the dimensions stated in his said notice to be procurable instead of to the dimensions described in the Contract or originally ordered by the Engineer; or

(ii) to make some other variation whereby the need to supply such materials to the dimensions described in the Contract or originally ordered by the Engineer will be avoided.

(3) This Clause shall apply irrespective of whether the materials in question are to be supplied in accordance with the Contract directly by the Contractor or indirectly by a Nominated Sub-contractor.

1. "HAVING USED HIS BEST ENDEAVOURS THE CONTRACTOR CANNOT": "We think best endeavours means what the words say. They do not mean second best endeavours ... they do not mean that the limits of reason must be overstepped with regard to the cost of the services. But short of this qualification the words mean that the Great Central Company must broadly speaking leave no stone unturned ..."

2. "WITHOUT UNDUE DELAY OR ADDITIONAL EXPENSE". There is no clarification of what delay is "*undue*". Apparently any additional expense, provided it is not trifling, is enough to entitle the contractor to operate this clause. Presumably expense, whether in the price for the material or transport costs, etc., is "*additional*" if it would not be incurred in supplying material in the other measure.

3. "ANY ADDITIONAL COST OR EXPENSE INCURRED BY THE CONTRACTOR AS A RESULT OF ANY DELAY ARISING OUT OF THE CONTRACTOR'S DEFAULT UNDER THIS SUB-CLAUSE SHALL BE BORNE BY THE CONTRACTOR". The contractor also bears his own costs of delay prior to timely action by the engineer under sub-cl. (2)—N. 6. The contractor is not specifically required to pay any extra costs incurred by the employer, but such costs may be recoverable as damages for breach of contract by the contractor in failing to give notice in time.

4. "AS SOON AS PRACTICABLE". *See* p. 163, N. 3.

5. "THE ENGINEER ... IF HE IS SATISFIED THAT THE CONTRACTOR HAS USED HIS BEST ENDEAVOURS". If the engineer is not so satisfied the implication is that he leaves the contractor to suffer the additional expense and (without any extension of time) the delay due to the contractor's own failure to use his best endeavours to get materials in the specified dimensions. Despite his right to liquidated damages, or at least in theory to forfeiture of the whole contract, if the contractor does not make up for the time lost, the delay may

(d') *Sheffield District Ry. Co.* v. *Great Central Ry. Co.* [1911] 27 T.L.R. 451.

be detrimental to the employer, and the engineer may be under some pressure to act.

It is suggested that in any case where difficulty is likely to arise the engineer should keep in touch with the contractor's ordering of materials so that he can supplement the contractor's endeavours if necessary (being careful not to give instructions or orders that could lead to claims). Indeed it is possible to write into the contract a clause giving the engineer the right to intervene in ordering materials, etc., where the contractor is failing in his duties. If difficulties are not avoided in this way, the engineer may agree to take one of the steps set out in sub-cl. (2) (a) or (b) although he has no duty to do so, provided the contractor agrees that this action is a concession to him out of which he will have no claim to extra time or money.

6. "INSTRUCT THE CONTRACTOR PURSUANT TO CLAUSE 13 . . . OR . . . GIVE AN ORDER TO THE CONTRACTOR PURSUANT TO CLAUSE 52". *See* under those respective clauses and cl. 44 for the rights of the contractor to an extension of time and payment. Under cl. 13 the contractor is entitled only to cost of delay or disruption, not for example of having to pay an exorbitant price or extra transport costs to obtain material in the measure specified. In such a case the engineer normally will act under para. (b) of this clause; if he unreasonably refuses to do so the contractor's remedy in arbitration is not very satisfactory (p. 302, N. 13).

The contractor is given no right to payment of costs for delay or disruption prior to the engineer's instruction or order, so that it is in the contractor's interest to give notice under sub-cl. (1) as soon as possible. If the contractor then suffers loss because the engineer does not act under sub-cl. (2) "*As soon as practicable*", the contractor will have a right to compensation for the engineer's breach of that sub-clause (p. 418).

SPECIAL CONDITIONS

72. The following special conditions form part of the Conditions of Contract. (Note: Any special conditions which it is desired to incorporate in the conditions of contract should be numbered consecutively with the foregoing conditions of contract.)

The difficult task of drafting special conditions is discussed on pp. 5 7, 25 6 and 440. The possibility of altering the Conditions has been mentioned in several places, most important cls. 13 (p. 76) and 40 (2) (p. 133, N. 12).

CONTRACT PRICE FLUCTUATIONS

This clause has been prepared by the Institution of Civil Engineers, the Association of Consulting Engineers and the Federation of Civil Engineering Contractors, in consultation with the Government in its revised form, for use in appropriate cases as a Special Condition of the Conditions of Contract for use in connection with Works of Civil Engineering Construction Fifth Edition dated June 1973.

(1)[1] The amount payable by the Employer to the Contractor upon the issue by the Engineer of an interim certificate pursuant to Clause 60 (2) or of the final certificate pursuant to Clause 60 (3) (other than amounts due under this Clause) shall be increased or decreased in accordance with the provisions of this Clause 1(a) if there shall be any changes in the following Index Figures compiled by the

Department of the Environment and published by Her Majesty's Stationery Office (H.M.S.O.) in the Monthly Bulletin of Construction Indices (Civil Engineering Works):

   (a) the Index of the Cost of Labour in Civil Engineering Construction;

   (b) the Index of the Cost of Providing and Maintaining Constructional Plant and Equipment;

   (c) the Indices of Constructional Material Prices applicable to those materials listed in sub-clause (4) of this Clause.

The net total of such increases and decreases shall be given effect to in determining the Contract Price.

   (2) For the purpose of this Clause:

   (a) "Final Index Figure" shall mean any Index Figure appropriate to sub-clause (1) of this Clause not qualified in the said Bulletin as provisional;

   (b) "Base Index Figure" shall mean the appropriate Final Index Figure applicable to the date 42 days prior to the date for the return of tenders;

   (c) "Current Index Figure" shall mean the appropriate Final Index Figure to be applied in respect of any certificate issued or due to be issued by the Engineer pursuant to Clause 60 and shall be the appropriate Final Index Figure applicable to the date 42 days prior to:

     (i) the due date (or extended date) for completion; or

     (ii) the date certified pursuant to Clause 48 of completion of the whole of the Works; or

     (iii) the last day of the period to which the certificate relates;

whichever is the earliest.

     Provided that in respect of any work the value of which is included in any such certificate and which work forms part of a Section for which the due date (or extended date) for completion or the date certified pursuant to Clause 48 of completion of such Section precedes the last day of the period to which the certificate relates the Current Index Figure shall be the Final Index Figure applicable to the date 42 days prior to whichever of these dates is the earliest.

   (d) The "Effective Value" in respect of the whole or any Section of the Works shall be the difference between:

     (i) the amount which in the opinion of the Engineer is due to the Contractor under Clause 60 (2) (before deducting retention) or the amount due to the Contractor under Clause 60 (3) (but in each case before deducting sums previously paid on account) less any amounts for Dayworks Nominated Sub-contractors or any other items based on actual cost or current prices[2,3,4,5] and any sums for increases or decreases in the Contract Price under this Clause;

and:

     (ii) the amount calculated in accordance with (i) above and included in the last preceding interim certificate issued by the Engineer in accordance with Clause 60.

     Provided that in the case of the first certificate the Effective Value shall be the amount calculated in accordance with subparagraph (i) above.

   (3) The increase or decrease in the amounts otherwise payable under Clause 60 pursuant to sub-clause (1) of this Clause shall be calculated by multiplying the Effective Value by a Price Fluctuation Factor which shall be the net sum of the products obtained by multiplying each of the proportions given in (a) (b) and (c) of sub-clause (4) of this Clause by a fraction the numerator of which is the relevant Current Index Figure minus the relevant Base Index Figure and the denominator of which is the relevant Base Index Figure.[6,7]

   (4) For the purpose of calculating the Price Fluctuation Factor the

proportions referred to in sub-clause (3) of this Clause shall (irrespective of the actual constituents of the work) be as follows and the total of such proportions shall amount to unity:

   (a)   0·   *   in respect of labour and supervision costs subject to adjustment by reference to the Index referred to in sub-clause (1)(a) of this Clause;

   (b)   0·   *   in respect of costs of provision and use of all civil engineering plant road vehicles etc. which shall be subject to adjustment by reference to the Index referred to in sub-clause (1)(b) of this Clause;

   (c) the following proportions in respect of the materials named which shall be subject to adjustment by reference to the relevant indices referred to in sub-clause (1)(c) of this Clause:

        0·   *   in respect of Aggregates
        0·   *   in respect of Bricks and Clay Products generally
        0·   *   in respect of Cements
        0·   *   in respect of Cast Iron products
        0·   *   in respect of Coated Roadstone for road pavements and bituminous products generally
        0·   *   in respect of Fuel for plant generally
        0·   *   in respect of Timber generally
        0·   *   in respect of Reinforcing steel ("(cut bent and delivered)" added in January 1979 revision) and other metal sections
        0·   *   in respect of Fabricated Structural Steel;

   (d)   0·10   in respect of all other costs which shall not be subject to any adjustment;

Total   1·00

(5) Provisional Index Figures in the Bulletin referred to in sub-clause (1) of this Clause may be used for the provisional adjustment of interim valuations but such adjustments shall be subsequently recalculated on the basis of the corresponding Final Index Figures.

(6) Clause 69—Tax Fluctuations—shall not apply except to the extent that any matter dealt with therein is not covered by the Index of the Cost of Labour in Civil Engineering Construction.

* To be filled in by the Employer prior to inviting tenders.

1. OPTIONAL CONTRACT PRICE FLUCTUATIONS CLAUSE. This clause is supplied loose leaf in the Conditions. The "*appropriate cases*" when it should be used as a special condition are, according to Government policy, contracts with an initial period of more than one year. A special adaptation is published for use in place of this clause "where ... required to make special provision for adjustment of Price Fluctuations in respect of Fabricated Structural Steelwork only or predominantly ... together with a negligible amount of Civil Engineering work". Alternatively for mixed works the two clauses may both be included with a third published clause to regulate the relationship between them.

The clauses are producing practical problems of under- or over-recovery, but most are not related to issues of legal interpretation.

(e) In *Re Sanders Construction Pty. Ltd. and Eric Newham (Wallerawang) Pty. Ltd.* [1969] Q.D.R. 29 the Supreme Court of Brisbane held that it was immaterial that the application of a formula for increases in the cost of labour might result in payment to a sub-contractor of an amount greater than that in fact paid out by the sub-contractor on account of such extra cost.

1(a). RETENTION. There has been controversy about whether retention is deducted from payment to the contractor under this clause. It is suggested with respect that the official guidance that it is deducted is quite correct. The doubt has been based on the opening and concluding words of sub-cl. (1) which can be read as meaning that increases under this clause are added to interim certificates rather than included in them. But, more importantly, sub-cl. (2) (*d*) refers to "*the amount . . . due . . . under Clause* 60 (2) . . . *or Clause* 60 (3) . . . *less . . . any sums for increases or decreases in the Contract Price under this Clause.*" Sub-cl. (3) also refers to "*The increase or decrease in the amounts otherwise payable under Clause* 60 *pursuant to sub-clause* (1) *of this Clause.*" Cl. 60 (1) and (2) are quite specific in directing that amounts to which the contractor is entitled "*in connection with all other matters for which provision is made under the Contract*" are to be included in interim certificates with retention deducted.

On the merits, if there is inflation the cost to the employer of making good any defects or completing the works on the contractor's default will increase correspondingly, and therefore there is reason why retention should be deducted from price increases. But there is no provision for increasing the limit of retention under cl. 60 (4).

2. "LESS ANY AMOUNTS FOR DAYWORKS NOMINATED SUB-CONTRACTORS OR ANY OTHER ITEMS BASED ON ACTUAL COST OR CURRENT PRICES". It has been suggested that the words here "*based on actual cost of current prices*" qualify the exclusion from the "*Effective Value*" of "*amounts for Dayworks Nominated Sub-contractors*", so that dayworks not so based are included and therefore subject to the operation of this clause. It is questionable whether that is the natural reading of the phrase on the run of the words, particularly as it may be difficult to decide whether or not dayworks are so based, and under cl. 59A (5) (a) the contractor is always reimbursed on the basis of cost for payment to nominated sub-contractors.

If the official view is right, presumably dayworks governed under cl. 52(3) by the F.C.E.C. Schedules without alteration are to be regarded as based on current prices, although the percentage addition for statutory charges and the fixed rates for plant in the schedules are not always up-to-date with recent inflation. Where the contractor fixes his own rates and prices in a special daywork schedule in the bill, then the amounts eventually payable are no more based on current prices or actual costs than any other rates in the bill. Where the bill directs the contractor to add or deduct a percentage from the F.C.E.C. rates and prices, it may be argued that the results are still "*based on*" the actual costs and current prices allowed in those schedules. The contractor may be advised to clarify the position in his tender if he is relying on protection by this clause against inflation affecting dayworks.

3. FLUCTUATIONS IN VALUING VARIATIONS. In any case where a "*fair valuation*" of a variation has to be made, the contractor is entitled to payment at current prices, even in a fixed price contract in which this clause is not included. Where work would otherwise fall to be valued at rates and prices in the bill or on the basis of such rates and prices, the contractor may argue that although in fixing his rates and

(*f*) I.C.E. Conditions of Contract Standing Joint Committee, in Guidance Note 1. "*The contents of this Guidance Note do not purport to be a legal interpretation but they do form the unanimous view of the C.C.S.J.C. on what constitutes good practice in the use of the Fifth Edition*". The committee consists of members appointed by the sponsors of the Conditions.
(*g*) Guidance Note 1 above.

prices he allowed for likely increases, his rates do not cover the full additional cost of carrying out extra work after the date of an increase, because the allowance was calculated in the expectation that some of the original contract work covered by the rate would be done before that increase. The contractor may claim that the extra work must be valued accordingly, and the claim has logic at least where the valuation is only to be "*based on*" bill rates. For application of the price fluctuation formula *see* p. 370.

It is suggested that in the context of cl. 52 "*conditions*" means physical conditions, and does not permit a general claim to revaluation on the grounds that a change in economic conditions has caused price and wage increases unforeseeable at the time of tender, in valuing variations under a wholly or partly fixed price contract.

4. GOODS AND MATERIALS. By cl. 60 (2) (b) interim certificates may include a percentage (not exceeding the percentage stated in the appendix to the form of tender) of the invoiced prices of goods or materials on site or vested in the employer under cl. 54 before delivery to the site. As such percentage is "*based on actual cost or current prices*" of the goods or materials it is excluded from the "*Effective Value*". The result is that this fluctuation formula is not applied to materials and goods until they are incorporated in the works and included in the next interim certificate. If goods or materials are on site or vested in the employer for a time during which the indices rise, when the formula is eventually applied the contractor will obtain a profit. Against that benefit the contractor will have to set the cost of insurance, storage and partial financing.

Clause 60 specifies no minimum percentage of the value of such goods and materials to be included in interim certificates (pp. 204 and 262). It is conceivable that the engineer may take into account the trend of rising prices in deciding what percentage (if any) it is proper to allow, particularly if goods are delivered to the site prematurely.

5. FLUCTUATIONS IN WAGES AND PRICES AS PART OF A DISRUPTION CLAIM. *See* p. 370.

6. FLUCTUATIONS IN WAGES AND PRICES AFTER THE DUE DATE FOR COMPLETION. Sub-cl. (2) (c) says that where the date of completion and last day of the certificate period are later than the due date for completion, it is the Final Index Figure applicable to the date 42 days prior to the due date which applies. The effect is to prevent the contractor recovering for increases in a period of his own delay, but not for increased costs due to the fact that more work is done after an earlier increase as a result of the contractor's slow progress (*see* p. 311, N. 9). The reverse effect of this limitation is that if prices fall after the due date for completion the contractor keeps the benefit.

Whenever the engineer or an arbitrator extends a date for completion that has already passed, under cls. 44 or 66, price fluctuations previously calculated by reference to the Final Index Figure 42 days prior to the due date for completion should be re-calculated. The re-calculation may

---

(*h*) Guidance Note 1 above interprets the clause in this way. There are special provisions about materials for the works in the fluctuation clause for fabricated structural steelwork (N.1 above).

perhaps be made under cl. 60 (7) (p. 272, N. 34), or the contractor should under cl. 66 seek a revision of the engineer's certificate.

7. LATE CERTIFICATION OF CLAIMS. The "*Current Index Figure*" normally is the "*Final Index Figure applicable to the date* 42 *days prior to . . . the last day of the period to which the certificate relates*". By cl. 60 (2) every certificate includes amounts due to the contractor from the beginning of the contract to the end of the relevant month less previous payments. The balance may have been earned by the contractor in the immediately preceding month, or prior to then, e.g. in the case of claims not admitted by the engineer for some months. This is particularly so in the case of the final certificate. Given the present tendency of index figures to rise, the contractor will gain unjustly if the index figure for the last date covered by the certificate, not of the month when the contractor incurred the relevant costs, is applied to such claims.

There is one specific limitation on the right to recover fluctuations on late claims: in all cases the latest Current Index Figure that is applied is the Final Index Figure applicable to the date 42 days prior to the due date for completion of the whole works or any relevant sections specified in the form of tender, however much later the claim or measurement may be certified.

Of course, the gain on late certification will apply in any case only to claims that are part of the "*Effective Value*" to which the index figure is applied, for example claims for rates based on bill rates under cl. 52 or it seems "*an appropriate increase or decrease of any rates or prices*" under cl. 56, and possibly "*such rate or price as in the circumstances . . . (the engineer) shall think reasonable and proper*" under cl. 52 (2), but not claims for which the valuation is "*based on actual cost or current prices*" (N. 1), which include a "*fair valuation*" under cl. 52 (2) and of course the various claims for cost listed in ch. 11.

In such a case the certificate actually relates to the several periods in which the matters included in the certificate arose. Unfortunately the wording of this clause as a whole is against applying different current index figures to the relevant proportions of the "*Effective Value*" (although cl. 1 (2) says that the singular includes the plural where the context requires). It must be accepted that the formula is intended to do rough justice, but the engineer should mitigate this defect by including claims in certificates as soon as possible.

Presumably in giving a decision under cl. 66 after the final certificate or in arbitration the price variation element is calculated as if the sum had been included in the first certificate after the costs were incurred.

If the contractor delays making a claim by not fulfilling cl. 52 (4) fully he will be in breach of contract and, it is suggested, the employer will be entitled to claim back any extra paid under this clause because of the delay, as damages for such breach.

It follows from what is said in this note that in a time of inflation the engineer should not combine into one certificate the valuation for two or more months, e.g. where the value of one month's work is below the minimum for certificate or the contractor delays with his monthly statement, but should issue separate certificates for the appropriate periods and apply the appropriate index figures to each.

The fact that the contractor will gain from a late valuation is an incentive to the engineer to make sure to include without delay in certificates the value of all work done and claims to date.

CHAPTER 10

The Bond

Form of Bond

(a) Is appropriate to an individual, (b) to a Limited Company and (c) to a Firm. Strike out whichever two are inappropriate.

BY THIS BOND (a) We ....
of .... in the
County of .... (b) We .... Limited
whose registered office is at.. in the
County of .... (c) We ....
and .... carrying on business in partnership under
the name or style of...
at .... in the
County of .... (hereinafter called "the Contractor"[1]) (d) and ....

(d) Is appropriate where there are two individual Sureties. (e) where the Surety is a Bank or Insurance Company. Strike out whichever is inappropriate.

.... of ....
in the County of .... and..
of .... in the County of ....
.... (e) and .... Limited
whose registered office is at.. in the
County of........................... (hereinafter called "the Sureties/Surety") are held and
firmly bound unto .... (hereinafter
called "the Employer") in the sum of.. pounds
(£ ....) for the payment of which sum the Contractor and the
Sureties/Surety bind themselves their successors and assigns jointly and severally[2] by
these presents.

  Sealed with our respective seals and dated this .... day of ....
19 ....

  WHEREAS the Contractor by an Agreement made between the Employer of the one
part and the Contractor of the other part has entered into a Contract (hereinafter called
"the said Contract") for the construction completion and maintenance of certain
Works as therein mentioned in conformity with the provisions of the said Contract.

  NOW THE CONDITION of the above-written Bond is such that if the Contractor
shall duly perform and observe all the terms provisions conditions and stipulations of
the said Contract on the Contractor's part to be performed and observed according to
the true purport intent and meaning thereof or if on default by the Contractor the
Sureties/Surety shall satisfy and discharge the damages sustained by the Employer
thereby[2a] up to the amount of the above-written Bond then this obligation shall be null
and void but otherwise shall be and remain in full force and effect but no alteration in
terms of the said Contract made by agreement between the Employer and the
Contractor or in the extent or nature of the Works to be constructed completed and
maintained thereunder and no allowance of time by the Employer or the Engineer
under the said Contract nor any forbearance or forgiveness in or in respect of any
matter or thing concerning the said Contract on the part of the Employer or the said
Engineer shall in any way release the Sureties[3,4]/Surety from any liability under the
above-written Bond.[5,6]

Signed Sealed and Delivered by the said }
  in the presence of:— }

The Common Seal of }
                                LIMITED }
  was hereunto affixed in the presence }
  of:— }
(Similar forms of Attestation Clause for the
  Sureties or Surety)

See conditions cl. 10 and notes, p. 56. For the engineer's duty to see that any bond specified is supplied in time, *see* p. 378, N. 13.

1. CHANGE OF CONTRACTOR AND SUB-CONTRACTOR'S BONDS. The bond is not affected by any sub-letting by the contractor, since he is still liable for the whole works, but if there is an assignment of the whole or any part of the works the bond should be specially extended to cover it.

It is entirely up to the main contractor whether or not he bonds domestic sub-contractors; the employer is not concerned because the main contractor and his bondsman are fully liable for their default. For the value to the employer of bonds by nominated sub-contractors *see* pp. 231-2.

2. "JOINTLY AND SEVERALLY" LIABLE. The employer may sue one or more of the parties for the whole amount due. A surety who pays more than his proper share may sue any co-surety for a contribution and the sureties are entitled to recover all they pay from the contractor, if they can, or to prove in his bankruptcy or liquidation.

2(a). DEFAULT. Note that this form of bond may be enforced against the surety only so far as the employer can prove damages because the contractor has not duly performed all the terms of the contract. Contrast the startling form of bond payable "on first of our demand without any conditions of proof", required by some foreign employers. _a

a

3. "NO ALTERATION ... AND NO ALLOWANCE OF TIME ... SHALL ... RELEASE THE SURETIES". Because very often he has given his guarantee for a friend without payment and without fully realising what he may be letting himself in for, the courts traditionally treat a surety sympathetically. This attitude may be a little out of place where an insurance company is guaranteeing a contract for a premium, but the rule which it has produced is nevertheless applied by the courts—that they will not allow the duties of a surety to be varied in any way without his consent:

> The honesty of a clerk and storekeeper was guaranteed. Later his office was altered to that of clerk only.
> Held: The surety was discharged. The contract guaranteed had been altered without his consent, and the courts will not judge the materiality of an alteration, unless it is quite obviously not to the sureties' disadvantage.

b

Therefore, unless there are terms in the bond equivalent to these, a surety may avoid liability very unjustly, e.g. where there are variations not authorised by the contract (pp. 169 and 172), or if a payment is made to the contractor before it is due under the contract.

Many insurance companies have their own forms of bond, which may not include these terms. Most companies will not insist on their strict rights if there is any change which frees them from liability, but it is not very satisfactory that they should be in a position in effect to decide whether or not to pay on a bond. Some of the larger companies treat a request to

(*a*) In *Edward Owen* v. *Barclays Bank International* [1978] 1 All E.R. 976 it was held that a bank which had given such a guarantee to a foreign bank that had in turn given a guarantee on similar terms to the employer was bound to honour the guarantee even though the Libyan employers were themselves the only party in default when they made the demand for payment.

(*b*) *R.* v. *Herron & Montgomery* [1903] 2 Ir.R. 474.

change their forms as if it were asking the Deity to alter the Ten Commandments, but the engineer should insist on the necessary changes. If they are not made, the engineer must notify the surety beforehand of every change intended and concession to the contractor outside the original contract, however minor, which is not always easy to remember, and an extra premium may be charged. Such bonds also usually will require rapid notice to insurers of actual or threatened default by the contractor, and failure to comply may invalidate the bond.

4. FRAUD AND NON-DISCLOSURE. A bond will not be binding if it is obtained by a material misstatement by the employer or engineer (not merely by the contractor), whether fraudulent or not. While a surety generally is bound to estimate the risk for himself, a bond will also be invalid, even if no actual misstatement is made, if the employer or engineer does not disclose any fact material to the risk which the surety would not reasonably expect to exist: for example, that the employer had agreed with a local landowner to have the works done at their joint expense and under the supervision of both their surveyors, or possibly that the employer knows from comparing tenders that there is a serious mistake in the accepted tender (p. 13).

5. COMPLETION ON DEFAULT. A surety has no legal right to take over and complete the work on default unless the right is given specifically by the bond. An insurance company surety is usually allowed to complete. The surety should in any case be kept informed of all developments.

6. RELEASE OF THE BOND. An insurance company or bank usually will limit the amount outstanding at any one time on bonds in force in favour of any one customer. As a result a common question is when does a bond cease to be in force. The answer is that, in the absence of a special clause in the bond, liability on a bond never does end at any clear cut moment. Only when it can be said that the contractor has no further obligation under or for breach of the contract can it be said that the surety can have no further liability under the bond. Now that the period of the contractor's liability is so uncertain in time (p. 431), therefore so too is the surety's liability. It may be many years before it is discovered that, in the words of this form of bond, the contractor did not "*duly perform and observe all the terms . . . of the said Contract*", e.g. by defective work first coming to light long after completion. The surety then becomes liable to "*satisfy and discharge the damages sustained by the Employer . . . up to the amount of the . . . Bond*", and until he does so the words of the bond say specifically that it "*shall be and remain in full force and effect . . .*".

It is becoming common to specify in the contract that the employer will release the bond on substantial completion or at the end of the maintenance period, and in the January 1979 revision of these Conditions, published at proof stage of this book, cl. 10 and this form of bond provide for release at the latter time. The employer is then taking a risk (about which the engineer will warn him if necessary) that he will have cause to regret the release if the works collapse or serious defects appear later and the contractor is insolvent.

(c) *Staff* v. *Eastbourne Local Board* (1869) 20 L.T. 339.
(d) See *Doe* v. *Canadian Surety Co.* [1937] S.C.R. 1 (Can.).
(e) *Slowey* v. *Lodder* (1901) 20 N.Z.L.R. 321 and *Ross* v. *Frain* (1908) 27 N.Z.L.R. 970.

CHAPTER 11

Key to 4th and 5th Editions
I.C.E. Conditions

This key provides only a brief summary of the clauses in the Conditions. Where the exact words or effects of the clauses and the general law are relevant the clauses and commentary in the text should be consulted. The four columns are not mutually exclusive.

Clause	Edition	1. Powers, rights and duties of the Engineer/Employer	2. Duties of the Contractor included in the Tender sum	3. Payments to and other rights of the Contractor	4. Orders, consents, notices, approvals, etc., required
1 (1) (c) & (d)	4th & 5th	To appoint and change the Engineer and Engineer's Representative.			Written notification to the Contractor.
1 (1) (g)	4th			The Contract Price.	
1 (1) (i)	5th			The Contract Price.	
1 (5)	5th			Right to "cost" specifically includes overhead costs on or off the site.	
2	4th & 5th	Engineer's Representative to watch and supervise Works (and test—4th ed. only). Engineer may delegate some of his powers to the Engineer's Representative.		To appeal to the Engineer from decisions of the Engineer's Representative.	Written notification to the Contractor of delegation.
2	5th	To employ assistants to the Engineer's Representative. The Engineer may delegate his powers (with stated exceptions) to any person responsible to the Engineer as well as to the Engineer's Representative.		Appeal to the Engineer's Representative from decisions of his assistants. Appeal to the Engineer from the decisions of other delegates.	Notification to the Contractor of names and functions of assistants. Prior written notice to the Contractor of delegation and determination of delegation.
2 (a) 39 (3)	4th 5th	Engineer may disapprove work or material not disapproved of by the Engineer's Representative.			

Clause	Edition				
3	4th & 5th		Not to assign the Contract or any part or benefit without consent.		Written consent of the Employer to assignment.
4	4th & 5th		Not to sub-let the whole Works. Not to sub-let part of the Works without consent. Liability for sub-contractors.		Written consent of the Engineer to sub-letting any part of the Works except where otherwise provided by the Contract.
5	4th		To construct, complete and maintain the Works. Provide everything specified in or reasonably to be inferred from Contract.		
8 (1)	5th		Ditto, specifically "subject to the provisions of the Contract".		
6	4th	Engineer to explain and adjust ambiguities or discrepancies in the Contract and issue instructions to the Contractor directing in what manner the work is to be carried out.		Reasonable additional sum if instructions referred to in column 1 involve the Contractor in expense which he did not and had not reason to foresee. Extension of time under cl. 44	Oral or written instructions by the Engineer.
5	5th	As above, except that the Engineer issues instructions under cl. 13.		Claim under cl. 13. Extension of time under cl. 44.	Written instruction by the Engineer.

Clause	Edition	1. Powers, rights and duties of the Engineer Employer	2. Duties of the Contractor included in the Tender sum	3. Payments to and other rights of the Contractor	4. Orders, consents, notices, approvals, etc., required
7	4th	Copyright in drawings, etc.— see p. 401.	(i) Provide himself any copies of drawings he requires in excess of two supplied free. (ii) Return drawings at end of contract. (iii) Keep one copy of drawings on Site for inspection by Engineer, E.R. or other authorised person.	Right of two free copies of drawings from the Engineer.	Contractor to give adequate notice in writing of further drawings or specification required.
6 & 7 (4)	5th	Copyright in the drawings and bill (except pricing) remains in the Engineer.	(i) and (ii) ditto. (iii) Specification also to be kept on Site and open for inspection.	Upon acceptance of the tender, right to receive from the Engineer two free copies of drawings, Conditions of Contract, the Specification and (unpriced) Bill of Quantities.	Authorisation from the Engineer to any other person to inspect drawings to be in writing. Ditto.
8	4th	The Engineer has power and authority to supply further drawings and instructions necessary for the adequate completion and maintenance of the Works.	To carry out and be bound by further drawings and instructions (subject to rights to extra payment specified elsewhere in the Contract).	Damages under the general law, including loss of profit, for delayed drawings and instructions (cl. 12).	Ditto.
7	5th	Ditto. The Engineer shall supply further or modified drawings and instructions necessary for the adequate completion and maintenance of the Works. "Works" means the permanent Works together with the Temporary Works, by cl. 1 (1) (l).	Ditto.	Reasonable cost and extension of time for cost or delay due to failure or inability of Engineer to issue at a time reasonable in all the circumstances drawings or instructions requested by Contractor and considered necessary by Engineer.	Adequate written notice from the Contractor to the Engineer of any further drawing or specification required.

Clause	Edition			
	4th & 5th			Damages under the general law (including loss of profit) for delayed inspections and other delays by Engineer or Employer not within cl. 7 or 8 (ch. 12).
8 (1)	5th	See under cl. 5 (4th ed.) above.		
8 (2)	5th	Full responsibility for adequacy, stability and safety of site operations and methods of construction, but not of Permanent Works or Temporary Works designed by the Engineer.		
9	4th & 5th	To execute the Contract Agreement.		
10	4th & 5th	Provide a bond if specified in the Tender.	Approve form of bond and guarantees.	
11	4th	To inspect and examine the Site, etc., satisfy himself as to nature of ground and sub-soil (so far as practicable), quantities, etc.		
	5th	Ditto—excluding reference to quantities (see cl. 56) and adding "communication with . . . the Site".		5th ed.—to take into account information on ground or sub-soil provided by or on behalf of Employer. Probably implied in 4th ed.

Clause	Edition	1. Powers, rights and duties of the Engineer/Employer	2. Duties of the Contractor included in the Tender sum	3. Payments to and other rights of the Contractor	4. Orders, consents, notices, approvals, etc., required
12 (1)	4th		Perform all obligations under the Contract and all matters and things necessary for proper completion and maintenance of the Works, except as thereinafter provided		
11 (2)	5th		Ditto—excluding words in italics and adding "except as . . . otherwise provided in the Contract"		
12 (2)–(7)	4th	On receipt of notice from the Contractor of unforeseeable conditions or artificial obstructions to admit facts and circumstances, or issue a suspension order under cl. 40, or variation order under cl. 51 or accept a quotation with or without admission of liability.		Reasonable cost of additional work and plant and unavoidable delay due to unforeseeable physical conditions or artifical obstructions, with a right to arbitration before completion on any dispute. Relevant rights where an Order is given by the Engineer under cl. 40 or 51. Extension of time under cl. 44.	(i) Prior written notice of additional work and plant due to conditions with all the other details specified. (ii) Estimate or quotation. (iii) Weekly returns and all necessary information and vouchers as required by Engineer. (iv) Written notice if further or more extensive conditions, etc., encountered.

Clause	Edition			
12 (2)–(4)	5th	On receipt of a notice of conditions, etc., as above to require the Contractor to give an estimate, or approve the Contractor's measures with or without modification, or give written instructions as to how the conditions, etc., are to be dealt with, or issue an order under cl. 40 or 51.	Reasonable cost of such additional work and plant plus reasonable percentage addition in respect of profit. Reasonable cost only of unavoidable delay or disruption. Immediate arbitration on any dispute. Extension of time under cl. 44 and appropriate rights if an order is given under cl. 40 or cl. 51. Possible remedy under cl. 13 if an instruction is given by the Engineer.	Cl. 52 (4) notice from the Contractor. Additional details specified (including the measures he is taking or proposing to take) are to be furnished with the notice if practicable or as soon as possible thereafter. The Engineer may approve in writing the Contractor's proposed measures with or without modification. Engineer to inform the Contractor in writing as soon as he decides to refuse a claim in whole or in part.
13 13 (1)	4th 5th	Construct, etc., works in strict accordance with the Contract to satisfaction of the Engineer and comply with his instructions and directions.	Relief for legal or physical impossibility.	
13 (2)	5th	See cl. 46, p. 344.		
13 (3)	5th		Reasonable cost beyond that reasonably to have been foreseen by an experienced contractor due to instructions pursuant to cl. 5 or 13 (1) which involve the Contractor in delay or disruption.	Oral or written instruction of the Engineer, etc. Notice by Contractor under cl. 52 (4).
Clause	Engineer			

Clause	Edition	1. Powers, rights and duties of the Engineer/Employer	2. Duties of the Contractor included in the Tender sum	3. Payments to and other rights of the Contractor	4. Orders, consents, notices, approvals, etc., required
14	4th	To require the Contractor to submit a programme showing the order of procedure and methods and written particulars of arrangements, Constructional Plant, Temporary Works.	To comply with the Engineer's requirements under this clause, as set out in column 1.		
	5th	Right to a programme within 21 days of acceptance of tender showing order of procedure and further details and information reasonably required. To require revised programmes. Right to request reasonable details of methods of construction including Temporary Works and calculations of stresses, strains and deflections.	Ditto, subject to rights set out in column 3.	To receive information from the Engineer within a reasonable period that methods submitted on request have his consent or of respects on which they fail to meet the requirements of the specifications or drawings or will be detrimental to Permanent Works. To receive design criteria from Engineer. Cost and extension of time if Engineer's consent to proposed methods of construction is unreasonably delayed or if the Engineer's requirements are unforeseeable	Oral or written requirements and requests for details, etc., from the Engineer. Written information from the Engineer to the Contractor of his decision on the Contractor's methods.

15	4th	To approve and withdraw approval of the Contractor's Agent. To give directions and instructions to the Agent on behalf of the Contractor.	Provide superintendence. A competent and authorised Agent to be constantly on the Works and superintending whole time.	Written approval of the Agent by the Engineer.
	5th	Ditto.	Superintendence by sufficient persons having adequate knowledge of operations (including methods, techniques, hazards and accident prevention). Agent to be in full charge of the Works and responsible for safety.	Ditto.
16	4th & 5th	To order removal from the Works of any person employed by the Contractor who misconducts himself or is incompetent or negligent.	Employ only careful, skilled and experienced persons (expressly including superintendents by the 5th ed.).	Possible claim under cl. 13 (3).
17	4th & 5th		Set out the Works and provide necessary instruments, etc., and labour. Carefully protect and preserve all benchmarks, pegs, etc. Rectify errors in setting out.	Expense of rectifying setting out, if an error is based on incorrect data supplied in writing by the Engineer or the Engineer's Representative.
18	4th & 5th	To require the Contractor to make boreholes or exploratory excavation.	Boreholes and exploratory excavations if a provisional sum (5th ed., or P.C. Item) is included in the Bill	Boreholes or exploratory excavations valued as a variation if no provisional sum (5th ed., or P.C. Item) is included in the Contract. Order in writing from Engineer.

Clause	Edition	1. Powers, rights and duties of the Engineer Employer	2. Duties of the Contractor included in the Tender sum	3. Payments to and other rights of the Contractor	4. Orders, consents, notices, approvals, etc., required
19	4th	To require lights, guards, fencing and watching.	Provide and maintain lights, guards, fencing and watching required by the Engineer or a competent authority.		
	5th	Ditto, adding "warning signs". Employer bound to have full regard to safety and keep the site orderly to avoid danger if he employs his own workmen to carry out work on the Site. The Employer is bound also to require his other direct contractors to have regard to safety and avoidance of danger.	Ditto, adding "warning signs". To have full regard for safety of all persons entitled to be on the site and keep the site (so far as it is under his control) and Works (so far as not completed or occupied by Employer) in an orderly state to avoid danger.		
20–25	4th & 5th	Check list of Insurance, p. 360.			
26	4th		To give notices required by, conform with, and keep the Employer indemnified against liability or penalty for breach of Acts, regulations or bye-laws.	Reimbursement of statutory and similar fees, and of rates and taxes in respect of the Site, construction thereon, and temporary structures elsewhere used exclusively for the Works. Employer warrants that planning permissions have been obtained	

5th	Ditto, but the Contractor is specifically relieved of liability for, and entitled to a variation or instruction to avoid breach of any Act, regulation or bye-law which is the unavoidable result of complying with drawings, specifications or instructions.	Ditto, plus rates and taxes on permanent structures used temporarily and exclusively for the Works. The Employer warrants that planning permissions have been or will be obtained only in respect of Permanent Works and Temporary Works specified or designed by the Engineer.	
26A 27	4th⟩ 5th⟩ To comply with Public Utilities Street Works Act 1950 and to indemnify the Employer against any breach save as provided. Not to commence work within two months of the notice by the Contractor referred to in column 4.	Extension of time and additional cost due to delay in having to serve the notice referred to in column 4.	The Employer must notify the Contractor in writing before commencement of the Works whether the Works or any part are Emergency Works or in Controlled Land or a Prospectively Maintainable Highway, and notify the Contractor similarly in respect of any variation. The Employer is to serve notices under P.U.S.W. Act. The Contractor must give 21 days notice before commencing any part of the Works (other than Emergency Works) in a Street, Controlled Land or a Prospectively Maintainable Highway, or commencing thereon part of the Works likely to affect apparatus of an Owning Undertaker. The notice is to state the date and place of intended commencement.

Clause	Edition	1. Powers, rights and duties of the Engineer/Employer	2. Duties of the Contractor included in the Tender sum	3. Payments to and other rights of the Contractor	4. Orders, consents, notices, approvals, etc., required
27 32	4th 5th	Right to fossils and articles of value, etc., discovered on Site.	To take reasonable precautions to prevent removal or damage to fossils, etc., and immediately acquaint the Engineer of discovery.	To carry out at expense of Employer the Engineer's orders as to disposal of fossils, etc.	Give order as to disposal of fossils.
28	4th & 5th		Indemnify the Employer against infringements of patent rights, etc. except where otherwise specified to pay tonnage, royalties, etc., for stone, clay, etc., or other materials.		
29	4th		All operations to be carried out so as not to interfere unnecessarily or improperly with public convenience or the access to use and occupation of public or private roads, etc., and to save harmless and indemnify the Employer in respect of claims demands, etc.		
	5th		Ditto and all work to be carried out without unreasonable noise and disturbance and contractor to indemnify Employer against liability for damages, etc.		

30 (1)	4th 5th	Contractor to use reasonable means to prevent highways, etc., being subject to extraordinary traffic.		See column 2.
30 (2)	4th	To give notice to the Engineer and proposals for protecting the highway and bridges which in probability will be damaged by the movement of a load and to carry out such proposals unless counter proposals are received from the Engineer within 14 days.		Costs and expenses of protection and strengthening as noted in column 2.
30 (2)	5th	Strengthen any bridges, alter or improve any highway to facilitate the movement of constructional plant equipment, etc., and to indemnify the Employer against all claims for damage caused by such movement.		
30 (3)	4th	To report any claim in respect of damage or injury to highways or bridges to the Engineer.	The Employer shall negotiate settlement of any claim in respect of damage or injury to highways or bridges and pay all sums due and indemnify the Contractor save and so far as such claims are not in the opinion of the Engineer due to any failure on the part of the Contractor.	

Clause	Edition	1. Powers, rights and duties of the Engineer Employer	2. Duties of the Contractor included in the Tender sum	3. Payments to and other rights of the Contractor	4. Orders, consents, notices, approvals, etc., required
30 (3)	5th	Ditto.	The Contractor to notify the Engineer of damage or of any claim in respect of damage to any bridge or highway. Where under any Act of Parliament or Statutory Instrument a haulier is required to indemnify the highway authority the employer shall not be liable for any costs, etc. In other cases the employer shall negotiate the settlement, etc. and indemnify the contractor in respect thereof and in respect of all claims, etc.	Save as the Contractor is liable under column 2, to be indemnified by the Employer in respect of all claims, etc.	
31 31 (1)	4th 5th		Afford all "reasonable facilities" for other direct contractors of the Employer, and for authorised authorities and statutory bodies.		
31 (2)	5th			Extension of time and cost if compliance with sub-cl. (1) involved the Contractor in delay or cost beyond that reasonably to be foreseen by an experienced contractor.	

32	4th		Except where otherwise specified in the Contract to provide all Constructional Plant, Temporary Works, materials and other things of every kind required for the construction, completion and maintenance of the Works.
	5th		*See* under cl. 27 (4th ed.) above.
33	4th & 5th	*See* column 2.	Clear the Site on completion and leave the Works clean to the Engineer's satisfaction.
34	4th	To require before Contract a certificate from the Contractor that the labour clauses (column 2) have been complied with for the three months preceding the date of Tender.	Pay and observe specified wages and hours and conditions of labour, recognise freedom of workpeople to be members of trade unions, display copy of this clause, be responsible for observance of the clause by sub-contractors.
34 & Form of Tender	5th	Ditto.	Ditto. Questions about observance of this clause to be referred to the decision of an independent Tribunal appointed by the Minister of Labour.

Clause	Edition	1. Powers, rights and duties of the Engineer Employer	2. Duties of the Contractor included in the Tender sum	3. Payments to and other rights of the Contractor	4. Orders, consents, notices, approvals, etc., required
35	4th & 5th	To require labour returns from the Contractor and prescribe forms and times for the returns. To require information respecting Constructional Plant.	See column 1.		
36	4th & 5th	To order samples and tests.	Materials and workmanship to be of the kinds described in the Contract and in accordance with the Engineer's instructions. To test materials and workmanship as specified. Supply assistance, instruments, etc. for examining, measuring and testing, and samples of materials for testing before incorporation in the Works.	Samples supplied at cost of the Employer unless clearly intended by or provided for in the Contract. Costs of tests borne by the Employer in the cases specified in the clause. Possible claim under cl. 13 (3).	
37	4th & 5th	Engineer and any person authorised by him to have access to the Works and other places specified.	To provide access as in column 1. and afford every facility for and assistance in obtaining access.		

38	4th & 5th	To examine and measure work before it is covered up or put out of view or permanent work is placed on foundations. To order uncovering or making of openings in the Works (and reinstatement).	Not to cover up work without the approval of the Engineer, and to afford full opportunity for the Engineer to examine and measure work before it is covered up. Obey Engineer's orders as set out in column 1.	Compensation under the general law of cl. 13 if the Engineer does not without unreasonable delay examine and measure work or notify the Contractor that he considers it unnecessary to do so (ch. 12). Expenses (5th ed., cost) of uncovering and making openings if the provisions of this clause are complied with and work and materials are found to be executed in accordance with the Contract	Notice from the Contractor to the Engineer when work or foundations are ready for examination. Notice from the Engineer to the Contractor that examination and measurement of work is unnecessary.
39	4th & 5th	The Engineer may order removal and replacement of materials or work not in opinion of the Engineer in accordance with the Contract. The Employer may employ others to do so on default by the Contractor and recover or deduct all expenses.	Obey Engineer's orders as set out in column 1. Pay extra expenses incurred by the Employer on the Contractor's default.		Order in writing from Engineer
39 (3)	5th	Failure of the Engineer or person acting under him by cl. 2 to disapprove work or materials does not prejudice their power subsequently to do so (see p. 130).			

Clause	Edition	1. Powers, rights and duties of the Engineer/Employer	2. Duties of the Contractor included in the Tender sum	3. Payments to and other rights of the Contractor	4. Orders, consents, notices, approvals, etc.; required
40 (1)	4th	To suspend progress of the whole or any part of the Works. To direct protection and securing of the Works.	To obey a suspension order and protect and secure the Works without extra payment if the suspension is otherwise provided for in the Contract, necessary for the proper execution of the Works, by reason of weather conditions, or by some default on the part of the Contractor, or for the safety of the Works.	Extra cost of suspension except as set out in column 2.	Written suspension order by the Engineer. Written notice by the Contractor of intention to claim costs within 28 days of the Engineer's order.
40 (2)	4th		As above.	Right to follow the procedure in column 4, and probably to damages for abandonment of the whole Works or a variation of rates under cl. 52 for omission of part of the Works.	The Contractor may serve 28 days written notice of abandonment or omission if whole or part of the Works are suspended by the Engineer's written order for more than three months. Notice, etc., of claim to costs under cl. 52 (4).
40 (1)	5th				
(2)				As above, unless the suspension is otherwise provided for in the Contract or continues to be necessary due to default on the part of the Contractor.	The Contractor may serve 28 days written notice to abandon the whole or omit parts of the Works if permission to resume work not given by the Engineer within three months from the date of suspension, subject as in column 3.

	Edition			
41	4th	To order commencement of the Works.	Commence the Works within 14 days of the commencement order. Proceed with the Works with due expedition, save as expressly sanctioned or ordered by Engineer or wholly beyond the Contractor's control.	Under the general law the order to commence is to be given within a reasonable time of the acceptance of the tender, unless otherwise agreed.	Written commencement order from the Engineer.
	5th	To notify the Date for Commencement of the Works.	Commence the Works on or as soon as reasonably possible after the Date for Commencement notified by the Engineer. Proceed with due expedition and without delay in accordance with the Contract.	Date for Commencement to be within a reasonable time after the date of acceptance of the Tender.	The Engineer to notify in writing the Date for Commencement of the Works.
42	4th	Give possession of so much of the site as required to enable Contractor to commence and proceed with construction of the works in accordance with the programme, etc.	Bear all expenses and charges for special or temporary wayleaves and additional accommodation outside the Site (but as to rates see cl. 26).	Extension of time and expenses for failure to give possession of the Site.	
	5th		Ditto.	Extension of time and cost as may be reasonable for failure to give possession of the Site.	Notices, etc., under cls. 44 and 52 (4).

Clause	Edition	1. Powers, rights and duties of the Engineer Employer	2. Duties of the Contractor included in the Tender sum	3. Payments to and other rights of the Contractor	4. Orders, consents, notices, approvals, etc., required
43	4th		Subject to the specification to complete the whole Works within the time stated in tender or extended time from the date of the order to commence under cl. 41.		
	5th		Ditto. and also complete any separate Section in the time stated in the Appendix to the Tender.		
44	4th	Engineer to determine extension of time to which Contractor is entitled. but is not bound to do so unless particulars given by Contractor.		Extension of time for completion of the Works for extra or additional work or other special circumstances of any kind whatsoever.	Full and detailed particulars from the Contractor to the Engineer within 28 days or as soon as practicable.
	5th	Ditto—on receipt of particulars or if he thinks fit. in the absence of particulars.		Extension of time for completion of the whole Works or a Section for variations. increased quantities. any other cause of delay mentioned in the Conditions. exceptional adverse weather conditions. special circumstances of any kind whatsoever.	Engineer to give notice to Contractor of his decision on the extension of time.

45	4th	No permanent work at night or Sundays without the Engineer's permission save where unavoidable, etc., for saving life or property or where rotary or double shifts are customary.	Assessment of extensions for Works or Section upon receipt of particulars; or if the Engineer thinks fit in absence of particulars. Review of extension as soon as possible after the original or extended date for completion whether a claim is made or not. Final review by the Engineer upon issue of the Certificate of Completion of the Works or Section, which review may not reduce an extension already given.	Full and detailed particulars within 28 days or as soon as reasonable in all the circumstances, but *see* column 3.
	5th	Ditto, applying to Permanent and Temporary Works, and excepting also work customarily carried out outside normal working hours.	Engineer to make review. *See* column 3.	The Engineer's written permission for night or Sunday work. The Contractor immediately to advise the Engineer or Engineer's Representative if such work is unavoidable.

Clause	Edition	1. Powers, rights and duties of the Engineer/Employer	2. Duties of the Contractor included in the Tender sum	3. Payments to and other rights of the Contractor	4. Orders, consents, notices, approvals, etc., required
46	4th	To notify the Contractor that progress is too slow for completion by the due date. Approve steps to expedite the Works.	(i) Whole of materials, etc., under cl. 5 and mode, manner and speed of works to be of a kind and conducted in a manner approved of by the Engineer. (ii) To take such steps as the Contractor thinks necessary and the Engineer approves to expedite progress of the Works so as to complete in the prescribed time. (iii) All work at night to be carried out without unreasonable noise and disturbance and the Contractor to indemnify the Employer against liability for noise and disturbance.	Extension of time if request for permission for night work is refused and there is no equivalent practicable method of expediting progress.	Written notification by the Engineer that expedition is required.
	5th	Ditto, specifically only if the rate of progress is unsatisfactory for any reason which does not entitle the Contractor to extension of time.	(i) Reproduced as cl. 13 (2). (ii) Ditto, to expedite Works or any Section. (iii) Reproduced as cl. 29 (2).	Permission requested for night or Sunday work not to be unreasonably refused.	Ditto.
47	4th	To liquidate damages and to deduct from monies due or which become due to Contractor.	To pay the liquidated damages stated in the Tender for delay in completing the Works.		

| 5th | To liquidate damages and to deduct from any sum otherwise payable. | If the Engineer notifies the Employer and the Contractor that the Contractor is not entitled to any further extension of time, the Contractor is liable to pay the liquidated damages specified in the columns in the Appendix to Tender:

col. 1
Weekly or daily sum for failure to complete the whole Works.
Proportionate reduction for a part of the Works (not being a Section or part of a Section) certified complete.
col. 2
Reduction in sum in col. 1 on completion of a Section for which separate completion date in the Tender, proportionate reduction on certified completion of a part of the Section.
col. 3
Sum for specific damage for late completion of a Section, subject to proportionate reduction where a part of the Section is certified complete. | Reimbursement of liquidated damages paid with interest if an extension of time is granted or increased on a review by the Engineer. | Engineer to notify the Employer and the Contractor as set out in column 2. |

Clause	Edition	1. Powers, rights and duties of the Engineer/Employer	2. Duties of the Contractor included in the Tender sum	3. Payments to and other rights of the Contractor	4. Orders, consents, notices, approvals, etc., required
48	4th	Duty to issue a Certificate of Completion when the whole Works are substantially complete, have passed any prescribed final test and the Contractor has given a written undertaking to finish any outstanding work in the Maintenance Period. Duty to issue a Certificate of Completion on the written application of the Contractor for any substantial part of the Works that is complete and occupied or used by the Employer. Discretion to give a Certificate of Completion for any other part of the Works. State expressly in the certificate if it is to include completion of any ground or surface requiring reinstatement.	To complete.	See column 1.	Written undertaking from the Contractor to finish any outstanding work. Written application from the Contractor for a Certificate of Completion of any substantial part of the Works completed and occupied and used by the Employer.
	5th	As above, save that on receipt of the notice and undertaking from the Contractor the Engineer must within 21 days either issue a Certificate of Completion stating the date of completion or specify the work to be done before issue of a Certificate, and in the latter			Written notice by the Contractor to the Engineer or Engineer's Representative with an undertaking to finish outstanding work.

Clause	Edition				
		case the Engineer must issue a Certificate within 21 days of completion of the work specified. Similar procedure for any part or Section for which a separate time for completion is specified in the Appendix to the Form of Tender. Similar procedure for part of the Works completed and occupied or used as above. Discretionary power to certify completion of part of the Works as above.			Written notice from the Engineer requiring maintenance work within the Maintenance Period or 14 days after its expiration.
49	4th & 5th	To require maintenance work.	Execution of maintenance work if necessary because of the Contractor's breach of contract.	Payment for maintenance work not due to the Contractor's breach of contract.	
		To have maintenance work carried out by others on the Contractor's default and recover or deduct the cost from the Contractor.	5th ed.—to carry out work outstanding at the date of completion under cl. 48 as soon as practicable after such date. As to continued liability after the Maintenance Period for defects due to breach of contract, see cl. 61.		
49 (5)	4th & 5th	Liability for injury or damage connected with permanent reinstatement, as specified.	Temporary reinstatement of any highway or road, and liability for injury or damage as specified.		

Clause	Edition	1. Powers, rights and duties of the Engineer/Employer	2. Duties of the Contractor included in the Tender sum	3. Payments to and other rights of the Contractor	4. Orders, consents, notices, approvals, etc., required
50	4th	To require the Contractor to search for the cause of defects, etc.	Cost of search for any defect for which the Contractor is liable	Cost of the search if the Contractor is not liable for the defect.	Search is to be required in writing by the Engineer.
50	5th	To require the Contractor to carry out searches, tests or trials to determine the cause of defects, etc.	Ditto in respect of cost of searches, tests or trials.	Ditto in respect of cost of searches, tests or trials.	Ditto
51	4th	The Engineer shall order a variation, as specified.			Prior variation order in writing by the Engineer or Prior oral order confirmed by the Engineer in writing or Prior oral order confirmed by the Contractor in writing and not contradicted in writing by the Engineer.
51	5th	Ditto. The Engineer shall also vary any specified sequence, method or timing of construction when necessary, etc.		Value of variation to be taken into account in ascertaining contract price.	Ditto. Any contradiction by the Engineer of the Contractor's confirmation must be "forthwith"
52 (1)–(3)	4th	To value variations, including power to vary rates and prices rendered unreasonable or inapplicable.		Valuation of variations: (i) At bill rates if applicable. (ii) At reasonable prices if no applicable rates. (iii) At reasonable and proper rates for any item of the Works where the nature or amount of an omission or	(i) As soon after the date of the order as practicable and in the case of extra or additional work before commencement of the work or as soon thereafter as is practicable. written notice by the Contractor to the

			addition renders a bill rate or price unreasonable or inapplicable. (iv) At dayworks if "necessary or desirable".	Engineer of his intention to claim extra payment or varied rate or Notice as above by the Engineer to the Contractor of his intention to vary a rate or price. (ii) Monthly accounts, etc., from the Contractor. (iii) The Engineer must give a written order in advance for dayworks. (iv) Daywork returns, receipts, and vouchers from the Contractor.
52 (4)	4th	To authorise payment in absence of monthly accounts if the Contractor notified his intention to claim at the earliest practicable opportunity.		
52 (1)–(3)	5th	To ascertain the valuation of variations after consultation with the Contractor.	Valuation of variation: (i) At rates and prices in bill where work is of similar character and executed under similar conditions. (ii) Where work is not of similar character, etc., rates and prices in the bill shall be used as a basis for valuation so far as may be reasonable. (iii) Fair valuation of work where (i) and (ii) do not apply. (iv) Reasonable and proper rates for any item of work where the nature or amount of a variation renders a bill rate or price unreasonable or inapplicable. (v) Dayworks if "necessary or desirable".	For (iv) in column 3, notice from the Engineer to the Contractor or vice versa before varied work is commenced or as soon thereafter as is reasonable in all the circumstances. For dayworks the Engineer must give written orders in advance. Daywork returns, receipts and vouchers by the Contractor.

Clause	Edition	1. Powers, rights and duties of the Engineer/Employer	2. Duties of the Contractor included in the Tender sum	3. Payments to and other rights of the Contractor	4. Orders, consents, notices, approvals, etc., required
52 (4)	5th	Right to instruct the Contractor to keep contemporary records or further contemporary records. Right to inspect records and to take copies.		Right to payment of a claim despite failure to comply with requirements (a) to (d) in column 4 "to the extent that the Engineer has not been prevented from or substantially prejudiced by such failure in investigating the said claim". Right to inclusion of the whole or part of a claim pursuant to any clause of the Conditions in interim certificates in so far as the Contractor has supplied sufficient particulars to enable the Engineer to determine the amount due.	(a) Written notice by the Contractor of his intention to claim a higher rate or price than that notified to him by the Engineer under cls. 52 (1) or (2) or 56 (2) within 28 days of notification. (b) Written notice by the Contractor as soon as reasonably possible after the happening of the events giving rise to the claim of his intention to claim additional payment pursuant to any clause of Conditions save cl. 52 (1) or (2). The Contractor to keep contemporary records as reasonably necessary to support any such claim. (c) The Engineer may instruct the Contractor to keep contemporary records or further contemporary records. (d) The Contractor to send to the Engineer as soon as reasonable after notice of claim a first interim account with full and detailed particulars of the amount claimed and the grounds of claim.

53	4th	(i) Constructional Plant, Temporary Works and materials owned by the Contractor or a controlled company vest in the Employer when brought on to the Site. (ii) In the event of forfeiture the Employer is entitled to hire Essential Hired Plant brought on the Site by the Contractor on the same terms as it was hired to the Contractor. (iii) The Employer may pay overdue H.P. instalments, etc., and recover or deduct the payments from the Contractor. Sell or return Plant, etc., not removed by the Contractor on completion and recover or deduct costs.	Not to remove Constructional Plant, Temporary Works or materials before completion (except hired plant, which does not include H.P. Plant) without the written consent of the Engineer (not to be unreasonably withheld).	Right to the exclusive use of plant, etc., vested in the Employer until forfeiture, etc. Revesting of plant upon removal from the Site with consent or completion of the Works.	Notification of name and address of the owner of Hired or H.P. Plant by the Contractor in writing to the Engineer on request, and a written certificate on request of the Employer's right under the agreement of hire to take over the hire of Essential Hired Plant. Request by the Employer in writing to hire Essential Hired Plant from owner and undertaking to pay outstanding hire, within 7 days of forfeiture becoming effective. Written consent of the Engineer to removal of Plant, etc.
	5th	As above, save "goods" also vest in the Employer. The Employer's right to hire on forfeiture applies to all Hired Plant. Arguably no hire purchase plant to be used by the Contractor, without special consent.	To incorporate this cl. 53 in sub-contracts. Liable for and to insure Plant vested in the Employer. Ditto.		As above.
54 53 (11)	4th} 5th}	Vesting does not imply approval of Plant or prevent inspection.			

Clause	Edition	1. Powers, rights and duties of the Engineer Employer	2. Duties of the Contractor included in the Tender sum	3. Payments to and other rights of the Contractor	4. Orders, consents, notices, approvals, etc., required
54	5th	The Engineer must check that the steps listed in column 4 are taken before including in a certificate payment for goods and materials not on the Site, and check Contractor's insurance. Upon written approval of the goods, etc. by Engineer same vest in Employer	To incorporate provisions similar to cl. 54 in every relevant sub-contract. Responsible for and shall insure against loss or damage to goods or materials vested in the Employer under this clause, and for the cost of handling and transportation.	To obtain payment before delivery to Site for goods and materials listed in the Appendix to the Tender (see cl. 60).	The Contractor: (i) Provides documentary evidence to the Engineer that ownership in goods and materials has passed to the Contractor. (ii) Suitably marks goods and materials, sets aside and stores them to the satisfaction of the Engineer. (iii) Sends schedule to the Engineer and invites him to inspect the goods and materials.
55 55 (1)	4th 5th		Quantities in the bill are the estimated quantities of the work only.		
55 (2)	5th	To correct an error or omission in the bill of quantities and value the extra payment due to the Contractor.		The value of work carried out in the case of any error in description in or omission from the bill of quantities.	
56 56 (1) & (3)	4th 5th	To value the work done by measurement.	To send a qualified agent to assist in measurement and furnish all particulars required by the Engineer or the Engineer's Representative	Right to attend on measurement.	Oral or written (5th ed., "reasonable") notice from the Engineer to the Contractor when he requires any part of the Works to be measured.

Clause	Edition			
56 (2)	5th	To determine an increase or decrease referred to in column 3 in consultation with the Contractor.		Appropriate increase or decrease of any rate or price rendered unreasonable or inapplicable where a difference between a billed and actual quantity by itself so warrants.
57	4th			Application of procedure in the Standard Method of Measurement save where a general or detailed description of work in the bill expressly shows to be contrary.
	5th			As above. The method may also be excluded by any statement in the bill.
58 & 59 58-59C	4th 5th	For a general explanation of these clauses refer to pp. 221-34.		
60	4th	The Engineer is to issue interim certificates (subject to the limit for such certificates stated in the Tender) for: (i) The estimated contract value of the permanent work. (ii) Such amount as the Engineer considers proper for materials delivered on Site. (iii) Such amount as the Engineer considers reasonable for Temporary Works or Constructional Plant itemised separately in the Bill—less a	To submit to the Engineer monthly progress statements of the estimated contract value of the permanent work.	Right to payment on each certificate within the time stated in the Tender from delivery of the certificate to the Employer. Payment of retention as set out in column 1. Interest at 5% p.a. on overdue certificates or retention.

Clause	Edition	1. Powers, rights and duties of the Engineer/Employer	2. Duties of the Contractor included in the Tender sum	3. Payments to and other rights of the Contractor	4. Orders, consents, notices, approvals, etc., required
		retention of the percentage and subject to the limit set out in the Tender. One half of the retention is released by the Engineer on certified completion of the whole Works and the other half 14 days after the expiration of the Period of Maintenance subject to the right to withhold from payment the estimated cost of work ordered under cls. 49 and 50 remaining to be executed. The Engineer may by any certificate correct or modify any previous certificate. The Engineer may withhold any certificate if the whole or any part of the Works are not being carried out to his satisfaction.			
60	5th	Interim certificates for: (a) (i) and (ii) substantially as above. (b) Estimated amounts due under other provisions of the Contract. (c) Such amount as the Engineer considers proper (but not exceeding the % of the value stated in the Appendix to the Tender) for goods or materials delivered on Site or the property in which has	To submit monthly progress statements (with amounts payable in respect of nominated sub-contractors listed separately) and a statement of final account and supporting documentation not later than three months after the Maintenance Certificate.	Right to certificates and payments in accordance with the following timetable: (a) Within 28 days of delivery of the Contractor's monthly statement the Engineer shall certify and the Employer pay the certificate less retention. (b) Certificates of completion in accordance with cl. 48. (c) Release of whole or part of first half of retention within 14 days of the date of	

vested in the Employer under cl. 54 before delivery.

Amounts payable in respect of nominated sub-contractors to be listed separately in certificates and every certificate is to be sent to the Employer with a copy to the Contractor.

(a) and (b) but not (c) are subject to a 5% retention up to the limit specified in sub-cl. (4). Release of retention as in 4th ed., but with partial release of the first half—i.e. $1\frac{1}{2}\%$ of the amount due in respect of a part or Section is released when it is certified complete.

Final certificate for the unpaid balance of the amount which in the Engineer's opinion is finally due under the Contract less all sums to which the Employer is entitled under the Contract up to the date of the Maintenance Certificate.

The Engineer may omit the value of any work or materials supplied or services rendered with which he is dissatisfied. For that or any other reason he may by any certificate delete, correct or modify any sum previously certified, subject to a restriction in respect of sums certified which the Contractor has paid or become bound to pay to a nominated sub-contractor.

issue of the Certificate of Completion of the whole or a Section or part of the Works.

(d) Release of the second half 14 days after the end of the last Period of Maintenance subject to deduction for works outstanding under cls. 49 and 50.

(e) Maintenance Certificate 14 days after expiry of the Period of Maintenance or later completion of any work ordered under cls. 49 and 50 (cl. 62 (1)).

(f) Not later than three months after the Maintenance Certificate the Contractor shall submit a statement of final account and supporting documentation.

(g) The Engineer shall issue the final payment certificate within three months of receipt of the Contractor's final account and of all information reasonably required for its verification. Interest at the rate specified in sub-cl. (6) if the Engineer fails to certify or the Employer to pay in accordance with this clause. Right to a copy of every certificate issued by the Engineer.

Clause	Edition	1. Powers, rights and duties of the Engineer/ Employer	2. Duties of the Contractor included in the Tender sum	3. Payments to and other rights of the Contractor	4. Orders, consents, notices, approvals, etc., required
61 & 62	4th	Engineer to issue a Maintenance Certificate 14 days after expiration of the Maintenance Period or later completion of any work ordered under cls. 49 or 50.	Possibly liable for defective work or materials in breach of contract despite the Maintenance Certificate.		Claim in writing by the Contractor before the Maintenance Certificate, or the claim is barred.
61	5th	To issue the Maintenance Certificate, as above, with a copy to the Contractor, but the Certificate does not relieve the Employer or the Contractor of any liability connected with the Contract.	*See* column 1. In particular the Contractor's liability for defective work or materials in breach of contract continues notwithstanding the issue of the Maintenance Certificate.		
63	4th & 5th	The Employer may forfeit the employment of the Contractor in the cases specified, with consequential rights. On forfeiture the Engineer is to determine with or without reference to the parties, etc... and certify the amount earned by or which would reasonably accrue to the Contractor in respect of work done at the time of expulsion and the value of unused or partially used materials, Constructional Plant and Temporary Works on the Site.	Liability to forfeiture. No further payment after forfeiture until expiration of the Period of Maintenance and the Employer's costs, damages and expenses have been certified by the Engineer, for which the Contractor is liable.		In cases (a)–(f) in sub-cl. (2), a written certificate of default by the Engineer, after prior written notice to proceed, 14 days written notice to remove materials from the Site or pull down and replace work, instructions not to sub-let (5th ed.), previous written warnings by the Engineer of lack of due diligence, as applicable. 7 days written expulsion notice by the Employer to the Contractor.

Clause (4th / 5th)	Column 1	Column 2	Column 3	Column 4
53 (4th)	The Employer may himself or by others complete the Works, using or selling Constructional Plant, Temporary Works and materials deemed to be his property under cl. 53, with deduction or recovery of costs. etc., under this clause and cl. 53.	Nor to remove Constructional Plant, Temporary Works or materials before completion (except hired plant, which does not include H.P. Plant) without the written consent of the Engineer.	Regard to the exclusive use of plant etc. vested in the Employer until 'forfeiture' etc. Resisting appeal upon removal from the Site with consent or completion of the Engineer.	Notification of name and address of the owner of Hired Plant by the Contractor in writing to the Engineer on request, and a written certificate on request of the Employer's right under the agreement of hire to take...
64 / 62 (4th / 5th)	The Employer may by his own or other workmen do urgent remedial or other work or repair necessary (4th ed., "for security"). Right to recover etc. resulting costs—column 2.	Liability for all costs and charges incurred by the Employer under this clause, if under the Contract the Contractor was liable to do the repairs, etc., at his own expense.		Engineer to notify the Contractor in writing as soon as reasonably practicable after the emergency...
65 (4th & 5th)	The Employer may determine the Contract on the outbreak of a war involving general mobilisation if the Works are not completed or completed so far as to be usable within 28 days from the date of the order for general mobilisation. Powers to sell Constructional Plant not removed from the Site by the Contractor with all reasonable dispatch after determination.	To remove Constructional Plant—column 1.	Alteration of maintenance duties if the Works are completed so far as to be usable within 28 days from the date of the order for general mobilisation. Payments after determination as specified in sub-cl. (5). Reduction of liabilities, payment in respect of damage, cost fluctuations as specified in sub-cl. (6).	Written notice to determine... from the Employer.
65A / 64 (4th / 5th)	The Contract ends automatically on frustration.		See column 1. Rights to payment on frustration as specified in this clause.	

Clause	Edition	1. Powers, rights and duties of the Engineer/Employer	2. Duties of the Contractor included in the Tender sum	3. Payments to and other rights of the Contractor	4. Orders, consents, notices, approvals, etc., required
66	4th & 5th	To refer a dispute back to the Engineer for a formal decision and to arbitration.		*See column 1.* Right to arbitration before completion on withholding of any certificate or any portion of the retention money, as to a certificate under cl. 63, or claim under cl. 12 (4th ed. by cl. 12 (6)) or "dispute ... as to any matter arising under Clause 12" (5th ed., cl. 66 (2)).	Engineer to state his decision in writing and give notice of it to the Employer and the Contractor. Request for arbitration within three months of notice of the Engineer's decision or expiration of the three months allowed for an Engineer's decision. 5th ed.— serve notice to concur in appointment of an arbitrator within one month. Application to the President of the I.C.E. to appoint an arbitrator if (4th ed.) the parties cannot agree, or (5th ed.) if they fail to appoint an arbitrator within one month of above notice to concur or if the chosen arbitrator declines the appointment or is removed by a court or is incapable of acting or dies and the parties do not fill the vacancy.
67	4th & 5th	Application of the Contract to Scotland.			
68	4th & 5th	Service of Notices.			
69	4th	As soon as practicable after notice from the Contractor the Engineer shall either direct the Contractor to supply materials		Right to give notice so as to require the Engineer to act as set out in column 1 if the Contractor cannot procure	Notice from the Contractor —column 3. Direction from the Engineer —column 1.

Clause	Edition	Provision	Valuation / Payment	Notice requirement
71	5th	in dimensions procurable instead of the metric or imperial measure described in the Contract or ordered by the Engineer, or to vary the Works to avoid the need to supply the materials to the dimensions that are not procurable.	materials in the required metric or imperial measure in sufficient time to avoid delay in performance of the Contract. Valuation of any variation.	Ditto. Notice where practicable to be given in time for any necessary design change to be considered and given effect to, and to avoid delay in performance of the Contract.
		As above, but the Engineer is to give an instruction pursuant to cl. 13 to supply the materials in the dimensions originally required, or an order under cl. 51 to supply the materials in the dimensions specified as procurable in the Contractor's notice or order a variation as above.	Right to give notice where despite having used his best endeavours the Contractor cannot obtain the materials in the measure required without undue delay or additional expense. Valuation of any variation. Remedies under cl. 13.	
70 69	4th 5th	Reduction in the Contract payments for decreases in the level of incidence of any labour-tax matter. The Engineer may take account of a reduction even if the Contractor fails to submit full details.	Payment of increases in the level or incidence of any labour-tax matter. The Contractor may incorporate a provision similar to this clause in any sub-contract. Payment to be included in all payment certificates.	The Contractor to give notice to the Engineer as soon as practicable after any change in level or incidence of a labour-tax matter, to keep contemporary records, submit full details of additions or deduction with his monthly statements.
71 70	4th 5th	Value Added Tax.		
72	5th	Special Conditions to be added as required.		
Loose sheet		Price variation formula.		

INSURANCE

Contractor's insurance, 5th edition

1. *All Risks policy in joint names of the Contractor and the Employer* (*cl.* 21)*:*

EXTENT OF COVER. Permanent and Temporary Works, unfixed materials and other things delivered to the site and Constructional Plant as defined in cl. 1 (1) (o), against all risks other than the Excepted Risks defined in cl. 20 (3) On damage due to the employer's negligence *see* p. 97. Goods and materials vested in the Employer before delivery must also be insured under cl. 54.

AMOUNT OF COVER. Full value of the above.
The full value of the works may be increased by variations and increased quantities and with inflation. The contractor and engineer will have to ensure either that there is a provision in the policy, e.g. by which the sum insured is increased by the same ratio as the final price bears to the original tender total (but such cover is usually subject to a maximum), or that the cover is increased from time to time. Inflation may continue to affect replacement cost between the date when the damage occurs and the time when reinstatement is reasonably possible. On the other hand cover at even the original tender total may be wasteful of premiums since a total loss of some work is virtually impossible. The employer may be encouraged to take advice from brokers before inviting tenders, as to whether any adjustment of cl. 21 is advisable for the particular works.

PERIOD OF COVER. From the Date of Commencement under cl. 41 until 14 days after the Certificate of Completion of the whole works or earlier Certificate of Completion in respect of any part or Section. Outstanding work in an undertaking under cl. 48 until such outstanding work is complete. Loss or damage in the Period of Maintenance under cl. 49 from any cause occurring prior to commencement of the Period, and loss or damage occasioned by the Contractor in the course of completing outstanding work under cl. 48 or complying with his obligations under cls. 49 or 50 (unless covered elsewhere).

PERMISSIBLE EXCLUSIONS. The Excepted Risks defined in cl. 20 (3). As to use or occupation by the Employer *see* p. 98. The necessity for repair/reconstruction of work not in accordance with the Contract, but *see* below. Wear and tear and gradual deterioration of plant, but *see* below. Consequential loss, but the Contractor may wish to seek cover for plant, etc., idle and loss of profit on constructing work twice, or the Employer his loss of profit due to delay for which the Contractor is entitled to an extension of time. *See also* p. 100, N. 6.

INADMISSIBLE EXCLUSIONS AND RESTRICTIONS. Faulty design or specification other than design within cl. 20 (3), and *see* p. 103. Damage or injury caused by work not in accordance with the Contract, or by wear and tear or gradual deterioration of plant.
Invariably the policy will have some Conditions which, although not specifically authorised by this clause, may have to be accepted—below.

ADVISABLE EXTENSIONS. Professional fees on reconstruction, cost of redrawing plans and documents, site clearance, etc., materials and plant off site and in transit and against any insurable Excepted Risks.

2. *Employer's Liability policy (cls. 23 and 24) with indemnity to principals clause:*

EXTENT OF COVER. Liability for bodily injury or disease sustained by employees of the Contractor.

AMOUNT OF COVER. Usually unlimited, and by the Employer's Liability (Compulsory Insurance) Act, 1969, not less than £2 million for claims relating to one or more persons from one occurrence.

PERIOD OF COVER. By statute, at all times whilst an employer.

PERMISSIBLE EXCLUSIONS. Radioactive contamination.

INADMISSIBLE EXCLUSIONS AND RESTRICTIONS. Liability undertaken by contract. The policy is likely to contain Conditions that the insured must take all reasonable precautions to avoid injury, against admissions of liability by the insured, etc. These Conditions are not permitted by the above Act, and insurers will not rely on them against the person injured so that they do not concern the Employer. Insurers reserve the right to recover from the Contractor damages paid despite breach of Condition, but are likely to do so only in most exceptional cases.

NECESSARY EXTENSIONS. Labour-only sub-contractors and their gangs to be deemed to be the Contractor's employees for the purpose of the policy (and payments to them accordingly included in the return of wages for premium calculation). Preferably the liability of the labour-master himself to his employees should be covered, to give his employees the advantage of insurance of the high degree of care owed by an employer to a direct employee (p. 93). Death or injury to hired-in operators of hired plant.

3. *Public Liability policy with indemnity to principals clause (cl. 23):*

EXTENT OF COVER. Liability for loss, injury or damage to any person or property whatsoever.

AMOUNT OF COVER. At least the amount stated in the Appendix to the Tender. The Contractor takes the risk of under-insurance and the cover should allow, e.g., for damage to valuable equipment of the Employer to be installed before completion, unless the plant is separately insured for the benefit of the Contractor.

PERIOD OF COVER. "Throughout the execution of the Works" by cl. 23— see p. 107, N.1. But as the Contractor's liability continues thereafter, an annually renewable policy is essential.

PERMISSIBLE EXCLUSIONS AND RESTRICTIONS. By the operative words the policy will almost invariably be restricted to "accidental" damage or injury. That is largely permitted by cl. 22 (b) (ii) to (iv)—p. 106, N.6. The restriction could cause difficulty where a contractor chooses to work in a way that will inevitably cause damage, but very few insurers will remove the limitation. Exclusion of injury to persons employed by the insured under any contract for service or apprenticeship is permissible. Liability arising from use of mechanically propelled vehicles when actually being used so as to require insurance under the Road Traffic Acts. All other use of vehicles and movable plant, and liability for damage to roads, etc., by such vehicles should be covered under this policy. Any condition requiring all reasonable precautions to prevent injury or damage should be objected to, but in any case will be interpreted narrowly by the courts.

INADMISSIBLE EXCLUSIONS. Liability assumed under a contract or agreement which would not otherwise have attached. Damage to property in the insured's care, custody or control unless restricted to the Works insured under the All Risks policy. Cls. 22 and 23 permit the Contractor to exclude damage to the Works from this policy, but since the Contractor will remain liable under the ordinary law for the Employer's consequential loss due to any damage to the Works resulting from the Contractor's negligence, which will not be covered under the All Risks policy, the Contractor may have to consider insuring his liability to liquidated damages or other liability to the Employer for such consequential loss. *See also* under "All Risks policy, Permissible exclusions", above. Any exclusion of property upon or in which the insured is or has been working should be deleted or restricted to "that immediate part of any property in which the Insured is or has been working".

4. *Road Traffic Act cover for vehicles and movable plant.*

General requirements as to cover, etc.
Policies to be with insurers and in terms approved by the Employer (cls. 21 and 23).

Where possible policies should be extended to cover or to waive insurer's subrogation rights against any director or partner in the Contractor's firm or company, offices, committees and members of the Contractor's canteen, and social sports and welfare organisations, and first-aid, fire and ambulance services, and other employees where possible.

Every exclusion, endorsement, schedule, or restriction of cover elsewhere should be carefully considered by the Contractor and the Engineer, and unless any restriction is clearly authorised by the Contract it should be brought to the Employer's attention, for legal or insurance advice as necessary. In the case of policies running for more than one works the Contractor should make certain that a restrictive endorsement will not be overlooked in respect of some subsequent works to which it may be relevant. The Contractor will also keep insurers advised of any change or extension in his activities.

Any special risks in the particular Contract should be brought to the attention of insurers before the policy is issued. All Conditions of the policies should be carefully complied with, and the policy consulted as soon as any difficulty arises that may give rise to a claim. Policies usually require notification to insurers of any occurrence that may give rise to a claim.

There may be various ways of obtaining the necessary cover, some cheaper than others. That is a matter for the Contractor's broker or other insurance adviser, and not for the Engineer.

Employer's insurance, 5th edition
1. The Permanent and Temporary Works against the Excepted Risks defined in cl. 20 (3), so far as insurable. For example, if procurable against non-negligent design failure—see p. 103, N. 11. The Employer should ensure that the full payment that will have to be made to the Contractor, including the Contractor's profit, is included. Professional fees on reconstruction, removal of debris, etc., should also be covered.
2. The Permanent Works within 14 days of certified completion of the whole, and similarly any Section or part certified complete.
3. Employer's Liability policy in respect of resident staff and other direct employees of the Employer.
4. Public Liability policy for the residuary liability of the Employer under cls. 22 (2) and 24.
5. The Employer may have to consider negotiating a special policy, where damage to neighbouring property, etc., is arguably an inevitable result of the Works—see "Public Liability policy, Permissible exclusions", above.
6. Road Traffic Act policies on resident staff or other employees' vehicles.
7. Loss of profit on delay to the works not covered by liquidated damages.
8. The Employer may take out a general contingency policy to protect against, for example, invalidity or lapse by non-payment of a premium of a contractor's policy.

Engineer's indemnity insurance—p. 397.

Insurance under the 4th edition I.C.E. Conditions
Both the Engineer and Contractor are placed in a difficult situation because these Conditions require the Contractor to provide insurance that is virtually unobtainable, in particular against inevitable damage to property unless it consists of interference with an easement or quasi-easement within cl. 22 (1) (c). Again, because of the very restricted terms of cl. 22 (1) (d), the Contractor may be liable for injury or damage due to the Engineer's original design, which it is also very difficult for the Contractor to cover. Careful consideration of the risks involved in the particular Works and the cover available may be necessary by the Engineer and the Employer's and Contractor's insurance advisers.

Alternative "wrap-up" insurance cover by the Employer on the whole project
Internationally there has been some movement towards provision of overall cover by the Employer instead of insurance divided between Contractor, Sub-contractors, Engineer and Employer. It is claimed that such insurance can provide gap-free insurance with more certainty and less cost, but the advantages and disadvantages of such cover are the subject of much debate. Certainly there are many contractual and insurance implications that are not always obvious and must be considered most carefully in amending these clauses and arranging the employer's policy, if all those concerned are to have the insurance protection on which they will be relying.

(a) F.I.D.I.C. Seminar on Project Insurance, reported in (1978) 42 The Consulting Engineer, at p. 46.

CHAPTER 12

Delay, Disruption
and Acceleration Claims

If execution of the works is delayed or disrupted by acts of the employer or of the engineer acting as his agent—e.g. delay by the engineer in supplying necessary drawings, instructions, or inspecting work under Conditions cl. 38 (1), delay due to late variations or by the employer in nominating or re-nominating a sub-contractor, or caused by a supplier or contractor employed directly by the employer—the contractor may claim compensation under one or more of the following headings:

(a) *"extra cost ... incurred"* in giving effect to an order under cl. 40 of the Conditions to suspend the works, or presumably where the arbitrator reverses an engineer's decision not to suspend the works. There is no requirement that the contractor must claim a suspension (only that when a suspension order has been given the contractor must give notice of claim under cl. 52 (4)). It may be that the engineer has a duty to give a suspension where a hold-up to the whole or any part of the works is *"necessary"* because they cannot in fact proceed, particularly where the engineer or employer is responsible for the cause of delay.

(b) As a variation, or as an ingredient in rates for a variation under cl. 52 (1)—p. 175, N. 10—or by re-rating under cl. 52 (2)—N. 12 to that clause on p. 188.

(c) Under cl. 42 the contractor is entitled to expenses if the employer delays in giving possession of the site in accordance with the contractor's programme. Presumably the contractor's programme must be reasonable. As to what is reasonable, *see* further on.

(d) Under cl. 27 (6) for delay caused in giving notice for the purpose of the Public Utility Street Works Act, 1950.

(e) The reasonable costs *"by reason of any unavoidable delay or disruption of working"* due to unforeseen physical conditions or artificial obstructions within cl. 12.

(f) *"cost as may be reasonable"* under cl. 7 for *"failure or inability of the Engineer to issue at a time reasonable in all the circumstances drawings and instructions requested by the Contractor and considered necessary by the Engineer"*. The ingredients in a claim under this troublesome clause are discussed on p. 49.

(g) Under cl. 13, for the actual issue by the engineer of *"instructions or directions which involve the Contractor in delay or disrupt his arrangements or methods of construction so as to cause him to incur cost beyond that reasonably to have been foreseen by an experienced contractor at the time of tender"*. The notes on this clause are on pp. 73–7.

(h) Under cl. 31 in respect of facilities for contractors or authorities, p. 119, N. 2.

(i) For breach of an implied term in the contract (p. 42 (b)) that the contractor will receive decisions from the engineer and employer in time so

as to avoid disruption of the planned expeditious and economic progress of
the works. A similar term may be implied for timely supply of goods that are
to be provided by or on behalf of the employer. It is clear that in so far as an
implied term would cover a cause of delay dealt with in any of the express
terms of the contract, particularly cl. 7, the implied term is displaced and the
express term governs (p. 50). Nevertheless there is still some room for an
implied term to apply to a decision of the engineer which is not an
instruction or drawing, e.g. delay in inspecting work under cl. 38, and refer
to p. 240, N. 6, on re-nomination.

a

a'

The notice requirements of cl. 52 (4) do not apply to such a claim in an
implied term (p. 194, N. 3).

In one unreported case it has been held that, particularly where a contract
says that the engineer has power to supply drawings and instructions "*from
time to time*" in the course of the contract (as in cl. 7), the court will imply
only a more limited duty than that referred to above, to supply drawings
and instructions within a reasonable time, and that what is a reasonable
time does not—

"depend solely upon the convenience and financial interests of the ...
(contractors). No doubt it is to their interest to have every detail cut and dried on
the day the contract is signed, but the contract does not contemplate that. It
contemplates further details and instructions being provided, and the Engineer is
to have a time to provide them which is reasonable having regard to the point of
view of him and his staff and the point of view of the Corporation, as well as the
point of view of the contractors.

In determining what is a reasonable time as respects any particular details and
instructions, factors which must obviously be borne in mind are such matters as
the order in which the Engineer has determined the works shall be carried out ...
whether requests for particular details or instructions have been made by the
contractors, whether the instructions relate to a variation of the contract which
the Engineer is entitled to make from time to time during the execution of the
contract, or whether they relate to part of the original works, and also the time,
including any extension of time, within which the contractors are contractually
bound to complete the works.

In mentioning these matters, I want to make it perfectly clear that they are not
intended to be exhaustive, or anything like it. What is a reasonable time is a
question of fact having regard to all the circumstances of the case."

b

(a) *Wells* v. *Army & Navy Co-op. Society* (1902), Hudson "Building Contracts", 4th ed., vol. ii,
346. Also relevant are *Demolition & Construction Co. Ltd.* v. *Kent River Board* [1963] 2
Lloyd's Rep. 7, and *Trollope & Colls Ltd.* v. *North West Metropolitan Regional Hospital
Board* [1973] 2 All E.R. 260, H.L. (set out above in the text on pp. 42–3).

(a') In *Thomas Bates and Son Ltd.* v. *Thurrock Borough Council*, The Times, October 23rd
1975, held that "If A promised B that C would supply goods to B in a reasonable time and C
did not supply them or supplied them late, B could sue A for damages for C's default. The
council employed "mass-producers of housing estates", specified in a building contract that
the producers' standard type of houses and standard components would be used, and
nominated the producers as suppliers of the components. The builders gave the producers
orders for the components as and when needed, but the components were supplied late. The
builders succeeded in a disruption claim against the council on the grounds that it was an
implied term of their building contract that the components would be supplied in time. Held
also that the council were entitled to recover from the producers the compensation paid to
the builders. There was an actual term in the building contract that the suppliers'
components "shall be incorporated in the ... works and shall be delivered to the site of the
works in accordance with a programme to be agreed between the Supervising Officer (of the
council)" and the producers.

(b) *Neodox Ltd.* v. *Swinton & Pendlebury B.C.* (1958) now reported in 5 B.L.R. 38, and
considered in *Fischbach and Moore of Canada Ltd.* v. *Noranda Mines Ltd.* (1978) 84 D.L.R.
(3d) 465.

With respect, whilst a reference to supply of drawings and instructions from time to time obviously means that all drawings and instructions need not be issued before the contract is let, it does not appear to imply that they need not be issued in time to allow the contractor to pre-plan and execute his work without disruption. The decision can hardly mean that the contractor is to have no remedy for delays in issuing instructions or drawings due to the private difficulties of the engineer and his staff or of the employer of which the contractor knew nothing and therefore could not

c   allow for when pricing his tender. Cl. 7 is now stated to apply whenever there is "*failure or inability of the Engineer to issue at a time reasonable in all the circumstances drawings and instructions*", but unfortunately does not clarify what "*circumstances*" are relevant. The inclusion of "*inability*" of the engineer may mean to make clear that private difficulties of the employer or engineer are not relevant.

The contractor may base his pricing on finishing the job before the completion date in the contract, and is perfectly entitled to do so if he can (p. 142, N. 6). However, notice to the employer to that effect even immediately after the work starts may be too late to give the engineer a reasonable time to meet the contractor's requirements. There may be a similar problem in relation to possession of the site and if the employer wishes to order variations at a late stage. A contractor in this position will best protect himself by a tender qualification requiring supply of drawings, specifications and details, possession of the site, instructions and variation orders in time to allow early completion in accordance with a programme

d   submitted before tender.

It is common for contractors to base disruption claims on the difference between the progress shown on pre-tender or contract programmes and actual progress, but that is not a sufficient basis of claim. To establish

---

(*c*) In *Unit Construction Co. Ltd.* v. *Liverpool Corpn.* (1972) 221 E.G. 459 it was held that the term to be implied into a contract, which was not in a standard form, was that the employers would make sites available to contractors erecting over three thousand buildings by a system method of construction "within times reasonable in all the circumstances of the case", and not "at such times as would enable ... (the contractors) acting reasonably, to achieve continuity of work on site and co-ordination between output at the factories and erection on the site and to complete the works within six years" (the contract period was six years). The learned judge stated that he had been in some doubt as to which of the alternatives should be implied. In this case the contractors knew when they made the contract of very considerable uncertainties about the availability of the site owing to the planning situation.

In *Gloucestershire C.C.* v. *Richardson* [1968] 2 All E.R. 1181, H.L. Lord Upjohn said (at p. 1188): "I am also of opinion ... the contractor did not receive instructions in 'due time' under cl. 18 (vi) (of the R.I.B.A. Conditions) as to recommencement of the work for which he had applied in writing. It is quite true that he was acquiescent in the delay but it was for the architect to make up his mind as to what was to be done and to give instructions accordingly. He cannot expect a contractor to keep together his men indefinitely and pay them to be idle on the site while he (the architect) waits supinely (as I think) on some report of an expert who in the end refuses to report to him." All work was stopped for two months, and the order to stop was given because defects, undetectable when they were supplied, developed in columns supplied by a nominated sub-contractor.

(*d*) In *U.S.* v. *Blair*, 321 U.S. 730, 64 S.ct. 82, 88 L.ed.1039, the contractor planned to finish the work before the completion date, but another contractor employed directly by the employer prevented this, although not completion by the contract completion date. Held by the U.S. Supreme Court that the contractor had no remedy against the employer, since the employer did not know of his plans when it entered into the contract with the other contractor, which was planned on the basis of the full completion time. It would, in the circumstances, have been unfair to place a duty to allow earlier completion on the employer, particularly since the contractor could not have been compelled to complete before the original date.

disruption the contractor must prove that he has been held up in fact by some cause for which the employer is responsible, and he must produce proof of the progress he would actually have made if he had not been delayed, not merely the progress he said he would make or intended to make. A programme may be some, but is by no means conclusive, evidence of the former.

In a recent unreported decision:

> The arbitrator in his findings of fact on a special case stated that "the result, in terms of delay and disorganisation, of each of the matters referred to (causes of delay for which the employers were responsible) was a continuing one. As each matter occurred its consequences were added to the cumulative consequences of the matters which had preceded it.... It is therefore impracticable, if not impossible, to assess the additional expense caused by delay and disorganisation due to any one of these matters in isolation from the other matters." Held: that "so long as the arbitrator does not make any award which contains a profit element, this being permissible under clauses 51 and 52 but not under clauses 41 (*sic*) and 42, and provided he ensures that there is no duplication ... (there is) no reason why he should not recognise the realities of the situation and make individual awards in respect of those parts of individual items of the claim which can be dealt with in isolation and a supplementary award in respect of the remainder of these claims as a composite whole".

This decision illustrates the extreme difficulties in assessing disruption claims, whether it is the contractor who is attempting to recover his real losses, or an employer defending an exaggerated claim. As a result arbitrators and courts are placed in a dilemma. The contractor should be fully compensated for actual losses due to real disruption, but it is harmful to the public and to responsible contractors if compensation is recovered for fictitious losses or losses due in fact to the contractor's own inefficiencies. *See further* p. 442 ff. The *Crosby* decision just cited has been embraced by contractors and their advisers with great enthusiasm, which might well be tempered by the following considerations:

(*a*) After completion the contractor is not entitled to disregard the original contract and claim on a *quantum meruit* his total costs of the works plus a profit, on the grounds that the works were disrupted by the employer.

(*e*) *J. Crosby & Sons Ltd.* v. *Portland U.D.C.* (1967) now reported in 5 B.L.R. 126. There is authority in other types of case that the courts will award damages even though the amount of the loss is uncertain and difficult to calculate. For example, the award to one of 50 finalists out of 6,000 who entered a newspaper competition offering engagements to 12 winning actresses, where the newspaper failed to give her a reasonable chance of being interviewed in accordance with the advertised rules: *Chaplin* v. *Hicks* (1911) 2 K.B. 786, C.A. "In all actions ... the character of the acts themselves which produce the damage, and circumstances under which these acts are done, must regulate the degree of certainty and particularity with which the damage done ought to be stated and proved. As much certainty and particularity must be insisted on, both in pleading and proof of damage, as is reasonable, having regard to the circumstances and to the nature of the acts themselves by which the damage is done. To insist upon less would be to relax old and intelligible principles. To insist upon more would be the vainest pedantry" *Ratcliffe* v. *Evans* (1892) 2 Q.B. 524, 532, 533, C.A.

(*e'*) *Morrison-Knudson Co. Inc.* v. *British Columbia Hydro and Power Authority* (No. 2) [1978] 85 D.L.R. (3d) 186, Can., in which the authorities are fully discussed. In exceptional cases U.S. courts have allowed recovery for disruption by a "total cost" claim for the difference between actual and bid cost, see *Sovereign Construction Co. Ltd.* 75-1 CCH Bd. Cont. App. Dec. 11, 251 and cases cited. No similar decisions elsewhere have been found. In the *Morrison-Knudson* decision it was said of a claim for acceleration that was at hearing for over 300 days: "If it is difficult to fix the amount for a breach it is no more difficult than to fix compensation for a personal injury ... It may be that the award will be remarkably similar to the result of a

The contractor's right is to payment of the original contract rates and prices plus only such additional sums for disruption as he can prove on the balance of probabilities to have been due to any of the causes of delay listed above and not to any cause that is a contractor's risk.

· (b) Despite the decisions that have been cited, showing that an arbitrator or court has some latitude to do practical justice in assessing compensation to the contractor, justice must also be done to the employer. The latitude applies only if it is not practicable for the contractor to prove his claim in full detail, and the possibilities for abuse have been recognised in another jurisdiction:

> "The primary lack is plaintiff's complete failure to link its accountant's general survey of the amount of time taken by the Government (in the requisitioning process) with the costs of the plaintiff's operations. We are reminded in general terms that for want of a nail a kingdom could be lost, but there is no evidence or attempt to show, even by illustration, that the delay on this or that car held up work on so many tanks for such-and-such approximate period … there is no effort to differentiate, even by general classes, between the reasonable and unreasonable Government delays and to show the special effect of the unreasonable delays. Other important causes of delay (such as dilatory sub-contractors) are ignored".

f

Contractor claimed over one million dollars extra on a contract to construct several buildings and electrical and mechanical installations. The Court accepted the trial commissioner's award of approximately one-fifth of that claim, including his findings and conclusion of law that the contractor's "total time" theory on which his claim was based was unacceptable. In accordance with that theory the contractor "simply takes the … overrun (between the original and extended completion dates), points to a host of individual delay incidents for which defendant was allegedly responsible and which 'contributed' to the overall extended time, and then leaps to the conclusion that the entire overrun time was attributable to defendant." The commissioner pointed out that the evidence demonstrated "that many of the incidents relied on by plaintiff were isolated and non-sequential and therefore could not possibly have caused any significant delay in the overall progress of the project. Furthermore, with respect to the great bulk of such incidents, plaintiff has failed to prove, or indeed even to attempt to prove, the crucial factors of the specific extent of the alleged wrongful delay to the project operations caused thereby. For the most part it had not even attempted a reasonable approximation based upon some rational theory." Nevertheless, it would have been unfair to dismiss the delay claim entirely because the record was sufficient to substantiate the contention that the defendant did cause actionable delay and to ascertain with a reasonable degree of accuracy the extent of such a delay to the project as a whole. Recovery was allowed on approximately one-tenth of the alleged specific items of delay.

g

Contractor attempted to introduce a complicated computer printout to demonstrate delays and cost overruns in a claim against the architect (*see* text below p. 398). The Californian Court of Appeal noted that the computer-operated accounting system did not distinguish between ordinary cost overruns and increased costs allegedly caused by the architect's negligence. Therefore, the printout was not proof that cost overruns were caused by such negligence.

h

---

quantum meruit and that some arbitrary figure will have to be used. But difficulty of assessment does not justify abandoning the attempt and making an award on … (the) basis (of *quantum meruit*)" (at pp. 448-9).

(*f*) *Commerce International Inc.* v. *U.S.* (1964) 338 F.2d 81, 89.

(*g*) *Bruno Law* v. *U.S.* (1971) 195 Ct.Cl. 370, 382 referring to a number of previous U.S. decisions to like effect. *See* p. 367 footnote (*e'*) for exceptional cases.

(*h*) *Huber, Hunt & Nichols, Inc.* v. *Moore* (1977) 67 C.A. 3d 278, 136 C.R. 603.

(c) It is claims for loss of overhead return and profit (as far as recoverable, below) that are most likely to produce a dividend for the contractor beyond his actual losses. The theory is that the contractor's site and management resources are his revenue earning instrument, and that insofar as they are detained on a contract by delay he will lose the earnings he would have made with them on some other contract out of which he would have paid his overheads and pocketed his profit. The reality is that in many cases, particularly where the delay affects a small part of a large contractor's total resources, the contractor's organisation has sufficient flexibility to cope with the extra time on site without sacrificing any other contracts that may be available, so that the contractor's total overhead return and profit is not in fact adversely affected by the delay, or not to the extent claimed on foot of the usual mathematical formula. On the other hand, where a major part of his resources are tied down on a site because of a delay, the ultimate length of which is not known, the contractor genuinely may be inhibited from tendering for other work at competitive rates: the edge may be taken off his tendering in a way not susceptible to very clear proof. The difficulty is to establish the real facts, and some indication of the proof necessary has been given:

"... the matter was put ... that in the time (of delay) ... they (the contractors) were unable to take on any other work, which they would have been free to do had the ... (works) been completed on time, and they lost the profit which they would have made on this other work. I think when there is a new trial every issue under this head should be open for the official referee to consider. It might be of some help to him not to be left only with the evidence of the plaintiffs' auditors on this point: possibly some evidence as to what this site organisation consisted of, what part of the head office staff is being referred to, and what they were doing at the material times, could be of help. Moreover, it is possible, I suppose, that an official referee might think it useful to have an analysis of the yearly turnover from, say, 1962 right up to, say, 1969, so that if the case is put before him on the basis that work was lost during 1966 and 1967 by reason of the plaintiffs being engaged upon completion of this block and, therefore, not being free to take on any other work, he would be helped in forming an assessment of any loss of profits sustained by the plaintiffs".

"The sum awarded (for the loss of profit) was arrived at on the basis of a gross profit calculated at 9 percent of the main contract figure of £232,000. Whether this was a satisfactory method of approach need not now be decided, although I have substantial doubts on the matter.... What is the proper sum to award under this head will depend upon the evidence called at the new trial. It was sketchily dealt with before the official referee, and I content myself with saying merely that the plaintiffs will need to do some hard thinking on how they should proceed to establish this item of damage."

(i) The efficiency of supervisors and managers may nevertheless be reduced by what has been called the "crisis mode of management"—Martin Barnes "Assessing the Cost of Disturbance", Journal of the Association of Surveyors in Civil Engineering, 1974 Nov., pp. 5–23.

(j) The formula extends the expected overhead return for the contract pro rata to the period of delay (text above p. 31). In practice the statement of the formula in Hudson's "Building and Engineering Contracts", 10th ed. by I. N. Duncan Wallace at p. 599 is cited by claimants as scripture although the limitations on the application of the formula because of the questions it begs are immediately mentioned in Hudson itself. The formula also may produce under-recovery for the contractor, where his overhead costs are increased above the level envisaged at the time of tender because of inflation in the period of delay.

(k) Peak Construction (Liverpool) Ltd v. McKinney Foundations Ltd. (1970) reported at 1 B.L.R. 114, C.A. 122 per Salmon L.J.

(l) Peak decision, above, per Edmund Davies L.J. at p. 126.

All the grounds of claim above on p. 364 except (b) and (i) have in common that they entitle the contractor to costs only (including overheads) as discussed on p. 31. The loss of the right to recover the profit he would otherwise have earned with his resources if they had not been tied up on the site due to the delay is a serious limitation on the contractor's recovery.

(d) A contractor may claim that labour or other resources were used or purchased at a late date because of employer's delay, and accordingly will seek an adjustment for any aspects of inflation not already covered by a price fluctuation clause in the contract. Since compensation for delay is based on actual cost, neither party is entitled to have it measured in a fixed priced contract by the standard fluctuation formula (p. 314), although they may agree to do so. Before making such an agreement the employer (or the engineer with his authority) should consider that the necessarily rough and ready results of the formula may be exaggerated, for example where the contractor did buy materials at the programmed time because he did not know there would be delay (p. 316, N. 1 and p. 318).

Even where the formula is part of the original contract, the contractor may claim to have it improved entirely to his benefit in valuing an employer's delay, e.g. by omitting the non-adjustable percentage. The contractor is not automatically entitled to such a change, since even with its limitations the formula does not necessarily produce a shortfall compared to actual costs.

Apart from conferring a right to compensation, delay may be so serious a breach of contract as to entitle the contractor to determine the contract and
m   refuse to go on with the works (p. 425); delay for more than three months may entitle the contractor to omit work or treat the contract as abandoned under cl. 40 (2) where there has been a suspension order (or presumably the contractor may excuse failure to execute the work by serving notice under cl. 40 (2) and persuading an arbitrator to hold that a suspension order should have been given by the engineer more than three months before he gave notice); delay outside both parties' control may frustrate the contract under cl. 64.

For disruption caused by the employer in occupying part of the works before completion of the whole *see* p. 161, N. 6.

The thorny problem of concurrent delays has already been mentioned (above, p. 139). Decided cases about similar but not identical issues in
n   different settings are not very helpful. The general rule would seem to be on principle that if the employer's actions do not actually delay the contractor because, for example, he was not in any case ready for drawings held back, or the contractor cannot prove which of several causes for only one of which the employer was responsible was the operative cause of the delay and his losses, having failed to discharge the burden of proving loss due to the action of the employer the contractor is not entitled to recover
o   compensation from him.

(*m*) *S. J. & M. M. Price Ltd.* v. *Milne, R.* [1968] 206 E.G. 313.

(*n*) *The Haversham Grange* [1905] P. 307, C.A.; *Carslogie S.S. Co.* v. *Royal Norwegian Government* [1952] 1 All E.R. 20 (concurrent repairs to ships damaged by two causes); *Baker* v. *Willoughby* [1969] 3 All E.R. 1528 (injury to leg in road accident, 3 years later injury by shooting as a result of which the leg was amputated, but held that did not reduce the compensation payable for the accident).

(*o*) ". . . there can be no recovery where the defendant's delay is concurrent or intertwined with other delays". *Commerce International* decision footnote (*f*) above, and other U.S. cases cited in that report at p. 90. .

Disruption problems may particularly arise as between several sub-contractors of the main contractor or direct contractors of the employer. A mechanical contractor's contract may state a particular date to start his work of erecting plant on foundations placed by others. He is then both bound and entitled to start on that day—p. 135, N. 1—and if he is not allowed to do so may suffer costs for which he may claim against the other party to his contract, whether the main contractor or employer. The other party may not have been able to provide the foundations in time because of strikes or because of delay in completing them by another sub-contractor or direct contractor. Nevertheless he will be liable to the contractor held up under most of the standard forms of contract and sub-contract, which do not give the employer or main contractor any right to extension of the time for providing possession of the site, etc., even for reasons outside his control. The employer or main contractor may not be entitled to pass liability for the compensation paid on to any other contractor who caused the delay if that contractor is entitled to an extension of time, as he will usually be under the standard forms for any delay outside his control.

The unfortunate position of the employer and the main contractor in the middle in this way may be eased by special contract terms, for example a "force majeure" clause by which he is relieved of liability for delays due to strikes, etc., and other causes beyond his control. To find a full and fair solution is a large problem which needs consideration by the industry.

By cl. 46 the engineer has a very useful power to order acceleration of the work necessary to ensure completion by the contract completion date. Varying views have been heard as to the possibility of a claim by a contractor for extra payment for acceleration if he completes the whole or part of the works before the contract date, but the position under the 5th edition I.C.E. Conditions appears to be reasonably clear, as follows:

(a) Under cl. 51 the contractor may claim for a variation if the engineer orders, or is bound to order, a change "*in the specified ... timing of construction (if any)*". This provision is discussed on pp. 175-7, where it is suggested that it does not give the engineer power to accelerate completion of the whole of the works.

(b) It is suggested that cl. 13 does not entitle the engineer to order the contractor to accelerate the whole or part of the works. That clause entitles the engineer to give instructions on any matter connected with the completion and maintenance of the works "(*whether mentioned in the Contract or not*)", not contrary to what is stated in the contract. Cl. 43 requires completion only by the time stated in the Appendix to the Form of Tender and subject to the contractor's right to an extension of time. A power to order acceleration would also cause difficulties about liquidated damages, which one would expect to be dealt with in the Conditions if such a power were intended to exist.

(c) The contractor does not appear to have any right to recover compensation from the employer merely because a refusal by the engineer to grant an extension or the amount of an extension granted is later increased by the engineer himself or an arbitrator (p. 417). But if the contractor is driven to expedite in order to avoid possible liability for damages or as a result of instructions by the engineer under cl. 46 or requirements under cl. 14 (2) because the engineer has failed to consider the contractor's right to an extension in good faith at the times at which he is directed to do so by cl. 44, then it seems that the contractor may have a claim. The claim is for damages for breach of contract by the employer by way of the failure of the engineer as his agent to administer the contract in accordance with its terms (p. 418).

(d) It follows that the contractor may refuse altogether a request by the employer or engineer to accelerate or require whatever payment he thinks fit for agreeing to do so.

(e) If the engineer orders the contractor to complete before what the engineer recognises to be the contract completion date or where the engineer refuses to grant an extension to which the contractor considers himself entitled, the contractor may refuse to obey and rely on his right to obtain an extension of time in arbitration and to upset in arbitration any purported forfeiture under cl. 63.

(f) If the contractor without agreeing extra payment in advance does accelerate in response to an order or a request by the engineer, e.g. that the contractor should try to make up lost time and the engineer will see about an extension if the contractor needs it, it seems that the contractor may be entitled to reasonable payment for the acceleration on an implied contract to pay for performance by the contractor beyond his existing contractual duty. The notice requirements in cl. 52 (4) do not apply to such a claim. As the engineer has no implied authority to make a new contract (p. 399), the contractor should check that the order or request is authorised by the employer. Indeed such is the uncertainty of the contractual position, that a contractor who considers that he is being ordered or harassed to accelerate should try to make direct contact with the employer and negotiate a special agreement, or at least notify the employer direct that he is implementing the employer's wishes on the basis that he will be paid extra for going beyond his contract (although that will not in itself guarantee that the contractor will be held entitled to extra payment).

(g) If the contractor is required to do extra work at an accelerated pace, the speed at which the work was done should be taken into account in the valuation under cl. 52 of the variation itself.

(q) Damages for acceleration were awarded in *Morrison-Knudsen Co. Inc.* v. *British Columbia Hydro and Power Authority* (No. 2) [1978] 85 D.L.R. (3d) 186 Can., where employers interfered with the exercise by the engineer of his duty to give extensions of time and directed the contractor to make up time lost for which he was entitled to an extension. *See also* the decision of the Supreme Court of South Africa in *Taylor Woodrow International Ltd.* v. *Minister of Health* (No. 1687 of 1977).

(r) *See* previous footnote.

CHAPTER 13

Relations of the Engineer with the Employer and the Contractor

THE ASSOCIATION OF CONSULTING ENGINEERS MODEL FORMS OF SERVICE AGREEMENT

It is perhaps most useful to deal with the legal relations of the engineer with his client and the contractor by a commentary on the model service agreements published by the Association. Form A is dealt with in detail below, and for the other forms *see* p. 406.

These service agreements are used widely, but it seems not as widely as they should be. Engineers who are retiring about fees may simply incorporate the agreement by letter instead of having it signed formally by the client, accepting employment, e.g., "on the terms and for the fees set out in the Model Form of Agreement 'A' of the Association", etc. Although not legally necessary a blank copy of the form should be enclosed, and rather than rely on his memory of the form the engineer should go through it to see if any changes are necessary for the particular contract (*see* especially cl. 4 and N. 41), which may be set out in the letter.

The schedule of fees only may be adopted by letter—but this is not completely satisfactory without, for example, cls. 3 or 9.

In writing an initial letter to the client on fees, the opportunity should be taken to draw several other matters to his attention (p. 397).

In 1970 the Association published revised "Conditions of Engagement", with an increase in fees, but these have not come into general use by public authorities.

MODEL FORM OF AGREEMENT "A" BETWEEN
A CLIENT AND CONSULTING ENGINEERS
for the
DESIGN AND SUPERVISION OF
WORKS OF CIVIL ENGINEERING CONSTRUCTION

MEMORANDUM OF AGREEMENT made the   day of
One Thousand Nine Hundred and
BETWEEN (name and address)
(hereinafter called "the Client")[1,2,3] of the one part and (names)

practising as Consulting Engineers[4] at (address)

under the style of (name of firm)

(who and the survivors or survivor of whom are hereinafter called
"the Consulting Engineers")[2,3,5] of the other part.

(*a*) General reading: D. Keating "Building Contracts" 4th ed. Hudson's "Building and Engineering Contracts" 10th ed. by I. N. Duncan Wallace.

WHEREAS the client
*has considered and approved the general proposals[6] recom-
mended in a report dated

  submitted by the Consulting Engineers, and/or
intends to proceed with the construction of†
(hereinafter called "the Works") and has requested the Consulting
Engineers to undertake and perform the duties hereinafter
mentioned which the Consulting Engineers have agreed to do upon
and subject to the terms and conditions hereinafter set forth.

*Delete if no
report submitted
but *see* cl. 4 (1).

†Here state briefly
the extent of the
works.

1. DEATH OF CLIENT. Because of the personal relationship involved the
death of the client may in some cases bring a service agreement to an end,
unless the agreement states otherwise. The engineer in that case is not
bound to work for his client's executors or administrators, but neither are
they bound to continue to employ him, even if they continue with the works,
and his authority ends automatically (N. 32).

2. BANKRUPTCY. For bankruptcy of the client *see* p. 426.
Bankruptcy of the engineer does not end his service agreement and he
may still carry it out, although his fees may be claimed by the bankruptcy
trustee. If the engineer does not complete the agreement the employer may
prove for damages in the bankruptcy.

3. ASSIGNMENT. The client cannot validly assign the agreement without
the engineer's consent (*see* p. 39, N. 1).
Cl. 15 below deals with assignment by the engineer.

4. "PRACTISING AS CONSULTING ENGINEERS". Anyone may practise as a
civil or consulting engineer—no qualification or registration is necessary by
law. But any person who holds himself out to be an engineer must show
reasonable professional skill in advising his client (N. 30). *See* the rules of
the Association, as to A.C.E. membership.

5. SURVIVORS. If the client in choosing a firm of consultants is relying on
the skill of a particular member of the firm he should consider naming that
member as the Consulting Engineer in this agreement, and not the firm, or
adding a special term altering this provision. Otherwise he will still be
bound to the firm under this definition even if that engineer (or indeed all
but one of the partners of a large firm) should die.

6. "WHEREAS THE CLIENT ... APPROVED THE GENERAL PROPOSALS", ETC.
See N. 7 below.

(*b*) For example, where the contract is to design works to meet the employer's taste or personal
requirements.
(*c*) The decision in *R.* v. *Breeze* [1973] 2 All E.R. 1141, C.A., that the defendant was guilty of an
offence under the Trade Descriptions Act, 1968, by calling himself an architect when he had
not completed the qualifying examinations, does not apply in the absence of a statutory
system of qualification and registration for engineers as there is for architects. But wrongful
use of qualifications such as "F.I.C.E." might infringe the Act, as might any false
representation of qualification by experience or apprenticeship (*see* the judgment of Lord
Widgery C.J. at p. 1144). Legislation does impose special control for certain works. By the
Reservoirs (Safety Provisions) Act 1930, a large reservoir may not be constructed unless a
qualified civil engineer (that is a member of a panel constituted for the purposes of the Act) is
employed to design and supervise.

NOW THESE PRESENTS WITNESS and it is hereby agreed and declared by and between the parties hereto as follows:

APPOINTMENT OF CONSULTING ENGINEERS

1. The Client hereby appoints the Consulting Engineers and the Consulting Engineers accept the appointment on the terms and conditions hereinafter set forth.

DUTIES OF CONSULTING ENGINEERS

2. The duties to be performed by the Consulting Engineers are:

PRELIMINARY STAGE

A. Preparing such drawings, estimates and other engineering documents as are necessary to enable the developed general proposals for the construction of the Works to be submitted for consideration by the Client[7] and to enable him to obtain approval in principle from any Government Department or Public Authority[8] concerned, including as may be applicable in the particular case:
  (i)   Making a normal topographical survey of the site.
  (ii) Initiating and controlling normal soil investigations.
  (iii) Investigating available data or information relating to the Works.
  (iv) Advising the Client on the necessity for any special surveys, investigations or tests referred to in Clause 4 which may be required for the proper design and construction of the Works, arranging for these to be carried out on his behalf[9] and considering and advising on the results of such special surveys, investigations or tests.
  (v)   Consulting any Architect[10] who may be appointed by the Client in regard to the architectural treatment of the Works and in consequence thereof making such reasonable modifications in the said drawings and estimates for the Works as may be approved by the Client.

DESIGN STAGE

B. (i)   Preparing:
       (a) designs and tender drawings,
       (b) specifications and schedules and/or bills of quantities, and
   (ii) Advising on appropriate conditions of contract, forms of tender and invitations to tender,[11] as may be necessary to enable the Works to be tendered for or otherwise ordered by the Client.

CONSTRUCTION STAGE

C. The administration of the Contract and the technical control of the construction of the Works, including as may be applicable in the particular case:
  (i)   Advising the client on tenders, tenderers,[12] prices and estimates for carrying out the Works. No tender shall be accepted or order placed by the Consulting Engineers except on behalf of the Client and with his authority in writing.[13]
  (ii) Advising on the preparation of any Contracts[10] relating to accepted tenders for carrying out the works.

    (iii)   Preparing bar bending schedules and any further designs and drawings necessary for the information of the Contractors to enable them to carry out the Works.

    (iv)   Examining Contractors' proposals and details.

    (v)   Advising the Client on the necessity for the inspection and testing of materials and plant supplied under the Contract and arranging for these to be carried out on his behalf.[9]

    (vi)   Advising the Client on the appointment of the resident site staff in accordance with the terms and provisions of Clause 9.

    (vii)   Issuing instructions to Contractors and making such site visits as the Consulting Engineers consider necessary.[14]

    (viii)   Issuing certificates for payment to Contractors.

    (ix)   Performing any duties which the Consulting Engineers may be required to carry out under any Contract for the execution of the Works—*provided that* they shall first have approved that Contract.

    (x)   Delivering to the Client on completion of the Works such records as are necessary for operation and maintenance.[15]

    (xi)   Assisting in settling disputes or differences which may arise between the Client and Contractors, excepting litigation and arbitration.

7. "CONSIDERATION BY THE CLIENT". Generally approval of plans, etc., by the client does not relieve the engineer of liability for mistakes; the client is entitled to assume that the plans are in order. But the client must give the engineer an opportunity to correct any mistake which he does find.

For the engineer to avoid liability for a defect in the works on the grounds of orders or interference by the client, he must prove that the client appreciated the effect of his orders. Where, for example, the engineer does not wish to annoy a client who wants economies, he cannot simply mention to the client in technical terms any risk there may be in a cheaper job, and if anything goes wrong argue that the decision was the client's. The client must be warned that the result is not guaranteed. *See also* p. 387, third and sixth cases.

It is vitally important for the protection of the engineer that all questions of policy and commercial risk are decided by the client and not the engineer—p. 397.

8. "APPROVAL IN PRINCIPLE FROM ANY GOVERNMENT DEPARTMENT OR PUBLIC AUTHORITY". See Conditions cl. 26, p. 109, and p. 390 (*g*). The engineer should of course see that approvals in principle are obtained as far as possible before the client is involved in expense.

9. "ADVISING THE CLIENT ON THE NECESSITY FOR ANY SPECIAL SURVEYS, INVESTIGATIONS OR TESTS . . . ARRANGING FOR THESE"—"ON THE NECESSITY FOR . . . INSPECTION AND TESTING". *See* p. 399.

10. "CONSULTING ANY ARCHITECT". There is an alternative form of service agreement for structural work where the client has appointed an architect—p. 406.

11. "ADVISING ON . . . CONDITIONS OF CONTRACT, FORMS OF TENDER AND INVITATIONS TO TENDER". Note that the engineer's duty is to advise on conditions of contract, not to make the final choice. For his own protection he should see that the choice is made by the client, of course with full advice as to the advantages and disadvantages of any form suggested. An early

letter should mention to the client the drawbacks of the I.C.E. Conditions, compared with the very strict conditions placing all risks on the contractor which it would be possible to draft. The engineer may then point out that use of strict conditions may dissuade contractors from tendering or result in higher starting prices (p. 438) and that it is for the client to make the choice. The contractor's rights to extra payment under the I.C.E. Conditions (key, p. 323 ff. and some of the problems may also be referred to specifically (e.g. cls. 13 and 40 (2)—see pp. 73 and 132) and of course the basic fact that the tender total is of limited significance since the works are measured on completion (p. 12).

The engineer also may have to ensure that the invitation to tender and tender procedure comply with requirements for public works in, e.g., local authority standing orders, directives of the Council of the European Community, etc.

Refer also to pp. 388–90 (b), (c) and (g) and item (ix) of this clause.

12. "ADVISING THE CLIENT ON TENDERS, TENDERERS". The engineer is bound to disclose any information he has and to have made reasonable enquiries about the skill and finances of a contractor whom he recommends, but he is not taken to guarantee the contractor and this may be made clear to the client.

Full enquiries are: how long the contractor has been in business; numbers, grades and qualifications and possibly names of principals and key personnel who will be employed on the works; particulars and references in connection with each contract for the past five years, and of any failure to complete; arbitration or litigation arising out of any previous contract with which the contractor or his principals or key personnel were involved; work on hand; list with particulars, including age and condition, of equipment available, intended to be purchased or to be rented and from whom (see particularly Conditions, p. 198, N. 5), the location of each item and date of delivery to the works; particulars of portions of the works which the contractor will want to sub-let and names of sub-contractors; a description of the contractor's intended arrangements, methods of construction and programme (p. 440 ff.); contractor's knowledge of local conditions and labour markets and numbers and grades of labour to be employed, on the works; detailed financial statement. This information is usually asked for in Instructions to Tenderers issued with the other tender documents, but direct enquiries of those who know the contractor's work may be particularly valuable.

These are very full enquiries and the engineer will use his discretion, but he should not recommend a contractor without putting all the facts before the client, unless he has found nothing which might lead to doubt and is positively satisfied in his own mind.

Some engineers are squeamish about reporting on tenderers. In fact even if he is negligent in giving a derogatory report the engineer will not be legally liable to the contractor provided he was acting in good faith, and not out of spite towards the contractor or other ulterior motive.

A bond is of course not a substitute for confidence in the contractor.

If the contractor's answers to enquiries are not true on any point material

(d) Halsbury's Laws of England, 4th ed., vol. iv, para 1138–1148, 1149 and 1150.
(e) Heys (or Hayes) v. Tindall (1861) R.R. 564, a case involving a house agent, but the position of the engineer appears to be clear on general principles of negligence.

in inducing the employer to give him the contract, the employer may be entitled to end the contract and to damages. Any officers, etc., of the contractor responsible for the statement may also be personally liable for damages, which can be important where the contractor is a limited liability company (*see* generally p. 60).

The engineer's advice on the detailed tender rates and on the capability and responsibility of tenderers is particularly important in the case of a remeasurement contract, as should be made plain to the client (p. 440).

13. "NO TENDER SHALL BE ACCEPTED OR ORDER PLACED ... EXCEPT ... WITH ... (THE CLIENT'S) AUTHORITY IN WRITING". *See* pp. 399–401. Before permitting the employer to accept a tender the engineer should see that the tender is clear, complete and in order (case, p. 2). If a bond is required he should make sure that it has been granted in favour of the employer, or that the bondsman has entered into a binding commitment to execute it immediately the tender is accepted. It is most dangerous to allow the contractor to start work before the bond position is regularised. If the bond eventually is not forthcoming it may not be a practical proposition for the employer to exercise his right (p. 56, N. 1) to replace the contractor, and having presumably advised the client that a bond is necessary the engineer will be in an embarrassing position if the contractor eventually defaults and there is no bond in existence.

14. "MAKING SUCH SITE VISITS AS THE ... ENGINEERS CONSIDER NECESSARY". *See* N. 26: "reasonably" is implied before "*consider*" — the engineer does not have an unfettered discretion to inspect or not as he thinks fit without risking liability for negligence (p. 386).

15. RECORDS FOR THE CLIENT. *See* N. 34, 35 and 36 for the ownership of documents generally and the engineer's lien on documents for his fees.

REMUNERATION OF CONSULTING ENGINEERS

3. The remuneration of the Consulting Engineers for the performance of the necessary services under Clauses 2A, 2B and 2C of this Agreement shall be a fee calculated on the basis and in the manner set out in Part I of the Schedule hereto.[16,17]

A. Subject to other arrangements such as interim payments on a quarterly or other basis, payments on account shall become due[18] as follows:

(i) 20 per cent of the said fee when such duties as may be applicable under Clause 2A have been completed.

(ii) A further 30 per cent of the said fee, together with the whole of the appropriate additional percentage fee provided for in the said Schedule, for the design of reinforced concrete and structural steelwork, when such duties as may be applicable under Clause 2B (i) (*a*) have been completed.

(iii) A further 20 per cent of the said fee when such duties as may be applicable under Clause 2B (i) (*b*) and (ii) have been completed.

(iv) The remaining 30 per cent of the said fee by monthly instalments as the work proceeds in proportion to the cost of the work carried out.

B. Payments under this Clause shall be calculated on the cost of the Works (or any portion thereof) as shown in an accepted tender or tenders or, where such cost is not accurately known, on the Consulting Engineers' best estimate of the cost of the Works (or of the relevant portion thereof) at the time payments become due. Such payments shall not be regarded as valuations of the duties performed at the respective stages but shall rank solely as payments on account towards the total fee ultimately payable and calculated on the cost of the Works, as defined in Clause 8 of this Agreement.

C.   Where the Works are the subject of more than one Contract, the instalments of the fee, as set out above, shall become due separately in respect of each individual Contract.

D.   Where the times of reaching the above stages are long delayed through circumstances over which the Consulting Engineers have no control, the Consulting Engineers shall be entitled to interim payments as determined by the amount of work performed by them.

16. FEES. If fees are not specially agreed the engineer is entitled to reasonable payment. What is reasonable is a question of fact and depends not only on the time spent but also on the responsibility involved, the nature and difficulty of the work, the standing and experience of the engineer and the merits of his work. The fee is based on the work done, and in the absence of agreement to this scale the courts will not imply that the engineer is to be paid simply a percentage of the cost of the works, although the scale is relevant in deciding what is reasonable, unless the client knew of the custom to pay the scale.

For the A.C.E. rules, etc., on the use of the scale, see p. 405.

The engineer must not without his client's consent receive in relation to his employment any payment from any other person. If, for example, he receives any commission from a contractor, even though he does not allow it to affect his judgment in advising on tenders, he must pay the commission over to his client. The engineer and the other party may also be liable for damages and have committed a crime.

17. LOSS OF FEES. The engineer will not be entitled to fees if the work is useless to his client due to his fault:

> Contract to build four-storey buildings. After plans had been made by the architects and a contractor employed the architects decided to have boreholes sunk. Finding that the ground was made-up ground they advised the client that two of the blocks of buildings would have to be resited and that in all cases concrete pile foundations were necessary.
> The client abandoned the scheme and it was held that the architects were not entitled to fees for their plans.

So an engineer employed to plan a building on the basis of an estimate of cost may not be entitled to payment if his design cannot be carried out for approximately that cost, but he should be given an opportunity to make

---

(f) *Brewer* v. *Chamberlain* (1949), Birkett J., unreported. In *Buckland* v. *Pawson & Co.* (1890) 6 T.L.R. 421 a surveyor was held entitled to recover fees at the scale rate from an employer who was himself a surveyor and had employed others and himself been employed on the scale, and to a similar effect *Graham & Baldwin* v. *Taylor, Son & Davis* (1965) Estates Gazette 305.

Perhaps the understanding attitude of the courts in assessing legal fees may be prayed in aid by engineers seeking reasonable payment in the absence of an agreed scale. In *Treasury Solicitor* v. *Register* [1978] 2 All E.R. 920 solicitors were awarded £8000 fees for 60 hours work on preparing a 9 page agreement and 20 page draft lease, because the transaction was valued at approximately £2 million.

(g) *Dalgliesh* v. *Bromley Corp.* (1953) 161 Estates Gazette 738.

380 ENGINEERING LAW AND THE I.C.E. CONTRACTS

h reasonable adjustments. In reported cases decided against the estimator the tenders received ranged from 20% to 50% above the estimate.

If the employer actually places a fixed limit on the cost before the plans are drawn up, the engineer will not be entitled to payment if the tenders exceed that limit at all unless the excess is trifling. Again the engineer should
i be given an opportunity to make reasonable adjustments.

For the engineer's liability for damages, which may be far greater than his fees, *see* p. 386. Damages may include repayment to the employer of part of the engineer's percentage fee, in so far as it is calculated on increases in the cost of the works due to extras or claims by the contractor arising from the engineer's negligence (pp. 389 (*e*) and 392 (*k*)).

18. "PAYMENTS ON ACCOUNT SHALL BECOME DUE". If the agreement is ended by justified dismissal of the engineer (p. 427) he is entitled to all fees which had become due under this clause and to all out-of-pocket expenses and fees on a time basis earned at the time of dismissal, subject to any right which the employer may have to claim damages (p. 427). But the engineer is not entitled to a proportion of his fees for a stage which is in progress at the time of dismissal, but not completed for payment — e.g. where he is dismissed in the course of carrying out the duties under cl. 2A or between monthly instalments (cl. 3 (iv)), and neither it appears is he entitled to fees due on completion in respect of an earlier stage because of an increase in the cost of the works. The ordinary rule applies that no part of the payment becomes due unless the specified work is substantially finished — p. 266, N. 27.

In the case of the death or illness of the engineer by statute a court or arbitrator may award the engineer or his representatives payment for work for which fees had not then actually become due.

REMUNERATION FOR ADDITIONAL SERVICES

4.   The Consulting Engineers shall be paid for additional services required by the Client in accordance with the Scale of Charges shown in Part II of the Schedule hereto, or as may be otherwise agreed, together with specialists' fees and out-of-pocket expenses in connection therewith. Such additional services shall include,[19] *inter alia*, work and advice in connection with:

(*h*) See cases collected in Hudson "Engineering & Building Contracts", 10th ed., pp. 144–146; U.S.A. cases collected in I. V. Werbin "Legal Guide for Contractors, Architects and Engineers", ch. 58, and "Legal Cases for Contractors Architects and Engineers", ch. 33; *Lea* v. *Medicine Hat City* [1917] 37 D.L.R. 1 Can.; *Pratt* v. *St. Albert Protestant Separate School District No.* 6 (1969) 5 D.L.R. (3d) 1, Alberta Sup. Ct., no recovery where original estimate of $206,512 increased on pressure from client to $243,145 and lowest tender $288,787 (increases of 18% and 37% respectively). Said *in Saxby and Pokorny* v. *Fowler* (1977) 3 Alta, L.R. (2d) 47m Can, that for architects to prepare a "*guesstimate*", a statement relating to the costs of construction without adequate factual information or by guesswork, with the intent that it would be relied on by a client in planning his finances, would be a negligent act; that although an architect cannot predict exactly what the bids will be and even if he refuses to guarantee the accuracy of his preliminary estimate of cost there is an implied condition that the final cost will be within a reasonable range of the estimate. The trend of prices known to the architect should be allowed for in his estimate, and when inflation intervenes before calling for tenders an architect is under a duty to make the necessary adjustments in his estimate. The facts of the case were complicated but the lowest bid was 20% above the architects' estimate and they failed to recover their fees.
(*i*) *Harvey* v. *Brown* (1920) 13 Q.S.R. 25 Can.; *Sharp* v. *Furber* [1939] 4 D.L.R. 775 Can.; *Flannagan* v. *Mate* (1876) 2 V.L.R. 157 Aus.; *Pearce* v. *Walker* (1905) 19 E.D.C. 80 S.Af.

(i)   Preparing any report or additional Contract Documents required for the consideration of alternative general proposals.[20]

(ii)   Parliamentary Powers, Ministerial Orders and Sanctions, Licences and Permits.

(iii)   Obtaining formal consents from outside Authorities,[21] or persons having rights or powers in connection with the Works or the site thereof.

(iv)   The valuation, purchase, sale or leasing of lands, or obtaining wayleaves.

(v)   All surveys other than that referred to in Clause 2A (i), and carrying out model tests or special investigations.[22]

(vi)   Preparing shop details for fabrication of steelwork, or other metal frameworks.

(vii)   Inspections or tests other than those normally carried out on site or by resident site staff appointed under Clause 9.[22]

(viii) Excessive delay on the part of the Client or of any Contractor or the taking by the Client of the Works or any part thereof out of the hands of any Contractor due to his failure properly to perform the relevant Contract.

(ix)   Litigation or Arbitration.

(x)   *

(xi)   *

(xii)   *

(xiii) *

(xiv)   *

* To be completed as necessary in special cases.

19. "ADDITIONAL SERVICES ... (WHICH) SHALL INCLUDE". It would be expensive for a client to have to employ another engineer to carry out extra work only, and it seems obviously to be implied, by this clause and the words *"perform the duties hereinafter mentioned which the Consulting Engineers have agreed to do"* in the opening of this form, that the engineer is bound (and therefore entitled) to do all additional work necessary for the project on payment of the extra fees. It may also be implied, despite (i) of this clause, that the engineer is not bound to do (and therefore may not insist on doing) additional work which is not reasonably related to or involves a complete transformation of the broad project for which he was originally appointed (*see* p. 172, N. 8). If it can be foreseen that any very unusual services may become necessary they should be added into this clause.

Any extra services which the client might later argue fall within the ordinary percentage should also be added here— e.g. possibly work at night, and *see* p. 406.

For extra fees where the works are damaged *see* cl. 10; where no resident is appointed *see* cl. 9.

20. "ALTERNATIVE GENERAL PROPOSALS". *See* N. 19 above.

21. "SANCTIONS, LICENCES ... PERMITS ... CONSENTS". *See* general conditions cl. 26, p. 109, and p. 390 (*g*).

22. SPECIAL SURVEYS, INVESTIGATIONS AND TESTS. On the wording of cl. 2 A (iv) and C (v) the engineer must have his client's special authority to order any of these services from specialists. For the position of the engineer and of the specialist if he has not, *see* N. 32.

ALTERATIONS OR MODIFICATIONS TO DESIGNS

5.   If, after completion of the duties under Clause 2A, any design whether completed or in progress or any specification, drawing or other document prepared in whole or part by the Consulting Engineers shall require to be modified or revised by reason of instructions received by the Consulting Engineers or by reason of circumstances which could not reasonably have been foreseen, such modification or revision and any consequential reproduction of documents shall be the subject of additional payment computed on a time basis in accordance with the Scale shown in Part II of the Schedule hereto, or such other basis as may be agreed, together with any appropriate reimbursements under Clause 6.

OUT-OF-POCKET EXPENSES

6.   In addition to the remuneration to be paid under other Clauses of this Agreement, the Consulting Engineers shall be reimbursed by the Client all out-of-pocket expenses actually and properly incurred by them in respect of:

  (i)   Printing, reproduction and purchase of all documents, drawings, maps and records;
  (ii)   Telegrams and telephone calls;[22A]
  (iii)   Travelling and hotel expenses and other similar disbursements;
  (iv)   Advertising for tenders and for resident site staff;

provided that the Consulting Engineers and the Client may agree on a lump sum or on an increase in the scale of fees to cover any or all of these expenses.

PAYMENT OF ACCOUNTS

7.   The times at which payments under Clause 3 become due are stated therein.
  The Consulting Engineers shall be entitled to render accounts for additional remuneration under Clauses 4 and 5, and for reimbursements under Clauses 4 and 6, as and when the additional services are provided or the expenses incurred, as the case may be.[23]
  All sums due to the Consulting Engineers under this Agreement shall be paid within forty days of the submission of their accounts.[24]

22A. Telex is not included in this list.

23. FEES ON A TIME BASIS AND EXPENSES are actually due immediately the work is done or the expense incurred, not when accounts are submitted — this may be relevant where the engineer is dismissed, N. 18, or for limitation of actions, p. 430.

24. "SHALL BE PAID WITHIN FORTY DAYS". For interest *see* p. 268, N. 29, and for the engineer's right in exceptional cases to end the service agreement for non-payment, *see* p. 426 (*b*).

7A.   All fees and charges set out in this Agreement and Schedule are exclusive of Value Added Tax, the amount of which, at the rate and in the manner prescribed by law, shall be paid by the Client to the Consulting Engineer. Where Value Added Tax is chargeable on Disbursements and Out-of-pocket Expenses; this will be based upon the VAT-exclusive cost of such outgoings.

COST OF THE WORKS

8. The cost of the Works or any part thereof shall be deemed to include:

(i) The cost to the Client of the Works, from whatever cause arising—including any payments made to the Contractors by way of bonus, incentive or *ex-gratia* payments, or settlement of claims, and before deduction of liquidated damages or penalties (if any) payable by the Contractors to the Client.[25] Such cost shall exclude:

(*a*) Administration expenses incurred by the Client.

(*b*) Professional fees and out-of-pocket expenses.

(*c*) Salaries, travelling, out-of-pocket and office expenses of resident site staff appointed under Clause 9, unless the Works are carried out by direct labour.

(*d*) Interest on capital during construction, and the cost of raising moneys required for carrying out the construction of the Works.

(*e*) Cost of land and wayleaves.

(ii) A fair valuation of any labour, materials, manufactured goods, machinery or other facilities provided by the Client, and of the use and waste (including all cost of repairs) of construction plant and equipment belonging to the Client which he shall require to be used in the carrying out of the Works.

(iii) Salaries, travelling, out-of-pocket and office expenses of resident site staff appointed under Clause 9, where the Works are carried out by direct labour.

(iv) The market value, as though they were purchased new, of any second-hand materials, manufactured goods and machinery incorporated in the Works.

(v) The cost of normal soil investigations.

25. "COST OF THE WORKS". Obviously includes payments to other contractors on forfeiture, etc., but not costs collateral to the works, e.g. indemnities paid to the contractor for liability to third parties under the general conditions cl. 22 (2). For fees on cost due to the engineer's negligence, *see* p. 380.

Items (*a*) and (*b*) of this clause are somewhat vague, and may need clarification for the particular works. For example, where the client is to supply housing, etc., for the consulting engineers it should be made clear whether the cost of such services is to be included in the cost of the works for computing fees (in cl. 19 (2) of the 1970 Conditions of Engagement, Schedule 2, they are specifically excluded).

For payment for work designed and later omitted *see* cl. 11 below.

SUPERVISION ON SITE

9. The Consulting Engineers shall, subject to the approval of the Client which shall not be unreasonably withheld, appoint such resident site staff as the Consulting Engineers consider necessary for the efficient supervision of work on site.[26] The full cost of such staff, including such expenses as are attributable to their employment and to their duties, shall be borne by the Client, and shall be refunded monthly to the Consulting Engineers. Alternatively, if mutually agreed, the Consulting Engineers may nominate such staff[27] for appointment and direct payment by the Client. In either case, such staff shall take instructions from the Consulting Engineers only. The Client shall at his own cost arrange for such local office accommodation, furniture, telephones, equipment and transport as shall be reasonably necessary for the use of the resident staff.[27A] In

the event of such resident staff not being appointed or not being available (due to sickness or other cause),[28] the Consulting Engineers shall be entitled to charge for any supervision additional to the site visits of inspection under Clause 2C (vii) in accordance with the Scale shown in Part II of the Schedule hereto.

26. DELEGATION TO SITE STAFF. It has been held that an architect is not bound to superintend minor details—these, but only these, he may leave to a representative:

> An architect left it to the employee's clerk of works to see that the protection specified in the plans for floors which were to be laid on damp earth was carried out.
> The architect was held liable when the clerk of works fraudulently failed to do this; had the architect supervised for the first block of buildings and then left it to the clerk only to see that the work for the second block was done in the same way, that might have been in order.

The 5th edition of the I.C.E. Conditions in cl. 2 now gives the engineer very wide powers of delegation vis-à-vis the contractor. However, that clause does not protect the engineer from liability to the client if he delegates too freely without special authorisation. The law may imply from the usage of the industry wider power to delegate than that allowed to an architect. The resident, for example, is generally a qualified engineer, with a status higher than the clerk of works in ordinary building work. The general practice in relation to the resident is set out in a booklet "Civil Engineering Procedure" published by the I.C.E. However, this includes in his duties examinations of the contractor's methods and redesign of work, items which it seems the engineer would in law be justified in delegating only subject to very close supervision. Where the works are abroad the engineer may be entitled to delegate more widely than otherwise to a resident. The engineer should clarify this uncertain situation in all cases by getting from his client at the outset defined authority to delegate.

The engineer is liable to his client for the act of a representative or other delegate:

(a) if the act was ordered by him;

(b) if the representative or delegate was acting (even fraudulently) within excess authority wrongfully delegated to him by the engineer;

(c) if he negligently appoints or acquiesces in the appointment of an incompetent representative or delegate or does nothing when his work shows that he is not competent, the engineer will be totally responsible for his activities;

(d) for the position where the employer insists on appointing or refuses to dismiss an incompetent representative, see N. 28.

(e) in the ordinary way the engineer is fully liable to his client (and to the public—p. 394) for the actions of any employee of his as if they were his own. If the engineer himself employs the resident (N. 27) it seems that the engineer will become fully liable for the resident's negligence, or any activity of his which infringes this service contract.

(j) Leicester Board of Guardians v. Trollope (1911), Hudson "Building Contracts", 4th ed., vol. ii, p. 419. In Lee v. Bateman (Lord) (1893), The Times, Oct. 31, an architect was held liable to his client for negligence when he relied without inspection on the opinion of the employer's clerk of works that beams did not require replacement in rebuilding premises after a fire.

27. "The Consulting Engineer shall, subject to the approval of the Client (etc.) ... appoint ... or nominate (site) staff". The engineer has ordinarily no implied authority to employ site staff—*see* p. 399. If the engineer does appoint the staff himself under this clause with the client's approval (which may not be unreasonably withheld) he will then have direct control, but as their employer he will also be liable for their wages if the client does not pay, and liable for any damage caused to third parties by their negligence (N. 26 (*e*)), and to the client for all their errors. Even if a member of the engineer's staff is to act as resident, it is probably better for the engineer to have him seconded to the employer.

By cl. 2 (3) a delegate must "*be responsible to the Engineer*", as to which *see* p. 35.

27A. "The full cost of ... (resident) staff ... shall be borne by the Client ... The Client shall at his own cost arrange for such local office accommodation, furniture ... equipment ... (etc.) as shall be reasonably necessary for the use of the resident staff". Where resident staff may do some design or other head office work covered by the consultant's fee, as well as having this agreed to in advance by the client (N. 26) it may be necessary to agree at the same time the part of the resident's salary, etc., to be allotted to the work and paid to the client by the consultant.

Disagreement about what accommodation or equipment is reasonable for the resident staff may be avoided by a list scheduled to this agreement.

28. "In the event of such resident staff not being appointed or not being available", etc. If the client refuses to agree to the appointment of necessary and competent site staff the engineer may not repudiate responsibility, but is bound to supervise with special care—obviously he may not rely on a resident if there is no capable resident to rely on. The client will, however, have broken a term of the engineer's contract, expressed here but probably implied in any case (p. 42 (*b*)), and will be liable to pay for any extra work which this throws on the engineer. In exceptional cases the engineer may despite this clause be entitled to bring his agreement with the client to an end, where for example the works are abroad and the absence of resident staff would put an impossible burden on him (*see* p. 425).

Damage or Destruction of the Works

10. If at any time before the completion of the Works any part of the Works or the equipment therefor shall be damaged or destroyed, the Client shall pay to the Consulting Engineers the appropriate remuneration for any additional work or expense resulting from such damage or destruction.

The employer may insure against these fees. p. 363.

(*k*) *Saunders* v. *Broadstairs Local Board* (1890), Hudson "Building Contracts", 4th ed., vol. ii, p. 164.

POSTPONEMENT OR ABANDONMENT OF THE WORKS

11. In the event of the whole or any part of the Works being postponed or abandoned, then the payment to be made to the Consulting Engineers for services performed in respect of that part of the Works so postponed or abandoned shall be calculated in accordance with Clause 3A of this Agreement, increased by one quarter, and in accordance with such other Clauses as may be applicable, having regard to the services performed prior to the Works being postponed or abandoned. If, within two years the postponed Works or any part thereof shall again proceed, then any relevant payments made under this Clause shall rank as payments on account towards the total fee actually payable and calculated on the cost of the Works as defined in Clause 8. Should additional services by the Consulting Engineers be required in connection with the resumption of postponed Works, the Consulting Engineers shall be entitled to charge for such additional services on a time basis calculated in accordance with the Scale shown in Part II of the Schedule hereto.

In the event of the Works or any part thereof being postponed for a period longer than two years, such Works or part thereof shall be considered to have been abandoned.[29]

29. POSTPONEMENT, ABANDONMENT OF THE WORKS. If the engineer is engaged for a project or works without more, then in law that amounts to a contract to allow him to do, and pay him, for the planning and supervision of the whole works, and if there is no express agreement for ending his contract he is entitled to damages for loss of profits (*see* p. 429) if the employer abandons the project at any stage, unless the works have been frustrated in the legal sense (p. 282).

The engineer may of course be employed from stage to stage — e.g. at first only to make plans.

By cls. 1–4 the engineer is given and accepts appointment for the whole project, so that he is bound and entitled to take up his duties if works which have been postponed eventually go on, subject to the two-year limit in this clause. This is more satisfactory to the engineer than employment from stage to stage and is fair to the client, since it is clearly implied that the engineer's rights on abandonment, etc., under this clause are in lieu of his right to claim loss of profits under the general law.

Where works are postponed or abandoned due to the engineer's fault he may lose all or part of his fees (N. 17) and may be liable to dismissal and damages (pp. 425, 426).

CARE AND DILIGENCE

12. The Consulting Engineers shall exercise all reasonable skill, care and diligence in the discharge of the duties agreed to be performed by them[30] and, in so far as any of their duties are discretionary, shall act fairly as between the Client and the Contractor.[31] Except in an emergency, the Consulting Engineers shall not, without the prior approval of the Client, authorise any modification of the Works involving a substantial extra cost.[32,33]

30A. THE ENGINEER'S DUTIES AND LIABILITY TO HIS CLIENT AS HIS AGENT. The engineer is bound to carry out his duties as agent for his client with "fair, reasonable and competent" skill. To amount to professional

(*l*) *Lamphier* v. *Phipps* (1831) 8 C. & P. 475, at p. 479. Refer also to p. 388 below on the decision ... *Ltd.* v. *Baynham Meikle* [1975] 3 All E.R. 99.

negligence it must generally be proved that the course taken was one which no professional man of ordinary skill would have taken if he had been acting with ordinary care:

An engineer employed to plan etc. a bridge did not himself test the soil, but accepted the results of borings carried out previously, which had been supplied to him at his client's request.
Held: Liable for negligence. *m*

Held: That failure to test the bearing capacity of soil to hold plant was not negligent because the consulting engineer was familiar with the character of the soil, and had obtained information about the soil from the city engineer. *n*

The site of a building was a garbage dump over a canal. The consulting engineer visited the site only once and did not examine the cores of two borings which had been made by a testing firm.
The engineer recommended a cheap method of construction without telling the client or his architect that the plan involved some risk and that there was an alternative which was foolproof.
Held: That before recommending the cheap method a more exhaustive examination of the soil should have been made; that the consultant was not entitled to rely on the results of percussion tests made by a soil testing firm, knowing the limitations of sampling tests. *o*

Architect employed to design a block of flats. The client was sued by a neighbouring owner for interference by the building with rights to light, despite alterations which the architect had made in the design to meet these rights, and settled the action by paying some damages. In proceedings by the client against the architect two experts gave opposing evidence as to whether the neighbour's rights were in fact infringed by the building as altered. Architect not liable. *p*

Surveyor instructed to inspect and give a "general opinion" on premises. After purchase on the faith of his report dry rot was discovered and defects in the roof, brick-work and ventilator. Surveyor liable. *q*

Negligence or not is a question of fact which must finally depend on the facts of the particular case, but it is settled that—
(a) The onus is on the client to prove negligence, but the failure of an ordinary engineering job is evidence of negligence. Failure of a new method in which the engineer does not profess experience is not:

An architect was employed to design a model house. The client specified that it was to have a flat roof, lead was not to be used and it was generally to be economical, and to include the latest improvements. The architect described to the client and recommended a patent form of flat roof which after a year's consideration was accepted by the client. The roof was completed according to specifications and plans supplied by the patentees.
The roof let in rain, but it was held (in 1853) that the architect was not liable. *r*

(m) *Moneypenny* v. *Hartland* (1826) 31 R.R. 672.
(n) *Lea* v. *Medicine Hat City* [1917] 37 D.L.R. 1 Can.
(o) *City of Brantford* v. *Kemp & Wallace-Carruthers & Associates Ltd.* [1960] 23 D.L.R. (2d) 640 Can.
(p) *Armitage* v. *Palmer* (1960) 175 Estates Gazette 315 C.A.
(q) *Sincock* v. *Bangs (Reading)* [1952] 160 Estates Gazette 134.
(r) *Turner* v. *Garland & Christopher* (1853) Hudson "Building Contracts", 4th ed., vol. ii, p. 1.

This case was border-line and the engineer should make his position and the risks involved clear from the beginning. *See also* N. 7.

(*b*) Failing to obey professional rules or practice where there is a usual or normal practice is evidence of negligence. The engineer might certainly be in a difficult position if he were to use a form of construction contract more favourable to the contractor than the I.C.E. 5th edition, without his client's clear and informed approval.

(*c*) It is normally a defence that the engineer followed the practice of a majority of the profession, but in exceptional cases the general practice may itself be negligent, and a member will pay for his profession's sin. The very prevalent practice of not explaining and getting the client's approval to the contractor's rights to extra payment in the conditions of contract might be a case in point—N. 11.

The more technical the subject matter the more a court is forced to rely on the evidence of experts in the defendant's profession. However, judges tend to believe that as practical men they understand engineering work, and they may take a strict view of the engineer's duties:

> Consultant structural engineers were employed by "package deal" building contractors to design a warehouse for their clients as a store for oil drums which were to be moved by fork-lift stacker trucks. The builders made known to the engineers the purpose for which the warehouse was required and in particular that the first floor would have to take the weight of loaded moving trucks.
>
> The engineers were aware of a British Standards Institution circular warning designers of the effect of vibrations caused by imposed loadings in such constructions, but they did not read the circular as a warning against vibrations in general and so did not take measures to deal with the random impulses of fork-lift trucks.
>
> After a time the first floor of the warehouse cracked and became dangerous, and costly remedial works were necessary to cure structural damage. The builders claimed against the engineers for the amount of their liability to their clients. It was found that the cracks had been caused by vibration produced by movement of loaded fork-lift trucks and that the floor had not been designed with sufficient strength to withstand that vibration.
>
> The engineers were held liable for negligence: a new mode of construction was to be employed and the engineers knew of the circular: there was evidence that other designers might have done the same as the engineers but that did not necessarily excuse them as other designers might have fallen short too.

(*s*) In *Clarke* v. *Adams* (1950) 94 Sol. Jo. 599, a case dealing with medical treatment, it was said that "there must . . . be a warning of danger as it would appear to a hypothetically reasonable man . . . the warning must be couched in terms which make it absolutely clear that it was a warning of danger". In *Reibl* v. *Hughes* (1977) 78 D.L.R. 35 Can. a surgeon who obtained consent to an operation without warning the patient that 4 per cent of such operations were fatal and another 10 per cent disabling was held liable when the patient suffered a stroke during surgery.

(*t*) In *Hill* v. *Harris* (1965) 2 All E.R. 358 a solicitor was held liable for negligence although he had followed a practice very common amongst solicitors. See also *Hucks* v. *Cole* (1968) 11? S.J. 483.

(*u*) *Greaves* v. *Baynham Meikle* [1975] 3 All E.R. 99, C.A. The judgment of the trial judge was capable of being read as a departure from the long established principle that a professional man is normally liable only if guilty of negligence, and in the previous edition of this book was suggested that the decision required careful consideration. On the subsequent appeal all three members of the court were at pains to clarify that judgment, by stressing that "in the ordinary employment of a professional man, whether it is a medical man, a lawyer or an accountant, an architect or an engineer, his duty is to use reasonable care and skill in the course of his employment" (pp. 104, 105 per Lord Denning M.R.) (although earlier his Lordship had said the question of the exact duty of an architect or engineer employed (*d*) If the engineer holds himself out as a specialist he must have the ordinary skill of those who specialise in the particular branch. The crucial point is the skill he expressly or impliedly holds himself out as having, so that he may be liable if he takes on work which is beyond his capacity:

> Architects supervising erection of a building issued certificates to a contractor of completion of electrical plant installation. The employer paid on the certificates. The installation was eventually discovered to be defective and useless. The fault could only have been discovered by an expert in that type of plant.
> Held: That the architects were under a duty to satisfy themselves that the installation was satisfactory before issuing certificates, either by special knowledge or by the report of an expert, and were liable to pay the employer damages for failing to do so.

(*e*) The more the construction contract allows the contractor extra payment for unexpected difficulties the more carefully the engineer must investigate the site and plan the work.

Where the client has to pay extra because difficulties are found during construction which the engineer should have allowed for, the engineer may argue that the client has suffered no loss from his negligence, because the original contract price would have been higher to cover the difficulties if he had found them in time and allowed for them in the contract. This is a weakish argument, because the extra price (or even expenses) payable when a mistake is found after a contractor has been given a contract has a habit of being higher than the price the contractor would have tendered for the work when competing for the job (*see* particularly p. 185, N. 7, and p. 435). And of course the client might not have embarked on the full scheme or constructed it on a different site if he had known the cost at the outset. It is suggested that, although the damages may be difficult to assess, a court may in appropriate circumstances award substantial damages in such a case.

(*f*) The engineer's work must be looked at as a whole, and it is suggested that the client cannot claim damages against the engineer (or deduct from his fees) for expenses paid the contractor for isolated minor delays by the engineer in supplying plans, etc., or for other minor errors inevitable in large-scale work. For example, in one case a mistake of £133 made by an apparently competent assistant of the engineer in calculating a certificate for £12,000.

---

design a house or a bridge "may require to be answered someday as a matter of law"). The other members of the court expressed no reservation in approving the long series of authorities from 1830 to 1967 establishing that an engineer ordinarily does not guarantee that works will fulfil their purpose, but is liable only if they fail to do so because of his negligence.

Because a package deal contractor will generally be held to give an absolute guarantee to his client that the works will be suitable for their purpose, unless the contract states otherwise, he may be concerned if he can to obtain a similar guarantee from an engineer carrying out the design for him, or give the engineer information on the purpose of the building that may be held to create such a guarantee by implication (p. 393). The engineer, on the other hand, should be astute if possible to restrict his liability clearly to professional negligence, leaving it to the package dealer similarly to restrict his liability to the client, particularly as the engineer's indemnity insurance may not cover a strict guarantee.

(*v*) *Philip & Leslie* v. *Transvaal Gold Fields Ltd.* (1898) 5 O.R. 54 S.Af.
(*w*) *See* footnote (*e*) p. 367 on award of damages by a court even though the plaintiff's loss is uncertain and difficult to value.
(*x*) *London School Board* v. *Northcraft* (1889) Hudson "Building Contracts", 4th ed., vol. ii, p. 147. However, the fact that an action for negligence normally is fought about a specific act or

It has also been held that an architect has a discretion to pass work with minor faults—"nothing rank bad"—where the contractor is "building down to a price", and that he is not liable to a deduction from his fees to cover them. This decision is doubtful—the engineer or architect generally has no power to alter the terms of the construction contract, and in this case the contract required the workmanship and materials to be the best of their kind, and the architect knew of the defects.

(g) The engineer is under a duty to have and use a reasonable working knowledge of the law relating to his job, e.g. to comply with statutes and bye-laws (see also N. 8); to advise on the clauses which should be in the construction contract, but not on the details of drafting; to look out for and make reasonable enquiries from his client as to private or public rights which may affect the works (see ch. 15); to acquaint himself within a reasonable time of major changes in the law, by legislation or decisions of the courts.

But the engineer is not bound to be a legal expert so that he is not liable for any detailed legal opinion he may be rash enough to give and the client to take, unless he holds himself out as having knowledge on which the client may rely.

(h) Failure to read one article in the journals might not, but failure to be aware of a series of warnings about particular materials or a method of construction would generally be negligence.

(i) As to supervision of the works:

"... the architect is not permanently on the site but appears at intervals it may be of a week or a fortnight ... When he arrives on the site there may be many very important matters with which he has to deal: the work may be getting behind hand through labour troubles: ... suppliers of materials or the sub-contractors may be lagging; there may be physical trouble on the site itself, such as, for example, finding an unexpected amount of underground water. All these are matters which may call for important decisions by the architect. He may in such circumstances think that he knows the builder sufficiently well and can trust him to carry out a good job; that it is more important that he should deal with urgent matters on the site than that he should make a minute inspection on the site to see that the builder is complying with the specifications ... It by no means follows that, in failing to discover a defect which a reasonable examination would have disclosed, in fact the architect was necessarily thereby in breach of his duty to the building owner so as to be liable in an action for negligence. It may well be that the omission of the architect to find the defects was due to no more than an error of judgment or was a deliberately calculated risk which in all the circumstances of the case was reasonable and proper."

---

omission operates harshly on an engineer responsible for numerous activities of his own and his subordinates in a major project. In the ordinary course of events it is likely that during a major project extending for many years there will be at least one error that taken in isolation may be classified as negligent, and even if the loss to the employer is a minor part of the cost of the project the loss to the engineer if he has to reimburse the client will be major compared to his fees.

(y) Cotton v. Wallis [1955] 3 All E.R. 373.

(z) Based on Crawford v. Charing Cross Hospital (1953) The Times, April 23rd and Dec. 8th, and see Roe v. Minister of Health [1954] 2 All E.R. 131.

(aa) East Ham Borough Council v. Bernard Sunley & Sons Ltd. [1965] 3 All E.R. 619, 625, 636, H.L. There is a belief that, partly because a decision that had to be made by the engineer in a few moments on site may be argued about for many days by half-a-dozen or more lawyers and many experts, what the courts demand of professional advisers as reasonable care and skill is not always in practice as realistic as this view.

A workman was seriously injured by collapse of an elevated concrete slab when he was helping to remove the formwork from underneath. Reinforcing mesh had been put into position on a Friday afternoon and evening, and ready-mixed concrete poured into the forms on the Saturday morning. Contrary to the structural engineer's plans the reinforcing mesh had been laid longitudinally along the slab that collapsed instead of transversely across its width, thus reducing the efficiency of the reinforcement. The routine inspections of the work by the architect took place on Tuesdays and Fridays as a result of an arrangement between the Managing Director of the building owners (who were doing the work by direct labour) and the architect for their mutual convenience. There had been an inspection on the Friday morning previous to the accident, before the reinforcement was in place. The building owners were negligent in removing the formwork prematurely, but it was held that the cause of the accident was the lack of proper reinforcement and the slab would have fallen down whenever the formwork was removed.

Held: That the architect was liable to the building owners for damages including the amount of the building owners' liability to the injured workman. The following is an excerpt from one of the judgments:

"Evidence was led at the trial of the practice of architects where an obligation for periodic inspection or supervision is accepted. Useful and persuasive as this evidence may be, it is not of course decisive of the legal obligations which such a retainer as an architect imports. But, as I would have expected, that professional evidence lends no support whatever to the respondents' submission that they were entitled to rely on the appellant's foreman to tell them when concrete was to be poured and to assume that none would be poured, without such notice, between the days of their routine inspections.

I am clearly of opinion that in law the respondents (architects) were not so entitled. They were bound to supervise the work, inspecting it with due skill and care. There can be no doubt that due skill and care in this case required them to supervise the work done in preparation for the pouring of concrete to form these slabs. The facts of this case bring out starkly the importance of the performance of this obligation. In my opinion, the respondents were bound to take reasonable steps to ensure that they inspected the formwork and the placed reinforcement before concrete was poured and the work covered up. They do not satisfy this by relying on the workmen whose work they were employed to supervise: in particular, they were not entitled to assume from past satisfactory performances of the foreman, that they would be notified of the readiness of the work for inspection and of the time for the pouring of the concrete. They were not engaged to supervise only such work as could be seen on the particular days of their routine inspections, or to attend to supervise only when advised that an occasion for supervision had arisen or was about to arise. They owed a duty to keep themselves informed of the progress of the work. They were bound, in my opinion, at least to have made reasonable arrangements of a reliable nature to be kept informed of the general progress of the work and, in particular, to be notified of the readiness of formwork and the placement of reinforcement for the pouring of concrete; these arrangements ought to have included clear and express instructions to the foreman that work of the kind in question must not be covered up till the respondents had inspected it or, at the very least had an adequate opportunity for its inspection. . . ."   bb

See also cl. 9.

(j) Typically, the engineer takes on vis-à-vis the employer the job of designing the whole works, on which his fee is calculated. Therefore unless

(bb) Florida Hotels Pty. Ltd. v. Mayo [1965] 113 C.L.R. 588 Aus. The quotation above is from the judgment of Barwick, C.J. at pp. 52, 53. See also text above, pp. 53–4.

he obtains special authority from his client, he is not entitled to delegate part of the design to others not employees of his:

An architect invited a firm of nominated sub-contractors to prepare the drawings for and construct a reinforced concrete frame, and approved the drawings. The building eventually failed after two years because the purlins were not strong enough to support the roof, and the portal frames built on sloping ground were not tied together at knee or ground level.

Held: The architect had no implied authority to delegate his design duties to and rely on the sub-contractors, even though there were qualified engineer directors of the firm, and was liable to his client.

Naval architects held liable to their clients for failure of zonolite or vermiculite concrete to meet the buoyancy requirements for display tanks for an oceanarium. The concrete was found to weigh more than the water. The clients had received assurances and guarantees from the representative of the material suppliers that the concrete would weigh less than half the water and meet their requirements. The representative had many years experience in the cement business and was backed by technical staff.

Held that the architects were not entitled to rely on the assurances by the material suppliers as a defence to liability to their clients. They should themselves have examined the suitability of the material beyond talking to the immediate suppliers and looking at an unhelpful pamphlet they had obtained. The use of the material was known to be somewhat experimental and other enquiries, from the head supplier of the concrete, for example, would have disclosed that it was not suitable.

Despite the first of these decisions, given so long ago, engineers have continued to delegate detailing and other design to nominated sub-contractors, and the problems created are discussed on p. 227.

(*k*) The engineer has various special duties under the construction contract, e.g. insurance (p. 96), and to see that notices are given in time (key, p. 324). Above all he must carry out his duties in time to allow the advance planning necessary in modern works (p. 365).

Three final cases to illustrate that the above categories are merely examples of the broad duty of care that the engineer owes to his client:

An engineer employed by an architect recommended to him that deep soil tests should be carried out, but the architect replied that the client would not approve the extra expense. The architect did not relay the engineer's concern to the client. After construction the building settled because of soil conditions that a deep soil test would have revealed. Held that the engineer owed a duty to inform the client directly of the need for deep soil tests; communication to the architect was not enough. Architect and engineer held jointly liable to the client.

Construction contract for a natural gas gathering system. Owner covenanted in the contract to make available to the contractor on maps or drawings all information in his possession concerning sub-structures, but expressly refused to guarantee the accuracy or completeness of such information. When asked by the owner's engineer appointed for the project to mark their existing lines on a map,

---

(*cc*) *Moresk* v. *Hicks* [1969] 2 Lloyd's Rep. 338, and see *Hamlyn Construction Co.* v. *Air Couriers* [1968] 1 Lloyd's Rep. 395.

(*dd*) *Sealand of the Pacific* v. *Robert C. McHaffie Ltd.* (1974) 51 D.L.R. (3d) 702 Can., 2 B.L.R. 74.

(*ee*) *District of Surrey* v. *Church* (1977) 76 D.L.R. (3d) 721 Can. That there was no direct contract in this case between the engineer and building owner (*see* text below) emphasises the duty of direct communication where there is.

one pipeline-owning company neglected to show a six-inch high-pressure line. Maps were passed on by the engineer to the contractor but not small-scale survey maps which the engineer did in fact have in his possession which showed the six-inch line. The contractor cut through the line and his plant was destroyed in the explosion and fire that resulted.

Owner held entitled to recover from the engineer the compensation he was found liable to pay the contractor for the loss of the plant. (The engineer was allowed a contribution of 25 % from the contractor and 25 % from the company which owned the line — *see* p. 404).

ff

Engineer's design for a thin wall to a prestressed circular concrete reservoir called for backfilling around the entire circumference in uniform layers of not more than six feet in depth. On completion leaks were discovered in one quadrant. Repairs of the leaks delayed completion of waterproofing in this quadrant. The contractor, not appreciating the need for uniform backfilling as designed, requested permission to proceed with backfilling the rest of the reservoir. The engineer without directing his mind to the consequences of such a modification on the design allowed the contractor to proceed with the non-uniform backfilling in order to expedite completion. Engineer found liable for the cost of repairs when the reservoir failed due to uneven loading on the thin-walled structure.

gg

Similarly the resident engineer and other site staff employed directly by the client owe to him a duty of reasonable care, having regard to their status and responsibilities. On employment of site staff by the engineer, refer to N. 27.

Special circumstances may even impose liability on an engineer merely because his design fails, without proof of negligence:

In the *Greaves* decision, above p. 388, it was decided that the special circumstances of the case were such as to imply into the contract a guarantee from the engineers to their package dealer clients that if the works were completed in accordance with the design they would be reasonably fit for use of the trucks. Therefore the engineers would have been liable for the lack of fitness of the works even if not due to negligence on their part.

If the engineer fails in any of these duties he may be liable to dismissal (p. 427), and lose his fees (N. 17). As the cases which have been cited show, he is on top of that liable as agent for all loss suffered by his client as a result of his negligence. For his liability for negligence in making decision as between the contractor and employer *see* N. 31.

30B. THE ENGINEER'S DUTIES AND LIABILITY TO THE CONTRACTOR AND OTHER THIRD PARTIES FOR HIS ACTIVITIES AS AGENT. Although this book so far has mainly been concerned with rights and duties created by agreement, whether between the contractor and the employer or sub-contractor or the employer and the engineer, it is obvious that one person may have a legal duty to another independent of any agreement between them. A motorist is liable to pay compensation to any pedestrian he runs down negligently even though he has made no prior agreement with the pedestrian not to run him down. The branch of the civil (as opposed to criminal) law covering duties imposed by the law itself is known as the law of tort. The most important torts are nuisance (ch. 15) and negligence. It is in

(*ff*) *Hensuet Bros. Ltd.* v. *Pan Canadian Petroleum Ltd.* (1977) 5 W.W.R. 681 Can.
(*gg*) *City of Prince Albert* v. *Underwood, McLellan & Associates Ltd.* (1969) S.C.R. 305 Can.

the widening scope given by the courts to the tort of negligence that the most significant developments in construction law affecting the engineer amongst others have taken place in the recent past, and are likely to take place in the near future:

(a) It is over half a century since the courts established liability independent of contract for negligently causing injury to the person or damage to the property of another (see p. 93, N. 4). So the engineer may be liable to the contractor and his workmen and to members of the public generally for injury or damage caused or contributed to by his negligence, in design or supervision, even though he has no contract with them. The most difficult problem of the extent of the engineer's liability for temporary works is discussed on p. 53.

(b) For almost thirty years the boundary of liability for negligence (in the absence of some contract creating wider responsibility) was fixed at liability for physical injury or damage. The courts feared that any relaxation of the boundary would open a floodgate to claims. Accordingly, it was formerly believed that the engineer under a construction contract could not in any circumstances be liable to a contractor who suffered purely financial loss by making a contract on the faith of misleading information or advice given to him negligently by the engineer, e.g. in a bill of quantities or drawings, etc., since there is no contract between them.

However, the House of Lords has held that the cases which laid down this principle were wrong, and that there may be liability for negligent misstatement of fact or negligent advice not merely where one party is employed by the other, but whenever there is a "*special relationship*" between the parties. There is some controversy as to the exact definition of a "*special relationship*", but it certainly includes the case of a person carrying on a business or profession involving the giving of advice calling for special skill and competence or holding himself out as having special access to information, who chooses to make a statement or give advice "*knowing that it is being relied on*", and does not warn the other party that he is not taking responsibility for it.

hh

The decisions referred to above had nothing to do with civil engineering. In applying the principle to engineering works it is to be expected that allowance will be made for the fact that the contractor is generally himself a skilled engineer and therefore in a position to evaluate statements made by the engineer, and indeed bound by the construction contract to do so as far as practicable (p. 56). But subject to that it seems the engineer will be liable to the contractor for damages if he makes any negligent statement about the conditions for the work, etc., in a form or in circumstances which imply that the contractor may rely on it—whether the statement is verbal or

(hh) *Hedley, Byrne & Co. Ltd.* v. *Heller & Partners Ltd.* [1963] 2 All E.R. 575, as interpreted in *Mutual Life Citizens Assurance Co. Ltd.* v. *Evatt* [1971] 1 All E.R. 150, P.C. and extensions discussed on p. 396 below. In the *Howard Marine* decision (p. 61 above, footnote (a')), Lord Denning points out that the principles in those two cases "speak of the 'gravity of the enquiry' and the seeking of 'considered advice'. Those words are used so as to exclude representations made during a casual conversation in the street; or in a railway carriage; or an impromptu opinion given offhand; or 'off the cuff' on the telephone. To put it more generally, the duty is one of honesty and no more whenever the opinion, information or advice is given in circumstances in which it appears that it is unconsidered and it would not be reasonable for the recipient to act on it without taking further steps to check it" (at p. 1141). Nevertheless the divided opinions of the members of the court in that decision itself illustrate the hazards of volunteering information however casually and however well-intentioned.

written, in or outside the contract documents. For example, if the engineer were to take it on himself to tell the contractor his conclusions about the conditions of the site on the basis of investigations made for the employer, without giving the contractor the detailed results of those investigations so that he could draw his own conclusions, or to mislead the contractor as to the difficulty of the works by negligent design criteria for the permanent works set out in the tender documents for the purpose of cl. 14 of the Conditions. Other examples are on pp. 81, N. 14 and 100.

A negligent misstatement may even be actionable by a party who suffers loss not by himself acting on the statement, but because it causes a third party to act to his detriment—examples are given on p. 399.

Although the contractor is the most likely party other than the client to wish to claim against the engineer, he is not in a unique position and the possibilities of redress for a negligent statement extend at least to any outsider with a "special relationship". In another jurisdiction supervisors have even been held liable directly to a surety under a performance bond for negligently certifying payment for defective work when the surety had to pay to have the work made good after the contractor's failure. *ii*

The engineer is certainly liable to the contractor as he is to any other person, for damages suffered in reliance on a fraudulent or reckless misstatement by him—that is, any statement which he makes without positively believing it to be true—whatever repudiation of responsibility he may make (*see* p. 60).

(*c*) A further extension of the boundaries of negligence has been commenced, and may well not be complete: Contractors, professional designers and supervisors, and even local authorities with the responsibility of making bye-law inspections, may be liable to an owner or occupier with whom they have no contract for the cost of rectifying a defect in a building which they negligently failed to prevent, provided the defect causes "present or imminent danger to the health or safety of occupiers". *jj*

(*d*) While for fear of letting loose a flood of claims the home courts have so far refused to extend further the liability for purely financial loss, it is clear that the last word has not been said on the very flexible principle of liability for negligence:

> "The position has now been reached that in order to establish that a duty of care arises in a particular situation, it is not necessary to bring the facts of that situation within those of previous situations in which a duty of care has been held to exist. Rather the question has to be approached in two stages. First, one has to ask whether, as between the alleged wrongdoer and the person who has suffered damage, there is a sufficient relationship of proximity or neighbourhood such that in the reasonable contemplation of the former, carelessness on his part may be likely to cause damage to the latter, in which case a *prima facie* duty of care arises. Secondly, if the first question is answered affirmatively, it is necessary to consider whether there are any considerations which ought to negative, or to reduce or limit the scope of the duty or the class of person to whom it is owed or the damage to which a breach of it may give rise. . . ." *kk*

(*ii*) *Peerless Insurance Co.* v. *Cerny & Associates Inc.* 199F. Supp. 951 and *Atna Insurance Co.* v. *Hellmuth Obata & Kassabaum Inc.* (1968) 392F. 2d 472.

(*jj*) *Anns.* v. *London Borough of Merton* [1977] 2 All E.R. 492, 498 H.L. in which a local authority was held, and builders said to be, liable to subsequent owners and occupiers of a house for rectifying inadequacy in foundations. See also *Batty* v. *Metropolitan Property Realizations Ltd.* [1978] 2 All E.R. 445, C.A.

(*kk*) *Anns* decision at p. 498.

Results in other jurisdictions perhaps confirm the wisdom of caution in extending liability:

> "An engineer advised the authorities to close certain valves while conducting tests at the city water system to discover the cause of normal water losses. After the valves were closed a fire broke out in a factory and there was not enough pressure in the city water system to cope with it. Held that the engineer as an expert was aware that closing the valves in one district would reduce the water pressure in the adjacent water district and generally increase the risk of fire damage, and was liable to the owner for the damage caused to the factory." [ll]

(e) It is necessary to digress here to illustrate the wide extent to which liability for negligence may affect parties to construction other than the engineer:

A party to a contract may be liable for a negligent misstatement in negotiations even though it is not referred to in the contract itself. So the employer may be liable to the contractor for a negligent misstatement apart from his liability under the Misrepresentation Act 1976 (text above p. 60). [mm]

It has been held by the High Court of Australia that as a matter of law a contractor may have a claim against an employer for negligence in compiling and furnishing site information, despite stringent terms in the contract requiring the contractor to inform himself about the site and local conditions and restricting his right to rely on information supplied by the employer. Clearly the contractor also may have a remedy directly against negligent site investigators. [nn]

A contractor has been held liable to an employer who made a contract with him for bulldozing work at an hourly rate on the faith of the contractor's negligent underestimate of the time it would take to do the job. [oo]

A hydro-electric commission has been held liable for a negligent estimate of the cost of heating electrically a proposed addition to a house which was to include an indoor swimming pool, for failing to point out that the commission had no experience in estimating heat loss in rooms containing swimming pools. [pp]

A nominated, or even domestic, sub-contractor or supplier may be directly liable to a building owner for defects in work done or goods supplied that create "present or imminent danger to the health or safety of occupiers", provided the owner can prove negligence on the part of the sub-contractor or supplier. But it [qq]

(ll) *Printed Terry Finishing* v. *City of Lebanon* [1977] A. 2d, 460 Supreme Court of Pennsylvania.

(mm) *Esso Petroleum Co. Ltd.* v. *Mardon Ltd.* [1976] 2 All E.R. 5, C.A., in which a tenant successfully counterclaimed for damages for a negligent estimate of the future throughput of a garage given to him by a representative of the plaintiffs in negotiations for a tenancy agreement. There was a special relationship between the plaintiffs and the tenant, because the plaintiffs had a financial interest in the advice and knew that the tenant was relying on their knowledge and expertise in seeking information which would affect his decision whether or not to enter into a tenancy agreement with them. *See also* the *Howard Marine* decision, text above p. 61 footnote (a').

(nn) *Construction Ltd.* v. *The Queen* (1974) 44 D.L.R. (3d) 82 Can. Contrast *Dillingham Constr. Pty. Ltd.* v. *Downs* (1972) 2 N.S.W.L.R. 49 and *George Wimpey & Co. Ltd.* v. *Territory Enterprises Pty. Ltd.* (1970) 45 A.L.J.R. 38. *Morrison-Knudson Int. Co. Inc.* v. *Commonwealth of Australia* [1972] 46 A.L.J.R. 265, and *see The Queen* v. *Walter Cabot Construction Ltd.* (1977) 69 D.L.R. (3d) 542.

(oo) *Young* v. *Cosgrave* (1963) N.Z.L.R. 967.

(pp) *Hodgins* v. *Hydro-electric Commission of Township of Nepean* (1972) 28 D.L.R. (3d) 174 Can.

(qq) There is no discernible reason why the *Anns* principle, above, should not apply to goods.

appears at the moment (and has been held in another jurisdiction) that the employer does not have a direct remedy merely because the goods do not function adequately if there is no such imminent danger.

qq'

See also text above p. 47 (contractor negligently failing to notify an ambiguity in the contract documents), p. 55 (contractor's possible responsibility in connection with the engineer's design), p. 81 (negligent design criteria supplied by the engineer, e.g. under cl. 14), p. 87 (error in setting out).

rr

The engineer must take such steps as he reasonably can to safeguard himself from the liability outlined in these notes, and from the threat and harassment of an action for negligence which can be ruinous whatever the result. He should particularly avoid taking on work outside his normal sphere, because a high proportion of negligence claims arise where an engineer decides that with a little research in the textbooks he can hold on to the fees for some specialist work that really should be handed on elsewhere. The engineer also should avoid taking it on himself to make policy or commercial decisions that should be made by the client. He may advise the client on the choice of contract form (p. 390), on the choice between nominated sub-contractors or several direct contractors (p. 233), on whether to hurry the works to tender without full drawings to avoid increases in prices due to inflation but taking the risk of disruption claims by the contractor, but the final decision on all these matters should be made by the client.

A more or less standard letter at the beginning of the relationship with the client may be useful, dealing with such matters, with fees and terms of agreement between them (p. 373), site investigation (p. 436), the form of construction contract, and making clear that if the client wants more than periodic inspections he must appoint resident staff. It probably would be professional negligence for the engineer to fail to point out to the client the problems of nominated sub-contracting (p. 221). The employer must be consulted also about liquidated damages (p. 153).

It is possible to do all this in a diplomatic letter which will not sour the relationship with the client, but indeed may help to convince the client that the engineer knows his business.

The other precaution is indemnity insurance. A specimen policy must be carefully vetted before the insurers are chosen. For example, there must be a clause by which insurers agree not to fight a claim if a Queen's Counsel advises that it is likely to succeed (so as to minimise the publicity of court hearings), and the insurers must waive their subrogation rights against employees of the insured. Unfortunately some engineers have found that, having paid premiums for some years, when they need the protection of their policy they do not have it. Most policies make it a condition of insurers liability that they receive notice as soon as any facts that may lead to a claim come to the notice of the insured (not necessarily an actual claim). A procedure in

---

(qq') *Ital-Canadian Investments Ltd.* v. *North Shore Plumbing and Heating Co. Ltd.* (1978) 4 W.W.R. 289 Can.

(rr) In *Cargill Grain Co. Ltd.* v. *Foundation Company of Canada Ltd.* (1977) 17 N.R. 41 the Supreme Court of Canada referred to French legal theory holding that contractors who "have questions on reading ... data and documents (supplied on behalf of the owner) ... have an obligation to inform the ... owner, thereby giving him the opportunity to make his decisions with full knowledge of the situation". It is possible that the same or an even higher level of duty would be reached through the law of negligence.

the engineer's office to make sure notice is given in time is essential. For the
rr' long period of insurance cover that is necessary, *see* p. 430.

It would hardly be the best public relations for an engineer to purport to
exclude liability by a term in his service contract or by a statement when
giving advice to his client, and in any case such a disclaimer may not be
effective in law — p. 432. The engineer may try to protect himself in giving
advice to others, for example he may state in a prominent place in the tender
documents that he accepts no responsibility to the contractor for
information in the documents or given in any way in connection with the
works.

31. ENGINEER'S DUTY OF FAIRNESS. The duties of the engineer under the
contract forms involving extra payment and other rights of the contractor
are collected in ch. 11. The special standard of conduct required by the
engineer in carrying out these independent duties is discussed at length in
ch. 14.

For a long time it was believed to be the law that the engineer is not
himself liable to his client for mere negligence in carrying out these special
duties on the grounds that liability might hamper his judgment. This
ss supposed exception to the engineer's personal liability has now been
overruled:

> Plaintiff having a house built paid interim certificates issued by the architect
> named in the construction contract. These certificates negligently included
> payment for work that was defective (one of the architects knew of the defects but
> failed to pass the information to the quantity surveyor who calculated the
> certificates). The contractor became insolvent before the defects were made
> good.
>
> The architects were held liable to make good the client's loss, for breach of
> their contract with the client to exercise reasonable care in performing their
tt > duties.

Of course the engineer is liable only for negligence and not for mere error
of judgment not due to lack of reasonable care.

This decision would appear to apply even to negligent failure by the
engineer to give a certificate under cl. 63, but the liability of the engineer in
making a decision under cl. 66 is still questionable — p. 293, N. 6.

In the previous edition of this book it was suggested that since the
engineer's 'quasi-arbitral' shield has been removed, the engineer could be
liable to the contractor in relation to his discretionary decisions. It has now
officially been confirmed that an architect (and therefore engineer) owes a

> "duty of care to the contractor arising out of their proximity: see the *Hedley
> Byrne* case. In *Sutcliffe* v. *Thackrah* the architect negligently certified that more
> money was due than was in fact due; and he was successfully sued for the damage
> which this had caused his client. He might, however, have negligently certified
> less money was payable than was in fact due and thereby starved the contractor
> of money. In a trade in which cash flow especially is important, this might have

(rr') Reading Madge Professional Indemnity Insurance. F.I.D.I.C. report on "Some aspects
of Professional Liability."
(ss) Chambers v. *Goldthorpe* [1901] 1 K.B. 624, approved in *Greenfield* v. *Major* [1958]
N.Z.L.R. 37.
(tt) Sutcliffe v. *Thackrah* [1974] 1 All E.R. 859 H.L. This important decision is also discussed
on p. 293 of the text.

caused the contractor serious damage for which the architect could have been successfully sued."

uu

A similar possibility of liability to the contractor exists if the engineer negligently gives a forfeiture certificate under cl. 63, or any decision that adversely affects the contractor under cl. 66. And the engineer may not merely be 'shot at from both sides' in relation to actions and decisions under the contract, but by third parties from many sides—p. 395.

vv

The engineer is fully liable for any damage caused to either his client or the contractor by his fraud or by acting in collusion with the other party. In the latter case the party with whom he colludes is liable jointly with the engineer. Note also that by the words of the clause the engineer has a specific contractual duty to his client to "*act fairly as between the Client and the Contractor*" in performing discretionary duties and will be liable to the client for failure to act fairly to the contractor not due to the client's instructions, where it involves the client in loss, in having to appoint a substitute engineer for example (p. 416).

32. ENGINEER'S AUTHORITY. The engineer acts as agent of the client and may attempt to commit the client, for example by accepting a tender on his behalf or by ordering variations. The engineer has authority to do this so as to bind his client only so far as the client authorises him before he acts, as in this clause, or retrospectively by ratifying what he has done.

But because it is difficult for outsiders dealing with the engineer to check his actual authority, they are entitled to a large extent to rely on appearances—if the client puts the engineer in such a position that he appears to a third party to have authority to act for him, the client is bound by the engineer's actions as if the engineer actually had his authorisation. Under cl. 51 of the Conditions, for example, the engineer is given very wide power to order variations, so that the engineer has apparent authority in relation to the contractor to do so, on which the contractor is entitled to rely. The employer of course is not bound if the engineer exceeds even such apparent authority, as well as his actual authority, for example by going outside the terms of the clause by the extent of the variation (p. 172) or by purporting to alter the contract or make any new contract:

A contract provided that the engineer should locate a racetrack as nearly as possible according to lines drawn on the plan and stake out the exact location. The contractor deviated from the specified grades in accordance with the engineer's stakes.

The deviation was held to be a breach of contract, since the construction contract gave the engineer power to vary the works by written order only.

ww

The practical problems of concessions to the contractor by the engineer are dealt with in N. 2 on p. 179.

Again, while cls. 2A (iv) and C (v) above make it clear that the engineer in relation to his client must have special authority before ordering investigations, tests, etc., at his expense, the courts might hold that from his appointment the engineer has apparent authority to order investigations

---

(*uu*) *Arenson* v. *Casson Beckman Rutley & Co.* [1975] 3 All E.R. 901, H.L.

(*vv*) This expression was used in the *Arenson* decision (p. 910).

(*ww*) *Courtney* v. *Provincial Exhibition Commission* (1906) 41 N.S.R. 71 Can.

obviously necessary so as to commit the client to pay any specialist who does them without knowing that they are not authorised. The position may be the same in relation to the appointment of site staff — N. 27. On the other hand it is quite clear that instructions to call for tenders do not give the engineer any apparent authority to accept a tender, so that any acceptance by him without special authority does not bind the employer.

For apparent authority flowing from a full-time office held by the engineer with the employer, *see* p. 59 footnote (*rr*).

This doctrine of apparent authority is for the protection of the contractor and other persons dealing with the engineer only; the engineer will therefore be liable for any loss he causes his client by acting beyond his actual authority but within his apparent authority, so as improperly to commit his client to a third party — for example by ordering extras within the general conditions cl. 51 but outside his authority under this clause (N. 33).

Apart from this liability to his client for exceeding his authority the engineer may also be liable to the contractor — if he represents that he has authority which he has not in fact been given by the client, and the contractor suffers loss by relying on his representation. The contractor will of course usually only suffer loss if the client is not bound by the engineer's actions because they fall outside the engineer's authority under the contract or other apparent authority as well as his actual authority, where for example the engineer orders an extra which is outside his powers under the construction contract (p. 172, N. 8). The engineer is liable only if he represents — by words or conduct — that he has authority and the contractor relies on his representation, not, e.g., where he purports to act under his ordinary powers in the contract to order extras and both he and the contractor mistakenly interpret the contract as authorising his order.

When it does arise this liability for warranty of authority is very strict, and the engineer will be liable even if he believed or had reasonable grounds for believing that he had authority, or that his action would be ratified by the employer.

In the same way the engineer may be liable to specialists, residents, etc., if he represents incorrectly that he has authority to employ them on his client's behalf.

Finally, if the engineer enters into a contract on his client's behalf without making it clear that he is acting as agent, he may be personally bound by the contract, which may be important if the client goes bankrupt:

> An architect wrote for quotations for fittings stating that he was acting for a client, but later he ordered the fittings without referring to a client.
> Held: He was personally liable to pay the suppliers for the fittings. If he had authority to make the order and his client was solvent he would of course have been able to recover the price paid.

> Engineer made a contract with a building company on behalf of owners of some property. He did not mention to the company the name of the owners or

(xx) *Waghorn* v. *Wimbledon Local Board*, Hudson "Building Contracts", 4th ed., vol. ii, p. 52 but see *Antisell* v. *Doyle* (1899) 2 Ir.R. 275. Since a quantity surveyor is not generally employed in civil engineering work, engineers, unlike architects, would have no implied authority to employ one, but the *Waghorn* decision might apply by analogy to other specialists.

(yy) *Beattie* v. *Ebury* (1872) L.R. 7 Ch. App. 777 aff. L.R. 7 H.L., 102, and *Jacobs* v. *Morris* [1902] 1 Ch. 816.

(zz) *Bergtheil and Young* v. *Stewart* (1900) 16 T.L.R. 177.

that he was acting on their behalf until the contract was made. He had, however, written and been written to with the qualifications "BE MICE" after his name, and had signed his letters as "Chartered Civil Engineer" so that it was clear that he was not acting on his own account, but professionally for a client.

Held that it was possible for a person who was in fact an agent to contract in such a way that he became liable to the other party. The judge admitted that it was uncommon to have a phrase "acting as agent" at the end of letters; nevertheless as the correspondence stood it was impossible to say that the engineer was acting as an agent, and the building company were entitled to assume that he was not.   *a'*

The engineer should therefore not place orders on his own behalf but only do so explicitly on behalf of his client, and as a matter of policy should have the acceptance of tender, etc., signed personally by the client.

33. "EXCEPT IN AN EMERGENCY . . . (THE ENGINEER) SHALL NOT, WITHOUT THE PRIOR APPROVAL OF THE CLIENT, AUTHORISE ANY MODIFICATION OF THE WORKS INVOLVING A SUBSTANTIAL EXTRA COST". This restriction probably represents an increase in the ordinary powers of the engineer *vis-à-vis* his client (N. 32) but it is in fact inconsistent with his independent position under the construction contract and his duty to act fairly stated in this clause itself. If the engineer considers a variation necessary he may in many cases be bound to order it, however large it is, and he must not be influenced by his client or the terms of his service agreement (*see* p. 169), but under this clause he may be liable to his client. If the client refuses to agree to a necessary change the contractor's right to arbitration at the client's expense and other remedies should be pointed out (p. 416). If that does not work, in view of his liability to the client the engineer should not order the variation, and leave the contractor to these remedies.   *b'*

The client is not specifically given control over instructions by the engineer, which under cl. 13 of the 5th edition I.C.E. Conditions may be very costly for the client.

INFORMATION TO BE SUPPLIED TO CONSULTING ENGINEERS

13. The Client shall supply free of charge all pertinent data and information and give such assistance as shall reasonably be required for the carrying out by the Consulting Engineers of their duties under this Agreement.

OWNERSHIP OF DOCUMENTS AND COPYRIGHT

14. All documents prepared by the Consulting Engineers in connection with the Works are the property[34] and copyright[35] of the Consulting Engineers, and the Client shall not be entitled, either directly or indirectly, to make use of such

(*a'*) *Sika Contracts Limited* v. *Gill*, The Times, April 27, 1978.

(*b'*) Although it is now clear that the courts will allow the engineer to be shot at by the contractor as readily as by his own client (p. 398), the position remains that the contractor is most likely to claim against the employer and not the engineer, and even if the engineer is joined in proceedings he will be entitled to an effective indemnity from his client if he warned him clearly of the contractor's rights and the client is solvent. On the other hand a variation order later found unjustified may affect the value or safety of the works or involve the employer in extra payment to the contractor with the engineer in the first line of fire for any attempt by the employer to recover his losses.

documents for the carrying out of any work beyond the Works to which this agreement relates,[36] without the prior approval of the Consulting Engineers.

34. "ALL DOCUMENTS ... ARE THE PROPERTY OF THE CONSULTING ENGINEERS". In the absence of a term to this effect all documents prepared by the engineer (except private notes, inter-office memos, etc., made for his personal use) belong to the employer, but the copyright (N. 35) belongs to the engineer. Under cl. 2C (x) above the client is entitled to record drawings, etc., but the engineer has a right to hold them until his fees are paid.

35. COPYRIGHT. In the absence of any special agreement with the client the engineer is entitled to the copyright in his plans and drawings, and in the contract documents prepared by him so far as they are original.

Copyright is infringed if a copy is made of any substantial part of a plan. A plan or drawing is protected, however, purely as an arrangement of lines, figures, etc., and the engineer cannot protect a new method or idea by claiming copyright in a plan which sets it out. An invention can be protected only if it qualifies for a grant of patent.

If the features of a structure are copied without a copy being made of the plans, where for example the client does keep the plans at the end of the work and uses only the originals for an extension to the works, the engineer's copyright may also be infringed.

The right to copyright generally continues during the life and 50 years after the death of the actual author or draftsman (not his employer in the case of an assistant, although the copyright belongs to the employer), so that drawings, etc., should be initialled.

Copyright is automatic so that the symbol © is not necessary, but it is useful, particularly for international protection. For this it should be followed by the name of the engineer claiming copyright (even if that is already given on the document) and the year of first publication.

There have been several recent decisions on copyright in plans:

An architect prepared plans for an application for planning permission to extend and rebuild a factory. The plans included a special and distinctive diamond-shaped feature which gave a very pleasing appearance to the building. Planning permission was granted on the basis of the plans. The architect sent to the clients his account for preparing the plans for the "Agreed nominal fee 100 guineas". He added to the account: "The copyright of the design remains with the architect, and may not be reproduced without his prior written consent." The account was paid. Subsequently the architect withdrew altogether from the project.

The clients went ahead with rebuilding the factory and some months later the architect saw that they had included in the building the distinctive diamond-shaped feature of his plans, although not much else from the plans. He claimed damages for infringement of copyright.

Held: That because the fee was nominal it did not carry with it an implied licence to use the architect's plans without paying anything for them, other than for the planning application. The nominal fee was far less than the R.I.B.A. scale fee (both parties were familiar with the R.I.B.A. conditions of engagement) and therefore the payment of this fee did not imply a right to use the plans for the building right through until its completion, which payment of the R.I.B.A. scale fee would have done.

(c') See generally Copinger and Skone James on "Copyright", 11th ed.

The measure of damages was held to be the fair remuneration which the clients would have had to pay the architect for a licence to use the copyright in the plans, assessed at £500.

This clause is sometimes changed so as to vest copyright in the client, who reasonably may not wish the engineer to build a project for another client with special features identical to his works.

36. "THE WORKS TO WHICH THIS AGREEMENT RELATES"—whether the engineer is employed for their construction or not, for example after his death or dismissal.

It is not made clear whether the client has a right to use the documents for reconstructing the works if they are damaged after completion. To use plans for this purpose is not an infringement of copyright in the ordinary way. For record drawings see cl. 2C (x).

NON-ASSIGNMENT

15.   The Consulting Engineers shall not have the right to assign or transfer the benefit[37] and obligations[38] of this Agreement or any part thereof, and the same shall automatically come to an end on the death of the survivor of them but without prejudice to the accrued rights of either party against the other under this agreement—*provided that* it shall be lawful for the Consulting Engineers at any time to take into partnership another Partner or Partners and that he or they or the survivor of them shall thenceforth be deemed to be included in the expression "the Consulting Engineers".[39]

37. "SHALL NOT . . . ASSIGN . . . THE BENEFIT . . . OF THIS AGREEMENT". *See* p. 39, N. 2.

38. "SHALL NOT . . . . ASSIGN . . . (THE) OBLIGATIONS OF THIS AGREEMENT". Irrespective of this clause the engineer cannot assign his duties to another so as to rid himself of them. If without assigning the contract he gets someone else to do the actual work he will be liable for any errors in the work delegated (p. 391 (*j*)) and may lose his right to fees (*see* p. 40, N. 4, and also N. 39 below).

The engineer is, of course, entitled to make use of assistants provided he retains control of the work and uses his own judgment in certifying. He is generally liable for the actions of his assistants as if they were his own (but *see* p. 389 (*f*)).

39. NEW PARTNER ENTITLED TO THE BENEFIT OF THE AGREEMENT. A partner need not legally be a whole-time member of the firm and may be a partner for a limited time, so that this is a major exception to the employer's right to object to assignment of the agreement.

(*d'*) *Stovin-Bradford* v. *Volpoint Properties Ltd.* [1971] 3 All E.R. 570, distinguishing *Blair* v. *Tomkins and Osborne* [1971] 1 All E.R. 468, where a licence was held to be implied from payment of the appropriate fee for the preliminary stage in accordance with the R.I.B.A. scale which was accepted as governing the engagement. *See* N. 36 in the text for the position under this agreement.

(*e'*) For a case where on the peculiar facts the architect did not lose his right to fees, see *Hamlyn Construction Co.* v. *Air Couriers* [1968] 1 Lloyd's Rep. 395.

ARBITRATION

16.   Any dispute or difference arising out of this Agreement[40] shall be referred to the arbitration of a person to be mutually agreed upon or, failing agreement, of some person appointed by the President for the time being of the Institution of Civil Engineers.[41,42]

ARBITRATION. *See* generally ch. 8. The Arbitration Act, 1950, of course applies, even though it is not mentioned.

40. "ANY DISPUTE OR DIFFERENCE ARISING OUT OF THIS AGREEMENT". These words cover a dispute as to frustration or repudiation of the agreement, but not as to whether it was void or voidable from the beginning, or a claim for rectification (*see* p. 291, N. 1). It is not certain that a claim by the client for damages for the engineer's fraud or negligence is subject to arbitration under this clause.

41. "PRESIDENT ... OF THE INSTITUTION". In forms, B, C and D, below, the name of the appropriate Institution must be added here. Where it is not the courts will nevertheless appoint an arbitrator if it is clear that the parties intended this clause to operate.

42. DISPUTES INVOLVING THE ENGINEER AND CONTRACTOR:

An employer sued his architect in the courts for negligence. The architect blamed the contractors and the employers sought to join the contractors in the court proceedings. The contractors applied for a stay of the proceedings in order to have the dispute dealt with by arbitration under the main contract. The court refused the stay in order to avoid duplicity of proceedings.

Even in a case where the engineer is bound by this service agreement, difficulties may arise in three-cornered disputes if the main contract is under, e.g., the R.I.B.A. form where the arbitrator is appointed by the President of the R.I.B.A. It appears from this decision that the courts will attempt to solve such problems by hearing the dispute and negativing the arbitration clauses unless the parties will agree on a single tribunal.

IN WITNESS whereof, etc.

SIGNATURE, ETC. *See* p. 22 for the full form.

(*f'*) For a discussion of the similar phrase "arising out of these conditions" in the R.I.B.A. Conditions of Engagement see *Kaye, Firmin & Partners* v. *Bronesky* [1973] 226 E.G. 1395. See also *The Eschersheim* [1976] 1 All E.R. 920, H.L.

(*g'*) *Davies, Middleton & Davies* v. *Cardiff Corp.* (1964) 62 L.G.R. 134.

(*h'*) *Taunton-Collins* v. *Cromie* [1964] 2 All E.R. 332, C.A. Although the convenience of avoiding hearings by both a court and an arbitrator is obvious, it is difficult to see the justification for depriving the contractor of his right to arbitration under his contract with the employer merely because the employer had a dispute with his own architect, with whom he had not made a service agreement incorporating an arbitration clause. This issue is likely to become most important with the extension of the right of one wrongdoer to recover a contribution to compensation paid from any other person liable for the same damage, whether in tort or for breach of contract, by the Civil Liability (Contribution) Act 1978.

SCHEDULE
PART I
SCALE OF FEES

FOR GENERAL CIVIL ENGINEERING

1. The fee shall be on the basis of a lump sum, plus a percentage of the cost of the Works as defined in Clause 8, in accordance with the appropriate line in the following table.

Cost of the Works			Fee
Up to	£10,000	.. .. ..	10 % of the Cost of the Works
From	£10,000 to	£30,000	£200 + 8 % of the Cost of the Works
From	£30,000 to	£50,000	£500 + 7 % of the Cost of the Works
From	£50,000 to	£100,000	£1,000 + 6 % of the Cost of the Works
From	£100,000 to	£250,000	£1,500 + $5\frac{1}{2}$ % of the Cost of the Works
From	£250,000 to	£500,000	£2,750 + 5 % of the Cost of the Works
From	£500,000 to £1,000,000		£5,250 + $4\frac{1}{2}$ % of the Cost of the Works
From	£1,000,000 to £2,000,000		£7,750 + $4\frac{1}{4}$ % of the Cost of the Works
Over	£2,000,000	.. ..	£12,750 + 4 % of the Cost of the Works

2. ADDITIONAL FEES ON THE REINFORCED CONCRETE PORTION OF THE WORKS— INCLUDING THE CONCRETE, REINFORCEMENT, PRESTRESSING TENDONS AND ANCHORAGES, FORMWORK, INSERTS AND ALL LABOURS, TOGETHER WITH THE RELEVANT PROPORTION OF "PRELIMINARIES"

Cost of Reinforced Concrete Portion	*Additional Fee*
Under £50,000	$3\frac{1}{2}$ % of the Cost of the Reinforced Concrete Portion of the Works.
From £50,000 to £200,000 ..	£500 + $2\frac{1}{2}$ % of the Cost of the Reinforced Concrete Portion of the Works.
From £200,000 to £400,000	£1,500 + 2 % of the Cost of the Reinforced Concrete Portion of the Works.
Over £400,000	£3,500 + $1\frac{1}{2}$ % of the Cost of the Reinforced Concrete Portion of the Works.

ADDITIONAL FEES FOR STRUCTURAL STEELWORK

3. For structural steelwork, the additional fee shall be one half of that for reinforced concrete.

BUILDING AND PLANT (REVISED)

4. In cases where (*a*) Buildings, with or without their associated engineering services, and/or (*b*) electrical and mechanical plant, form part of a Civil Engineering Project, the fees therefor shall be at the above scale, but calculated as if each of the groups is a separate Work—that is, the calculation of the fees therefor shall start afresh from the beginning of each scale, for each group.

ARCHITECTURAL SERVICES

5. If the services of an Architect are required by the Client to deal with the architectural treatment of the buildings, his fees shall be paid by the Client. If

architectural services are provided by the Consulting Engineers, an additional
fee shall be chargeable.

Note—The above fees do not apply in cases where the demands on the
Consulting Engineers' time are out of proportion with the estimated or
actual cost of the Works—e.g. alterations or additions to existing works.
In such cases, the remuneration payable shall be on a higher percentage
rate, or on a time basis calculated in accordance with Part II hereof, or as
may be otherwise agreed.

PART II
SCALE OF CHARGES ON A TIME BASIS

The Scale of Charges on a time basis shall be as follows:
  (i) Partners:
  (ii) Technical Staff: At the rate of 3s. 0d. [15p] per hour per £100 (or part
       thereof) of annual salary (including any bonus).
Time spent by clerical staff (unless otherwise agreed) shall not be chargeable.
Time spent by Partners and Technical Staff in travelling shall be chargeable.

Fees. The Association also publishes the following general guide:

CONDITIONS OF ENGAGEMENT AND SCALES OF FEES

...

REPORTS AND OTHER ADVISORY WORK

2.   For reports, or for advisory work, or for valuations of plant and
undertakings, the fee will be dependent on the professional standing of the
Member, on the matter under consideration and on any special circumstances.
In such cases, the fee will normally be computed on a time basis in accordance
with paragraph 6 hereof, or an agreed lump sum, or a combination thereof, or
alternatively computed as an agreed percentage of the estimated capital value.

An appointment to undertake advisory work of this kind may be covered by an
exchange of letters embodying the agreed terms of reference,

...

MODEL FORMS OF AGREEMENT

4.   The basic fee for the services to be rendered by the Consulting Engineers,
after the proposals recommended in their preliminary report have been
approved by the Client, is computed as a percentage on the cost of the Works.
The amount of the percentage fee and the duties which it covers are set out herein
in four Model Forms of Agreement "A", "B", "C" and "D", prepared for the use
by Clients and Consulting Engineers.

MODEL FORMS. Form "C" is for structural engineering work in buildings
and other structures where an architect has been appointed by the client,
and form "D" is for the design and supervision of engineering services and
associated equipment for building and other structures. The general clauses
in these forms are identical to form "A" except for differences in cls. 2–4 and
8 (9 in these forms) and a new cl. 6, all dealing with calculation of fees, and
differences in Part I of the scale of fees. There are also details of the
information to be provided by the client (cl. 14), and *see* N. 41 above. In
Form "C" cl. 10 deals with co-operation between the engineer and architect
in appointing resident staff, and there is a technical schedule to form "D".
Form "B" is for works principally of an electrical and mechanical nature.

VARIATIONS IN TERMS OF AGREEMENT

5. The Model Forms of Agreement are applicable in normal circumstances, but some variation of the terms set out in the Model Forms may be necessary in particular cases *where the amount of work required differs substantially from the normal*—for example, where:

  (i)   The design work is of an unusually complex character.
  (ii) The Works are to be constructed wholly or partly by direct labour.
  (iii) The Works are to be constructed by means of an abnormally large number of separate Contracts.
  (iv) A substantial proportion of the project involves alterations or additions to existing structures, plant or services.
  (v)   The completion of the project is retarded through circumstances over which the Consulting Engineers have no control—e.g. in order to spread the aggregate cost over an extended period.
  (vi) The project is exceptionally large and simple in character.
  (vii) The work is for a Client of long standing who regularly retains the same Consulting Engineers for the execution of the majority of his work.

FEES BASED ON TIME

6. Where fees are based on the time occupied, a Member is entitled to charge for work done by himself and by his technical assistants, but not (unless otherwise agreed) by his clerical staff. Alternatively, a Member may charge for his technical assistants on a time basis, together with a fixed fee for his personal services. A Member is entitled to charge for time spent by himself and his technical assistants in travelling.

The time rates currently in force are:

  (i) Partners: Dependent on the standing of the Member, on the nature of the work, and on any special circumstances, but not less than $3\frac{1}{2}$ guineas [£$3.67\frac{1}{2}$] per hour.

  (ii) Technical Staff: 3s. 0d. [15p] per hour per £100 or part thereof of annual salary (including bonus, if any).

All travelling, hotel and other out-of-pocket expenses, properly incurred by a Member or by his assistants on his Client's behalf, are reimbursable—either at actual cost or as may be otherwise agreed. An additional charge may be made for the use of special equipment.

INSPECTION WORK

7. Charges for inspection work, where not already covered by the basic fee, will usually be calculated as a percentage of the cost of the materials to be inspected, or on a time basis, or as a lump sum fee, or as a combination thereof. In addition, out-of-pocket expenses are reimbursable.

ARBITRATION, EVIDENCE, ETC.

8. (i)   When a Member acts as Arbitrator or Umpire, the fee shall be a lump sum, plus a charge of not less than 5 guineas per hour, depending on the nature of the reference and on the professional standing of the Member.

(ii) When a Member attends at Parliamentary Committees, Courts of Law, Arbitrations or Official Inquiries, the fee shall usually be a lump sum, plus an appropriate hourly charge—not less than three hours being chargeable for attendance, however short, either before or after mid-day adjournment. The Member is also entitled to a refresher for each day on which he is requested to hold himself in readiness to attend but is subsequently not required, in the sum of three hours' remuneration.

(iii) Fees are also chargeable on a time basis for work done by a Member's technical assistants, in accordance with paragraph 6 hereof.

(iv) When computing fees chargeable under this paragraph on a time basis, a Member is entitled to include time spent by him or his assistants in travelling, attendance at consultations, considering documents, making inspections, or otherwise qualifying for and preparing evidence. All travelling, hotel and other out-of-pocket expenses, properly incurred, are reimbursable—either at actual cost or as may be otherwise agreed.

AREA OF APPLICATION OF FEES

9. The fees referred to in paragraph 4 are intended primarily to apply to work carried out in the United Kingdom. For work overseas, it is impracticable to make definite recommendations as the conditions vary widely from country to country. There are added complications in documentation relating to import customs, conditions of payment, insurance, freight, etc. Furthermore, it is necessary to arrange for site visits to be undertaken by Partners or senior staff whose absence abroad during such periods represents a serious reduction of their earning power. The additional duties, responsibilities and non-recoverable costs involved, and the extra work on general co-ordination, therefore justify higher fees in such cases. Special arrangements are also necessary to cover travelling and other out-of-pocket expenses in excess of those normally incurred on similar work in the United Kingdom—including such matters as local cost-of-living allowances and the cost of providing home-leave facilities to expatriate staff.

CHAPTER 14

Conduct of the Arbitrator and Engineer

DISPUTES

Background. It is a mistake, often made, to believe that the conditions of contract are self-contained. They must on the contrary be read against the background of a large body of legal principles and decisions. The most far-reaching of those principles concern the conduct of the arbitrator and, to a lesser extent, the engineer. The two are grouped together because the engineer has a special role in some cases under the construction contract.

The courts originally took the view that the contractor's and employer's relationship with the engineer was akin to marriage. The rule was laid down that having agreed to obey the engineer's decisions, the contractor and employer generally must carry them out even if mistaken; but with the limitation that, as in marriage, the relationship might be dissolved for misconduct.

Over the years the effect of this rule has been reduced. At first with the introduction into contract forms of arbitration clauses which give the arbitrator wide powers to overrule decisions of the engineer, then by the Arbitration Act, 1950, which prevents appointment of the engineer as arbitrator also (below), and on top of that by the addition of contract terms which in some cases give the contractor a right to have disputes arbitrated while the works are still in progress. What it is hoped is the final stage is the very recent court decision discussed in the next section.

Despite all these changes, what may be called the independent role of the engineer is still vitally important.

The engineer's independent role. The engineer has a dual capacity. In performing some of his functions he is acting purely as agent of the employer, and is bound to consider the employer's wishes and interests only—for example, in deciding what power to delegate to a representative under cl. 2, or whom to nominate as a sub-contractor under cl. 58 (p. 236), or it appears in deciding whether or not to consent to sub-letting under cl. 4. However, the construction contract also places on the engineer in many circumstances the function of deciding on the rights of the parties under the contract according to his own opinion and acting accordingly. For example, in deciding whether the contractor is entitled to a certificate of payment, or on the length of an extension of time under cl. 44, or to give a forfeiture certificate under cl. 63.

These latter duties used to be called the quasi-arbitral or quasi-judicial duties of the engineer, because in performing them the engineer is bound to

(a) *Hatrick (N.Z.) Ltd.* v. *Nelson, Carlton Construction* [1964] N.Z.L.R. 72, see text p. 415.

409

act impartially and independently in finding the facts and applying the contract to them. However, previous decisions have recently been overruled, and it has been held that an architect (and clearly the decision applies to an engineer) is not to be classed as a quasi-arbitrator in
b performing these functions. In this decision the House of Lords was concerned to deny to an architect the ingredient in the status of quasi-arbitrator that would have deprived his client of a right to claim
c compensation from him for negligence. This desirable result does not alter the position that the engineer must apply the contract independently and fairly in deciding questions on which specifically or by implication he is
d required by the construction contract to exercise his personal judgment. Particular cases under the 5th edition I.C.E. Conditions are discussed on pp. 261 and 292. Note, however, that his position does not confer on the engineer any licence to substitute his own opinion as to what is fair or reasonable for the terms of the contract. The engineer's duty is to act and decide fairly in applying the contract; the obligation imposed on the contractor as a result is to be in accordance with the contract which may or may not be "fair" in the abstract.

Misconduct of arbitrator, of engineer. These topics are best dealt with by considering, in relation first to a full arbitrator and then to the engineer, two rules developed by the courts which experience has shown to be the essentials of elementary justice in deciding disputes: (*a*) No man may be a
e judge in his own cause; (*b*) both parties must know fully and be given an opportunity of putting forward their answers to the case which they have to meet:

(*b*) *Sutcliffe* v. *Thackrah* [1974] 1 All E.R. 859 H.L.; for facts *see* text above, p. 293.

(*c*) It has even been suggested by a learned Law Lord that an arbitrator may be liable for negligence, in *Arenson* v. *Casson Beckman Rutley & Co.* (1975) 3 All E.R. 901, 918, H.L. But that is a largely isolated view—*see*, for example, *Campbell* v. *Edwards* [1976] 1 All E.R. 785.

(*d*) "We do not in this case have occasion to consider whether nevertheless he (the architect) may have some duty to the contractor. . . . It has often been said, I think rightly, that the architect has two different types of function to perform. In many matters he is bound to act on his client's instructions whether he agrees with them or not; but in many other matters requiring professional skill he must form and act on his own opinion. Many matters may arise in the course of the execution of a building contract where a decision has to be made which will affect the amount of money which the contractor gets . . . for example, he (the architect) decides whether the contractor should be reimbursed for loss under (R.I.B.A. Conditions) cl. 11 (Variations), cl. 24 (Disturbance) or cl. 34 (Antiquities); whether he should be allowed extra time. . . . And, perhaps most important, he has to decide whether work is defective. . . . The building owner and the contractor make their contract on the understanding that in all such matters the architect will act in a fair and unbiased manner and it must therefore be implicit in the owner's contract with the architect that he shall not only exercise due care and skill, but also reach such decisions fairly holding the balance between his client and the contractor." *Sutcliffe* v. *Thackrah* per Lord Reid at p. 683, and to the like effect Lord Morris at pp. 862, 872 and 875, Viscount Dilhorne at p. 880 and Lord Salmon at p. 881 and in the *Arenson* case above, p. 910.

See also the one specific requirement in the I.C.E. Conditions that the engineer has the employer's consent before acting—cl. 59A (2) (c). The A.C.E. Service Agreement, cl. 12 (text p. 386), says specifically that "in so far as any of their duties are discretionary (the consulting engineers) shall act fairly as between the Client and the Contractor".

(*e*) These rules of natural justice do not apply as such to the engineer. (See *Sutcliffe* v. *Thackrah* above, text p. 293, and *London Borough Council of Hounslow* v. *Twickenham Garden Developments Ltd.* [1970] 3 All E.R. 326, at pp. 348, 349). The limited extent to which similar requirements do apply is discussed below (see also note (*j*)).

(a) JUDGE IN OWN CAUSE:

In an appeal against an assessment to rates, it was discovered that the judge who heard the appeal was at the time of trial the registered shareholder of five shares (out of a large total capital) in the company appealing. The judge had at the time of trial already contracted to sell the shares and believed that he had no interest in the company.

Held: That he was an interested party and was not competent to try the appeal. *f*

An arbitrator may therefore be disqualified if, for example, he is a shareholder in or particularly associated with one of the parties. An arbitrator might also be disqualified from arbitrating a dispute between the engineer and his client, if he had taken an active part as a member of a professional body in dealing with a complaint against the engineer's conduct.

The parties may, of course, consent to the arbitrator acting despite his interest. Formerly the rule was that a party could not complain that the arbitrator had an interest or bias which might affect his impartiality if he knew of this when he agreed to the particular arbitrator, even if that was by a general agreement to arbitrate made before any dispute had arisen. This rule was important because it meant that a contractor could not object when a dispute arose merely because, in the past very common, it was the engineer of the employer who was appointed arbitrator by the construction contract. The Arbitration Act, 1950, now provides that in the case of an *g* agreement to refer future disputes to a named arbitrator a court may revoke the authority of the arbitrator or restrain the arbitration on the grounds that the arbitrator is not or may not be impartial, although "the party complaining knew or ought to have known at the time when he made the agreement that the arbitrator because of his relationship towards any other party to the agreement or his connection with the subject matter might not be capable of impartiality".

Known interests do not disqualify the engineer from deciding between the contractor and employer. The contractor is in particular taken to know that the engineer will generally have prepared the contract; will have estimated the cost of the work and so will want to avoid extras; may have made mistakes in the plans involving extra cost which again he will want to keep down; and may wish to minimise the extension of time for any delay which he causes the contractor, for which he may be liable to the employer. The engineer will be disqualified if he has any exceptional interest which the contractor did not know of when he made the contract—e.g. where the engineer had actually promised the employer (not merely estimated) that *h* the works would not cost more than a certain figure.

A difficult question is the extent to which the ownership of shares in an employer company which is not disclosed to the contractor will disqualify the engineer under this heading:

In 1854 an action was brought to disqualify Brunel as certifier under a contract, on the grounds that unknown to the contractor he held shares in the

(*f*) *R.* v. *Storks* (1857) 29 L.T. (O.S.) 107.

(*g*) Sec. 24 (1).

(*h*) *Kimberley* v. *Dick* (1871) L.R. 13 Eq. 1, and *Kemp* v. *Rose* (1858) 114 R.R. 429. In *Fraser* v. *Hamilton Corp.* (1912) 32 N.Z.L.R. 205 it was said that the latter case can be supported only on the ground that the assurance as to price given by the architect was equivalent to a binding undertaking.

railway company employer. The judges dismissed the action, with some doubt, on the grounds that as Brunel was principal engineer of the employer company it was "known amongst engineers and must have been known by Mr. Ranger (the contractor) that it was an ordinary case for the engineer to hold shares", and that the interest in the outcome of the contract which the engineer had by reason of holding shares was trifling compared to his interest known to the contractor due to his official connection with the company.

i

One can therefore only take the lawyer's escape route when the law is not clear by saying that the question must be one of degree. Certainly if a seemingly independent consultant has a substantial interest in an employer company, particularly if he has a controlling interest or is on the board, contractors should be told before contract.

The reverse of course applies. The Association of Consulting Engineers rules expressly state that a member shall not have any financial interest in any contracting or manufacturing company with which he may have to deal on behalf of clients.

(*b*) FAIR HEARING. The scrupulous hearing by the courts of the arguments of a party who seems to be obviously in the wrong often exasperates non-lawyers, and one may avoid hearing one side to a dispute for fear of being argued out of a preconceived decision. Nevertheless, experience of deciding disputes underlines the extraordinary dangers there are in listening to one side only, however informal the dispute or however obvious the case may seem to be, and the courts will apply this second rule absolutely strictly to the conduct of an arbitrator:

j

    An official arbitrator visited land which was the subject matter of the dispute, in the company of the engineer of one of the parties only. The award was set aside although it was not proved that the arbitrator discussed the dispute on this visit, since his conduct might give rise to suspicion.

    The arbitrator wrote to the solicitors for both parties indicating that before the hearing he would view the property concerned in a building arbitration. Although the arbitrator had not in fact viewed the premises, one of the parties conducted his case on the basis that a view would take place and called no expert evidence. The arbitrator did not view the property, nor notify that party of his change of intention so that he could make representations about it. The

k

arbitrator's award was set aside.

It follows that the arbitrator must act fairly between the parties: "if he does, or offers to do, anything for one, he should do the same, or offer to do

l

the same for the other". If the arbitrator receives a communication from or sends a communication to one party, which should be avoided as far as possible apart from statements of claims, etc., he should send a copy to the other party, and he should avoid hearing any verbal evidence about the dispute even in the absence of both parties. The parties and their advisers should help the arbitrator to maintain this independent position.

    This rule also does not apply fully to the engineer in performing his

(*i*) *Ranger* v. *G.W.Ry.* (1854) 5 H.L.C. 72.
(*j*) *The State (Hegarty)* v. *Winters* [1956] Ir.R. 320. But see *Rokopoulas* v. *Esperia Spa*, The Times Feb. 8, 1978.
(*k*) *Micklewright* v. *Mullock* (1974) 232 E.G. 337.
(*l*) W. T. Creswell "Handbook of Procedure and Evidence in Arbitration", 2nd ed., p. 55.

independent duties, since he may have to consider his own conduct and decisions as agent; it is accepted that the completely open mind of an arbitrator cannot be expected of him. The mere fact that before finally deciding he has expressed a strong view on a contractor's claim (in one case that it was "simply outrageous") does not automatically disqualify him. *m* Nevertheless the engineer will be disqualified for fraud, whether he is acting for his own purposes or in collusion with the employer, or if he fails to act independently of his employer in carrying out these duties. His duty is to give his decisions "according to his own conscience and according to what he conceives to be the right as to the work done, and for that purpose he has no right to obey any order or any suggestion by these people who are called his masters. For that purpose they are not his masters. He is . . . to act fairly and honestly as between them and the contractor": *n*

A contractor's estimate showed $7,406 due for interim payment. This was not disputed by the architect but he refused to issue a certificate because a bye-law submitted by the City Council to raise the balance of the money necessary to pay for the works had been turned down by the ratepayers. The contractors stopped work, after giving the Council notice that they would do so because they had no money with which to pay workers. The Council acted to forfeit the contract.

Held: That the Council were parties to the architect's wrongful refusal to certify, and that the attempted forfeiture was therefore invalid. *o*

Contractor recovered payment without a final certificate because the architect, although he would have given a certificate if left to his independent judgment, refused to do so on instructions from the employers and their solicitors. The architect had "abdicated his judicial office". In particular it was the duty of the architect to have consulted an independent solicitor. Although the architect said that he told the employers' solicitor that he was consulting him as his own solicitor, it was impossible for the employers' solicitor in the circumstances to advise with an unprejudiced mind and with due regard to his duty to the employer on the one hand and the architect on the other. *p*

A contractor recovered payment without the certificate specified in the contract because unknown to him the superintendent was a relative of and owed a large sum to the employer. *q*

The engineer is not bound to shun his client in making such decisions. He must act fairly to the employer also, and keep him in touch with disputes, and the employer may, if he believes that the engineer is over-looking facts

---

(*m*) *Cross* v. *Leeds Corp.* (1902) Hudson "Building Contracts", 4th ed., vol. ii, p. 339. *Hatrick (N.Z.) Ltd.* v. *Nelson, Carlton Construction* [1964] N.Z.L.R. 72, holding that the rules of natural justice as such do not apply to an architect deciding under a construction-contract. This decision is summarised on p. 415 of the text below.

(*n*) *McDonald* v. *Workington Corp.* (1893) Hudson "Building Contracts", 4th ed., vol. ii, 228, at p. 230 per Lord Esher M.R. See also quotations in footnote (*d*), p. 410.

(*o*) *Alberta Building Co.* v. *Calgary City* (1911) 16 W.L.R. 443 Can.

(*p*) *Watts* v. *McLeay* (1911) 19 W.L.R. 916 Can. (the reference to "judicial office" must now be read in the light of the decision in *Sutcliffe* v. *Thackrah* (p. 293)). See also *Hickman* v. *Roberts* [1913] A.C. 229. In *Panamena Europa Navigacion* v. *Leyland & Co. Ltd.* [1947] A.C. 428 it was said that a surveyor was not disqualified merely because he consulted with the employers, their solicitors and counsel, since his opinion was formed before, and not affected by, the consultation (per Lord Thankerton at p. 444). An engineer who consults with his employers' lawyer without taking independent advice risks, at the least, involving himself unnecessarily in a severe cross-examination as to whether he allowed his decision to be influenced improperly.

(*q*) *Ludlam* v. *Wilson* (1901) 21 C.L.T. 554 Can.

of arguments in his favour, point them out forcefully for the engineer's
consideration.

The essential point is that the decision must be the engineer's and he may
not allow the employer to override his judgment. The client should not
make, and the engineer should not allow himself to be influenced by, any
suggestion that because the employer is paying the piper he is entitled to call
the tune which the engineer is to play in carrying out his independent duties.

It appears clear that the general position is no different where the
engineer actually named in the contract is a local authority engineer or
otherwise in the full-time service of the employer. There is no parallel with
the relaxation of the rule about interest, which has been discussed. The
employed engineer may act independently or not when it comes to the
crunch of a difference of opinion with his employer in administering
the contract; there is no mid-way. That despite his ordinary duty of
obedience to the employer a whole-time engineer is under a duty to the
contractor to act independently has been assumed by the courts in several
cases.

The employer's own interest in having an engineer (whether full-time or
not) who preserves his independence has been explained perfectly by
Brunel:

> You may have seen that a great appeal case before the Lords, affecting claims
> of some hundreds of thousands, has just been finally decided in favour of the
> Great Western Railway Company after fourteen years of litigation; and this
> favourable decision was entirely obtained by carefully prepared specifications,
> and by my not having departed in any single case, in years of correspondence,
> from the letter and spirit of the contract, and particularly from the fact
> strongly commented upon by Lords Cranworth and Brougham that I had
> maintained my position of umpire between the Company and Contractor. It is,
> then, as essential to the Company as to the contractor and to me that I should
> maintain that position.

If necessary the engineer should forcefully draw to his client's attention
the above quotation and the legal effects of interference. If his client insists
on interfering despite this warning, the engineer, in view of his contractual
liabilities to his client, may be wise to obey the order and leave the
contractor to his remedies (p. 416). The growing problems created by
pressures on the engineer's independence are discussed on pp. 445-6.

(r) *Brennan & Hollingsworth* v. *Hamilton City* (1917) 37 D.L.R. 144 Can., at pp. 155-156 and
the cases cited there, and *Hatrick (N.Z.) Ltd.* v. *Nelson, Carlton Construction* below.
Some engineers undoubtedly do have the misconception that their special role in law requires
them to mete out unequal treatment to their own client compared to the contractor. Whereas
they will listen fully to the representations and arguments of the contractor on a dispute they
may not even tell the client that a dispute has arisen, and consider that any representations
from the client are a reflection on their own standing. Performance of the engineer's duty to
keep the client informed and to listen to his representations undoubtedly may be open to
misinterpretation by those suspicious of the pressures that may be applied to him,
particularly by a valued client, but nevertheless the duty exists. The engineer will have to
balance his duties so as to satisfy his own conscience, and keep good records of his
discussions so as to be able to satisfy others.

(s) e.g. *Page* v. *Llandaff* etc. *R.C.* (1901) Hudson "Building Contracts", 4th ed., vol. ii, p. 316;
Young v. *Ballarat, Comss.* (1879) S.V.L.R. 503 Aus.; and important decisions in *Perini Corp.*
v. *Commonwealth of Australia* [1969] 2 N.S.W.R. 530 and *Morrison Knudsen Co. Inc.* v.
British Columbia Hydro and Power Authority (No. 2) [1978] 85 D.L.R. (3d) 186 Can.

(t) Letter dated May 26th, 1854 reproduced in "The Life of Isambard Kingdom Brunel" by
Isambard Brunel, reprinted in 1971, at p. 478. The case referred to is *Ranger* v. *G.W.Ry.*, text
above p. 412.

It has also been suggested that the engineer may be disqualified for lack of discreet conduct, irrespective of influence by the employer:

A contractor's claim for certificates for £2,600 for work done was refused by the architect on the grounds that the work was unsatisfactory.

The contractor asked two of his suppliers to meet the architect to find out what the architect was complaining about, since the architect had given no details. The architect told them that the work was completed except for £200 in value and would be finished in two or three weeks. Despite this the architect then ended the contractor's employment, refused to have anything to do with a joint examination of the works, made no account of the state of the work at the time of forfeiture, and finished the work himself for his employer. Held: disqualified. *u*

But in a recent case:

The certificate of an engineer that the contractor had failed to make satisfactory progress, on which the employer ended the contract, was attacked on the grounds that the engineer had failed in his independent duties. The basis of the attack was that on the morning of the day of forfeiture the engineer had shown from his action that he held the opinion that the contractor should be allowed to continue with the work, but after two one-hour discussions on the same day with the employer, who was "definite about taking the work out of (the contractor's) hands", he gave the necessary certificate.

It was decided that there was no evidence that the engineer had been swayed by the employer in making the only decision on which he was bound to act independently—that the contractor had failed to make due progress so as to entitle the employer to take the works out of his hands. The engineer was bound to bow to the employer on the policy question of whether the right to forfeit which had arisen should be used. In the absence of evidence that the engineer when he gave his certificate had lost the essential attribute of impartiality and independence, the certificate stood. *v*

The extent to which the engineer is bound to hear the contractor's case before deciding under cl. 66 of the Conditions is particularly doubtful. The reference in cl. 66 itself to evidence and arguments before the engineer is relevant (p. 302, N. 15), and cl. 52 requires consultation with the contractor before a variation is valued. *See also* cl. 63 (3). It seems that the engineer at the least will be legally disqualified if he is refusing to consider a claim or dispute on its merits at all—if he is clearly saying: "I have made up my mind and whatever I may hear I shall stick to my opinion". Despite this *w* uncertain legal position, if the engineer deigns to learn only one lesson from lawyers, the one he should choose if he wishes to do justice and to save himself and his clients unnecessary trouble is to make it a personal rule to deal equally with the contractor and the employer, and to see that the contractor knows the case he has to answer at the earliest possible time. This means much more than listening to the contractor; the benefit of the rule will be lost if the engineer listens to the contractor's story with a consciously or unconsciously closed or biased mind, because he has already committed himself to a decision, with a hostile mind because he is trying to shift the

(*u*) *Pawley* v. *Turnbull* (1861) 66 R.R. 327, and see discussion of *Hickman* v. *Roberts* [1913] A.C. 229 at p. 468 of Hudson. "Building & Engineering Contracts", 10th ed. by I. N. Duncan Wallace.

(*v*) *Hatrick (N.Z.) Ltd.* v. *Nelson, Carlton Construction* [1964] N.Z.L.R. 72.

(*w*) See *Hatrick (N.Z.) Ltd.* v. *Nelson, Carlton Construction* [1964] N.Z.L.R. 72 at p. 86, followed in *London Borough Council of Hounslow* v. *Twickenham Garden Developments Ltd.* [1970] 3 All E.R. 326, and *Cross* v. *Leeds Corp.* (1902) Hudson "Building Contracts", 4th ed., vol. ii, 339, at p. 341.

blame for his mistakes, or even with a sceptical mind because he believes that as a commercial being the contractor is of a lesser breed.

It is also the engineer's job—and one of the most difficult things to do—diplomatically to reduce pressure all round where necessary so that disputes are considered objectively, and to see that the parties understand each other's points of view. Angry correspondence, which from their different standpoints will very often convey totally different impressions to the writer and to the reader, is particularly harmful. As in other fields where there are conflicts of interest, a high percentage of engineering disputes are due simply to failure of real communication between those involved.

The above applies particularly to the engineer if he gets himself personally involved in a dispute. He must watch any bias towards proving himself right, and be prepared to reverse a decision at the last moment if he is persuaded that it was wrong. However acute the frustration may be, he is also not free to carry on a quarrel with the contractor, even if he is right, if it is more in the interest of the works to give way.

In short then, since there is no human tendency so strong as that of assuming the worst of others, the engineer will avoid much unnecessary litigation and arbitration if he appreciates the special responsibilities of his work and avoids doing anything that "might reasonably give rise to suspicion that justice is not being done"—"anything at any time which could make fools suspect".

Effect of engineer's misconduct. If the engineer fails to act fairly and impartially when he is bound to do so, his decision will not bind. That is not always important, because the contractor may, in any case, have the engineer's decisions overruled in arbitration. The principle is, however, very important in cases of forfeiture (p. 305, N. 21) and in entitling the contractor to sue without a certificate for payments withheld and some difficult cases (discussed below). In addition, if the employer wrongfully interferes with the independence of the engineer he will be guilty of a breach of contract, which will usually be sufficiently serious to entitle the contractor to end the contract and recover full compensation (p. 425).

The employer may not be a party to misconduct by the engineer in the first instance, but it appears that he will nevertheless become liable for breach of contract if he refuses to change the engineer after becoming aware of his misconduct. Therefore in some cases it may be wise for the contractor, before taking action, to call on the employer to remove and replace a disqualified engineer under cl. 1 (1) (c).

If the engineer is guilty of misconduct the contractor may, of course, follow the procedure in cl. 66 for settlement of claims, but in referring back to the engineer disputes (including a dispute as to whether there is misconduct) he should say specifically that he is doing so without prejudice to the claim that the engineer is disqualified from deciding. Where,

(x) *Jackson* v. *Barry Ry. Co.* [1893] 1 Ch. 238, at p. 246.

(y) *R.* v. *Taylor ex. p. Vogwill* (1898) 14 T.L.R. 185.

(z) See *Panamena Europa Navigacion* (*Compania Limitada*) v. *Frederick Leyland & Co. Ltd.* [1947] A.C. 428—"If the appellant had taken the contrary view of their surveyor's function (under the contract) it would have been their duty to appoint another surveyor to discharge that function, and if they had refused to appoint another surveyor, the respondents would clearly have been absolved from the necessity of obtaining the surveyor's certificate; the respondents are equally so absolved when the appellant's wrongful view of their surveyor's function prevents the appellant from obtaining the certificate" (Per Lord Thankerton at p. 436.) See also *Alberta Building Co.* v. *Calgary City* (1911) 16 W.L.R. 443 Can. (text p. 413) and *Burden* v. *Swansea Corp.* [1957] 3 All E.R. 243.

although he knows the facts suggesting such disqualification, the contractor accepts the engineer's decisions without protesting, he may be held to have waived (p. 157, N. 11) the right to claim later that the engineer was disqualified.

A contractor may, however, wish to avoid the delay of operating cl. 66, by which the engineer has three months within which to make his decision and in some cases under that clause arbitration may not be opened until completion of the works. It is arguable that the works cannot be completed if there is no independent and fair engineer to make decisions and give instructions. But the clause in fact provides for the situation where the engineer fails altogether to give a decision, there is no procedure for getting a dispute to arbitration without first referring it to the engineer, and the requirement that all disputes should be submitted to the engineer in the opening of the clause and the denial of arbitration before completion later on are worded very widely. In any case, a contractor who tried to by-pass this clause would take the risk that if it were decided eventually that the engineer was not, in fact, guilty of misconduct, the arbitration would have to be postponed whilst other disputes were referred back to the engineer and the works completed.

Where money is clearly due to the contractor under the terms of the contract and an engineer misconducting himself is wrongfully withholding a certificate, the contractor is entitled to sue in the courts for the amount which should have been certified despite the absence of a certificate. The employer will not be granted a stay of the proceedings so as to compel the contractor to go to arbitration (p. 302, N. 16), unless the employer can show that there is a genuine dispute as to whether the engineer is guilty of misconduct or the certificate due. *aa*

Contractor's remedies for engineer's decisions that are unreasonable. The remedies discussed in the last section, coupled with the very wide words of cl. 66 of the general conditions, which entitle the arbitrator to "*open up review and revise any decision opinion*", etc., of the engineer, therefore give the contractor much protection. However, the protection may not be total. It appears that the contractor has no effective remedy merely because a decision of the engineer which was unreasonable but not involving misconduct is reversed by the arbitrator after completion, unless the contract gives him a specific right to extra payment, as it does where compliance with the decision results in a variation within cl. 51. For example, if the engineer, acting in good faith, gives an unreasonably short extension of time which is increased by the arbitrator, the arbitrator is not *per se* entitled to award the contractor compensation for any acceleration which he may have undertaken to complete by the date fixed by the engineer (*see* fully p. 371 on acceleration claims). See also p. 305, N. 21, p. 85, N. 5, and below.

The doctrine which applies in these cases is that in so far as the engineer is independent of control by the employer, the employer does not warrant that the engineer will act reasonably and is not liable merely because he does act unreasonably—the contractor takes the advantages and disadvantages of the engineer's independence. Difficulties created by this doctrine have been revealed by an unreported decision:

Specified that excavations were to be timbered with suitable timber or alternate forms of sheeting as and where necessary to the satisfaction of the

(aa) *Panamena Europa, etc.* v. *Leyland & Co. Ltd.*—see previous note.

engineer. An arbitrator found that the resident engineer unreasonably required timbering in places where excavation by machine and battering of the sides of the trenches to a slope would have been satisfactory, by his decisions unreasonably prevented the contractors excavating by machine in other lengths, and also unreasonably prohibited the laying of pipes until trenches were excavated for long lengths in bad ground. The contractor had protested at the time and claimed extra payment, but the engineer had refused to issue a variation order.

The general conditions provided that the work was to be carried out under the direction and to the satisfaction of the engineer.

Held: That the contract gave the engineer power to determine the method of working; the employers did not warrant his competency or skill or that his decision would be reasonable provided that he was honest. Held in addition that a direction by an engineer intimating the manner in which work was to be done in order to satisfy him could not in the absence of a specific method of carrying out the work being required by the contract, amount to a variation of the works.

bb

The relevance to the I.C.E. Conditions of the decision is doubtful. It is suggested that a specific method of carrying out the works was, in fact, stated—timbering "as and where necessary"—and that therefore the provision of timbering where it was not strictly necessary would have been a variation in the quality of part of the works within cl. 51 (1). In addition cls. 13 and 14 now deal with the problem of instructions causing loss to the contractor and control of temporary works to a large extent, although unfortunately not exhaustively (pp. 73–84). Where these clauses do not apply it remains difficult to imply into the contract (p. 42 (*b*)) any general agreement by the employer to take liability for unreasonable decisions by the engineer.

cc

Where the contract does say specifically that the engineer will not act unreasonably, then an unreasonable decision will be a breach of the promise in the contract by the employer that such a decision will not be made, for which the contractor will have the usual remedies, principally damages (p. 427). An example is cl. 46.

A distinction must be drawn also between an unreasonable certificate or decision of the engineer and his failure to administer the contract. It is suggested that the employer does contract with the contractor that the engineer will perform his administrative duties—i.e. will consider at the times specified in the contract and according to correct principles whether the contractor is entitled to a certificate or extension of time, etc. If that is so, failure by the engineer to administer cl. 44 or 60, for example, as opposed to merely giving unreasonable certificates or decisions under these clauses, may entitle the contractor to the remedies for breach of contract (pp. 261 and 371).

dd

(*bb*) *Neodox Ltd.* v. *Swinton & Pendlebury B.C.* (1958) now reported in 5 B.L.R. 38.

(*cc*) It is suggested that to some extent the learned Judge in the *Neodox* case (previous note) begged this question in saying that "In a contract in which there is no specific method of carrying out particular operations . . . set out, and which provides merely that they should be carried out under the Engineer's directions and in the best manner to his satisfaction, I find great difficulty in seeing how a direction by the Engineer intimating the manner in which the operation must be carried out in order to satisfy him can be a 'variation of or addition to the works'. It seems to me to be no more than what the contract itself calls for . . . (p. 47)".

There was the special circumstance in that case that the engineer's decision as to the quality of the work carried out was final and not subject to arbitration. The decision in *Sutcliffe* v. *Thackrah* [1974] 1 All E.R. 859, H.L. (text p. 398) does not appear to alter the position.

(*dd*) *Panamena Europa Navigacion (Compania Limitada)* v. *Frederick Leyland & Co. Ltd.* [1947] A.C. 428. *Perini Corp.* v. *Commonwealth of Australia* [1969] 2 N.S.W.R. 530 is an interesting decision relevant to this point—"I am also of opinion that the obligation created by the implied term on the defendant (employer) is to ensure that the Director of Works (the engineer) gives his decision . . ." per MacFarlan J. at p. 545.

CHAPTER 15

Liability for Nuisance

Occupiers of property in the neighbourhood of the site and the public generally have rights which may restrict development and must be allowed for in carrying out works—*see* the I.C.E. Conditions, cls. 22, 29, 42 (2), 45 and 49 (5), and for the engineer's duties, p. 390 (*g*).

These rights fall under the following main headings:

1. Nuisance and allied liability. The occupier of land or buildings has a right to object to anything injurious coming from neighbouring land and causing him damage, e.g.:

> Dust and grit from a power station; sparks from machinery; vibrations from pile driving; electricity escaping from a generating station or high-tension cable; dumped waste slipping down a hill; sewage directed through a surface water drain to a cesspool on private land; water escaping from a reservoir; the smell of sulphuric acid and sulphate from a petrol depot; noise from a petrol depot at night, ranging from 64 to 83 decibels.

To be actionable a nuisance must cause damage either by physical injury to the neighbouring premises or property on them, or by interfering with the comfort or convenience of the occupiers. Generally there is no protection for special sensitivity:

> A manufacturer of brown paper sued for injury to his stock caused by heat produced by a neighbouring manufacturer. He failed because it was proved that his stock was particularly sensitive and that an ordinary business would not have been affected.

Interference with comfort or convenience particularly must be such as would be considered a substantial inconvenience by the average man. The question is one of degree and the test is elastic, depending partly on the locality—"a dweller in town cannot expect to have as pure air as if he lived in the country", but "it does not follow that because I live, say, in the manufacturing part of Sheffield I cannot complain if a steam hammer is introduced next door, or ... worked so as to render sleep ... almost

(*a*) General reference: S. L. Newcombe "The Law of Easements", 4th ed. Gale on "Easements", 13th ed. by M. Bowles.

(*b*) *Manchester Corp.* v. *Farnworth* [1930] A.C. 171; *Powell* v. *Fall* [1880] 5 Q.B.D. 597; *Hoare* v. *McAlpine* [1923] 1 Ch. 167; *Eastern and S.A. Telegraph Co. Ltd.* v. *Capetown Tramways Co. Ltd.* [1962] A.C. 381; *A.G.* v. *Cory Bros.* [1921] 1 A.C. 521; *Gibbings* v. *Hungerford & Cork Corp.* [1904] 1 Ir.R. 211; *Rylands* v. *Fletcher* (1868) L.R. 3 H.L. 330; *Halsey* v. *Esso Petroleum Co. Ltd.* [1961] 2 All E.R. 145; *Halsey* etc. above. These cases fall within two distinct legal categories—the law of nuisance proper and the rule in *Rylands* v. *Fletcher*. The differences in liability between the two categories are not likely to be of practical interest to any save lawyers, but for further reading see n. (*a*).

(*c*) *Robinson* v. *Kilvert* (1889) 41 Ch. D. 88.

(*d*) *Colls* v. *Home & Colonial Stores Ltd.* [1904] A.C. 179 at p. 185.

419

impossible, although previously ... my house was a reasonably comfortable abode".

It is no defence to liability for nuisance that the acts complained of are in the public interest, unless the nuisance is authorised by statute:

> Plaintiff complained of noise caused by a cement manufacturing company quarrying near his house. An injunction was granted to stop the work, although the company pointed out that it was the principal supplier of cement to the building trade in Ireland and that an injunction would result in a shortage of cement throughout the country.

Nor is it generally a defence that the acts are a reasonable use of property and that all possible care has been taken to reduce the nuisance. The only exception to this rule is that temporary acts for the ordinary use of land and buildings are not actionable, e.g. pulling down and reconstructing a building, including hoardings, scaffolding, etc., but strictly provided no more inconvenience is caused than is reasonably necessary:

> A builder who had contracted to take down and rebuild premises had possible access by three narrow passages. He used one of these passages solely because it was shortest and most convenient. The plaintiff lost trade because this blocked the entrance to his shop in the passage.
> Held: The contractor should have used all three passages so as to reduce the inconvenience and, as far as possible, have done the work in the early morning or late evening. His actions were described as of the "selfish and not the social man".

> The defendants used pneumatic drills and power hammers to extend windows. The plaintiff complained that the noise was making work in his offices impossible, and an injunction was granted to stop use of these tools during office hours.

> Contractors employed to place a girder in the first floor of a building and to extend stanchions to support it.
> Held: Both the contractors and their employer were liable for dust affecting a second-floor tenant because they had not used dust sheets, and for noise because they had made no effort to arrange the work to suit the tenant, a music teacher.

There are also various statutory offences and powers to prevent nuisances harmful to health, e.g. the Public Health Acts, 1936 61, the Clean Air Acts, 1956 and 1968. There are important new controls in the Control of Pollution Act, 1974, dealing with disposal of waste, pollution of the atmosphere or water (below) and noise (including vibration). In particular the local authority is given wide powers to impose requirements on the way in which construction work is carried out. They may by notice specify the plant or machinery that may be used, the hours during which the work may be carried out and the level of noise permitted. Contractors may be wise to allow in their tender prices for meeting the increased public concern for the environment.

2. Public nuisance. Any act which obstructs the public right of passage

---

(e) *Rushmer* v. *Polsue and Alfieri Ltd.* [1906] 1 Ch. 234 at p. 250.
(f) *Bellew* v. *Cement Ltd.* [1948] Ir.R. 61.
(g) *Fritz* v. *Hobson* (1880) 14 Ch. D. 542, and see p. 552.
(h) *Le Gor* v. *Transworld Airlines* (1963) C.L.Y.
(i) *Matania* v. *National Provincial Bank* (1936) 155 L.T. 74.
(j) See particularly Control of Noise (Code of Practice for Construction Sites) Order, SI 1975 No. 2115, and Kerse "The Law Relating to Noise".

along the highway or any navigable waters or makes it dangerous is actionable as a public nuisance:

> Workmen placed a ladle of molten lead on a fire pail on open land beside a highway. Their employer was held liable for injury caused by the lead to a child who veered from the footpath. [k]

Other examples are buildings projecting into the highway, structures beside the highway which are allowed to become dangerous, excavations adjoining the highway which are not fenced properly.

What has been said as to the defences to an action for private nuisance applies to public nuisance also.

There are also provisions in the Highways Acts 1959–71, about obstruction of highways, fencing of works, deposit of building materials, etc., and other legislation that may be relevant, such as the Deposit of Poisonous Waste Act, 1972.

3. Water. A riparian owner, that is, an owner of any stretch of the banks, may:

(a) Object to any obstruction of a natural stream which prevents it reaching him fully or throws it back on his land. He may also object if water is taken from the stream, subject to the right of other riparian owners to take water without restriction for domestic purposes and for cattle in connection with the use of the banks, and for other riparian purposes provided no actual loss is caused in the flow of water.

(b) Object to pollution, which is alteration of the natural character or quality of water, reducing its fitness for any purpose for which it could be used in its natural state. It includes, apart from the obvious cases, discharge of hot water which increases the temperature, or adding hard water to a soft water stream. And the owner does not have to prove any actual loss, so that it is no defence that the water was already polluted or even that he does not, in fact, use it (but as to an injunction *see* p. 430).

Pollution of underground water is actionable, but not taking or obstructing the water, except in the case of an underground stream in a defined channel:

> In the course of road construction an aqueduct which carried water from a reservoir was diverted, and certain water mains repositioned. Excavations were dug to a depth below the water table level near the plaintiffs' land, and kept dry by pumping. The plaintiffs complained that the pumping resulted in abstraction of the water percolating beneath their land, and that this caused very serious settlement to the buildings on their land.
>
> Held: The plaintiffs had no cause of action in law. [l]

There is, in addition to this law of nuisance, the Control of Pollution Act,

(k) *Crane* v. *South Suburban Gas Co.* [1916] 1 K.B. 33. An individual may recover damages for public nuisance only if he can show special and particular damage, as distinct from the general inconvenience suffered in common with the general public. The remedy for the inconvenience to the public is a criminal indictment or other statutory criminal proceedings, or an injunction at the suit of the Attorney General. A contractor whose operations are affected may be able to show special damage—in *Rose* v. *Miles* (1815) 66 R.R. 405 a public navigable creek was obstructed by a large barge, and the plaintiff recovered damages for the impediment to his barge, as a result of which he had to transport the cargo a great distance over land.

(l) *Langbrook Properties Ltd.* v. *Surrey County Council* [1969] 3 All E.R. 1424, affirming an old principle which had been criticised.

1974, dealing with precautions to prevent pollution, a wide system of control and criminal sanctions for water polluters.

4. Lateral support for land. The owner of land has the right to prevent his neighbours causing his land to subside, e.g. by excavating near the boundary of their own land. But there is no right to prevent the owner of adjoining land withdrawing support provided by underground water only and not by minerals, by pumping, draining, etc. Silt and other semi-fluids are, however, classed as minerals:

> The defendants in carrying out excavation work on their property cut through a stratum of running silt, so that the plaintiff's land subsided.
>
> Held: The silt was in the nature of wet sand rather than muddy water and the defendants were liable.

m

5. Subjacent support for land. To excavate under another's land is trespass, and even if different owners are entitled to the surface of land and to the minerals underneath the land the owner of the minerals may be liable if in working them he causes subsidence of the surface of the land. There is liability unless the natural right of subjacent support is clearly taken away by the instrument granting the mineral rights.

6. Support for buildings. There is no natural right to lateral nor, probably, subjacent support for buildings on land as opposed to the land itself, but this and the right to support from buildings may be acquired (below). And if withdrawal of support from land would have caused subsidence even if it had not been built on the withdrawal is actionable and damages will be awarded for the damage to the building as well as for the damage to the land. In addition there is liability for negligent withdrawal of support from lands or buildings, for example by negligence in not properly supporting excavations.

n

7. Right to air coming through a shaft or defined opening in a building, but not merely a flow of air to open ground or to a chimney (but *see* N. 11 below).

o   **8. Rights of way and wayleaves.** For acquisition *see* below.

p   **9. Ancient lights.** The right is to a reasonable amount of light only. The question is not what light has been taken away, but what is left; reduction of light is not actionable (except where there has been a grant of an exceptional amount of light by the adjoining owner below), unless the light which remains is below the level ordinarily required, so as to make the building uncomfortable or inconvenient for ordinary use. No mere length of use will create a right to more light than that ordinarily required.

p'

(*m*) *Jackson* v. *Sutton Gas Co.* [1899] 2 Ch. 217.
(*n*) *Dorset Yacht Co.* v. *Home Office* [1970] 2 All E.R. 294 and *Bognuda Upton* v. *Shearer* [1972] N.Z.L.R. 741.
(*o*) Reading: "Pipes, Mains, Cables and Sewers" by H. W. Williamson.
(*p*) Reading: B. Anstey and M. Chavasse "The Right of Light".
(*p'*) But this statement of what has been traditionally believed to be the law may need to be revised following the decision in *Allen* v. *Greenwood* [1979] 249 E.G. 139, in which the Court of Appeal held that the high degree of light needed by a greenhouse had been acquired by use.

Efforts have been made to have the courts accept some definite test for deciding whether an interference with light is actionable, particularly:

The 45-degree rule, i.e. that where there is 45 degrees of unobstructed light through a particular window there is no actionable nuisance.

That if 50% of a room is lit to above grumble point (1/500th part of the light received from the sky on a dull or overcast day with uniform diffusion of light) there is no actionable nuisance.

The first test is barely relevant; the second the courts accept as of some help and they will hear evidence based on modern methods of measuring light. But they insist that a rigid test is out of place and that the question must ultimately be decided from a common sense point of view:

For some time A had used the part of his shop nearest the window for showing samples of cloth to customers, which needed more than the ordinary amount of light. The erection of a theatre, whilst not reducing the general level of the light in the room below that which would ordinarily be required, seriously reduced the direct light coming through the window.

Held: The test must be applied flexibly and as a person cannot complain because his light is below the grumble point in corners, it follows that "a person may expect a reasonable amount of direct light where he might expect to find it, that is, near the window in a room laterally lighted, even if that direct light is above the grumble point. ... The practical minimum tolerable is different from the theoretical minimum tolerable of the experts and differs for different parts of the room in which different ordinary purposes are ...satisfied." *q*

10. Party walls. A neighbour may also have rights in boundary walls, or to support from a common wall which divides properties, and generally the neighbour's consent is necessary for any change in the whole wall. But in London, under the London Building Acts (Amendment) Act, 1939, the part owner of a wall, on following the proper procedure, may improve, etc., a party wall if he wishes to build on or against it. Similar local regulations apply elsewhere.

11. Restrictive covenants. The title deeds under which the site land is held may contain restrictions on its use for particular purposes, or to protect e.g., the view or privacy of neighbouring buildings, which cannot become protected merely by long enjoyment. It may be possible to insure against enforcement of old or outmoded restrictive covenants or they may be modified or discharged by the Lands Tribunal or the Courts.

As to planning and other statutory restrictions *see* Conditions, cl. 26, p. 109.

Natural rights and acquisition of easements. The rights in headings 1 to 5 above are natural rights, which are automatically attached to land and buildings and do not have to be specially acquired. But the right to object to a particular interference with a natural right (except a public nuisance) may be lost if the interference continues without interruption for 20 years openly and to the knowledge of the other party. So that if a factory causes a

(q) *Smyth* v. *Dublin Theatre Co.* [1936] Ir.R. 692 at p. 704. In *Ough* v. *King* [1967] 3 All E.R. 859 the Court of Appeal accepted that in deciding whether light is reduced below an acceptable level regard is to be had both to locality and to "the higher standards expected for comfort as the years go by" (per Lord Denning at p. 861), and that the fifty-fifty rule is not now a universal rule.

nuisance by noise or vibration for 20 years the owner will generally be entitled to continue to do this.

The rights under headings 6 to 9 are easements, that is, rights not naturally attached to land or buildings, but which may be acquired:

(a) By written grant from the owner of the neighbouring land; or

(b) generally the owner of buildings which have existed for 20 years will be held to have acquired a right of support and light by long enjoyment, and other easements will be acquired by 20 years' uninterrupted use; or

(c) by implied grant. For example, an owner of land who conveys or leases part expressly or impliedly for building or similar purpose is held (if there is nothing to the contrary in the deed) impliedly to grant a right of support from the land which he retains for any buildings erected on the land conveyed. This rule may be extended to similar cases:

> The plaintiff and defendant had grants of adjacent plots from Liverpool Corporation for building purposes. Both were bound to build according to plans approved by the Corporation.
>
> Held: The plaintiff was entitled to prevent the defendant excavating so as to endanger the house he had built.

r

In exactly the same way a right to light may be impliedly granted. And the right to an exceptional amount of light may also be acquired by implication, where property is leased or sold for a particular purpose envisaged by both parties at the time of the lease or sale:

> Property was let in the vicinity of Hatton Garden for the business of a diamond merchant.
>
> Held: The tenant had acquired a right to the exceptional amount of light necessary for his business and enjoyed by the property at the time it was leased, and was entitled to prevent building on neighbouring land also owned by his landlord.

s

Particularly, therefore, where site land has in the recent past been in the same ownership as neighbouring land the possibility of easements affecting it which are not apparent must be considered.

On the other hand, if the owner of land conveys away part of it, unless he expressly reserves it he will have no right to any light for buildings on the land retained by him as against the land granted away. The principle is that a grantor will not be presumed to detract from his own grant.

Extinguishment of easements. Finally, an easement may be lost not only by being expressly given up, but by being impliedly abandoned. This may give trouble if it is not thought about in time, where a building with rights to light is destroyed or taken down and eventually replaced. Delay in rebuilding may be evidence of abandonment, and it is particularly necessary to keep records of the position of the original windows, since the rights will also be lost if the windows of the new building do not correspond to any substantial extent with those of the old so as to receive part of the same cone of light.

(r) *Rigby* v. *Bennett* [1882] 21 Ch. D. 559. And see Law of Property Act, 1925, Sec. 62.
(s) *Herz* v. *Union Bank* (1854) 66 E.R. 287.

CHAPTER 16

Remedies for Breach of Contract

The right to end the contract for breach. When there is a breach of contract by one party the reaction of the other party is very often to wish to throw up the whole contract and refuse to carry out his part. The ordinary remedy for breach of contract is, however, damages (below), and it is only in exceptional cases that a party may under the ordinary law bring a contract to an end because it has been broken. If, for example, the employer is late in paying on an interim certificate, the contractor may not be inclined to do further work for which he may fear the employer will not be able to pay him, but generally he must carry on with the work and merely sue the employer for the payment due; only in some exceptional cases may he end the contract (*see* below).

The right to end the contract under the general law for breach, which is in addition to any special rights in the contract, exists then only:

(i) If a party repudiates the contract—that is, expressly or by his conduct refuses absolutely to perform it, e.g. the contractor abandons the works before they are substantially complete.

(ii) If a party commits a major breach that goes "to the root" of the contract. Whether or not a breach goes to the root of the contract depends on the importance given to the term broken by the parties when they made the contract, which must be gathered from the wording of the contract and the surrounding circumstances, or whether the breach renders further commercial performace impossible or deprives the party not in breach of substantially the whole benefit which the contract intends him to receive.

For example:

(*a*) Delay does not generally go to the root of a contract unless it shows that the party cannot or will not carry out the contract eventually or time is of the essence of the contract. The parties may expressly state in the contract that "time is of the essence", or the courts may also imply from the circumstances of a contract that time is intended to be of the essence, for example, in a sub-contract to deliver machinery, Finally, time may normally be made of the essence, if after delay by one party the other serves a notice requiring him to complete his part of the contract within a reasonable time:

The defendant ordered a body for a Rolls-Royce chassis. The date for delivery was March 20, 1948. The body was not completed on that date, but as the defendant continued to press for delivery he was held to have waived (*see* p. 157, N. 11) the right to insist then that time was of the essence.

(*a*) General reference: "Sutton & Shannon on Contracts", 7th ed., Cheshire & Fifoot "The Law of Contract", 9th ed.

On June 28 he was promised that the body would be ready in two weeks' time, and on the following day he wrote to say that he would not accept delivery after the 25th July.

Held: By giving reasonable notice the defendant had revived time as of the essence. As the car was not delivered on the date reasonably fixed by the notice, he was entitled to refuse to accept delivery.

Had the defendant in this case been held not entitled to end the contract he would still have been entitled to deduct from the purchase price of the car any tangible damages he had suffered because of the delay, but in this sort of case it is, of course, very difficult to prove tangible loss. For that reason also, apart from cases where the guilty party may not have the means to pay any damages awarded, the right to end the contract may be the only really effective remedy.

For the employer's special rights of forfeiture under the I.C.E. Conditions *see* p. 275, and to take part of the works out of the contractor's hands, p. 127.

(*b*) If the employer does not pay on an interim certificate (or fees on account to the engineer) when payment becomes due, this breach may go "to the root" and give the contractor (or engineer) a right to refuse to do any more work and to bring his contract to an end. Whether it has this effect or not is a question of degree, and the only general guidance given by the courts is that the answer depends on the size of the breach in relation to the contract as a whole and the degree of probability or improbability that it will be repeated, and, of course, having regard to the fact that the time for payment is not ordinarily of the essence of the contract. Recent decisions suggest that in deciding this question the courts may take a realistic view of the importance to the contractor of regular and punctual interim payment.

Where the employer insists on repeatedly paying late, he may be held to have shown his intention not to be bound by the contract so that the contractor may be entitled to rescind. The contractor in the case of delay in paying may improve his position by serving notice on the employer that he will end the contract unless the payment due is made within a reasonable time—(*a*) above.

If the employer is actually made bankrupt or goes into liquidation, it seems that the engineer or contractor may always refuse to do work or provide materials on credit unless payment is guaranteed.

The same principles apply where the contractor fails to pay a subcontractor.

For interference by the employer with the engineer which may entitle the contractor to rescind *see* p. 416, and for failure of the engineer to administer the contract, p. 418. For the contractor's special rights to end the contract where the works are suspended *see* p. 130, and *see* cl. 69 of the F.I.D.I.C. International forms.

(*b*) *Rickards (Charles) Ltd.* v. *Oppenheim* [1950] 1 All E.R. 420, C.A.

(*c*) *Withers* v. *Reynolds* (1831) 109 E.R. 1370, and see *Mersey Steel Co.* v. *Naylor* (1884) 9 App. Cas. 434.

(*d*) See e.g. *Gilbert-Ash (Northern)* v. *Modern Engineering (Bristol)* [1973] 3 All E.R. 195, the second quotation from the judgment on p. 269 of the text above. American courts take a realistic view of the contractor's position—"in a building or construction contract ... covering a long period of time and involving large expenditures, a stipulation for payments on account, to be made from time to time during the progress of the work, must be deemed so material that a substantial failure to pay would justify the contractor in declining to proceed". *Guerini Stone Co.* v. *P. J. Carlin Const. Co.*, 248 U.S. 334, 63 L. Ed. 275.

(*e*) *Re Sneezum, ex. p. Davies* [1876] 3 Ch. D. 463.

(c) Whether dismissal of the engineer is justified depends again on the same points—has he shown that he does not intend to or cannot carry out his duties, under his service contract or implied by law, or failed in his duty in a major way? The leading case, which held that disturbing fellow employees by boasting of (not merely having) illicit relations with a neighbour's wife will justify dismissal, is not, of course, of any interest to engineers. The following case (although it involves a full-time employee and not an independent agent) illustrates the principles applied by the courts:

An employee by an oversight damaged a valuable printing press in his charge. Held: That while a single act of carelessness will not normally justify dismissal, it may where valuable property or injury to others is involved.

Obviously lack of skill is more serious than carelessness, and bad faith in relation to the client (see e.g. p. 379, N. 16) most serious of all.

Recent legislation protecting employees in respect of dismissal is outside the scope of this book.

As a result of these rules, a party to a contract may be faced with a difficult decision. Where there is no special clause in the contract which applies, as we have seen to end the contract under the general law rather than only sue for damages may be the most effective remedy for a breach of contract, but it may be very difficult to be certain that it is justified in law. Legal advice before such action is attempted is advisable, since if a party tries to end the contract and it is held that this was not justified, he will himself have repudiated the contract, and the other party may then be entitled to end the contract validly and to recover damages.

The right to end the contract when it exists is, of course, generally in addition to and not in substitution for the right to damages (below). And the contractor having ended the contract may choose either (i) damages for breach of the original contract—i.e. loss of profit (below) and the contract rates for the work already done, or (ii) to claim only for the work already done on a new implied contract by the employer to pay a reasonable price for it. If he chooses the latter, a reasonable price is fixed for all work actually done without reference to the contract rates and whatever the form, even pure lump sum, of the original contract, so that this alternative may be useful to a contractor if his tender prices and rates were cut low.

For the time for arbitration where the contract is ended in this way see p. 307, N. 22.

Damages are the ordinary remedy for a breach of contract. They are awarded to the injured party to put him, as far as money can, in the position in which he would have been had the contract been carried out. The problem is that the consequences of a breach of contract may be endless. If the contractor fails to complete the works on time the damage to the employer may drive him to bankruptcy, so that eventually he loses everything. Obviously a line has to be drawn somewhere in settling the liability of a defaulter, and some losses may be too remote to be recoverable in law.

(f) Baster v. London & County Printing Works [1889] 1 Q.B. 901.
(f') There may be exceptional cases where fundamental breach so frustrates the whole contract as to terminate it irrespective of any action by the innocent party: Harbutt's "Plasticine" Ltd. v. Wayne Tank and Pump Co. Ltd. [1970] 1 All E.R. 225 and Photo Production Ltd. v. Securicor Transport Ltd. [1978] 3 All E.R. 147, C.A.

The basic rule, therefore, is that compensation will generally be awarded only to cover damage which is of the kind that follows naturally in the usual course of things, from the type of breach committed. Damages for exceptional or unusual loss may be recovered only if it could reasonably be supposed that had the parties considered the matter at the time of the contract it would have been within their contemplation as a serious possibility in the event of the breach which in fact occurred. The question of what amounts to a *"serious possibility"* is a question of fact to be decided by the application of common sense to the particular circumstances, and provided that the loss which could be contemplated was of the type which had in fact occurred, the defendant is liable for the whole of the loss although the amount is greater than the parties would have contemplated. For example:

(a) Where the works are obviously required for a profit-earning business the contractor will generally be liable for the employer's loss of ordinary business profits if there is any delay in completion. The contractor will not be liable for loss of special profits unless he knew when he made the contract that they might be lost by delay:

> A contractor agreed to build a large boiler for a laundry company, but was late in delivery in breach of contract.
> The contractor was held liable for the amount of the profits that the boiler could have been expected to earn the company in the ordinary way, but not for the loss of extraordinarily profitable contracts that the company had agreed to carry out with the new boiler, and of which the contractor knew nothing when he made the construction contract.

For the position where there is a liquidated damages clause *see* p. 149.

(b) The loss of profit that he would have made had he been allowed to complete in the ordinary way is the loss to a contractor who is not allowed to carry out the work, or where part of the works is wrongly omitted (pp. 171–2, and *see* p. 427 on the alternative to such damages). For disruption claims refer to ch. 12, p. 364.

(c) The ordinary damages awarded to the employer when the contractor fails to start the works is the difference between his and the next satisfactory tender; if he does not complete the works, the difference between the contract price and the actual cost of having the building completed, together with any loss of profits for delay ((a) above). In the case of defects, if the cost of making good is disproportionately high and the defects are not serious, the arbitrator or court may award the employer damages to cover only the reduction in value of the works because of the defects, and not the full cost of making them good (p. 128). For damages for interference with use of the works due to defects *see* p. 165, N. 11.

(d) A sub-contractor who causes delay which involves a main contractor in liability for liquidated damages under the main contract will be liable to pay as damages to the main contractor a sum equal to the full main contract liquidated damages (however small a part of the main works his sub-contract works may be) if he knew when he entered into the sub-contract of

---

(g) Different degrees of "contemplation" have been propounded in different decisions on this rule, but the statement in the text is taken from the majority judgments in the latest decision, by the Court of Appeal in *Parsons (Livestock) Ltd.* v. *Uttley Ingham & Co. Ltd.* [1978] 1 All E.R. 525, following *Koufos* v. *Czarnikow Ltd.* [1967] 3 All E.R. 686, H.L.

(h) *Victoria Laundry (Windsor) Ltd.* v. *Newman Industries Ltd.* [1949] 1 All E.R. 997.

the provision for liquidated damages in the main contract—whether or not the damages were actually referred to in his sub-contract. The main contractor in any case will be entitled to recover his own standing time, etc., costs.

(e) Where the engineer is wrongly dismissed or a project wrongly abandoned (see p. 386, N. 29) he is entitled to his fees for the work done and to damages equivalent to the profit element in the fees which he would have earned had he been allowed to complete his contract. It is generally assumed that the engineer is not entitled to any additional damages for not being allowed to actually do the work even though that might have added to his reputation, but it is possible that the courts would allow the engineer damage for loss of the publicity of having his name shown on the works, etc., by analogy with decisions relating to actors.

(f) Expenses incurred by a party before the contract and made futile by the breach of contract may be recoverable—p. 19.

(g) For recovery by the contractor of damages for the engineer's failure to administer the construction contract see p. 418.

(h) For disruption claims see ch. 12.

(i) The employer is not entitled to any substantial damages if a technical breach of specification does not cause him any actual loss. But for the engineer's powers to order rectification see pp. 126 and 130.

Mitigation of damages. Finally, in relation to damages, the mere fact that one party has broken a contract does not put him completely out of court—he must pay compensation, but may not be mulcted. The other party is therefore under a duty to take all reasonable and prudent steps to mitigate the damage resulting from a breach. For example, the employer

(i) Sub-contractors often seek to avoid having payment of a part of the main contract liquidated damages proportionate to the value of the sub-contract works specified in the sub-contract. The result may be not that the sub-contractor avoids liability for liquidated damages, but that he is liable for the full amount of the main contract damages if he holds up the main contract works, since a sub-contractor usually will know the liability for liquidated damages which the main contractor will incur. It is specified in the standard forms of sub-contract that the sub-contractor has knowledge of the terms of the main contract.

(j) *Herbert Clayton & Jack Waller Ltd.* v. *Oliver* [1930] A.C. 209, H.L., and *Joseph* v. *National Magazine Co. Ltd.* [1958] 3 All E.R. 52. There has been a notable liberalisation of damages for breach of contract in awarding damages for mental or emotional distress in some cases, such as breach of an employment contract in *Cox* v. *Philips Industries Ltd.* [1976] 3 All E.R. 161.

(k) *Olive Ackland (Canterbury) Ltd.* v. *Gedge* [1972] 224 E.G. 2019. No damages awarded where only one nail per tile used to fix Old Kent tiles, even if the specification that "each tile pegged at $1\frac{1}{4}$ inch galvanised nails" was to be read as requiring two nails per tile. It was clear on the evidence that the one-nail method was regarded as having definite advantages over the two-nail method and was the prevailing practice in a very large percentage of cases.

(l) Whenever there is a breach of contract by one party the duty of the other to mitigate his losses should not be overlooked—"No doubt the measure of damages and the plaintiff's duty and ability to mitigate are logically distinct concepts. . . . But to some extent, at least, they are mirror images, particularly in cases of damages for breach of contract: for the measure of damages can be, very frequently, arrived at only by postulating and answering the question, what can this particular plaintiff reasonably do to alleviate his loss and what would be the cost to him of doing so at the time when he could reasonably be expected to do it?": *Radford* v. *De Froberville* [1978] 1 All E.R. 33, 44.

In that case the defendant in breach of a contract with his neighbour failed to build a party wall on his own land. Held that the neighbour was entitled to recover the cost of building the wall at the date when he should reasonably have brought the case to a hearing. The damages were not to be reduced by the delay between the breach going back to 1968 and the start of proceedings in 1973, even though that was a time of high inflation, because during that period there had remained a reasonable probability that the defendant would carry out the

must act reasonably thriftily when entitled to employ another contractor to complete the works, although he need not complete in the cheapest possible way and, since he is the innocent party placed in a difficult situation, the courts will not scrutinise his conduct too severely.

Specific performance and injunction. The courts will not always allow a party in effect to buy the right to commit a wrong by paying damages for breach of contract. They may, therefore, order specific performance of a contract; that is, order a party to actually perform his contract on pain of imprisonment for contempt of court. The courts will not usually make that order in the case of a construction contract, largely because damages are generally an adequate remedy to either party for any breach; nor will they keep a party to a personal relationship against his wishes, so that they will not order specific performance of the service agreement.

m

The courts may also, by way of an injunction, order a party not to do something, particularly not to cause a nuisance or infringe an easement (ch. 16). For example, they may order work to stop on a building which will obstruct a right of light, or even order a building to be pulled down. This can, of course, lead to ransom by anyone with the good luck to own property with a right of light, etc., in the way of a large project, so that the courts have been given power to refuse an injunction to protect such a right and to merely award damages for any actual loss suffered instead. The courts will use this power sparingly:

> Part of the defendants' land slipped into the plaintiffs' land. The defendants had offered to buy the plaintiffs' land, but they refused to sell.
> An injunction was granted ordering the defendants to take all necessary steps to support the plaintiffs' land, although it would cost £35,000 to do so and the land was worth only £1,500. This decision of a County Court Judge was upheld by the Court of Appeal, and only reversed by the House of Lords.

n

Limitation of actions. For obvious reasons a party may not delay indefinitely in bringing proceedings to enforce a claim. Various time limits are laid down by statute, e.g. for actions in tort (p. 393), proceedings must generally be issued or arbitration commenced (p. 295) not later than six years from the wrong, with the major exception that for actions for personal injuries the period is normally three years. The time limit for breach of contract is twelve years if the contract is under seal (p. 4), six years if it is not. Unfortunately the law on the crucial issue of when the period starts to run is no longer certain. In the case of liability for physical damage to property or injury to the person caused by negligence it is clear that the wrong is not complete until at the earliest the other party suffers the

work. Once proceedings had been started the defendant was not entitled to complain that it was unreasonable for the plaintiff to delay building the wall for himself before the damages were assessed, particularly where his right to any damages was being contested.
Contrast the decision in *Dodd Properties (Kent) Ltd.* v. *Canterbury C.C.* (1978) 248 E.G. 229, where damages for distortion of the framework of a garage premises during construction of a multi-storey car park on adjoining land were assessed as at the date of damage, although the cost of repairs had trebled by the time the proceedings were heard ten years later.

(*m*) The possibility of an order for specific performance being granted of a building contract was discussed but not decided in *London Borough Council of Hounslow* v. *Twickenham Garden Developments Ltd.* [1970] 3 All E.R. 326, 350.

(*n*) *Morris* v. *Redland Bricks Ltd.* [1969] 2 All E.R. 576.

damage or injury—until then, of course, there is no reason for that party to sue. On the other hand it appears still to be the law in theory that the time limit for a claim made for breach of contract commences to run with the last relevant breach, even if at that time the party claiming could not have known of the breach (subject to some extensions of the period, particularly in the case of fraudulent concealment of a defect). But the developing liability for negligence threatens to envelop other causes of action (pp. 393–7), and on such liability it seems that the limitation period will only start to run when the loss is suffered or the person claiming discovers or ought reasonably to have discovered a defect. Even a party who has a contract with the wrongdoer for construction, design or supervision apparently may ignore the contract and claim in negligence against an engineer or contractor, where the contractual period of limitation has expired because the defect was hidden for some time.

o

p

Thus the efforts by the courts to do full justice to those harmed by negligence has the unfortunate repercussion for contractors and engineers that, even when they have retired from business, they or their successor may be visited with liability for defects in works completed many years before. Insurance covering the full period at risk is essential.

Actions brought within these time limits are generally perfectly valid in law despite delay, but delay may, of course, cast doubts on the genuineness of a claim, and the courts may refuse an injunction, e.g. where a party has stood by and allowed a building to be completed before claiming.

In the 5th edition I.C.E. Conditions this long period of liability is not restricted, and liability for defects in the works and to indemnify the employer against damage done by the works to themselves or the property or person of others continues despite the issue of the maintenance certificate—cl. 61 (2), p. 274, and on the bond p. 322, N. 6.

Legislation protecting remedies for breach of contract. The courts have long tried without full success to prevent abuse of freedom of contract by commercial and public bodies in a position to dictate their terms, however unfair, or to take advantage of consumers who do not read printed forms of contract until too late. Parliament has now intervened with the Misrepresentation Act 1967 (60) and the Unfair Contract Terms Act 1977.

The 1977 Act is both wide in scope and in some respects not clearcut, so that, although they are hardly within the real mischief aimed at, it is necessary to consider many possible effects the Act may have on these Conditions on the way to reaching the conclusion that the actual effects are likely to be small.

The Act first of all absolutely invalidates any attempt by a contract term or notice to exclude or restrict liability for death or personal injury resulting

(*o*) See generally on this important extension *Clark* v. *Woor* [1965] 2 All E.R. 353 and *King* v. *Victor Parsons & Co.* [1973] 1 All E.R. 206. In the latter case the period was extended because the defendants built on foundations which they knew were unsuitable.

(*p*) See *Esso Petroleum Co. Ltd.* v. *Mardon Ltd.* [1976] 2 All E.R. 5, C.A.; *Batty* v. *Metropolitan Property Realizations Ltd.* [1978] 2 All E.R. 445, C.A.; *Midland Bank Trust Co. Ltd.* v. *Hett, Stubbs & Kemp* [1978] 3 All E.R. 571. Various tests for the start of the period are mentioned in *Sparham-Souter* v. *Town and Country Development (Essex) Ltd.* [1976] 2 All E.R. 65, C.A. and *Anns* v. *London Borough of Merton* [1977] 2 All E.R. 492, H.L., for an action in negligence for the cost of remedying defects in a building. The courts are now generally reluctant to have a limitation period start before the person damaged has a realistic chance to sue.

from negligence, and similarly invalidates exclusion or restriction of
liability for negligence in the case of other loss or damage "except insofar as
the term or notice has satisfied the requirement of reasonableness". Cls.
21-24 of the Conditions do not appear to infringe this section and as to cl.
20 dealing with damage to the works *see* p. 97.

Another provision of the Act with wide scope says that where one
contracting party deals "on the other's written standard terms of business
... the other cannot by reference to any contract term ... when himself in
breach of contract, exclude or restrict any liability of his in respect of the
breach ...". Many clauses in these Conditions give the contractor rights to
extra payments where there has been no breach of contract at all by the
employer, cls. 12 and 13 are the prime example, and on those clauses this
section can have no effect. But there are several clauses that restrict the
contractor to recovery of "*cost*" only although arguably there has been a
breach of contract by the employer. For example, the remedies under cls. 7,
14(6), 27(6), 40(1), 42(1) for unreasonable delay by the engineer or the
employer (ch. 12). In any of those cases, the contractor may claim loss of
profit (and possibly loss of return with which to pay overheads—p. 31) on
the grounds that the exclusion in the clause of his right·to do so is
invalidated by the Act. To succeed with that argument the contractor has to
overcome several obstacles:

(*a*) To establish that the contract is on the employer's written standard
terms of business. The better interpretation of that phrase is that the
standard terms do not have to be unique to the other party to the contract,
but merely frequently used by him as they stand. Therefore, these
Conditions used by the Department of Transport or any of the many public
authorities and private employers who habitually use them will qualify. On
the other hand, an employer who wishes to have a factory built and has not
before promoted civil engineering works, and who decides to use these
Conditions would not appear to be subject to this section.

(*b*) Even where the section applies to his contract, the restriction will be
valid if the employer discharges the burden of proving "that the term shall
have been a fair and reasonable one to be included having regard to the
circumstances which were, or ought reasonably to have been, known to or
in the contemplation of the parties when the contract was made". The Act
gives no guidance as to what is or is not reasonable under this section, but in

(*q*) Section 2. The Act came into force on 1st February 1978 and applies to contracts made on
or after that date, and also to notices attempting to exclude liability under the Occupiers
Liability Act 1957.
(*r*) Section 3. The section also protects a "consumer" whatever the norm of contract, that is a
person not making the contract in the course of business. Obviously that protection is
unlikely to be relevant to civil engineering works, even where it is the employer who is seeking
to rely on the Act (below).
(*s*) There is controversy about whether a clause in a contract may escape this section on the
grounds that properly interpreted it is not a limitation on liability created by the contract but
defines and limits in the first instance the extent of the liability being undertaken. For
example, it may even be argued that by cl. 7 the employer does not undertake at all that
drawings will not be late, merely that if they are late he will pay the contractor's costs, so that
as long as he pays for delay he is not in breach of contract. That argument is unlikely to be
accepted by the courts—text p. 61 above, footnote (*a*). But the issue is open where
information is given on specific terms that no liability for it is accepted—"A man cannot be
said voluntarily to be undertaking a responsibility if at the very moment when he is said to be
accepting it he declares that in fact he is not." *Hedley Byrne & Co. Ltd.* v. *Heller & Partners
Ltd.* [1963] 2 All E.R. 575, 613.
(*t*) Section 11.

relation to another provision ingredients mentioned include the relative bargaining strength of the parties, whether the customer knew, or ought reasonably to have known, of the existence and extent of the term (having regard, among other factors, to any custom of the trade and any previous course of dealing between the parties).

Although it is the term and not the contract as a whole that is to be judged and it is not unknown in drafting committees for the representatives of the one section of an industry to accept an unreasonably unfavourable term in return for an unreasonably favourable term elsewhere in a standard contract, it is unlikely that the courts will deprive the employer of the benefit of a term in these Conditions negotiated as they have been over several years with representatives of all sides of the industry, including representatives with the task of protecting the interests of contractors. For the courts to teach contractors their own business would seem to be going beyond the purpose of the Act and they have recognised the special nature of these Conditions (p. 45, footnote (ee)).

In addition, there is no doubt that claims for loss of profit are particularly troublesome and capable of abuse (p. 369).

Cl. 51 permitting the engineer to make omissions from the works is another clause of the Conditions that surprisingly might be argued to fall within the ambit of the Act. Subject again to the two limitations that have been discussed above ("other's written standard terms" and the "reasonableness" test) the Act strikes down any term by which a party claims to be entitled "to tender a contractual performance substantially different from that which was reasonably expected of him, or ... in respect of the whole or any part of his contractual obligation, to render no performance at all". Although an omission of part of the works for which the employer will then not pay might be held prima facie to fall within this section, given the purposes of and limits on (p. 172, N. 8) cl. 51, with the ancient and widespread use and acceptance by contractors of such a term, and the quite different purpose for which this provision of the Act is designed, there can be little doubt that even a court most zealous to protect the contractor would uphold the clause.

Subject to the same two limitations, the Act also prevents "making the liability (for breach) or its enforcement subject to restrictive or onerous conditions; ... excluding or restricting any right or remedy in respect of the liability ... excluding or restricting rules of evidence or procedure". This restriction is relevant to the notice terms of the Conditions (cl. 52(4) particularly, and list in ch. 11) where they apply to claims that are essentially for breach of contract: nevertheless there can be little doubt that those terms satisfy the "*reasonableness*" test, and that any special terms written into the contract to supplement those requirements should similarly be valid unless very severe (p. 442).

The Act generally must be kept in mind in adding special contract restrictions on any rights the contractor would have ordinarily for breach of contract, whether the restriction is in special conditions or the specification or bill. An example is given in N. 6, p. 125.

The Act may have work to do in the construction industry on other standard forms of contract. For example, on several clauses of the Institution of Mechanical Engineers, etc. model forms, such as the clauses usually

(*u*) Section 3.
(*v*) Section 13.

restricting liquidated damages for delay to one-half per cent per week and a maximum of five per cent of the contract price. Where the employer has to invite tenders for supply of plant whether by sub-contractors to be nominated or by direct contractors even though he knows that he may not obtain tenders on the form he will offer a fair form of contract, leaving it to tenderers to introduce the model form so as to establish that the contract is on "the other's written standard terms of business" and obtain the protection of the Act directly or through the main contractor (but see p. 240 N. 2 (a)).

Many adjectives might be applied to the home-produced sub-contract forms dictated by some large main contractors, but "reasonable" is hardly one of them. The Act may have much to do between main contractors and sub-contractors.

Although outside the scope of this book, it may be mentioned that where these Conditions or a package deal contract form emanates from the contractor, then the Act applies in reverse to the direction dealt with in this note, and terms protecting the contractor (such as very low liquidated damages or restrictions on liability for defects or damage) may be affected.

CHAPTER 17

Tendermanship and Claimsmanship

The problem. Lawyers should tread humbly outside their own strictly legal business. As they are often reminded, their experience is limited mainly to dissecting the mistakes of others with the advantage of hindsight, and no legal argument has ever driven a pile.

However, there undoubtedly are problems about the contractual framework of the construction industry, and it is felt appropriate in this book to examine attitudes and procedures that might help to reduce them. Unfortunately, and it is hoped coincidentally, in the three and a half years since unsolicited advice on disputes was given to the industry in the previous edition of this book the problems have become worse and not better. At the same time the references in this chapter show the growing concern in the industry to grapple with this aspect of construction.

The fundamental factor surely is that a civil engineering contract cannot be as simple and clear-cut as a contract for sale of a pound of butter. It is utopian to believe that while works become more complex it will be possible to find a formula for producing cut-and-dried final accounts without argument. The realistic aim must be greater professionalism in framing contracts and contract procedures, in distributing risks and in distinguishing between good and bad claims.

Such improvement is vitally important both for the industry itself and for the public benefit. Claims and disputes are wasteful. They divert personnel from the creative function of construction in which they are trained at much expense to the unproductive and unsatisfying chore of arguing, arbitrating and litigating. A high proportion of disputes are concerned with deciding whether the employer or contractor is to bear the cost of waste of resources—rectification or repetition of work, standing time of plant and labour while arguments rage about changes in design or methods of construction to deal with problems that should have been envisaged and planned for in advance. In addition, reputable tenderers lose contracts to the disreputable, and the employer is misled by the tender price. The rewards go to the lucky and litigious instead of the efficient. Much of the works is paid for on cost plus without any real incentive to efficiency. Above all, a contract system intended to produce a co-operative effort from parties who have a joint duty to complete satisfactory works for the employer is converted into a battle of antagonists.

It is very sad that the situation has been reached where it can even be suggested of a great industry, as it has been, that efficiency in the pursuit of payment pays better than efficiency in site work. And this problem should not be represented as a conflict between the interests of contractors and the interests of engineers and employers. Neither side of the industry benefits. Contractors do not make more profit overall, because competition ensures that in seeking contracts they allow in their starting prices for the money to be earned at the end in claims.

The title of this chapter summarises the vicious circle that causes this state of affairs to continue. The contractors justify claimsmanship by alleging that employers and their advisers place unpriceable and unfair risks on them; engineers justify harshness in contracts and hostility in administration of contracts on the grounds of the claims habits of some contractors. The following factors do seem relevant to any improvement:

1. Site information. An employer who is prepared to pay a fair price will give the contractor full information about the works he wants constructed. In particular it is absurd that major works should be founded on the fiction that the contractor bases his tender on site investigations that were not made (the unlimited investigations which in the past the contract told the contractor to make during the short tender period) and not on the investigations that were in fact made (by the employer). The recognition by the 5th edition of the I.C.E. Conditions and the general law that the contractor is entitled to take into account in his pricing site information provided by the employer (pp. 60–3) will produce benefits if coupled with responsible attitudes on both sides of the industry.

A responsible employer will spend the necessary money for an adequate and not merely notional site investigation, properly planned and executed by a specialist chosen for competence and not cheapness. He will in particular avoid making site investigations in one area and building the works elsewhere. The information supplied will enable the contractor to allow in his tender for site conditions of which a substantial risk is foreseeable, to plan his operations with sufficient flexibility to deal efficiently with any such conditions that eventuate, rather than having turmoil on the site, delay and hasty solutions whenever conditions are less than ideal.

All the serious detriments mentioned at the beginning of this chapter apply if cl. 13 of the Conditions is interpreted by engineers or arbitrators so as to free the contractor from responsibility where he loses out on a calculated gamble to ignore in his pricing risks that at the time were foreseeable as real and substantial. In particular, it is for engineers and arbitrators to deal firmly with any irresponsible efforts by contractors to base claims on unrealistic (and sometimes retrospective) deductions from site information. If they do not, employers may be disinclined to give information that will be used as a stick with which to beat them—the vicious circle again.

Exactly how much then should the employer tell, and in particular should any interpretation of factual data be given to the contractor or should he be left to provide it for himself? Some say that the employer should tell all and take responsibility for all he tells. Some say he should tell, but should add the traditional Irish rider "mind you I said nothing" by excluding from the contract any guarantee of factual or other information and even excluding cl. 12 itself. Others take a more complicated position, as in cl. 11 of the F.I.D.I.C. International Conditions.

a

b

(*a*) Construction Industry Research and Information Association Report 79 "Tunnelling Improved Contract Practices" (1978), Chapter 3.

(*b*) It has been suggested that "Logically such clauses (which entitle the contractor to extra payment for unforeseen difficulties) contradict the policy on which they are based, since if the risk is truly unforeseeable, it is unlikely that, without such a clause, there would be a material difference in the contract price" (Hudson "Building and Engineering Contracts", 10th ed. by I. N. Duncan Wallace at p. 569).

That comment of course begs the question. An experienced and reputable contractor will

If the employer supplies a detailed site investigation based on many boreholes, it will hardly be necessary or practicable for a tenderer to verify it by an equally extensive investigation in the time permitted for tender, and were he to make one or two boreholes which were found to give information inconsistent with the employer's results, it might be difficult to draw any firm conclusion from them in the face of the previous detailed investigation. There may, of course, be cases where it is practicable and necessary to supplement an investigation; for example, by a borehole between two far apart boreholes made in the employer's investigation on the line of a projected sewer.

On the other hand, there is "a view ... that site investigation reports are not adequately studied and applied at the tender stage and only seriously brought into use in order to sustain claims for extra costs when things have gone wrong." [c]

As a result the choices open to the employer about giving site information should not be made on legal grounds divorced from the realities. The choice should aim to enable the employer to give to the contractor, and the contractor within reasonable limits to rely on, information which the employer is in the best position to find out, and to cause the contractor to discover the information that he can best find out for himself, for example, that needed for his special methods of construction. In that way the project will start with the maximum combined knowledge about the site, on which those involved may safely budget and price and, perhaps more important, plan the works in advance.

The employer certainly should take the precaution of supplying the information with the tender documents but not as part of the contract and of saying that at least any interpretation supplied is not warranted or guaranteed. Great care must be taken in abbreviating or interpreting information. Obviously, as far as possible the information should be compiled with the purpose for which the contractor will use it in mind, since information can rarely be sufficiently comprehensive or the language in which it is expressed sufficiently unambiguous not to be (or claimed later to be) misleading if it is used for some purpose not foreseen by the compiler. There is a serious danger in the engineer obtaining information for his design purpose and then supplying it to a contractor who may unknown to the engineer rely on it for a different purpose, in pricing or devising some construction method. A suitable and specific warning to discourage unreasonable deduction and extrapolation from the information may have to be given. If careful selection of tenderers has not been made it may be prudent only to give factual data with no interpretation whatsoever. [e]

in pricing know that there are risks ranging from the totally unforeseeable, through the improbable up to the probable. Where there is no cl. 12 he will mark the line above which risks must be priced lower than in the case of a tender for which cl. 12 operates. For totally unforeseeable risks he will add a percentage based on his experience of the particular class of work. At the same time in repeating from the last edition of this book this comment on the Hudson criticism, the reservation must be admitted that not all tenderers are both reputable and experienced. There is some evidence that the level of tenders received is not always affected by the contents of the conditions of contract particularly in times of shortage of work. The result is that no loosening or tightening of the contract can avoid the need to select the contractor carefully — text below.

(c) C.I.R.I.A. report, above, p. 18.

(d) See above, p. 58 and p. 62, footnote (b').

(e) There is a longer discussion of this topic and other issues dealt with in this chapter, in the paper by the author on "Contractual Issues— can the Contract help?". Proceedings of the Conference on Management of Large Capital Projects published by the I.C.E. in 1978. Many of the other papers and discussions are also relevant.

2. Pricing contingencies. The ideal solution is to eliminate problems of risk-sharing whenever possible: for example, by giving the contractor an opportunity to price extra work and delay which will occur if a risk materialises. Method- and time-related charges are a move in this direction, and a contingency may be fully described and priced in a bill item under which it is to be measured if it materialises. In this way the employer has an incentive to carry out site investigations, etc., to define the contingency closely so that the contractor's price for it is as low as possible, and may pass over a tender if the tenderer's methods are such that his price is unreasonably high. Again, the wastage is avoided that occurs in thinking about problems for the first time when they appear, with expensive plant and labour standing idle.

This approach contrasts with cl. 56 of the 5th edition, by which the contractor may be entitled to "*appropriate increase or decrease of any rates*" for any change in quantities, with no guidance as to what may be appropriate. Apart from the obvious precautions of care in preparing bills, and in examining the contractor's rates to ensure that they are not unbalanced and his methods to ensure that they are not too inflexible or peculiar to deal economically with any change from the quantities in the bill, it is open to the engineer to go further and give, e.g., rock quantities for excavation in provisional steps, so that the contractor prices separate items for, say, 1,000 cu. metres of rock, for from 1,000 to 2,000, and so on. The contractor in this way is under pressure and has an improved chance to plan in advance at the tender stage what he will do if the various quantities eventuate, and to price the effect on his working accordingly. The method of itemisation should be explained clearly in the bill, and within the steps priced no change of rate will be appropriate under cl. 56.

It is strange that the pricing of risk items in this way is resisted by both sides. Some contractors prefer the possibility of claiming extra costs to an opportunity to price a contingency, and indeed rely on such claims to make up for low tenders. On the other hand some employers and engineers prefer to refer to risks as generally or obliquely as possible, presumably in the hope of finding a contractor who does not know what he is doing and will not allow for them fully in his price. The wisdom of employing a contractor who does not know what he is doing is somewhat doubtful (below), and these two attitudes are equally reprehensible and short-sighted. It is a sorry start to a project when they meet each other.

3. Fair contract conditions. It is for the advisers of employers to explain to them the importance of fair contract conditions, and to regard it as a matter of professional ethics not to put forward tricky conditions of contract or specifications. The easy way out for the engineer or lawyer of drafting terms which give every conceivable protection to the person who is employing him, so as to avoid any criticism if things go wrong, disregards the adverse effects which such terms may have on the clients' interests in putting up the price (but *see* footnote (*b*) above) or in the attitude of the contractor in performing the job and in harassing the employer with claims at the end. Legislation now encourages the draftsman to be fair—p. 431 above.

Due for abandonment, for example, are common clauses dealing with services. More often than not every effort is made by special conditions to place on contractors the risk of unknown and untraceable services and the delay by undertakers in removing services. It is to be hoped that cl. 31 (2) of the 5th edition will lead to practical steps actually to avoid the commonly vast disruption to works from services found too late and delay in diversion (for which employers must pay eventually, directly or indirectly) rather than, as often in the past, a public employer doing nothing more constructive than indolently passing liability for the faults of another public body on to a private contractor.

There has been much discussion as to whether building and civil engineering standard conditions are moving too far in favour of the contractor. It can certainly be said that in revising standard contract forms the tendency has been to start work without any consideration of basic principles, and what one might call a philosophy of risk is lacking. The draconian view which seeks to place all risk on the contractor and the belief that a contractor should be safeguarded against all risks and in effect guaranteed his costs plus a profit on all work done are both an over-simplification. Each risk has to be examined separately and it may be that different solutions are appropriate as between public and private contracts, for example.

It must not be forgotten that one cannot easily have it both ways—create trust whilst by the contract safeguarding minutely against betrayal. If an employer pays overriding attention from the beginning to contractual matters, he telegraphs to the contractor that he is distrusted, and goodwill and cooperation are dissipated from the start. No general rule can be laid down. The contents of the contract and of the management applied to any works must have primary regard to the record and character of those who have to be managed. They must reflect and vary with the degree of trust or mistrust that is justified, which in turn depends on the selection of tenderers—below.

On the other hand it may be fair for an employer in some cases to require the contractor to be an insurer against risks, given that the contractor is in the construction business and in a position to spread risks over a number of jobs, so that what he loses on the swings on one contract he may gain on the roundabouts of others where he includes for risks but they do not occur. If he takes on such a role there should be no presumption that the contractor is entitled to compensation merely because he has lost money. There is no noticeable move by contractors to give back payment to employers on works that are very profitable because risks allowed for do not materialise. Reneging on freely accepted risks will do as little for the construction industry as it would do for the insurance industry (and should not be encouraged by arbitrators).

Insurers choose and define carefully the risks they will run, fixing their premiums accordingly. Progress in this area in construction will consist of recognising this insurance element and developing the type of expertise which the insurance industry is said to possess, in assessing risks, deciding which may and may not be accepted, distributing appropriate premiums over several jobs, and defining the risks in precisely drafted terms. It is one thing to accept risks after careful analysis of what is involved and with the necessary advance planning to meet them if they occur (both financial and in flexibility of working methods), another to accept a risk unknowingly and be caught unprepared when luck fails.

(*f*) Principles of distributing risk are discussed in ch. 2 of the Construction Industry Research and Information Association Report 79: "Tunnelling—Improved Contract Practices" (1978), and references cited there.

Again, what is put on paper in the contract must be workable in practice. For example, the right to an extension of time for delay beyond his control is a reasonable protection to the contractor, but the difficulty of evaluating claims for extension and the lack of confidence of engineers and arbitrators in enforcing liquidated damages has given the industry a bad name for delay. It is also extremely difficult in practice to evaluate claims for disruption payments by contractors, and this may result either in the contractor not getting full compensation for the tangible and intangible results of disruption for which the employer is responsible or in the employer paying for the contractor's inefficiency (p. 367). What is essential is that the contract should reward incentive and enterprise, flexibility and adaptability. Unless very carefully administered by engineers and arbitrators rights to extra payment or time, although justified in the abstract, may in practice reduce the contractor's incentive to struggle hard to minimise difficulties.

The "harassment" factor also must be recognised. Perfectly fair rights to claim given to contractors can be used unscrupulously to harass engineers and employers into capitulation on claims that are trumped up or exaggerated. It is to be hoped that the I.C.E. Conditions of Contract Standing Joint Committee will consider carefully the many areas in the 5th edition that may encourage such activities by vague expressions, undoubtedly well-meaning in their intention to allow flexibility because of the wide range of cases covered, but it is suggested not taking full account of the practical realities.

4. Better drafting. It has been suggested that "the old and well-tried method of preparing contract documents by means of the previous set, a scissors and a pot of 'Gloy' has still much to commend it". One would like to see a reference to an engineer's mind added-to that list, as it is quite essential that the contract terms should pass through the mind of an engineer aware of any peculiarities of the particular project, before issue to tenderers.

Although one would not guess it to be the case from the 5th edition of the I.C.E. Conditions, lawyers have developed principles of good drafting which might usefully be studied by engineers before writing specifications, changes to standard forms or tender qualifications (p. 5). Even the extreme of paying a lawyer's fee at that stage may avoid much larger fees for clearing up the debris when the harm has been done.

5. Selective tendering. The aim of comparing tenders is to predict which tender will produce the most satisfactory combination for the employer in standard of workmanship, completion time and price. The fact that under the new I.C.E. Conditions there is no contract price at all should finally end the belief that the starting-out total of the bill of quantities is a reliable guide even to the last of these elements. It is the duty of the engineer to disabuse the employer of any such notion. Included in the matters to be considered must be the reputation of the contractor. The sooner selective tendering produces tender lists free of contractors who deliberately put in low prices with the intention of making up on claims, the better not only for the public but also for responsible contractors who bid a fair price with the intention

(g) F. R. Oliver, Informal Discussion, "Contract Conditions and Procedures", The Institution of Civil Engineers, Oct. 5th, 1972. Some of the statistics about the prevalence of claims given at that discussion are frightening.

of doing a good job. Selective tendering should also help to avoid another situation that breeds claims, in which a contractor starts work with the chill realisation that he is well below the average price of other tenderers and will have to try to make up accordingly on his standard of work and inventiveness in claims.

The faith of some employers that lawyers and contracts will give them satisfactory control over a contractor who, under open tendering, is accepted with virtually no examination to see that he has the resources, integrity and capability to perform as he is contracting to do, is touching but contrary to all the evidence. One cannot think of any area of choice—whether of employee, physician, hairdresser or tailor—where a similar procedure would be contemplated for a moment.

Selective tendering can, of course, be abused to punish a contractor for making a justified claim, and there are problems about new entrants to the industry. Nevertheless, if it is true that prevention is better than cure the industry will have to face up to the implications of selectivity. The facts necessary for selection may be obtained among other ways by carefully prepared enquiries to tenderers, and the law cannot be used as an excuse for lack of firmness or courage in reporting on tenderers (p. 377).

6. Information and procedures under the 5th edition. It will be a mistake if the past practices under the 4th edition of the I.C.E. Conditions are applied without re-thinking to the 5th edition. The changes in the conditions amount to a new ball game to which the practice in inviting tenders and administering contracts must adapt. For example, if the engineer is to avoid a conflict between his requirements and instructions and the contractor's arrangements, with claims as the result, then it is not even sufficient to obtain information about those arrangements as soon as the contract starts. The information should be required in the instructions to tender and vetted before contract for suitability and flexibility to deal with contingencies (and the engineer may have to probe into the information rather than merely receiving it passively, for it has been said that some of the most misleading information about likely methods of construction comes to engineers at the bidding stage).

Again, the engineer may minimise claims under cl. 14 by giving in the tender documents full details of his requirements for temporary works and also the design criteria of the permanent works. Precautions of this kind are not expedients to sidestep proper claims, but a legitimate way to ensure that the contractor has all the material on which he can fairly price what he is to do and therefore will have no reasonable grounds to complain of unexpected difficulties.

An oddity of the industry is the assumption that both parties must be allowed to play with some cards up their sleeves. The reticence of some employers about site investigations and services has been discussed. Contrariwise, one finds the contractor arguing for new rates on the basis of the alleged make-up of his tender with no insistence on the engineer's part that the actual estimating papers are produced (although if there is arbitration they will have to be disclosed on an order for discovery, p. 298). Where the contractor refers in claims to allowances, percentages, breakdown of rates, methods of working and so on said to be taken from his tender, there is no reason why the engineer should not refuse to take such matters into account in his decisions unless the contractor proves them by producing his original tender papers.

Engineers must develop the expertise to use effectively their very extensive contract powers to deal with bad work, disregard of safety and unjustified claims. At least the contract should be read or re-read before some irrevocable step is taken and it is too late; memory of the document should never be relied on. The various new procedures under the 5th edition, for example reviewing extensions of time, must be carried out. The engineer must also consider whether he will take control of the works by special terms in the specification, to minimise the necessity for instructions that may produce claims (pp. 74 and 82), and in administering the contract he will keep in mind all the new grounds for claims (key, p. 324).

7. Programmemanship. A sub-species of the manoeuvring that unhappily occurs in response to efforts of one party to obtain information from the other is the practice of some contractors of either failing to supply and update programmes, or deliberately supplying over-optimistic programmes. The aim of the latter expedient is to place the contractor in the situation that he can the more readily claim disruption for alleged late drawings, etc.

Unfortunately the Conditions give the engineer no real sanction to enforce his right to programme and other information (p. 78). All that the engineer can do is to be alert to programmemanship, and at a meeting if necessary challenge the contractor to justify his programme, recording in minutes the contractor's protestations which may later be used in evidence against him and refuse to accept a programme if it is unrealistic (p. 80, N, 5). Since any such stratagem suggests that the contractor is not unconscious of the possibilities of manufacturing claims, it is for the engineer to monitor particularly closely his progress and the extent to which he is or is not held up for drawings or instructions (and in extreme cases to advise his clients to amend their select tender lists accordingly).

8. Records. It is increasingly the practice of contractors to claim for cumulative and general losses due to disruption which it may not be possible to prove in detail—effects on morale and on productivity, reduction in output by workmen when they know that there is not a steady flow of work in front of them, and so on. Experience of the contrast in productivity between works that run smoothly and works which are impeded for any reason makes it quite clear that such claims may be justified. An understanding that this is so by engineers (and the courts—see p. 365) is essential if pre-planning and co-operation in the industry are to develop as they must in the public interest.

At the same time it is perfectly clear that some of the elaborate literary efforts put forward as disruption claims are works of fiction rather than fact. It is all too easy for a contractor who finds at the end of a contract that he has lost money to exaggerate the minor delays inevitable in large-scale work and to distort the real sequence of events by alleging delay caused by the engineer when in fact he was not in any case ready to do the work involved. The result is a wildly exaggerated disruption claim costed out in the vaguest possible way. Provided his lawyers create the maximum confusion at the arbitration about what actually happened on the works (and the standard arbitration procedure almost seems designed to help to that end—below) he can hope for a substantial award from an arbitrator.

It should also be mentioned that although arbitration can and frequently is conducted on the basis of hindsight, work obviously cannot be built by hindsight. That might be remembered by, and may if necessary be pointed out to, engineers who tell a contractor how he could have avoided disruption only in arbitration several years after the disruption has passed.

It is grossly unfair both to employers and contractors that the mechanism to determine the actual full costs of disruption to a contractor, and to divide them from the costs due to his own inefficiency, is lacking more often than not. To improve the mechanism it is necessary to have better arbitration procedure (below) and better records.

A party to a dispute, particularly if there is arbitration, will learn three lessons (often too late): the importance of records, the importance of records and the importance of records. It is impossible to exaggerate the extent to which lawyers can find unexpected grounds, often quite real, on which to cast doubt on evidence if it is not backed by meticulously established records. It must also be remembered that the arbitrator will know nothing about the history of the works, which must be reconstructed for him with all complexities and nuances, from the records available.

That is why cl. 52 (4) of the new I.C.E. Conditions is so important. If the requirements of the sub-clause are followed by contractors and firmly insisted on by engineers and arbitrators, then contemporary records should be available on most disputes. A danger, of course, is that more time is spent on recording what is happening, for fear of disputes, than on engineering work to make sure that the right things do happen to build the works. Indeed a breakdown of the average time spent by agents, contract managers, resident staff and engineers on or in anticipation of disputes, as opposed to engineering matters, might even now produce alarming figures. That is part of the overall problem being dealt with in this chapter. The only suggestion that can be offered is that both contractor and engineer should have an established procedure for record-keeping, that will work more or less automatically and painlessly to produce the minimum records necessary. They should then be alert in any case of incipient dispute to consider as soon as possible and chart out carefully a system of supplemental records—a detailed and well-thought-out scheme rather than piecemeal and often incomplete information. It should be kept in mind that the purpose of notice procedure is not to harass the contractor, but to ensure good management..Instead of trying to describe what is required in the contract in the usual convoluted and often practically unworkable legal language, it is suggested that the Conditions might say simply that the contractor is to supply or co-operate in preparing notices, returns, graphs, charts and other management tools following a procedure and specimen forms attached to the contract.

Diaries can also be invaluable and those keeping them should be supplied with a list of subject headings for entries, to be reviewed each day. While tailoring of records is to be avoided because it is usually obvious as well as immoral, it is reasonable for diarists to keep in mind the possibility that their work may have to be produced to the other side in arbitration (pp. 298–9). and refrain from entering hasty and ill-considered opinions that they themselves may no longer hold after a few days' reflection. Important

h

(*h*) In *Oldschool* v. *Gleeson* (*Construction*) *Ltd.* (1976) 4 B.L.R. 105, 117 the judge refused to rely on a site agent's diary because he concluded that the agent was not anxious to record criticisms or complaints when they were made, since the diary did not record warnings on behalf of the employer although there was other evidence that a warning had been given.

matters should be stated in writing to the other party at the time, and indeed contemporaneous records should be agreed wherever possible.

Full use should also be made of progress meetings. The engineer may have a list of topics to run through at every meeting: for example, a question to the contractor as to whether he is held up or anticipates that he will be held up for lack of any drawings or instructions. If the contractor says he is not then he will not later be able to claim the contrary; if he says he is then he can be required to spell out his case, which can be examined at the time and the extent of any hold-up recorded. The contractor in turn should have a system for collecting before progress meetings any cases of actual or future disruption, etc., from his various supervisors.

While microscopic examination should be unnecessary, minutes and other records put forward by one party should be very carefully checked by the other as soon as they are received. Unfortunately because of the attitude of the law unnatural alertness is to some extent necessary in relation to written records (pp. 5–6), and the witness box or chair is a very uncomfortable place for a witness who is maintaining under cross-examination that he did not actually mean what he appeared to say in writing, or that a letter or minutes to which he did not object does not actually represent what happened.

Obviously there should be concentration on collecting 'real' first-hand evidence while it is fresh, by way of photographs, tests, etc. as the works proceed, rather than on argument and confusing and increasingly strident correspondence by which each party concentrates more on trying to build the file than the works.

Although the emphasis in cl. 52 (4) (e) is on notices and records to prevent the engineer being prejudiced in investigating claims, proper management documents of the kind that have been advocated should also aim to forestall or minimise disruption or other losses, whoever is going to bear them. In that respect the employer is entitled to benefit of the skill of both the engineer and contractor. It is difficult to see why the attitude to actual or potential difficulties that are contractual should differ from other management problems, where the first step should be for those involved to sit down together and make a plan for dealing with the difficulty, not to start fighting between themselves. Again a common-sense procedure for co-operation drafted in ordinary sensible language can be incorporated into the contract by reference, leading to a joint plan of campaign tailored for the particular problem.

9. Research and education. The industry has been long on declarations that more education and research is needed about contract procedures, but short on action. One hopeful development in respect of arbitration is mentioned below, but much more is necessary as part of the general management training of engineers. Speculation and extreme and unbalanced views on one side or another are not a substitute for research on the many complex problems involved in distributing risk and maintaining that distribution throughout the works. The research that has been done on bills of quantities and method-related charges supplies a model for the future. If even a small percentage of the money and manpower resources spent on dealing with conflicts could be diverted, preventative research and education would be luxuriously financed and staffed.

Obviously any improvement achieved in this way will not be speedy, but that is an argument for making a start as soon as possible.

10. Personalities. An unknown, but probably high, proportion of disputes are due to personality clashes, particularly at site level. Should not both sides of the industry be more prepared to change staff in such a case, rather than regard it as loss of face not to keep their original appointees fighting to the finish?

11. Independence and reasonableness of the engineer and other supervisors. The essence of the contract system is that the contractor does work for the employer on credit. In the complications of accounting for civil engineering works the contractor would be at the mercy of an unscrupulous employer if an independent engineer of integrity were not interposed between them to decide what should be paid for work done and when it should be paid. Therefore if engineers cease to function independently and fairly the contract system embodied in the I.C.E. Conditions also must cease to exist.

It is of course a matter of opinion whether that would be a bad development. There are many who believe that it is unrealistic to expect independent conduct where the engineer is himself involved in a dispute. Perhaps it is naïve to believe otherwise, but the system has worked for a long time in the keeping of engineers of integrity. It is disconcerting to hear many lawyers and others denigrate the system simply because it is unique and they know nothing of its history and the way in which it has actually worked.

There undoubtedly are signs of a steady erosion of the role of the engineer named in the contract, under many pressures. These pressures include increased claimsmanship—back again to the vicious circle. Government auditing procedures control the engineer in flagrant breach of the construction contract. Professional jealousy towards the engineer in local government from his colleagues in other professions, and by full-time engineers for some reason employed by many employers to watch their consultants by way of hiring a dog and barking themselves, cannot be ruled out as another cause of the disenchantment professed for the system in some quarters.

What is certain is that while the system exists, and until something better is produced, it is a fraud on the contractor for the employer to make a construction contract based on an independent role of the engineer, and either by a private service agreement or pressure during the contract to curtail that independence. It is also unwise legally (p. 416), and a lawyer representing a contractor will be happy to go into arbitration with an engineer who can easily be discredited for unfair conduct during the course of the contract. An employer has little grounds to complain if a contractor saddled with a biased engineer retaliates in kind, and in any case an engineer with a guilty conscience is unlikely to administer the contract well, particularly because he will lack the moral authority that may be more important than legal powers. Because it is so important in minimising

i

j

k

(*i*) The importance of maintaining the independence of the engineer is stressed by the I.C.E. Conditions of Contract Standing Joint Committee in Guidance Note 2A, and in ch. 5 of the C.I.R.I.A. report, above. Representatives of several government departments and other public authorities were on the working party which produced the report.

(*j*) Is a rather grudging recognition of the special role of the architect detectable in the latest decision on the subject? *Sutcliffe* v. *Thackrah* [1974] 1 All E.R. 859, H.L. discussed in the text on p. 293 and p. 398.

(*k*) The 3rd edition of the F.I.D.I.C. International Conditions cls. 2 and 69(1)(d) has taken a step in the direction of honesty.

disputes, the standard of conduct required of the engineer is discussed separately in ch. 15.

Also certain is that the operation of the system must be monitored, and consideration given to publishing a code of conduct for guidance of engineers (and why not also expert witnesses and lawyers?). Such a code would make it easier for the engineer to convince his client to respect his independence. Generally it is difficult to accept that the bodies representing engineers are doing all they can to sustain the system, despite the fact that their members are the prime losers from its decline.

Unfortunately there is not always a successfully selective choice of engineer or resident staff. Supervisors who do not know what they are doing will refuse every request by the contractor, and rigidly administer the specification. Only development in technical knowledge will produce realistic specifications, instead of standards that often resemble railway rule books in the sense that if enforced strictly the works can hardly be done. The present system gives enormous power to the engineer or resident staff which is virtually untouched by the conditions of contract and a fruitful source of acrimony and dispute.

As in other spheres there is no substitute for competence and balance, and training and education (including education in professional responsibility) are the long-term solutions.

12. Legal mechanisms. It might be considered an understatement to say that the contribution of the legal profession to the construction industry is not as great as it might be. In place of aid in drafting a clear-cut and just contractual framework and in producing sensible results to disputes, there is over-emphasis on legalistic drafting and interpretation of contracts (p. 5), and distortion of arbitration.

It is too much to expect that engineers alone will be able to convince lawyers and judges that they are not performing a very useful function by clinging to the jargon they find most comfortable although it is incomprehensible to those for whom their work is intended, or in spending days arguing about and often distorting words that had to be chosen by the engineer in minutes. At the same time, history suggests that change in law and legal procedures comes only from ruthless and self-confident pressure from outside. Given its contribution to the livelihood of the legal profession, the construction industry is entitled to apply that pressure.

Arbitration was originally intended as a straightforward means of having disputes decided by a technical man, with the great advantage that the parties are free to adapt the procedure for their particular needs. In the past lawyers have been allowed to distort the procedure, but there is no reason why the industry cannot take control again and tailormake a procedure for construction disputes. It is to be hoped that the Institution of Civil *l* Engineers' Arbitration Procedure (p. 301) will advance in that direction. In addition there have been experiments elsewhere with conciliation pro- *m* cedure, and suggestions that an arbitrator or at least agreed fact-finder

(*l*) The Arbitration Bill 1978, introduced into the House of Lords at the proof stage of this book, proposes changes in control of arbitrators by the courts that may be very significant for the construction industry, but does not restrict the development of procedure advocated above.

(*m*) South African Institution of Civil Engineers etc. General Conditions of Contract 1972. Information is that the procedure is not used a great deal in practice.

should come on the site while the facts of the dispute are still fresh and sense may prevail about the future of the works.

The notion that the arbitrator should know virtually nothing about the particular case until the hearing starts is justified only if it is considered that because the Bar provides a corps of professional advocates they should be given as much to do and as much room for manoeuvre at the hearing as possible. Cl. 52 (4) of the 5th edition should ensure that in most cases there are written records available of the events being arbitrated, and make it possible for each party to state his case very fully in writing, with all relevant documents annexed before the hearing. The Arbitration Act 1950 does not contain any rules about pleadings in arbitration, and there is no reason why pleadings should follow the court format.

In this way the oral hearing will be used, as it should be, merely to deal with crucial points by cross-examination of witnesses on matters of real contest. Unlike judges, engineer arbitrators generally are trained and prefer to work on written evidence and details presented in writing, and concentration on the papers should make it more likely that awards will be based on a proper analysis of the issues. Consider, as an analogy, how lengthy the meetings of the I.C.E. would be if the papers were produced for the first time at the meetings and read out by the contributors. More important, how much less acute would be the consideration and analysis of the papers by the members.

Needless to say the success of procedure that makes full use of written records depends on the arbitrator mastering the documents for the hearing, but without reaching any conclusions until he has heard all the evidence: keeping an open but not an empty mind and making sure the parties appreciate the extent of his work beforehand so that they do not spend the hearing telling him what he already has learned from the records.

The Institution's training scheme for arbitrators should give to arbitrators the confidence and skill to regulate the procedure before them fruitfully. It is important that this training should be designed not to produce legalistic second-class judges, but arbitrators applying what is good for civil engineering in the present judicial outlook and procedure, and discarding what is bad. Indeed what is needed is a careful blend of common law and continental procedures, as they have been developed in different countries: the notion that one system, and that a court system, must be used in whole is preventing progress.

The result of the present procedure is that very often the parties are driven to a settlement without either of them being satisfied that justice has been done; alternatively, too often they persevere to the bitter end of the proceedings, and conclude eventually that the game was not worth the candle. In some cases a party with a thoroughly bad case (whether claim or defence) may still succeed in obtaining a settlement because his opponent cannot face the demands and uncertainties of a long arbitration. That is to give an advantage to a party who is unreasonable, indifferent to justice and with large resources.

Fortunately only a small proportion of cases actually reach arbitration, but a rational, fair, relatively speedy and inexpensive system will have a beneficial influence well beyond such cases, in inducing parties to behave reasonably because of the knowledge that they will not get away with anything by threatening or actually holding an arbitration.

(n) C.I.R.I.A. report, above, chs. 5, 6.

13. Crux of the matter. Concentration in this chapter on the remedies for cases where the behaviour of one of the parties is less than ideal should not be allowed to obscure the realities that there are severe limits both to what can be achieved and what has to be achieved in this way. Contracts are intended for a minority of cases where the normal restraints break down, often in circumstances of extreme misfortune. The industry only works so far as most employers, engineers and contractors show responsibility and good faith and teamwork even in areas that lawyers and accountants cannot or do not reach. If that ceases to be the case, as it will if the abuses of a minority make honesty and responsibility bad policy to a sufficient degree for the majority, civil engineering will no longer be a very pleasant or worthwhile activity for those engaged in it, and the public interest too will suffer drastically.

Case List

Index

Legislation is grouped under the heading Acts of Parliament and Statutory Instruments. The I.C.E.'s (Institute of Civil Engineers) Conditions of Contract are listed under the heading 'Clauses'.